Centre for Innovation in Mathematics Teaching
University of Exeter

C000069758

PURE MATHEMATICS

Writers David Burghes
David Cassell
Tim Cross
John Deft
Jon Middle
William Thallon

Editor David Burghes

Assistant Editors Nigel Price
Derek Jackson
Betty Elkins

Heinemann Educational

Heinemann Educational
a division of Heinemann Educational Books Ltd.
Halley Court, Jordan Hill, Oxford OX2 8EJ

OXFORD LONDON EDINBURGH
MADRID ATHENS BOLOGNA PARIS
MELBOURNE SYDNEY AUCKLAND SINGAPORE
TOKYO IBADAN NAIROBI HARARE
GABORONE PORTSMOUTH NH (USA)

ISBN 0 435 516 04 3

First Published 1994 with corrections

94 95 96 10 9 8 7 6 5 4 3

Typeset by ISCA Press, CIMT, University of Exeter

Printed in Great Britain by The Bath Press, Avon

PURE MATHEMATICS

This is one of the texts which has been written to support the AEB Mathematics syllabus for A and AS level awards first available in Summer 1996.

The text, which covers the Pure Maths Module 1, is a development of the Foundation Mathematics Core text written for the AEB Coursework syllabus.

The development of these texts has been coordinated at the

Centre for Innovation in Mathematics Teaching

at Exeter University in association with Heinemann and AEB. The overall development of these texts has been directed by David Burghes and coordinated by Nigel Price.

Enquiries regarding this project and further details of the work of the Centre should be addressed to

Margaret Roddick
CIMT
School of Education
University of Exeter
Heavitree Road
EXETER EX1 2LU.

CONTENTS

ACKNOWLEDGEMENTS

This text has been developed from an earlier version, published specifically for the CIMT/AEB Mathematics syllabus and based on the philosophy of the Wessex Project. I am particularly grateful to the original authors and to Bob Rainbow (Wessex) and John Commerford (AEB) for their help and encouragement in the development of the original resources.

This revised version and associated texts have been written for the new AEB Mathematics syllabus and assessment, which will be examined for the first time in Summer 1996. I am grateful for the continued support from AEB through its mathematics officer, Jackie Bawden, and to the staff at Heinemann, particularly Philip Ellaway.

Finally, I am indebted to the staff at CIMT who work with dedication and good humour despite the pressure which I continually put upon them. In particular, I am grateful to Nigel Price for the revisions and editing of the text, to Derek Jackson and Betty Elkins for checking the mathematics and to Liz Holland, Margaret Roddick and Ann Tylisczuk for producing camera ready copy.

David Burghes

(Series Editor)

PREFACE

Mathematics is an important technique for the solution of problems in almost any area of society today. It has been of crucial importance in the advancement of space travel, telecommunications, computing, power generation and environmental issues. The use of mathematical models to predict whale populations has done much to conserve current stocks whilst the solution of the equations of motion for ballistics has helped design rockets of awesome power which can pinpoint targets. Mathematics in the hands of people and governments can be used for the benefit or destruction of mankind. Whatever view you take, however, its power cannot be ignored.

This particular text aims to develop mathematical topics and concepts, illustrating how the techniques can be used in practical ways. Some mathematical themes are important for their own sake and this is also recognised. Nevertheless, the main theme behind this book is to provide a comprehensive text which covers the main topics in the Inter Board Core published by SEAC for implementation for examinations in Summer 1996.

This text has been produced for students and includes examples, activities and exercises. It should be noted that the activities are **not** optional but are an important part of the learning philosophy in which you are expected to take a very active part. The text integrates

- **Exposition** in which the concept is explained;
- **Examples** which show how the techniques are used;
- **Activities** which either introduce new concepts or reinforce techniques;
- **Discussion Points** which are essentially 'stop and think' points, where discussion with other students and teachers will be helpful;
- **Exercises** at the end of most sections in order to provide further practice;
- **Miscellaneous Exercises** at the end of most chapters, providing opportunities for reinforcement of the main points of the chapter.

Discussion points are written in a special typeface as illustrated here.

Note that answers to the exercises are given at the back of the book. You are expected to have a calculator available throughout your study of this text and occasionally to have access to a computer.

Some of the sections, exercises and questions are marked with an asterisk (*). This means that they are **not** central to the development of the topics in this text and can be omitted without causing problems.

Note that this reprint has included in the Appendix the use of partial fractions for integration. The determination of partial fractions is in the current AEB syllabus for Pure Mathematics.

This text is one of a series of texts written specially for the new AEB Mathematics syllabus for A and AS level coursework. The framework is shown opposite. Essentially each module corresponds to an AS level syllabus and two suitable modules provide the syllabus for an A level award. Optional coursework is available for students taking any of the three applied modules

Mechanics, Statistics and Discrete Mathematics.

Full details of the scheme are available from
AEB, Stag Hill House, Guildford GU2 5XJ.

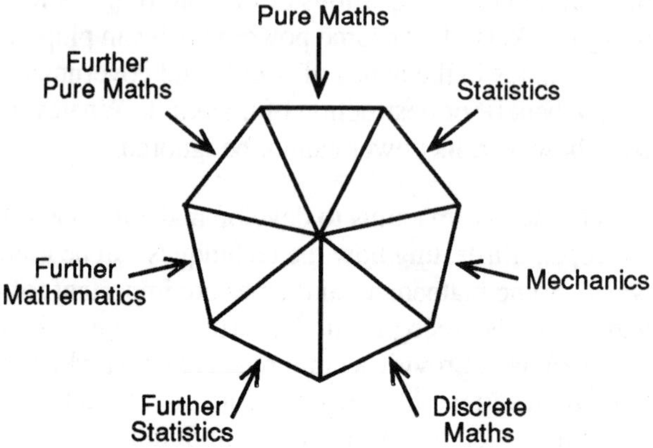

We hope that you enjoy working through the book. We would be very grateful for comments, criticisms and notification of any errors. These should be sent to

Margaret Roddick
CIMT
School of Education
University of Exeter
EXETER EX1 2LU

from whom full details of other CIMT publications and courses for both teachers and students are available.

1 THE NATURE OF MATHEMATICS

Objectives

After studying this chapter you should

- appreciate the different aspects of mathematics;
- be able to understand how simple mathematical models are constructed to solve problems;
- understand the power and limitations of mathematical analysis;
- have revised the laws of indices.

1.0 Introduction

You are starting off on a course of mathematical study leading to an A-level or AS award in Mathematics. Although the **starting point** of your course is clearly defined from the work that you have done in your GCSE Mathematics course, the **end point** is not so clearly defined, since it depends on your interests and ability.

Those who are more interested in Physics and Technology will probably take further mathematical study with **Mechanics**, whilst those interested in Biology or Geography need a good grounding in techniques in **Statistics**, and those specialising in Business Studies will need further work in **Decision Mathematics**.

All these areas are mathematical and the extent of the topic can be illustrated by the fact that it is possible to take not just one A-level, but two or even three A-levels in mathematical subjects. This text is based on the current 'common core', which all A-levels in mathematics have to cover. Whilst the syllabus for the common core is quite prescriptive, the aim is to show why and how to apply the various topics under study. Of course, not all mathematical topics are immediately useful and some have historically been developed for their own sake with their applications coming later.

The first task, though, will be to see some of the ways in which mathematics is developed and used; in particular its uses

- to explain
- to predict
- to make decisions

will be illustrated in the next section.

1.1 Case studies

Bode's law

In 1772, the German astronomer, *Johann Bode*, investigated the pattern formed by the distances of planets from the sun.

At the time, only six planets were known, and the pattern he devised is shown below. The distances are measured on a scale that equates 10 units to the Sun - Earth distance.

The fit between actual distances and Bode's pattern is remarkably good.

Planet	Actual distance	Bode's pattern
Mercury	4	$0+4 = 4$
Venus	7	$3+4 = 7$
Earth	10	$6+4 = 10$
Mars	15	$12+4 = 16$
-	-	-
Jupiter	52	$48+4 = 52$
Saturn	96	$96+4=100$

What do you think is the missing entry?

There are also planets further out than Saturn.

Find the next two numbers in Bode's pattern.

In fact, the data continues as shown here

Planet	Actual distance
Uranus	192
Neptune	301
Pluto	395

Can you give an explanation of how Bode's Law can be adapted for this extra data?

Wind chill

When the temperature drops near zero, it is usual for weather forecasters to give both the expected air temperature, and the **wind chill** temperature - this is the temperature actually felt by someone, which depends on the wind speed and air temperature. So, for example, the wind chill temperature for an actual temperature of

0° C and wind speed of 10 mph is given by -5.5° C.

For $v > 5$ mph, the wind chill temperature is given by

$$\boxed{T = 33 + \left(0.45 + 0.29\sqrt{v} - 0.02v\right)(t - 33)}$$

where t° C is the air temperature and v mph the wind speed. This formula was devised by American scientists during the Second World War, and is based on experimental evidence.

Example

Find the wind chill temperature when

(a) $t = 2^\circ\text{C}, \quad v = 20$ mph;

(b) $t = 10^\circ\text{C}, \quad v = 5$ mph;

(c) $t = 0^\circ\text{C}, \quad v = 40$ mph.

Solution

(a) When $t = 2, \quad v = 20$,

$$\begin{aligned} T &= 33 + \left(0.45 + 0.29\sqrt{20} - 0.02 \times 20\right)(-31) \\ &= -8.8^\circ\text{C}. \end{aligned}$$

(b) When $t = -10, \quad v = 5$,

$$\begin{aligned} T &= 33 + \left(0.45 + 0.29\sqrt{5} - 0.02 \times 5\right)(-43) \\ &= -9.9^\circ\text{C}. \end{aligned}$$

(c) When $t = 0^\circ\text{C}, \ v = 40$ mph,

$$\begin{aligned} T &= 33 + \left(0.45 + 0.29\sqrt{40} - 0.02 \times 40\right)(-33) \\ &= -16.0^\circ\text{C}. \end{aligned}$$

What is the significance of a wind speed of about 5 mph?

Heptathlon

The Heptathlon is a competition for female athletes who take part in **seven** separate events (usually spread over a two day period). For each event, there is a point scoring system, based on the idea that a good competitor will score 1000 points in each event. For example, the points scoring system for the 800 m running event is

$$\boxed{P = 0.11193\,(254-m)^{1.88}}$$

where m is the time taken in seconds for the athlete to run 800 m.

What points are scored for a time of 254 seconds?

Example

What points are scored for a time of 124.2 seconds, and what time would give a point score of 1000?

Solution

For $m = 124.2$,

$$P = 0.11193\,(254-124.2)^{1.88}$$

$$\Rightarrow \quad P = 1051.$$

(Scores are always rounded down to the nearest whole number.)

Now, to score 1000 points requires a time of m seconds where

$$1000 = 0.11193\,(254-m)^{1.88}$$

$$\Rightarrow \quad (254-m)^{1.88} = 8934.15$$

$$\Rightarrow \quad 254-m = (8934.15)^{\frac{1}{1.88}}$$

$$\Rightarrow \quad m = 254-126.364$$

giving $\quad m = 127.64.$

All track events use a points scoring system of the form

$$\boxed{P = a(b-m)^c}$$

with suitable constants a, b and c.

Suggest an appropriate formula for the points system in the track events in the Heptathlon.

Simple pendulum

The great Italian scientist, *Galileo*, was the first to make important discoveries about the behaviour of swinging weights. These discoveries led to the development of pendulum clocks.

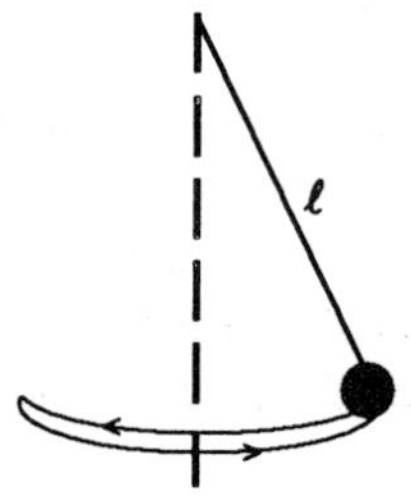

Activity 1 Period of pendulum swing

Attach a weight at one end of a light string, the other end being fixed. Let the pendulum swing freely in a vertical plane and for various lengths of pendulum, ℓ, in metres, find the corresponding times in seconds of one complete oscillation (known as the **period**) - it is more accurate to time, say, five oscillations and then divide the total time by 5. On a graph, plot the period, T, against the square root of the pendulum length, $\ell^{\frac{1}{2}}$. What do you notice?

In fact, the two quantities are related by the formula

$$\boxed{T = 2.006\,\ell^{\frac{1}{2}}}$$

Example

What pendulum length gives a periodic time of 1 second?

Solution

If $T = 1$ then

$$1 = 2.006\,\ell^{\frac{1}{2}}$$

$$\Rightarrow \quad \ell^{\frac{1}{2}} = \frac{1}{2.006} = 0.4985$$

$$\Rightarrow \quad \ell \approx 0.25\text{ m}.$$

Activity 2

Construct a simple pendulum with $\ell = 0.25$ m, and check its periodic time.

Perfect numbers

These are numbers whose divisors (excluding the number itself) add up to the number. Excluding the number 1, the first perfect number is 6, since

$$6 = 3\times2 = 1\times6$$

and $\quad 3+2+1 = 6.$

Activity 3

Test the numbers 7, 8, ... , 30 in order to find the next perfect number. (You might find it useful to write a short computer program to test whether any number is perfect.)

You have probably realised by now that perfect numbers are pretty thin on the ground!

Example

Are the following numbers perfect :

(a) 220 (b) 284 (c) 496?

Solution

(a)
$$\begin{aligned} 220 &= 220\times 1 \\ &= 110\times 2 \\ &= 55\times 4 \\ &= 44\times 5 \\ &= 22\times 10 \\ &= 20\times 11 \end{aligned}$$

and $1+2+4+5+10+11+20+22+44+55+110 = 284$.

Hence 220 is not a perfect number.

(b)
$$\begin{aligned} 284 &= 284\times 1 \\ &= 142\times 2 \\ &= 71\times 4 \end{aligned}$$

and $1+2+4+71+142 = 220$.

Hence 284 is not a perfect number (but note its connection with 220).

(c)
$$\begin{aligned} 496 &= 496\times 1 \\ &= 248\times 2 \\ &= 124\times 4 \\ &= 62\times 8 \\ &= 31\times 16 \end{aligned}$$

and $1+2+4+8+16+31+62+124+248 = 496$.

Hence 496 is a perfect number.

In fact 496 is the third perfect number, and 8128 is the fourth. Although there are still many unknown results concerning perfect numbers, it has been shown that

(a) all **even** perfect numbers will be of the form

$$2^{n-1}\left(2^n - 1\right)$$

when n is a prime number. This number is in fact perfect when $2^n - 1$ is prime;

(b) all even perfect numbers end in 6 or 8;

(c) the sum of the inverses of all divisors of a perfect number add up to 2

e.g. for 6, $\frac{1}{6}+\frac{1}{3}+\frac{1}{2}+\frac{1}{1}=2.$

Activity 4 Perfect numbers

Given that the fifth and sixth perfect number are 33 550 336 and 8 589 869 056 respectively, copy and complete the table below.

n	$2^n - 1$	prime	$2^{n-1}\left(2^n - 1\right)$	perfect
2	3	✓	6	✓
3				
5				
7				
11				
13				

You probably noticed in the example above that 220 and 284 are connected through their divisors. They are called **amicable pairs** (they are the smallest numbers that exhibit this property) and are regarded as tokens of great love. In the Bible, for example, Jacob gave Esau 220 goats to express his love (Genesis 32, verse 14).

Activity 5 Amicable pairs

Write a short program to generate amicable pairs, and use it to find the next lowest pair.

Day of the week

The algorithm below gives a method for determining the day of the week for any date this century. The date used as an example is 3 March, 1947.

1.	Write $y = \text{year}$.	$y = 1947$
2.	Evaluate $\left[\frac{y-1}{4}\right]$ ignoring the remainder.	$\left[\frac{y-1}{4}\right] = \left[\frac{1946}{4}\right] = 486$
3.	Find $D =$ day of year. (Jan. 1st $= 1, \dots,$ Feb. 1st $= 32$, etc.)	$D = 31 + 28 + 3 = 62$
4.	Calculate $s = y + \left[\frac{y-1}{4}\right] + D.$	$s = 1947 + 486 + 62$ $= 2495$
5.	Divide by 7 and note remainder, R.	$\frac{s}{7} = \frac{2495}{7} = 356,$ with remainder $R = 3$
6.	The remainder is the key to the day: $R = 0 \Rightarrow$ Friday, $R = 1 \Rightarrow$ Saturday, etc.	Hence 3 March 1947 was in fact a Monday.

Activity 6

(a) Use the algorithm to find the day of the week on which you were born. Note that if the year is divisible by 4, it is a leap year and February has 29 days!

(b) Analyse how and why this algorithm works.

Bar code design

Nearly all grocery products now include an identifying Bar Code on their wrapper (supermarkets now use them both for sales checkout and stock control). There are two types of EAN (European Article Numbers) - 13 digit and 8 digit. The shortened 8 digit code will be considered here. A possible example is shown opposite. The number has three parts.

0039 9104

0 0	3 9 9 1 0	4
↑	↑	↑
retailer's code	product code	check digit

The check digit is chosen so that

$$3\times\left(1^{st}+3^{rd}+5^{th}+7^{th}\text{ numbers}\right)+\left(2^{nd}+4^{th}+6^{th}+8^{th}\text{ numbers}\right)$$

is exactly divisible by 10. For the numbers above

$$3\times(0+3+9+0)+(0+9+1+4)$$

$$=3\times12+14=36+14=50$$

which is divisible by 10.

If the check digit is in error, the optical bar code reader will reject the code.

Example

Find the check digit for the EAN codes :

(a) $5021421x$ (b) $0042655x$.

Solution

(a) Denoting the check digit by x, the number

$$3\times(5+2+4+1)+(0+1+2+x)=3\times12+3+x=39+x$$

must be divisible by 10, so x must be 1.

(b) Similarly

$$3\times(0+4+6+5)+(0+2+5+x)=3\times15+7+x=52+x$$

must be divisible by 10, so x must be 8.

If the optical bar code reader makes one mistake in reading a number, will it always be detected?

Another 8 digit EAN is shown opposite. It has left and right hand guide bars and centre bars. In between there are 8 bars of varying thickness. Each number is represented by a unique set of 2 bars and 2 spaces. As can be seen in the magnified version of 5, each number code is made up of 7 **modules**.

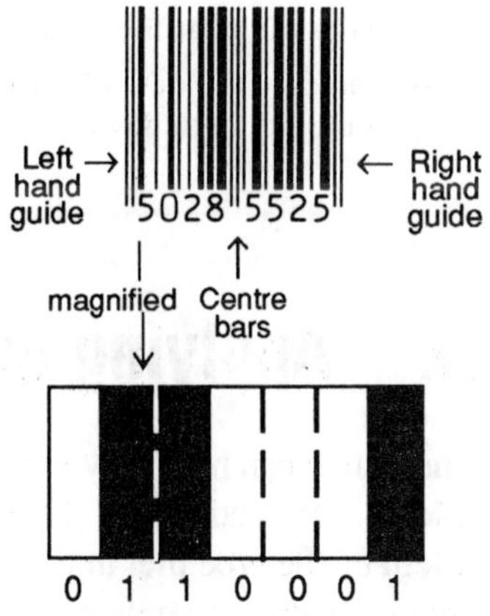

Left hand 5

The digit 5 is written as 0110001 to indicate whether a module is white (0) or black (1).

All left hand numbers start with 0 and end with 1, and use a total of 3 or 5 black modules. Right hand numbers are the complement of the corresponding left hand code e.g. right hand 5 is 1000110.

Activity 7

Design all possible codes for left hand numbers, and use 8 digit examples found on products to identify the code for each number.

The seven case studies in this section have demonstrated a variety of uses of mathematics. They have ranged from the practical design problem in Bar Codes and Bode's pattern for planetary distances to the development of perfect numbers (which as yet have no obvious applications). Mathematics embraces all these concepts, although it is the practical application side that will be emphasised where possible throughout this text. This aspect will be considered in greater depth in the next section.

Exercise 1A

1. Use the wind chill temperature formula to find its value where

   (a) $t = 0°C$, $v = 20$ mph

   (b) $t = 5°C$, $v = 20$ mph

   (c) $t = -5°C$, $v = 20$ mph.

   Plot a graph of wind chill temperature against air temperature, t, for $v=20$ mph. Use your graph to estimate the wind chill temperature when $t = 10°C$ and $v = 20$ mph.

2. The points scoring system for the high jump event in the Heptathlon is given by

   $$p = a(m-b)^c$$

   where $a = 1.84523$, $b = 75.0$, $c = 1.348$ and m is the height jumped in centimetres. Find the points scored for a jump of 183 cm, and determine the height required to score 1000 points.

3. An algorithm for determining the date of Easter Sunday is given at the top of the next column.

   Use it to find the date of Easter next year, which is given by the pth day of the nth month.

Step	Number	Divide by	Answer	Remainder (if needed)
1	$x =$ year	100	$b =$	$c =$
2	$5(b+c)$	19	-	$a =$
3	$3(b+25)$	4	$r =$	$s =$
4	$8(b+11)$	25	$t =$	-
5	$19a+r-t$	30	-	$h =$
6	$a+11h$	319	$g =$	-
7	$60(5-s)+c$	4	$j =$	$k =$
8	$2j-k-h+g$	7	-	$m =$
9	$h-g+m+110$	30	$n =$	$q =$
10	$q+5-n$	32	-	$p =$

*4. Write a computer program to determine the date of Easter Sunday for the next 100 years. Illustrate the data using a histogram.

5. Find the check digits for these EAN codes :

   (a) 0034548*   (b) 5023122*.

6. Determine whether these EAN codes have the correct check digit :

   (a) 00306678   (b) 06799205.

1.2 Applying mathematics

Mathematics can be a very powerful tool in solving practical problems. An example of this is given below with an optimisation problem of the type met in the commercial world, as well as two further case studies showing how mathematics is used to solve problems.

Metal cans

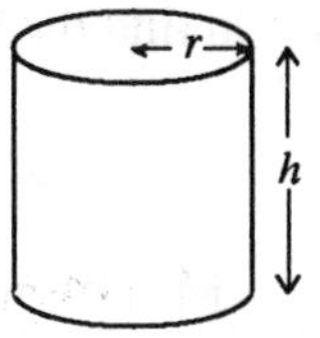

The most popular size of metal can contains a volume of about 440 ml. As they are produced in millions each week, any savings that can be made in their manufacture will prove significant. Part of the cost of making steel cans is based on the amount of material used, so it might be sensible to design a can which minimises the amount of metal used to enclose the required volume.

To analyse this problem, you must find an expression for the total surface area of a can. Suppose the cylindrical can has radius r and height h, then total surface area,

$$S = \text{curved surface area} + \text{top area} + \text{base area}.$$

What are the dimensions of the rectangle used for the curved surface area?

Assuming that no metal is wasted, an expression for the total surface area is given by

$$S = 2\pi rh + \pi r^2 + \pi r^2$$

$$\Rightarrow \quad S = 2\pi rh + 2\pi r^2. \qquad (1)$$

The formula for S shows that it is a function of two variables, r and h. But in reality it is a function of only one variable since r and h are constrained by having to enclose a specified volume.

You should be familiar with the formula for the volume of a cylindrical can:

$$V = \text{area of cross section} \times \text{height}$$

or, in this case

$$440 = \pi r^2 h. \qquad (2)$$

This equation can be used to find an expression for h which is substituted into (1) to eliminate h.

From (2)

$$h = \frac{440}{\pi r^2} \qquad (3)$$

and substituting into (1) gives

$$S = 2\pi r\left(\frac{440}{\pi r^2}\right) + 2\pi r^2$$

giving

$$\boxed{S = \frac{880}{r} + 2\pi r^2} \qquad (4)$$

What happens to S if r is very small or large? Does it make sense?

The problem is to find the value of r which minimises the total surface area S.

Activity 8 Minimising packaging costs

Draw a graph of S as given by equation (4), for x values between 1 and 10. (If you use a graphic calculator, you will need to enter the equation in the form

$$y = \frac{880}{x} + 2\pi x^2$$

where y replaces S and x replaces r.)

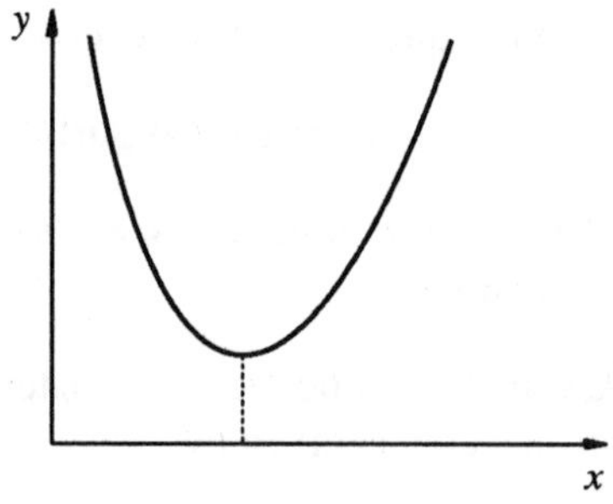

Use your graph to obtain an estimate of the base radius which would make the surface area of the can a minimum. (If you know how to 'magnify' a portion of the graph, you may be able to make a better estimate by concentrating on the part of the graph close to the minimum.)

Also find the corresponding optimum height from equation (3).

You have made a number of assumptions in finding this optimum value of r. To complete the analysis, you must find out whether this solution, based on minimising the total surface area, is in fact used in practice.

Activity 9 Validating the result

Find the dimensions of the usual size of a can containing 440 ml. Do they agree with your theoretical result? If not, suggest what assumptions should be modified.

In practice, the aesthetic look and feel of an object might be more important than minimising the total surface area of the packaging.

Can you suggest objects where the packaging is clearly not based on minimising the material used?

Returning to the metal can problem, there is one particular case where aesthetic appeal would not be important, and that is in the design of cans for trade use (e.g. hotels, caterers). You will see later that for these cans, your model does indeed provide the basis for deciding the optimum dimensions.

Reading age formula

Educationalists need to be able to assess the minimum reading age of certain books so that they can be appropriately catalogued, particularly for use with young children.

You are probably aware that, for example, it is much easier and quicker to read one of the tabloids (e.g. 'The Sun') than one of the quality 'heavies' (e.g. ' The Guardian').

What factors influence the reading age of a book, newspaper or pamphlet?

There have been many attempts at designing a formula for finding the reading age of a text. One example is known as the **FOG Index.** This is given by

$$\boxed{R = \frac{2}{5}\left(\frac{A}{n} + \frac{100L}{A}\right)} \qquad (5)$$

where the variables are defined for a sample passage of the text by

A = number of words

n = number of sentences

L = number of words containing three or more syllables (excluding '-ing' and '-ed' endings).

Activity 10

Find four or five books of varying reading difficulty. First estimate the minimum reading ages for each of these, then use the FOG formula to compare the two sets of data.

Of course, the whole concept of a designated reading age for a particular book is perhaps rather dubious. Nevertheless, the problem is a real one, and teachers and publishers do need to know the appropriate order for their reading books.

The two case studies above illustrate the idea of a **mathematical model**; that is a mathematical description of the problem. For the metal can problem the mathematical model is described by the equations (1) and (3), leading to the mathematical problem of finding the value of r which minimises

$$S = \frac{880}{r} + 2\pi r^2 .$$

In the second problem, the reading age formula, the mathematical model is essentially given by equation (5).

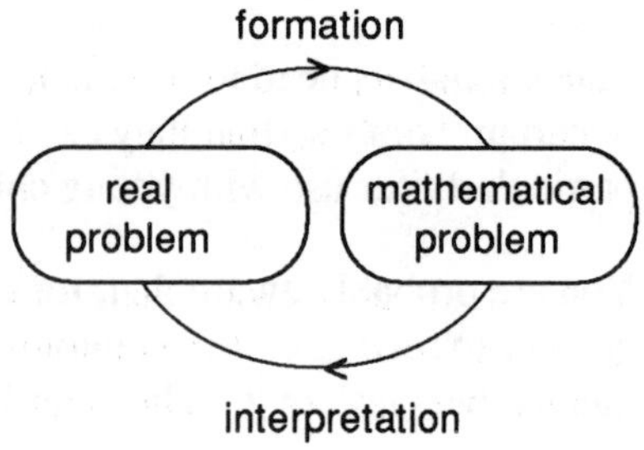

The translation of the problem from the real world to the mathematical world can be summarised in the diagram opposite. The model is formed from the real problem by making various assumptions, whilst the solution to the mathematical problem must be interpreted back in terms of the real problem. This will be illustrated in the next example.

Handicapping weight lifters

In weight lifting, there are nine official body weight classes. For some competitions, it is important to be able to compare lifts made by competitors in different classes. This means that some form of handicapping must be used.

There are a number of models that have been used to provide a form of handicapping. For example if

L = actual lift (in kg)

W = competitor's weight (in kg)

L' = handicapped lift,

then two possible solutions are

(a) $L' = L - W$

(b) $L' = L/(W-35)^{\frac{1}{3}}$.

The first method was used for some time in a television programme (TV Superstars) in which competitors of different weights competed against each other in a number of sports events. The second method, called the O'Carroll formula, is used in more serious competitions in order to find an overall winner.

Example

The best lifts (for the 'snatch' lift) for eight competitors are given on the following page, together with their weight. Use the two models to find an overall winner.

Competitor	Weight (in kg)	Lift (Snatch) (in kg)
1	52	105.1
2	56	117.7
3	60	125.2
4	67.5	135.2
5	75	145.2
6	82.5	162.7
7	90	170.3
8	110	175.3

Solution

The handicapped lifts are shown below.

Competitor	W	L	$L-W$	$L/(W-35)^{\frac{1}{3}}$
1	52	105.1	53.1	40.9
2	56	117.7	61.7	42.7
3	60	125.2	65.2	42.8
4	67.5	135.2	67.7	42.4
5	75	145.2	70.2	42.5
6	82.5	162.7	80.2	44.9 ←
7	90	170.3	80.3 ←	44.8
8	110	175.3	65.3	41.6

For the first method, the winner is competitor number 7, but the second method makes competitor number 6 the winner.

Whilst mathematics is a precise science, applications to real problems require both an understanding of the problem and an appreciation that, whilst mathematics can provide answers and give precise explanations based on particular assumptions and models, it cannot always solve the real problem. Mathematics can help to design multi-stage rockets that work, but it can't necessarily help to solve the problem of world peace. Often mathematical analysis can help in making the best decisions, and, for example the success of mathematical modelling is shown by the fact that man has stepped on the moon. You should, though, be aware that most problems in real life are more complicated than a single equation or formula!

Exercise 1B

1. Repeat the analysis for finding the minimum surface area of a metal can where the volume enclosed is 1000 ml. Determine the values of r and h which minimise the surface area.

2. A mathematical model for the reading age of a text is given by

$$R = 25 - \frac{N}{10}$$

where N is the average number of one syllable words in a passage of 150 words. Use this model to find the reading age of a number of books. Compare the results with those found in the case study outlined in Section 1.2.

3. Use the handicapping model

$$L' = L / W^{\frac{2}{3}}$$

to find the winner of the competition described in the case study in the section before this exercise.

4. Horseshoes are made by blacksmiths taking straight strips of iron and bending them into the usual horseshoe shape. To find what length of strip of iron is required, the blacksmith measures the width, W inches, of the shoe and uses a formula of the form

$$L = aW + b$$

to find the required strip length, L inches. Use the following data to find estimates for a and b:

Width W (inches)	Length L (inches)
5	12
5.75	13.50

1.3 Number

Before moving on it is important to check that you are familiar with some basic terminology and notation for numbers. Note that

(i) $\mathbb{R}$ represents the set of all real numbers

(ii) $\mathbb{Z}$ represents the set of all integers;

i.e. $\{\ldots, -2, -1, 0, 1, 2, 3, \ldots\}$

(iii) $\mathbb{N}$ represents the set of positive integers (sometimes called the natural numbers)

i.e. $\{0, 1, 2, 3, \ldots\}$

(iv) $\mathbb{Q}$ represents the set of rational numbers; that is,

numbers that can be written in the form $\frac{a}{b}$ where a and b are integers and $b \neq 0$; for example,

$$\frac{1}{2}, \frac{1}{8}, \frac{5}{14}, \frac{21}{13}, -\frac{5}{2}, 2, \ldots$$

Why is 2 a rational number?

It is sometimes convenient to represent this system in set theory notation, by a Venn diagram of the form opposite.

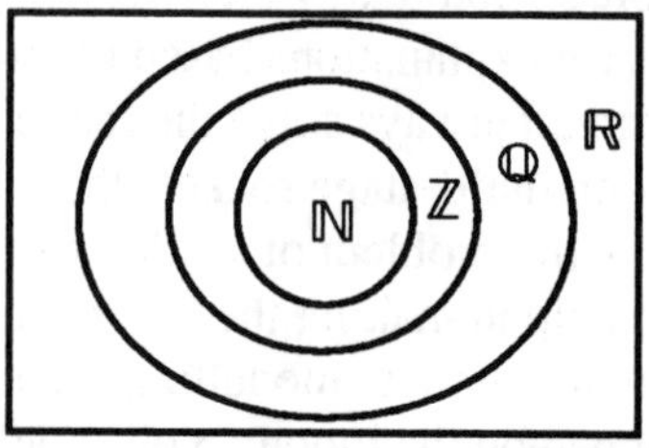

You can see that $\mathbb{N}$ is a subset of $\mathbb{Z}$, $\mathbb{Z}$ a subset of $\mathbb{Q}$, $\mathbb{Q}$ a subset of $\mathbb{R}$ or, in set theory notation

$$\mathbb{N} \subset \mathbb{Z} \subset \mathbb{Q} \subset \mathbb{R}$$

Activity 11

Draw a Venn diagram of the type shown opposite and show which set the following numbers are in, by marking them on the diagram. The first three have already been inserted .

$$5, \frac{7}{2}, -3, -\frac{9}{4}, 7, 0, \sqrt{2}, \frac{21}{4}, -5, \pi$$

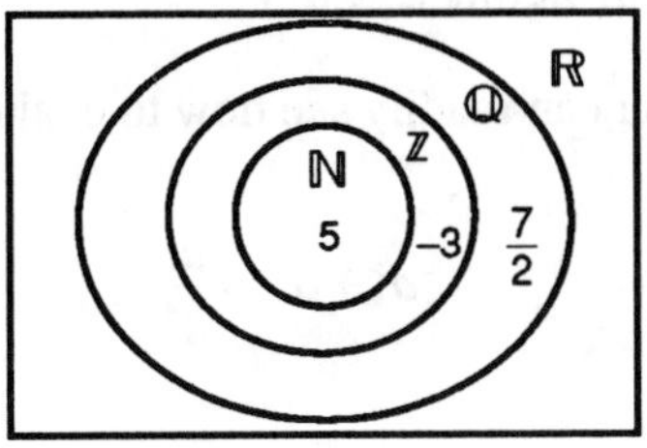

What type of numbers are $\sqrt{2}$ and π?

Any number which cannot be expressed in the form $\frac{a}{b}$ where a and b are integers ($b \neq 0$), i.e. is **not** rational, is called an **irrational** number.

Both $\sqrt{2}$ and π are irrational numbers. You will meet a proof that $\sqrt{2}$ is irrational in Section 6.8.

1.4 Indices

You have probably met the concept of indices before, but for revision purposes or in case you haven't, you should note that a^2 is shorthand notation for $a \times a$. Similarly

$$a^3 = a \times a \times a$$

$$a^4 = a \times a \times a \times a$$

and so on. Note also that

$$a^3 \times a^4 = (a \times a \times a) \times (a \times a \times a \times a)$$

$$= a \times a \times a \times a \times a \times a \times a$$

$$= a^7$$

In general, you can write

$$\boxed{a^n \times a^m = a^{n+m}}$$

where n and m are positive integers. Similarly

$$\boxed{a^n \div a^m = a^{n-m}}$$

which is illustrated by

$$a^4 \div a^3 = \frac{a \times a \times a \times a}{a \times a \times a}$$

$$= a$$

and here $4 - 3 = 1$.

What about $a^3 \div a^4$?

You can readily see how to evaluate this by noting that

$$a^3 \div a^4 = \frac{a^3}{a^4}$$

$$= \frac{(a \times a \times a)}{(a \times a \times a \times a)}$$

$$= \frac{1}{a}$$

But $3-4=-1$, and you can write

$$a^4 \div a^3 = a^{-1};$$

that is, by definition,

$$a^{-1} = \frac{1}{a}.$$

Similarly

$$a^{-2} = \frac{1}{a^2} \quad \text{etc.}$$

With this notation, the results boxed earlier are true for any integer values of m, n, and not just positive values.

Finally in this section, note that

$$\boxed{\left(a^m\right)^n = a^{mn}}$$

for integers m and n. For example, if $m=3$ and $n=4$,

$$\left(a^3\right)^4 = a^3 \times a^3 \times a^3 \times a^3$$

$$= (a \times a \times a) \times (a \times a \times a) \times (a \times a \times a) \times (a \times a \times a)$$

$$= a^{12}$$

and $mn = 3 \times 4 = 12$.

Activity 12

Verify the three boxed results when

(i) $m=2,\ n=3$

(ii) $m=-2,\ n=4$

(iii) $m=-2,\ n=-3$.

One important use of indices is in **standard form.**

A number in standard form is given by

$$x \times 10^{\alpha}$$

where x is a number such that $1 \le x < 10$ and α is an **integer**.

For example

$$48.2 = 4.82 \times 10^{1}$$

$$2004 = 2.004 \times 10^{3}$$

Example

Write each of these numbers in standard form

(a) 397 (b) 76500 (c) 0.92 (d) 0.00618

Solution

(a) $397 = 3.97 \times 10^{2}$

(b) $76500 = 7.65 \times 10^{4}$

(c) $0.92 = 9.2 \times 10^{-1}$

(d) $0.00618 = 6.18 \times 10^{-3}$

It is also sometimes easier to manipulate with numbers expressed in standard form. For example

$$\begin{aligned} 0.78 \times 0.021 &= (7.8 \times 10^{-1}) \times (2.1 \times 10^{-2}) \\ &= (7.8 \times 2.1) \times 10^{-1-2} \\ &= 16.38 \times 10^{-3} \\ &= 0.01638 \end{aligned}$$

but it is only for very large (or very small) numbers that this method is important.

Exercise 1C

1. Write in standard form

   (a) 42 (b) 0.42 (c) 0.0157

   (d) 195.2 (e) 2387.96 (f) 0.0028

2. Write as ordinary decimal numbers

   (a) 2.7×10^{2} (b) 3.52×10^{-2}

   (c) 7.01×10^{-1} (d) 5.65×10^{1}

3. Write in standard form and then find an approximate answer to

   (a) 17.2×33.1 (b) 0.49×23.8

   (c) 0.72×0.94 (d) $(0.31)^2$

   Use a calculator to check your answers.

4. Use a calculator to evaluate the following. Give your answers in standard form.

   (a) $(7.2\times10^{-2})\times(1.6\times10^{-1})$

   (b) $(2.74\times10^{-3})\times(5.02\times10^{2})$

   (c) $(1.14\times10^{-1})\times(3.145\times10^{-1})$

5. Use numbers expressed in standard form to find an approximate answer to

   (a) $98.15+0.219$ (b) $0.05128+0.477$

   Use a calculator to check your answers.

6. Light travels at a speed of 186 000 miles per second. Express the number in standard form and then find in standard form the speed of light in miles per hour.

   How far does light travel in one year, again giving your answer in standard form?

7. The mean radius of the earth is approximately 6500 km. What, in standard form, is the approximate distance round the equator?

2 USING GRAPHS

Objectives

After studying this chapter you should

- be able to illustrate simple functions with a graph;
- understand what is meant by mapping, domains and ranges;
- be able to identify if a function is odd or even or neither.

2.0 Introduction

Graphs can be used to quickly get an idea of how one quantity varies as another quantity changes. This can be very useful when trying to solve a wide range of problems. An illustration is given in the first activity which deals with currency exchange.

Activity 1 *Conversion rates*

Conversion rates between different currencies are often displayed in bank windows. You may either assume the rates given below, or find out the current rates from a local bank, to draw 3 graphs showing the number of francs, dollars and Deutschmarks you can buy for any number of pounds sterling up to £50.

£1 = 10.5 Fr   £1 = \$1.65   £1 = 2.90 DM

Use your graphs to do these conversions.

(a) £25 into francs, (b) \$35 into pounds, (c) 80 DM into francs.

Banks usually charge a fixed commission of about £2 every time they change currency for you. On the same three pairs of axes you drew earlier, draw conversion graphs which take this commission into account. What are the values of the conversions given above now?

Another problem which can be readily illustrated graphically is that of temperature conversion. You are probably familiar with the rule for conversion from degrees Celsius (° C) to degrees Fahrenheit (° F). You multiply by 9, divide by 5 and add on 32.

This can be written as a mathematical formula

$$F = \frac{9}{5} \times C + 32.$$

Instead of using algebra you can draw a graph of F against C and use it to convert from degrees Celsius to degrees Fahrenheit.

Activity 2 Temperature conversions

Since $32°\text{F} = 0°\text{C}$ and $212°\text{F} = 100°\text{C}$, plot these two points on a graph and draw a straight line to join them. Use your graph to convert

(a) $30°\text{C}$ to $°\text{F}$ (b) $10°\text{C}$ to $°\text{F}$ (c) $100°\text{F}$ to $°\text{C}$.

The lowest possible temperature is $-273°\text{C}$. Can you use your graph to find the corresponding temperature in Fahrenheit?

2.1 Mappings, domains and ranges

Very often when trying to solve a problem you may produce a rule which links one quantity with another. For instance, the speed of a car may be linked with its braking distance, or two currencies may be linked by their rate of exchange. Once a rule or formula has been produced, it is tempting to draw a graph illustrating it, to help solve the problem. However, not all of the graph may be relevant.

Activity 3 What happens at $x = 0$?

Use a graph plotting program or calculator to draw the graphs of

$$y = \frac{1}{x} \text{ and } y = \sqrt{x}.$$

What happens to the first graph when $x = 0$? Why do you think this happens?

Why do you think there is no graph when $x < 0$ for the second equation?

Another example is given by the relationship between pressure and volume. For a fixed amount of any gas, kept at a fixed temperature, pressure and volume are linked by the formula

$$p = \frac{k}{v},$$

where p is the pressure, v is the volume and k is a constant.

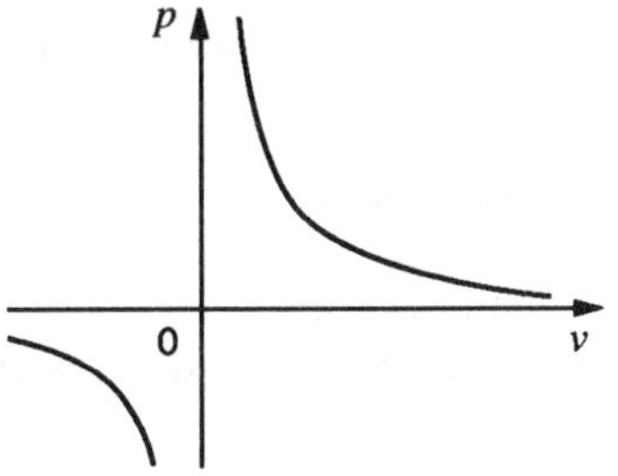

The graph for this formula is shown opposite. It shows that the pressure of the gas gets higher as the volume gets smaller in the right half of the graph. Then the pressure 'jumps', so that it is negative as soon as the volume is negative. This does not make sense. A gas cannot have a negative volume, so the left 'branch' does not exist. To show that $p = \frac{k}{v}$ can only be used for positive values of v, the formula can be written as

$$\boxed{p = \frac{k}{v},\ v > 0}$$

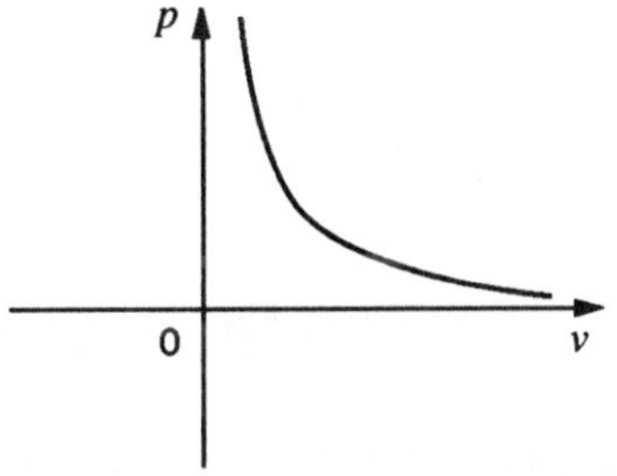

The figure opposite shows the graph of this rule, which now makes sense. As the volume increases, the pressure gets closer to zero. As the volume gets closer to zero, so the pressure gets higher - but the volume never actually equals zero.

Mapping diagrams

The equation $p = \frac{k}{v}$ can be thought of as a way of linking a value of the volume, v, with a value of the pressure. For instance, if $k = 10$, then $p = \frac{10}{v}$. So if $v = 1$, $p = \frac{10}{1} = 10$.

Thus 1 is 'sent' or 'mapped' to 10 by the equation.

If $v = 2$, $p = \frac{10}{2} = 5$. So 2 is 'mapped' to 5.

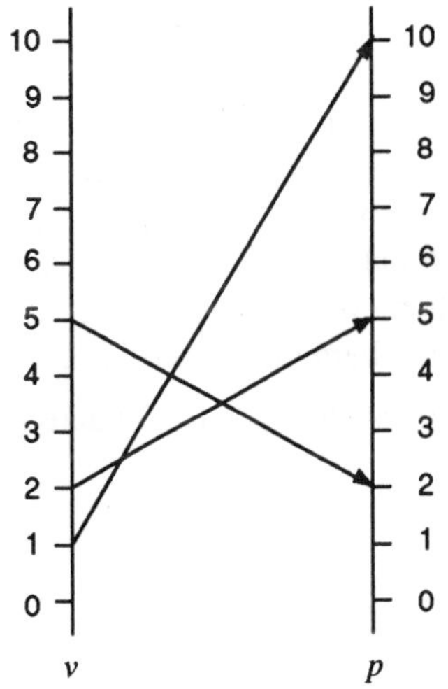

The figure opposite shows how several possible values of v are mapped to corresponding values of p. The formula $p = \frac{k}{v}$ is a **mapping** - it links the values in one set of numbers (here the set of volumes) with another set of numbers (the set of possible pressures). The set of all possible volumes, greater than zero, is called the **domain** of the mapping. The set of all possible pressures (again, any number greater than zero) is the **range** of the mapping.

Another example of a possible mapping is $F = \sqrt{T}$, $T \geq 0$. The domain is any number greater than or equal to zero. This mapping is rather different to $p = \frac{k}{v}$, however, as it gives two 'answers' for every value in the domain. For instance, $\sqrt{4}$ is +2 or −2, since $(+2)^2 = 4$ and $(-2)^2 = 4$. The figure opposite shows the graph of F. The range of F is any number, positive or negative.

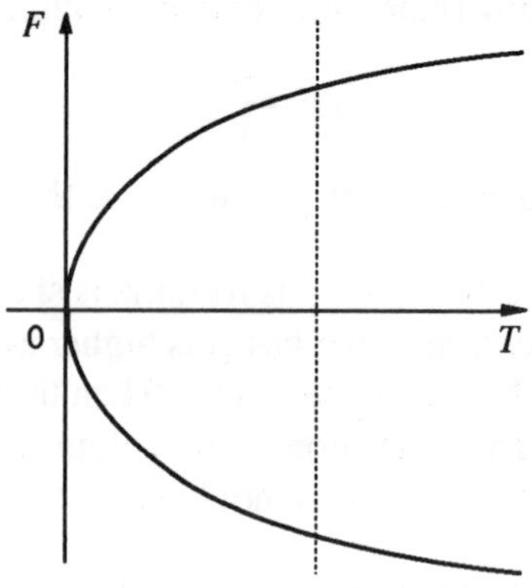

A mapping which gives one, and only one value, for every number in its domain is called a **function**. So the mapping

$$p = \frac{k}{v},\ v > 0$$

is a function, but the mapping

$$F = \sqrt{T},\ T \geq 0$$

is not, as it gives more than one answer for some members of its domain.

Changing the rule to get a function

Notice that the domain can be vital when deciding if a mapping is a function or not. For example, if the domain of $p = \frac{k}{v}$ is any value of v, positive or negative, including zero, the mapping ceases to be a function. This is because when $v = 0$, p cannot be calculated.

However, it is possible to adapt the rule for F to make it into a function. Suppose

$$F = +\sqrt{T},\ T \geq 0$$

which means that F is the positive square root of T. The graph of this mapping is shown opposite. If a vertical line is drawn across the graph, it will cross the graph only once. (In the previous figure a vertical line will cross the graph only twice - showing that there are two members of the range for each member of the domain). In fact mathematicians avoid this problem by usually agreeing that $\sqrt{x}$ means the positive square root.

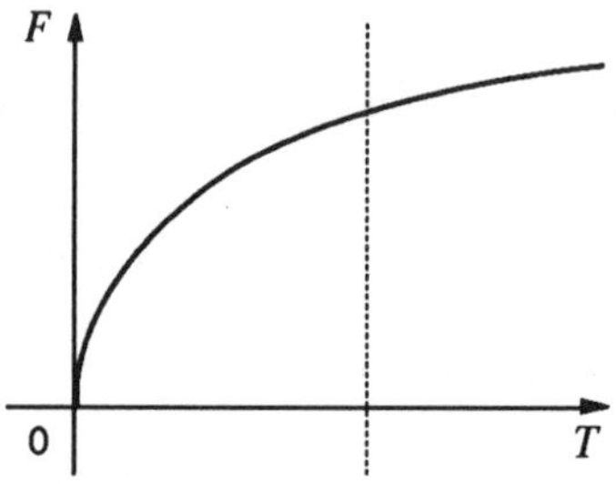

Number sets

Sets of numbers which are often used as domains or ranges have names, so that they can be described accurately. These were introduced in Section 1.3.

Any number on a number line, including fractions and decimals and any number in between them, is called a **real** number. The set of 'real' numbers is denoted by $\mathbb{R}$. Unless otherwise stated, you can usually assume that a domain is the real number set, or a part of it. Other commonly used sets of numbers are the **integers**, which are the positive and negative 'whole' numbers

$$..., -2, -1, 0, 1, 2, ...$$

Other domains and ranges are usually described using set notation, like the range in this next example.

Example

The table below shows the current postal rates in the U.K. for first class letters.

Weight up to	60 g	100 g	150 g	200 g
Postage	25p	38p	47p	57p

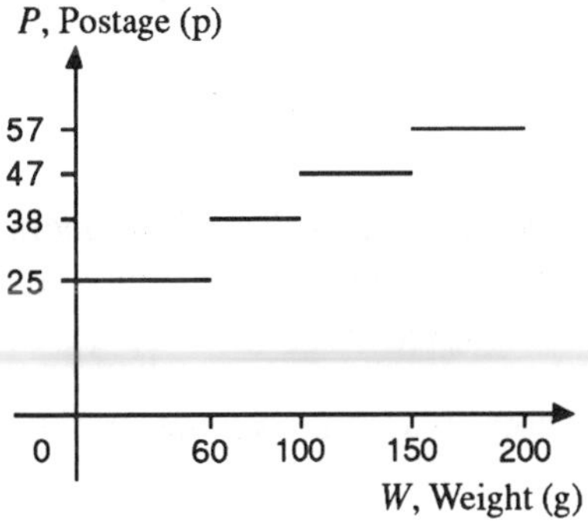

This is a mapping from part of the real numbers (between 0 and 200), to a 'discrete' range. This means that the range contains only certain values. In this case, the range is the set of numbers $\{25, 38, 47, 57\}$. The graph of this mapping is shown opposite.

A vertical line drawn across the graph will cut it only once, so this mapping is a function, even though it does not appear to have a 'formula' of the usual sort. It is possible to write down a kind of formula, however ;

$$\text{Postage, } P = \begin{cases} 25 \text{ for } 0 < W \le 60 \\ 38 \text{ for } 60 < W < 100 \\ ....\text{etc.} \end{cases}$$

The value of P changes in steps as the weight increases, so it is necessary to have different rules for different parts of the domain.

Activity 4

Use a graph plotting program or a graphic calculator to make sketches illustrating the following rules. By looking at the sketches, decide on a domain which will make the rule a function.

(a) $y=\frac{1}{x-5}$ (b) $y=\frac{3-x}{1-x}$ (c) $y=+\sqrt{x-2}$

(d) $y=1-x^2$ (e) $y=\frac{1}{x^2}$ (f) $y=\frac{2}{1-x^3}$.

Function notation

Returning to the mapping of volume to pressure met earlier in this section, another way of writing the mapping or function is illustrated by

$$p: v \mapsto \frac{k}{v},\ v \in \mathbb{R},\ v>0.$$

This is read as p is the function which maps v to $\frac{k}{v}$ where v is any real number greater than zero. The more usual way of writing a function is

$$p(v)=\frac{k}{v},\ v \in \mathbb{R},\ v>0$$

which illustrates that p is a function of v. In what follows the second method will generally be used, but you should be aware of the alternative.

Another example is given by the function

$$F: t \mapsto +\sqrt{t},\ t \in \mathbb{R},\ t \geq 0$$

or in the usual notation

$$F(t)=+\sqrt{t},\ t \in \mathbb{R},\ t \geq 0.$$

Hence, when $t=4$, $F(4)=+\sqrt{4}=2$, and in general if $t=a$,

$$F(a)=+\sqrt{a};$$

when $t=b^2$,

$$F\left(b^2\right)=+\sqrt{b^2}=b.$$

Exercise 2A

1. f is a function defined by the equation

   $f(x) = x^2 + 2.$

   Find the value of

   (a) $f(2)$ (b) $f(-1)$ (c) $f(0)$

   (d) $f(a^2)$ (e) $f(1-a)$

   (where a is a constant real number).

2. g is defined by $g(x) = \frac{1}{x}$

   Find the value of the following if possible

   (a) $g(1)$ (b) $g(-1)$ (c) $g(0)$

   (d) $g(a^2)$ (e) $g(1-a)$

   (where a is a constant real number).

3. For each of the following rules, use a graphic calculator or computer to make a sketch, for values of x between −10 and +10. Use your sketches to work out a domain for each mapping which will make each one a function.

   (a) $f: x \mapsto \frac{1}{x^3}$ (b) $g: x \mapsto x^5$

   (c) $h: x \mapsto \frac{1}{x+2}$ (d) $m: x \mapsto +\sqrt{1-x}$.

4. The wind chill temperature, T°C, depends on the actual temperature, t°C, and the wind speed, v mph; an appropriate formula for T is given by

   $T = 33 + \left(0.45 + 0.29\sqrt{v} - 0.02v\right)(t - 33)$

   for $t > -273°$, $v \geq 5$. Sketch a graph of T against t for varying wind speeds; for example $v = 10$, 15 and 20 mph.

2.2 Some important graphs

Many of the functions which arise from problems can be 'built up' from simpler functions. In this section you will see how some of these simpler functions behave by looking at their graphs. This will help you to sketch more complicated functions later on.

Activity 5 Some well known curves

(a) Use a computer or calculator to make sketches of the following curves on the same pair of axes. Make the sketches for values of x between −2 and + 2, and the y values between −20 and + 20.

$$y = x,\ y = x^2,\ y = x^3,\ y = x^4,\ y = x^5,\ y = x^6.$$

Which points do all the curves pass through? What happens to the curves between $x = 0$ and $x = 1$ as the power of x increases? What happens as the power increases for values of x greater than 1? Try to predict what the curves $y = x^7$ and $y = x^8$ will look like and check your answer on the computer or calculator.

(b) Sketch these curves on separate axes with x-axis from −2 to 2 and y from −10 to 10.

$$y = x^2,\ y = x^4,\ y = \frac{1}{x^2},\ y = \frac{1}{x^4}$$

Describe any symmetry these graphs have.

(c) Now sketch these graphs on four pairs of axes like the ones you have just used.

$$y = x,\ y = x^3,\ y = \frac{1}{x},\ y = \frac{1}{x^3}$$

Describe any symmetry these graphs have. (Use the term 'rotational symmetry' in the description).

Activity 6 Odd and even powers

The first four graphs in part (b) of Activity 5 were all for even powers of x, whilst the graphs in part (c) were all for odd powers of x. Use the knowledge you have gained from these graphs to describe the symmetry of the following graphs. Then check your answers by using a computer or calculator to see the graphs.

(a) $y = x^{10}$, (b) $y = x^{11}$, (c) $y = \frac{1}{x^5}$,

(d) $y = x^2 - 3$, (e) $y = x^3 + 1$, (f) $y = x - 2$.

Were you surprised by any of the graphs? If so, try to find out why you were wrong.

Activity 7 Fractional powers

It is possible to find the value of a fractional power. Chapter 9 covers this in more detail. Using your graph plotting device, sketch these curves on the same axes, with x values from -1 to $+2$ and y values from -1 to 8.

$$y = x^{\frac{1}{2}},\quad y = x^{\frac{1}{3}},\quad y = x^1,\quad y = x^{\frac{3}{2}},$$

$$y = x^2,\quad y = x^{\frac{5}{2}},\quad y = x^3.$$

Which points do all the curves have in common?

What happens as the power of x increases when x is between 0 and 1, and when x is more than 1?

Do all the curves exist for x values less than zero?

Shapes of graphs

The graph for any power of x will pass through the points (0, 0) and (1, 1). When x is between 0 and 1, the higher the power of x, the lower the result becomes. For example

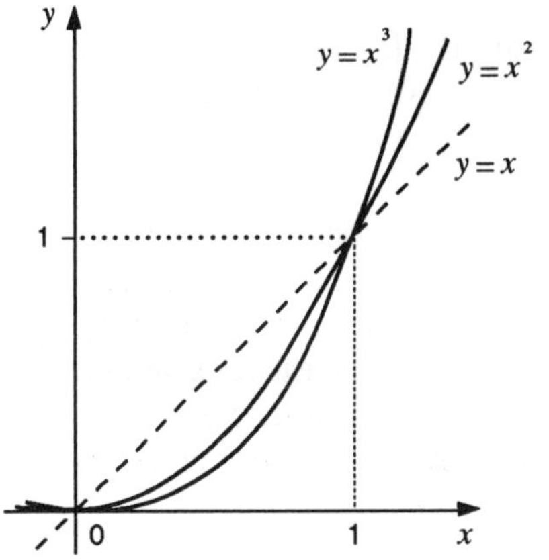

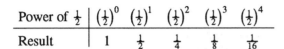

Power of $\frac{1}{2}$	$(\frac{1}{2})^0$	$(\frac{1}{2})^1$	$(\frac{1}{2})^2$	$(\frac{1}{2})^3$	$(\frac{1}{2})^4$
Result	1	$\frac{1}{2}$	$\frac{1}{4}$	$\frac{1}{8}$	$\frac{1}{16}$

This means that the graphs of powers of x get 'flatter' as the power increases when x is between 0 and 1. This is shown in the figure opposite.

When x is larger than 1, the higher the power of x the larger the result:

Power of 2	2^0	2^1	2^2	2^3	2^4
Result	1	2	4	8	16

This means that the curve of a higher power of x will be higher than the curve of a lower power when x is greater than 1. So the curve of a higher power 'overtakes' the curve of a lower power when $x = 1$. This is illustrated above.

*Odd and even functions

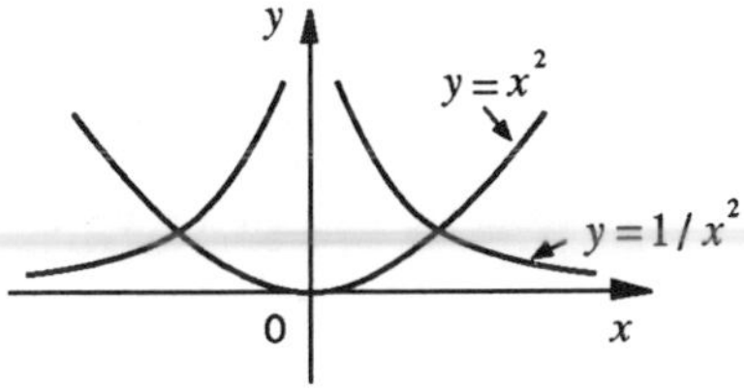

The curves for even powers of x are symmetrical about the y-axis. Any function whose curve has the y-axis as a line of symmetry is therefore called an **even** function. The graph of two even functions are shown opposite.

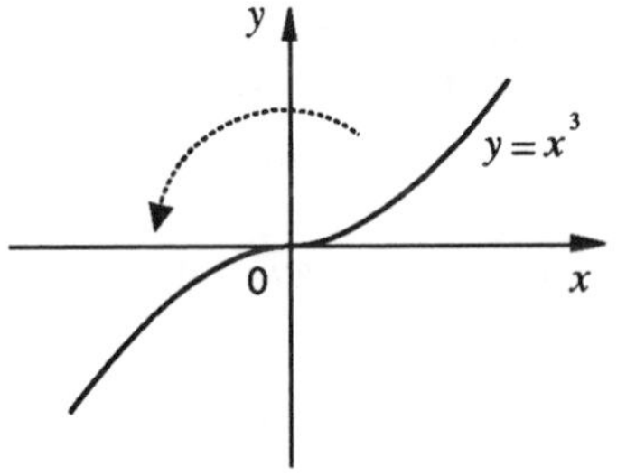

Curves for odd powers of x have two fold rotational symmetry about (0, 0). That is, the right hand side of the curve can be rotated through 180° about (0, 0) so that it fits onto the left hand side. This is illustrated for the graph of $y = x^3$. Functions having graphs with this kind of rotational symmetry are called **odd** functions.

Obviously, if you know already that a function is even or odd, you can easily sketch the whole of its graph if you know one half of it.

Example

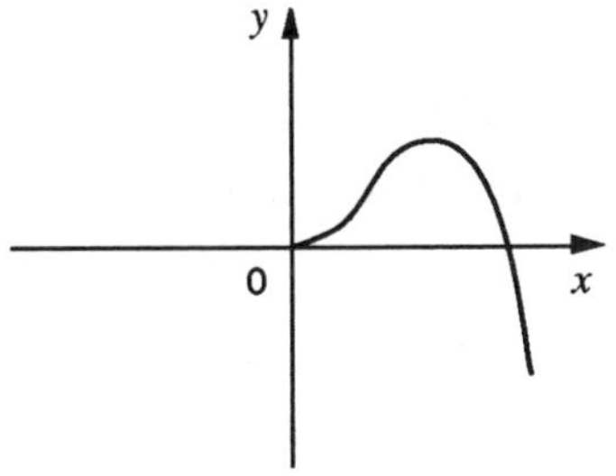

One part of the graph of $y = f(x)$ is shown opposite. Complete the curve assuming that

(a) $f(x)$ is even,
(b) $f(x)$ is odd.

Solution

(a) If $f(x)$ is even, the curve must be symmetrical about the y-axis, so the curve will be the one shown opposite.

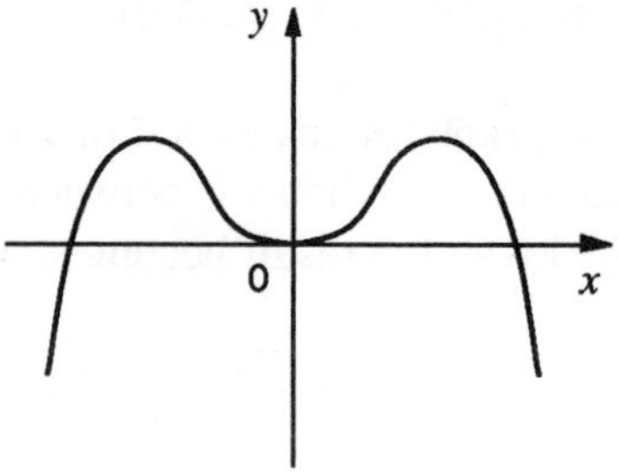

(b) If $f(x)$ is odd, the curve has two fold rotational symmetry about (0, 0). This produces the graph below.

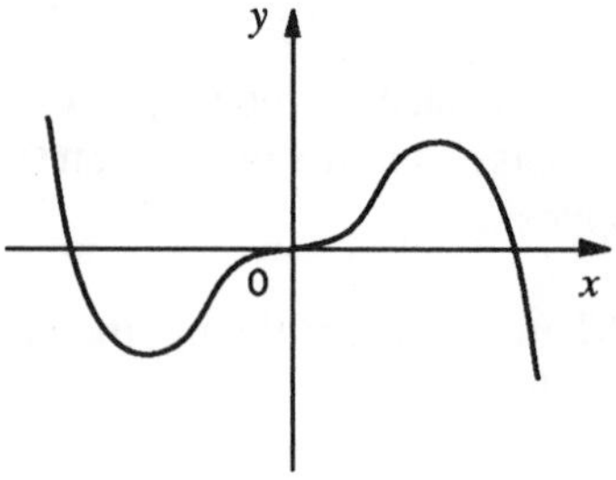

Most functions are neither even nor odd. For a function to be even, its equation must only contain even powers of x. For a graph to be odd, only odd powers of x may appear. (There are some functions which are not usually given in terms of powers of x, like the trigonometrical functions, which are even or odd however). A mixture of odd and even powers of x means the graph is neither odd nor even.

Example

Is $y=(x+1)^2$ even?

Solution

When the brackets are multiplied out the reason the function is **not** even is clear :

$$\begin{aligned} y &= (x+1)^2 \\ &= (x+1)(x+1) \\ &= x(x+1)+1(x+1) \\ &= x^2+x+x+1 \\ &= x^2+2x+1. \end{aligned}$$

This equation contains an even power (x^2) and an odd power (x), so the graph does not have reflection symmetry about the y-axis. The graph is sketched opposite. It is symmetrical, but about the line $x=-1$, not the y-axis.

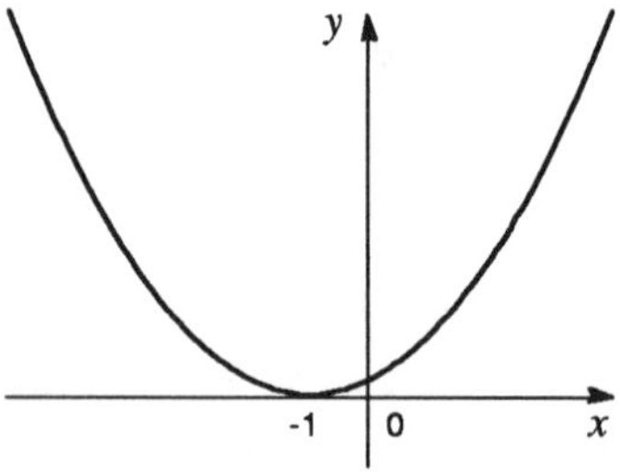

An alternative way of defining odd and even functions is to say that

$$f(x) \text{ is even if } f(-x)=f(x)$$
$$f(x) \text{ is odd if } f(-x)=-f(x).$$

Example

Are the following functions odd, even or neither?

(a) $f(x)=x^2+1$ (b) $f(x)=x^3$ (c) $f(x)=\frac{1}{x+1}$, $(x \neq -1)$.

Solution

(a) $f(-x) = (-x)^2 + 1 = x^2 + 1 = f(x)$ – hence even.

(b) $f(-x) = (-x)^3 = -x^3 = -f(x)$ – hence odd.

(c) $f(-x) = \dfrac{1}{-x+1} \neq \pm f(x)$ – hence neither even or odd.

*Exercise 2B

1. Decide whether the graphs illustrate an even function, an odd function, or neither:

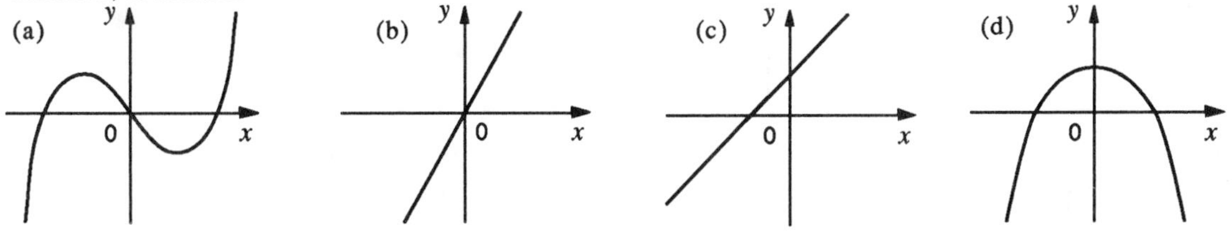

2. Copy and complete the following curves, assuming that the function each represents is i) even, and ii) odd.

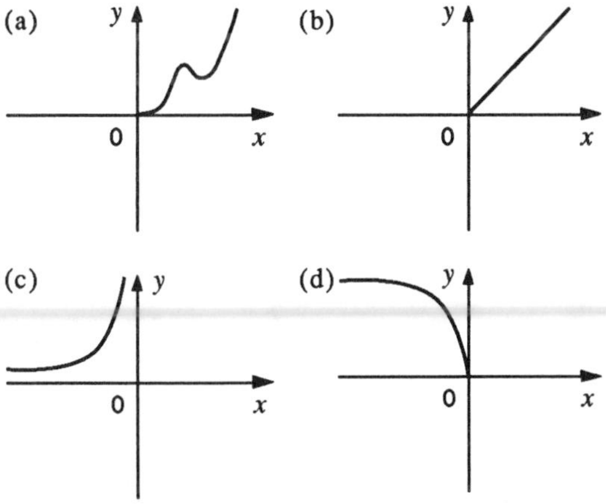

3. By looking only at the equation decide whether these functions are even, odd or neither.

   (a) $y = 3x$ (b) $y = 3x + 1$

   (c) $y = (x+2)^2$ (d) $y = x^2 + 2$

   (e) $y = \left(x^2 + 2\right)^2$

   (You will need to multiply out any bracket. Also note that a constant number can be thought of as an even power of x. For instance $2x^0 = 2 \times 1 = 2$ as $x^0 = 1$.)

2.3 Miscellaneous Exercises

1. Many shoes give both their U.K. size and European equivalent. For example,

   English adult size 12 = European size 47

   English adult size 5 = European size 38

   Use this information to construct a conversion graph between the two sizes. What does English size 0 correspond to in terms of European size?

   (English adult size 0 is in fact equivalent to junior size 13).

2. Give a reason why the domains for each of these functions are unsuitable, and give a domain that is acceptable. Also state the range.

   (a) $f(x) = \dfrac{1}{\sqrt{x}}$, $x \in \mathbb{R}$

   (b) $f(x) = \dfrac{1}{x-3}$, $x > 0$

   (c) $f(x) = \sqrt{6-x}$, $x > 0$

   (d) $f(x) = \dfrac{1}{(x-2)(x+3)}$, $x \in \mathbb{R}$.

3. Which of the graphs below represent functions?

(a)

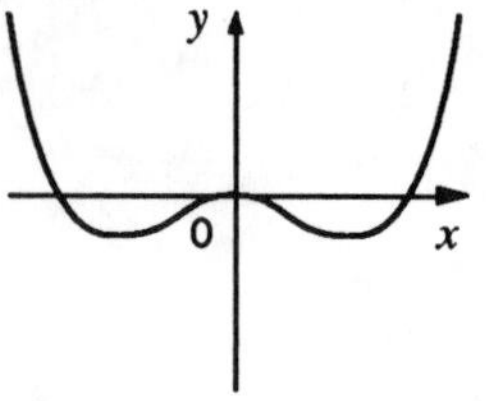

(b)

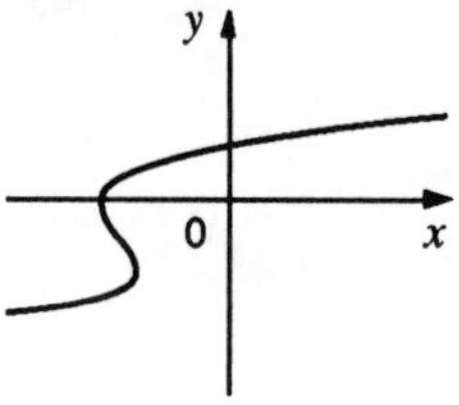

(c)

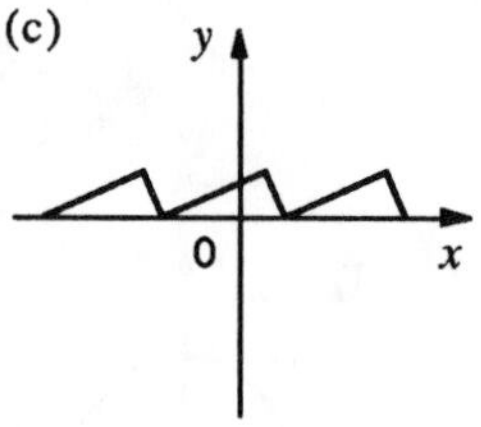

(d)

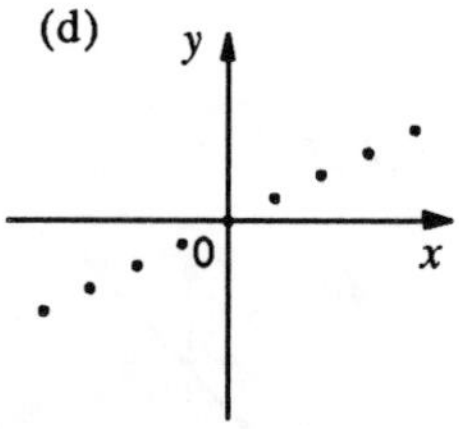

(e)

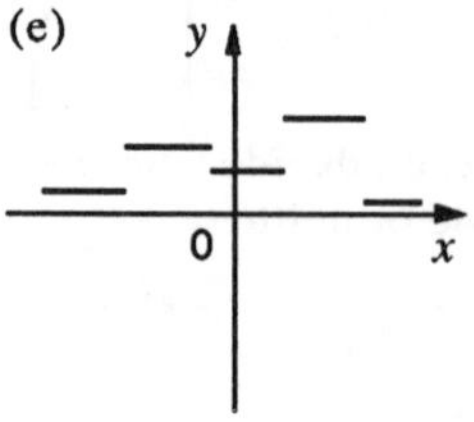

4. Let $f: x \mapsto \dfrac{1}{x^3 - 8}$, $x \in \mathbb{R}$, $x \neq 2$. Find:

(a) $f(0)$ (b) $f(1)$ (c) $f(-1)$ (d) $f(-2)$.

*5. State whether each of the following graphs represents an even or an odd function, or neither.

(a)

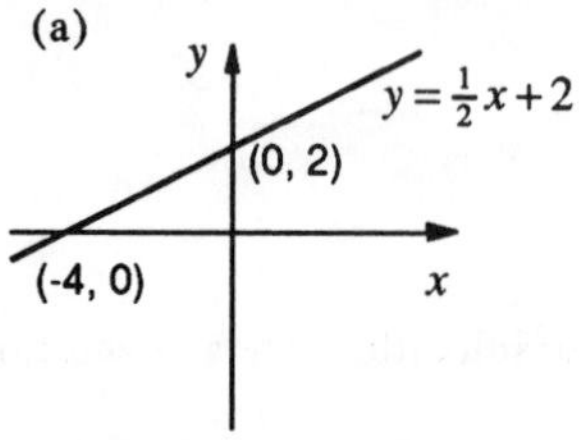

(b)

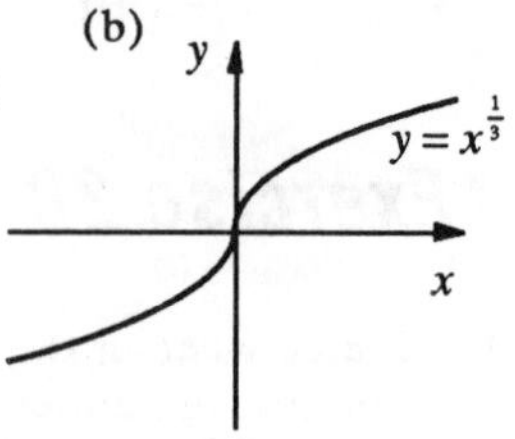

(c)

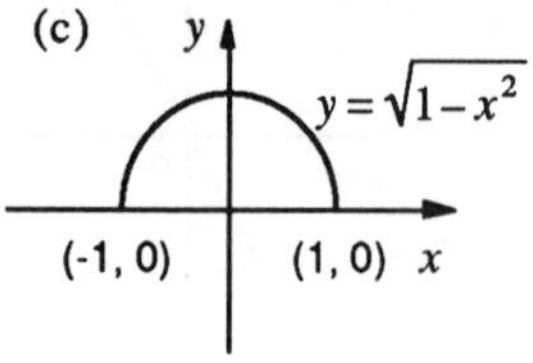

3 FUNCTIONS

Objectives

After studying this chapter you should

- understand what is meant by a composite function;
- understand the difference between $f(g(x))$ and $g(f(x))$;
- know what is meant by the inverse of a function;
- be able to sketch the graph of a function's inverse.

3.0 Introduction

You have now met a number of functions. Some have represented practical relationships whilst others have been simply mathematical functions. In this chapter, you will extend these ideas by looking at how two functions can be used to define another function, and considering how to find inverse functions, and what they represent. Whilst many of the functions to be studied will be quite complex mathematically, it is the practical application of mathematics which motivates the need for those extensions.

3.1 Composite functions

You have already met some quite complicated functions in the first two chapters. In this section you will see how **composite** functions can be built up, and why they are an important concept in mathematics. The idea of a composite function is introduced with a practical currency exchange rate example.

Example

A bank in the U.K. offers the exchange rate

$$£1 = \$1.7$$

plus an administration payment of £2 for each transaction. A similar shop in U.S.A. offers the exchange rate

$$\$1 = 1.6 \text{ marks}$$

plus an administration payment of $3 for each transaction. How many marks will you actually receive if you first exchange £10 into dollars in the U.K., and then into marks in the U.S.A?

Solution

It is easy enough to solve this problem in two numerical stages. Firstly the £10 is changed to dollars. Taking away the £2 transaction payment, leaves you with $\$1.7 \times 8 = \$13.6$.

Secondly the \$13.6 are changed into marks, remembering to take off \$3 transaction payment. So you have

$$10.6 \times 1.6 \text{ marks} = 16.96 \text{ marks}.$$

A more general approach is to form two functions to represent the two transactions. If t = amount in £, x = amount in \$ and y = amount in marks, then for the first transaction

$$\begin{aligned} x &= 1.7(t-2) \\ &= 1.7t - 3.4 \end{aligned}$$

and, since x is a function of t, write

$$x(t) = 1.7t - 3.4. \qquad (1)$$

Similarly, for the second transaction

$$\begin{aligned} y &= 1.6(x-3) \\ &= 1.6x - 4.8 \end{aligned}$$

and write

$$y(x) = 1.6x - 4.8 \qquad (2)$$

to show that y is a function of x. Since x in turn is a function of t, you can write y as a function of t by substituting (1) in (2) to give

$$\begin{aligned} y(x) = y(x(t)) & \\ &= 1.6x(t) - 4.8 \\ &= 1.6(1.7t - 3.4) - 4.8 \\ &= 2.72t - 5.44 - 4.8 \\ &= 2.72t - 10.24 \end{aligned}$$

i.e. $$f(t) = 2.72t - 10.24 \qquad (3)$$

where $$f(t) = y(x(t)).$$

Does equation (3) give the correct solution when $t = 10$?

The composite function $y(x(t))$ is written for short as $y_o x$.

Example

The functions f and g are defined by

$$f(t) = 4t - 3$$

$$g(t) = 2t - 1$$

Find the composite functions $f_o g$ and $g_o f$.

Solution

$$f_o g = f(g(t)) = f(2t-1)$$

$$= 4(2t-1) - 3$$

$$= 8t - 7.$$

whereas

$$g_o f = g(f(t)) = g(4t-3)$$

$$= 2(4t-3) - 1$$

$$= 8t - 7.$$

In this case the two composite functions $f_o g$ and $g_o f$ are identical. This is not generally true as you will see in the activity below.

Activity 1

The function f and g are defined by

$$f(x) = x^2 + 1$$

$$g(x) = x - 1$$

Is $f_o g = g_o f$ for any value of x?

As you should have seen composite functions are **not** usually commutative. That is, in general $f_o g \neq g_o f$. For instance, if

$$f(x) = x + 3,\ x \in \mathbb{R}$$

and $\quad g(x) = 2x,\ x \in \mathbb{R}$

then $f(g(x)) = f(2x)$

$= 2x + 3$ for $x \in \mathbb{R}$.

Similarly $g(f(x)) = g(x+3)$

$= 2(x+3)$

$= 2x + 6$ for $x \in \mathbb{R}$.

The two composite functions are clearly different for all values of x. Also note that, because the range of the function which is applied first is the domain for the second function, it is essential that the range of the first is suitable as a domain for the second.

Example

If $h(x) = \frac{1}{x}$, $x \in \mathbb{R}$, $x \neq 0$ and $m(x) = x - 2$, $x \in \mathbb{R}$, find suitable domains for the composite function $m_o h$ and $h_o m$.

Solution

Although $m(h(x)) = \frac{1}{x} - 2$, $x \in \mathbb{R}$, $x \neq 0$ is a function, there is a problem with the composite function $h(m(x))$.

$$h(m(x)) = h(x-2)$$

$$= \frac{1}{x-2}.$$

If the domain is chosen to be $x \in \mathbb{R}$, $x \neq 0$ which is the domain of the first function m, then x can be equal to 2.

However, $h(m(2)) = \frac{1}{2-2} = \frac{1}{0}$, and this does not exist.

So $x \in \mathbb{R}$, $x \neq 0$ is not suitable as a domain for $h_o m$.

If $x \in \mathbb{R}$, $x \neq 2$ is chosen as the domain, $h_o m$ will be defined for all the values given in the domain.

Exercise 3A

1. Work out composite functions $f_o g$ and $g_o f$ for each of the following pairs of functions. In each case, state a suitable domain for the composite function. (You may find a sketch of the composite function graph made with a computer or calculator helpful when checking your answer.)

   (a) $f(x) = x - 1$ and $g(x) = x^3$

   (b) $f(x) = +\sqrt{x}$ and $g(x) = x - 2$

   (c) $f(x) = \frac{1}{x}$ and $g(x) = x + 1$

   (d) $f(x) = x^2 - 1$ and $g(x) = \frac{1}{x}$

   (e) $f(x) = x + 3$ and $g(x) = x - 3$

   (f) $f(x) = 6 - x$ and $g(x) = 6 - x$.

2. Find the composite function $f_o g$ and $g_o f$ if

   $f(x) = 1 + \frac{1}{x}$ and $g(x) = x^2$.

3. Find the composite function $h_o f_o g$ if $f(x) = x - 3$,

   $g(x) = x^2$ and $h(x) = \frac{1}{x}$.

3.2 Inverse functions

In Chapter 2 you met the function that transforms degrees Celsius to degrees Fahrenheit, namely

$$F = \frac{9}{5}C + 32. \qquad (1)$$

Suppose you wanted to find the formula that gives degrees Celsius in terms of degrees Fahrenheit, then taking 32 from both sides

$$F - 32 = \frac{9}{5}C$$

and multiplying by $\frac{5}{9}$ gives

$$\boxed{C = \frac{5}{9}(F - 32)} \qquad (2)$$

This is an example of an **inverse** function.

Example

If $y =$ number of dollars and $x =$ equivalent number of pounds and $y = 1.7x$, express x in terms of y.

Solution

You must make x the subject of the formula when $y = 1.7x$.

This gives $x = \frac{y}{1.7}$

(in fact, exchange rates from dollars to pounds and pounds to dollars are not in practice equivalent, and there is usually a transaction charge)

Activity 2 Kepler's third law

In 1619 the astronomer *Kepler* announced his third law of planetary motion (dedicated to James II of England) which stated that the periodic time of a planet, T, is related to its average radius of orbit, say R, by the formula

$$T = kR^{\frac{3}{2}}.$$

Find the inverse function which expresses R as a function of T.

A special notation is introduced for inverse functions. For example, the temperature conversion formula, with x now denoting degrees Celsius and y degrees Fahrenheit,

$$y = f(x) = \frac{9}{5}x + 32 \qquad (3)$$

can be rearranged to give, $y - 32 = \frac{9}{5}x$ and $x = \frac{5}{9}(y - 32)$.

The inverse function is denoted by f^{-1}, so

$$f^{-1}(y) = \frac{5}{9}(y - 32).$$

Since y could be any variable, we can rewrite the inverse function as a function of the variable x as

$$f^{-1}(x) = \frac{5}{9}(x - 32). \qquad (4)$$

Note that the meaning of the variable x is different in (3) and (4). In (3), it represents the temperature in degrees Celsius, so that, for example, $20°\mathrm{C}$ will transform to $\frac{9}{5} \times 20 + 32 = 36 + 32 = 68°\mathrm{F}$. Whilst in (4), x represents degrees Fahrenheit, so that $77°\mathrm{F}$ transforms to $\frac{5}{9} \times (77 - 32) = \frac{5}{9} \times 45 = 25°\mathrm{C}$.

Example

Find the inverse of $f(x) = \dfrac{1}{1-x} + 2$, $x \in \mathbb{R}$, $x \neq 1$, and state the domain of the inverse function.

Solution

Let $f(x) = y$, so that

$$y = \frac{1}{1-x} + 2$$

$$\Rightarrow \quad y - 2 = \frac{1}{1-x}$$

$$\Rightarrow \quad (1-x)(y-2) = 1$$

$$\Rightarrow \quad 1 - x = \frac{1}{y-2}$$

$$\Rightarrow \quad x = 1 - \frac{1}{y-2}.$$

This formula gives the inverse function as

$$f^{-1}(y) = 1 - \frac{1}{y-2}.$$

Replacing y by x, this becomes

$$f^{-1}(x) = 1 - \frac{1}{(x-2)}.$$

As $f^{-1}(x)$ is the inverse of $f(x)$, its **domain** will be the **range** of $f(x)$. This is because its task is to map members of the original range back onto the corresponding members of the domain.

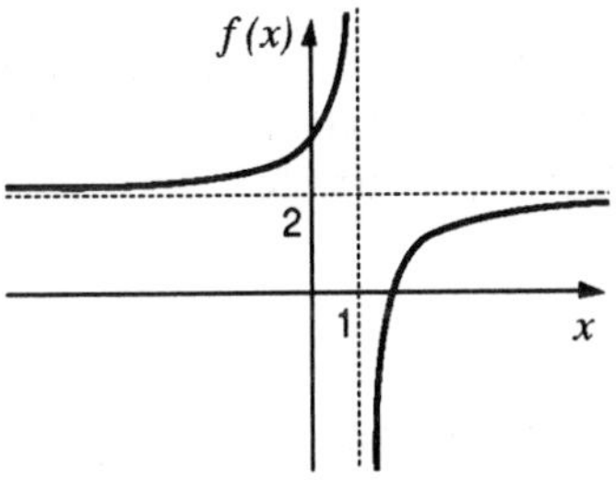

The figure opposite shows the graph of $f(x)$. The range is all the real numbers, except 2. There is no value of x for which $f(x) = 2$, as shown by the horizontal dotted line.

So the domain of $f^{-1}(x)$ is the set of real numbers, except 2. This means the full definition of $f^{-1}(x)$ is

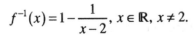

$$f^{-1}(x) = 1 - \frac{1}{x-2}, \; x \in \mathbb{R}, \; x \neq 2.$$

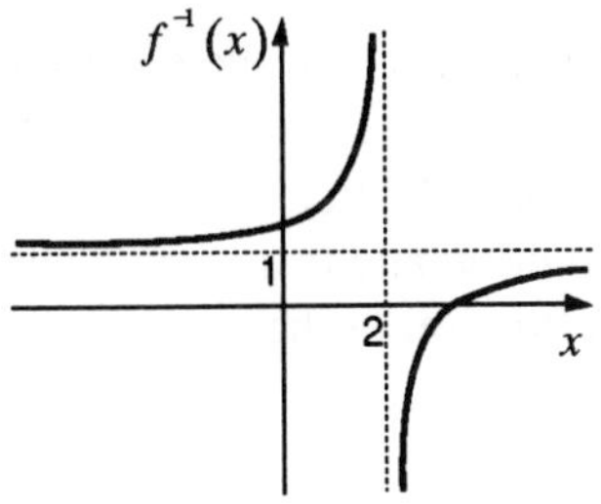

The graph of $f^{-1}(x)$ is shown opposite.

(Note also that the range of $f^{-1}(x)$ is the domain of $f(x)$).

Exercise 3B

Find the inverses of these functions.
State the domain of each inverse.

1. $f(x)=x+2, x \in \mathbb{R}$
2. $f(x)=4x-1, x \in \mathbb{R}$
3. $f(x)=4x-2, x \in \mathbb{R}$
4. $f(x)=x, x \in \mathbb{R}$
5. $f(x)=1-x, x \in \mathbb{R}$
6. $f(x)=\frac{3}{x}, x \in \mathbb{R}, x \neq 0$
7. $f(x)=\frac{1}{x+2}, x \in \mathbb{R}, x \neq -2$
8. $f(x)=\frac{1}{5-x}+2, x \in \mathbb{R}, x \neq 5.$

3.3 Symmetry about the line $y=x$

Functions and their inverses have an interesting geometrical property as you will see below.

Activity 3 The graph of an inverse function

Below is a list of functions, each with its inverse. On graph paper, plot and draw the graph of a function, together with its inverse, on the same axes. Repeat this process for each function in the list. Use the same scale on both axes. Use values of x between -6 and $+6$, and y values between -12 and $+12$.

(a) $f(x)=2x, f^{-1}(x)=\frac{1}{2}x;$

(b) $f(x)=x-4, f^{-1}(x)=x+4;$

(c) $f(x)=x^2, (x \in \mathbb{R}, x \geq 0), f^{-1}(x)=+\sqrt{x}, (x \in \mathbb{R}, x \geq 0).$

Describe the relationship between the graph of each function and that of its inverse. You may find drawing the line $y=x$ on each pair of axes helpful.

In the previous Section 3.2, the inverse of the function $f(x)=\frac{9}{5}x+32$ was found to be $f^{-1}(x)=\frac{5}{9}(x-32)$.

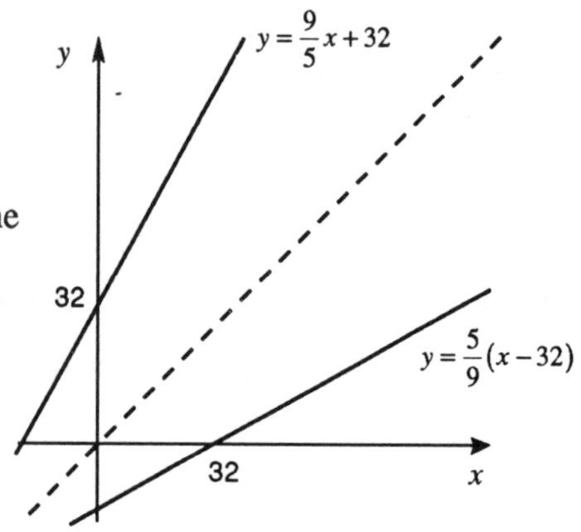

The figure opposite shows the graphs of these two functions on the same pair of axes. The dotted line is the graph $y=x$. These graphs illustrate a general relationship between the graph of a function and that of its inverse, namely that one graph is the **reflection** of the other in the line $y=x$.

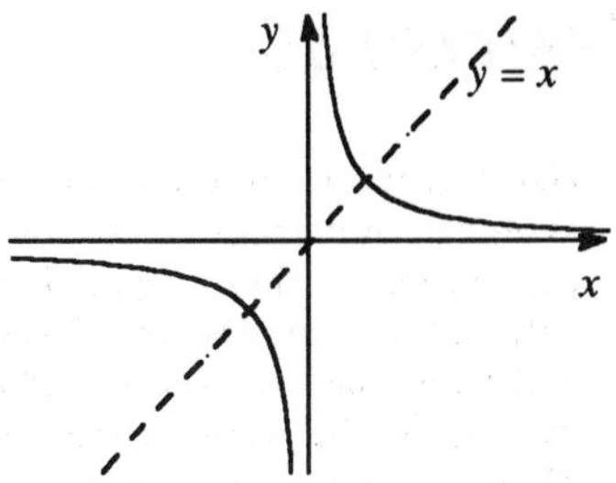

There is an interesting group of functions which have graphs that are symmetrical about the line $y = x$. The figure opposite shows such a graph, for the function $f(x) = \frac{1}{x}$. The graph of its inverse function will be the reflection of this curve in the dotted line, but as the curve is symmetrical about this line, the inverse function will be the same as the function itself.

A function which is its own inverse is called a **self inverse** function. In this case, if $f(x) = \frac{1}{x}$, then $f^{-1}(x) = \frac{1}{x}$ too.

One final point that is worth noting is that

$$f\left(f^{-1}(x)\right) = f^{-1}\left(f(x)\right) = x.$$

For example, you have already seen that if $f(x) = \frac{9}{5}x + 32$,

then $$f^{-1}(x) = \frac{5}{9}(x - 32).$$

Now $$f\left(f^{-1}(x)\right) = f\left(\frac{5}{9}(x - 32)\right)$$

$$= \frac{9}{5}\left(\frac{5}{9}(x - 32)\right) + 32$$

$$= x - 32 + 32$$

$$= x,$$

and similarly for $f^{-1}\left(f(x)\right)$.

Activity 4

If $f(x) = 4x - 3$, find $f^{-1}(x)$ and check that

$$f\left(f^{-1}(x)\right) = f^{-1}\left(f(x)\right) = x.$$

Exercise 3C

1. Use a graphic calculator or computer to make sketches of each of these functions. (You can plot and draw them if you do not have a calculator or computer at hand). Use values of x and y between –5 and +5 and on each pair of axes show the graph of the inverse function. You will find that superimposing the line $y=x$ is helpful. Use the same scales for x and y.

   (a) $f(x)=x+3$ (b) $f(x)=x^3$ (c) $f(x)=-2x$

   (d) $f(x)=\frac{-1}{x}$ (e) $f(x)=4-x$ (f) $f(x)=\frac{1}{x^3}$.

2. For (b) and (c) in Question 1 above check that $f\left(f^{-1}(x)\right)=f^{-1}\left(f(x)\right)=x$.

3. Copy the graphs below and sketch the graphs of the inverse functions.

   (a)

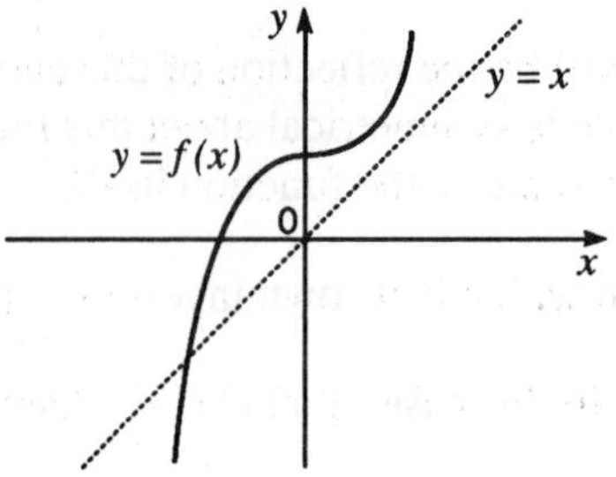

   (b)

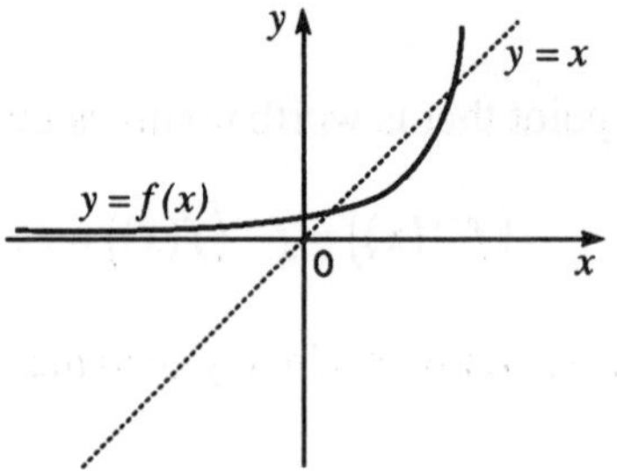

3.4 Functions with no inverse

In Section 2.1 you saw that for an algebraic rule, or formula, to be a function, the rule must map each member of the domain to one and only one member of the range. That is, it must give only one answer. So, for example, if $y^2=x$ then it is not possible to express y as a function of x since $y=\pm\sqrt{x}$; that is, for $x=4$, $y=\pm 2$, *etc.* One value of x gives two values of y. However, $y=\sqrt{x}$, $x\geq 0$, is a function, as there is only one number that is the positive square root of x, for any real number x, which is greater than zero.

You can tell if a mapping is a function from its graph. If a line parallel to the y-axis crosses the graph in more than one place, the mapping is **not** a function. For instance, the figure opposite shows that the value x=2 in the domain is mapped to three values in the range, so this is not the graph of a function.

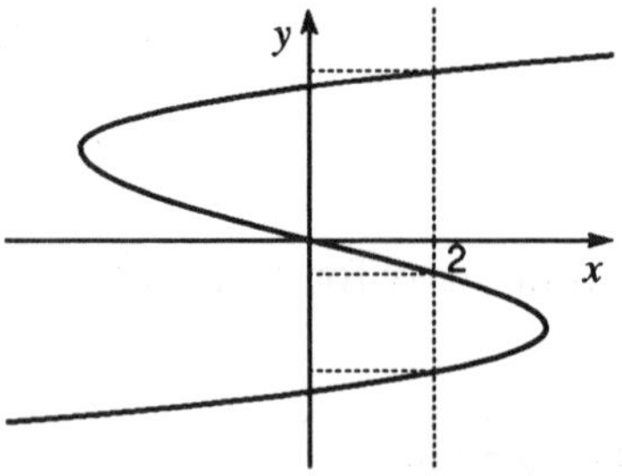

A **many to one** function will map different members of its domain to the same member of the range. An example of such a function is

$$f(x)=x^2, x\in\mathbb{R}.$$

For instance $f(3)=3^2=9$ and $f(-3)=(-3)^2=9$. So two values in the domain, 3 and – 3, are mapped to the same value in the range, namely 9.

Activity 5

Use a calculator or computer to draw the graph of $y = x^2$ for values of x between -3 and $+3$. Use the same scales on both axes. Draw on the same pair of axes the graph of the inverse mapping, by using the reflection property.

Does the graph represent a function?

If the domain of $f(x)$ is changed from $x \in \mathbb{R}$ to $x \in \mathbb{R},\ x \geq 0$, make a sketch of $f(x)$ on new axes. Also show what the graph of the inverse must look like on the same pair of axes. Is this the graph of a function?

Activity 6

An even function has a graph which is symmetrical about the y-axis. Draw some sketchs of functions which are even, like the one shown opposite. Then show on the same axes what the inverse mapping should look like.

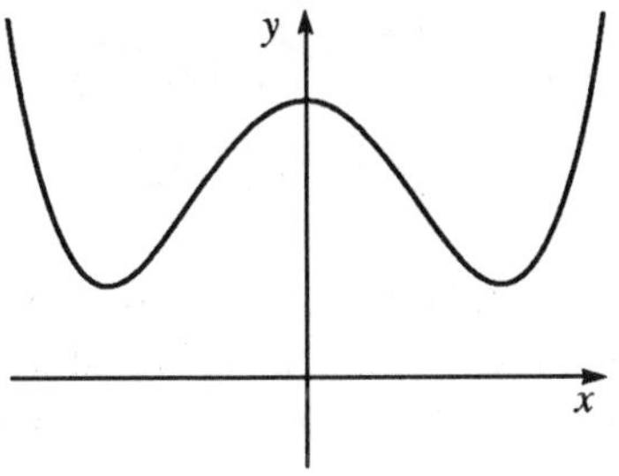

A many to one function maps different values in the domain to the same value in the range. The graph of a many to one function can be crossed in more than one place by a line parallel to the x-axis, as shown opposite.

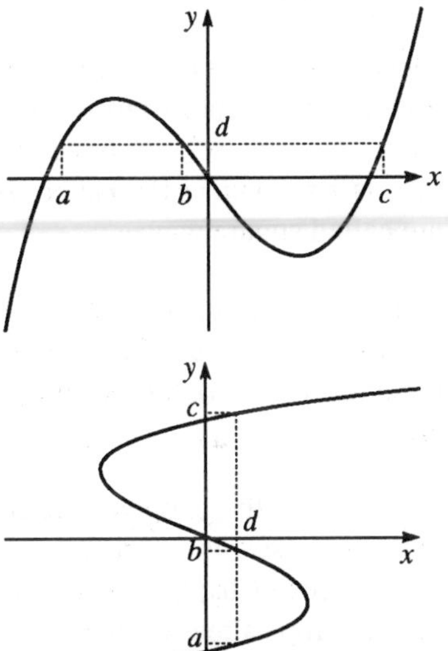

The inverse of such a function must therefore map the same value to different members of the original function's domain. In the graph opposite, d must be mapped to a, b and c. This means that the inverse **cannot** be a function, (as it does not send every member of **its** domain to only one member of its range).

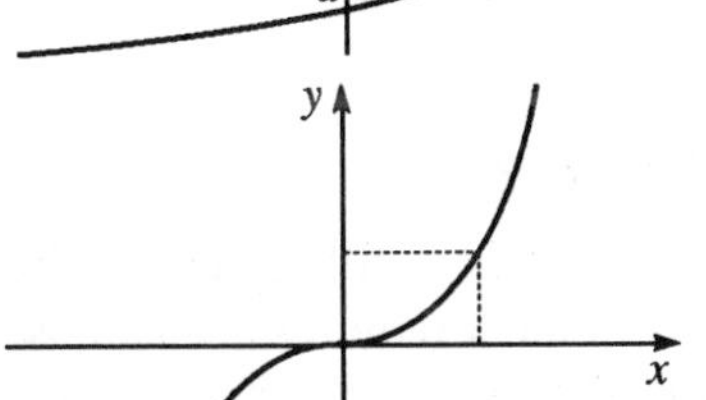

So a many to one function cannot have an inverse function.

If a function is to have an inverse, the function cannot be many to one - it must be **one to one**. That is, every member of its domain is mapped to its own unique member of the range. The graph of such a function can only be crossed by a line parallel to the x-axis **once**, as shown in the figure opposite.

Exercise 3D

Use a graphic calculator or computer to sketch the graphs of these functions. Check whether a horizontal line can be drawn which crosses each graph in more than one place to decide whether each graph is one to one or many to one. For the functions which are one to one draw the graph of the inverse function in each case using the reflection relationship.

1. $f(x)=x^2+2,\ x\in\mathbb{R}$
2. $f(x)=x^3+2,\ x\in\mathbb{R}$
3. $f(x)=\frac{1}{x^2},\ x\in\mathbb{R},\ x\neq 0$
4. $f(x)=(x+1)^2,\ x\in\mathbb{R}$
5. $f(x)=x^3+x^2-6x,\ x\in\mathbb{R}$
6. $f(x)=x^3-9x^2+27x-27,\ x\in\mathbb{R}$
7. $f(x)=\frac{1}{x-2}+1,\ x\in\mathbb{R},\ x\neq 2$
8. $f(x)=3,\ x\in\mathbb{R}$.

3.5 Modelling repeating patterns

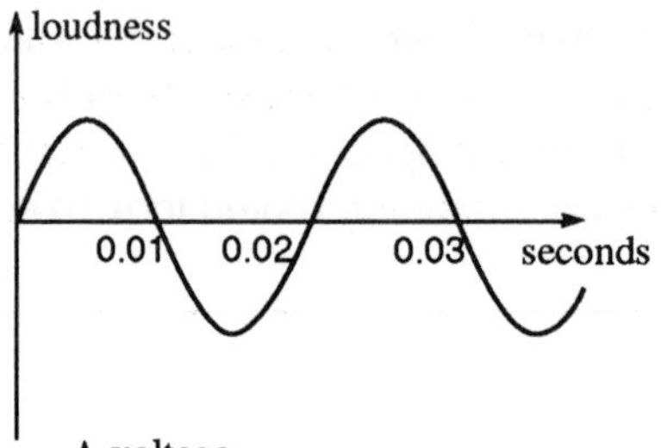

The sound produced by a tuning fork is a wave shape when its 'loudness' is plotted against time. This is shown in the first graph opposite. This wave repeats itself after 0.02 seconds - the **period** of the wave.

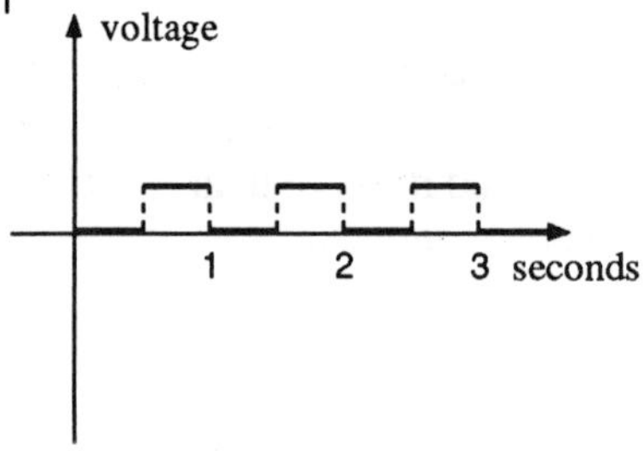

Electronic clocks count **beats** produced by an internal circuit. Some circuits, for instance, can be made to produce a voltage which repeats itself as shown in the second graph. The period here is 1 second, as the pattern is repeated after this time. These are called square waves.

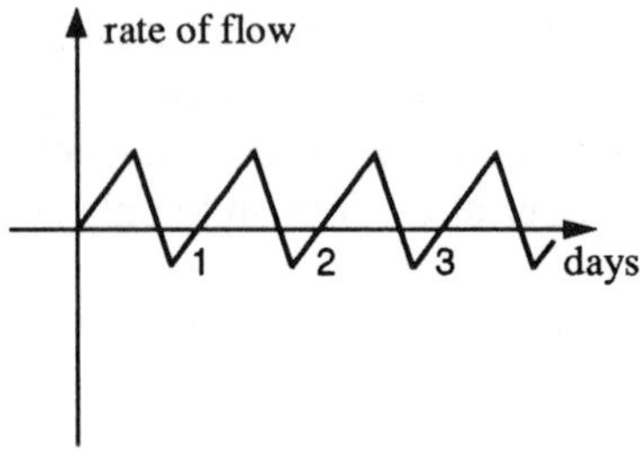

A number of living organisms, especially plants, exhibit repeating cycles of behaviour. For instance, a plant's stem may conduct sap to its leaves in a daily repeating pattern, as shown in the third graph.

Patterns like these are very common. The most important among them are based on trigonometric functions, and these are covered separately in Chapter 10. However, some can be modelled with the functions already covered.

Example

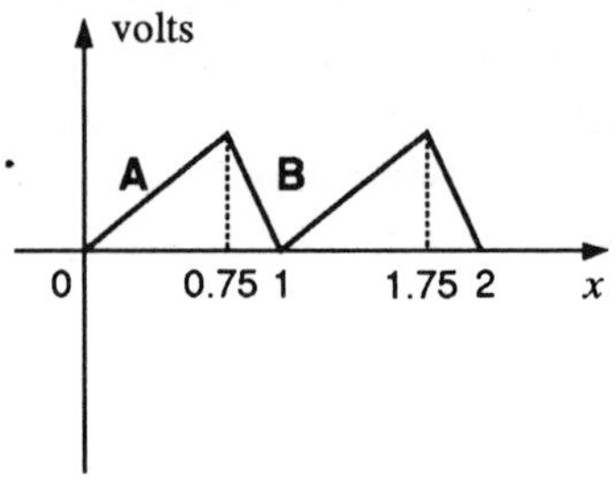

A 'sawtooth' oscillation is a pattern which occurs in electronics. An engineer requires such an oscillation to have the shape shown opposite, repeating once every second.

The equation of the line marked A is $y = \frac{8x}{3}$. The equation of the line marked B is $y = -8x + 8$. So the function which models the first 'tooth' is $f(x) = \begin{cases} \frac{8}{3}x, & 0 \le x \le 0.75 \\ -8x+8, & 0.75 \le x \le 1 \end{cases}$

The period of the function is 1 second, and this completes the definition of the function.

Example

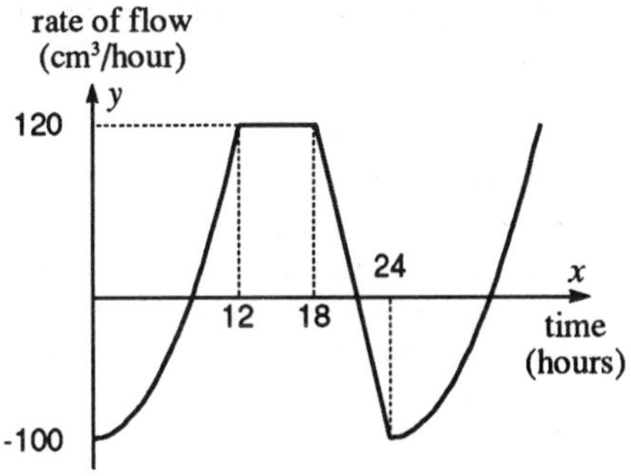

The rate of flow of sap in a certain species of plant is thought to follow the pattern as shown opposite. A positive rate of flow means the flow is upwards.

The section of the graph for values of x between 0 and 12 is the graph of

$$y = \frac{220}{144}x^2 - 100.$$

The part when x is between 12 and 18 is constant at 120, so its equation for these values of x is $y = 120$. The last part of the cycle, when x is between 18 and 24, is given by the graph of

$$y = -\frac{220}{6}x + 780.$$

So the function which models this pattern is

$$f(x) = \begin{cases} \frac{220}{144}x^2 - 100 & \text{for } 0 \le x \le 12 \\ 120 & \text{for } 12 \le x \le 18 \\ -\frac{220}{6}x + 780 & \text{for } 18 \le x \le 24 \end{cases}$$

with a period of 24 hours.

Example

Sketch the graph $f(x) = \begin{cases} x & \text{for } 0 \le x < 2 \\ 0 & \text{for } 2 \le x \le 3 \end{cases}$

when $f(x)$ has a period of 3 units, for values of x between –3 and 6.

The solution is shown opposite.

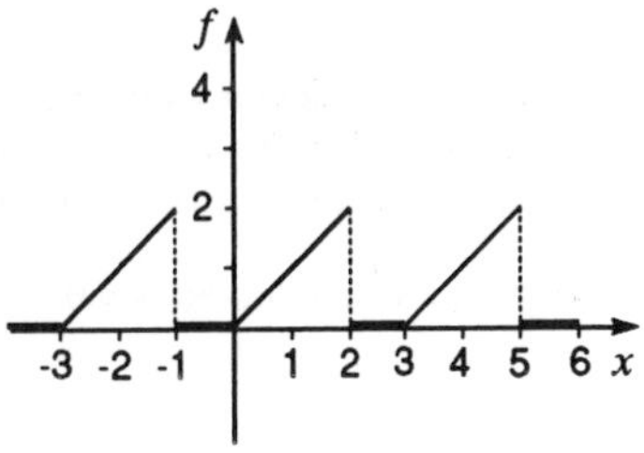

Exercise 3E

1. A square wave generator produces a voltage that is given by the function $f(x)$, where

$$f(x) = \begin{cases} 0 \text{ if } 0 \le x \le \frac{1}{2} \\ 1 \text{ if } \frac{1}{2} < x \le 1 \end{cases}$$

and $f(x)$ has a period of 1 unit. Draw the graph for values of x between 0 and 3.

2. The stock level of coal at a small power station (in thousand tonne units) can be modelled by the function

$$f(x) = 20 - 2x \text{ for } 0 \le x \le 7$$

where x is the number of days. The function has a period of seven days. Draw the graph of the function for values of x between 0 and 21. What is the lowest level the stocks ever reach, and how regular are the deliveries? Why would the following function be unlikely to represent a stock level problem:

$$g(x) = 20 - 2x \text{ for } 0 \le x \le 10?$$

3. Draw the graph of $f(x)$ for values of x between 0 and 12, where

$$f(x) = \begin{cases} 1-(x-1)^2 \text{ for } 0 \le x \le 2 \\ (x-3)^2 - 1 \text{ for } 2 \le x \le 4 \end{cases}$$

$f(x)$ has a period of 4 units. You may need to plot and draw the first 'cycle' of the pattern.

4. Plot and draw the graph of the function below, showing a full two periods of its cycle.

$f(x)$ has a period of 2 units. You may need to plot and draw the first 'cycle' of the pattern.

$$f(x) = \begin{cases} \frac{1}{2}x^2 \text{ for } 0 \le x \le 1 \\ \frac{1}{x} - \frac{1}{2} \text{ for } 1 \le x \le 2 \end{cases}$$

3.6 Miscellaneous Exercises

1. Using a graphic calculator or computer to make sketches of the following functions decide whether each has an inverse function or not. If an inverse exists, find the algebraic rule for it, and state its domain.

(a) $f(x) = 3x - 2, x \in \mathbb{R}$

(b) $f(x) = 4 - 3x, x \in \mathbb{R}$

(c) $f(x) = x^2 - 1, x \in \mathbb{R}$

(d) $f(x) = x^2 - 1, x \in \mathbb{R}, x \geq 0$

(e) $f(x) = (x-3)^2, x \in \mathbb{R}$

(f) $f(x) = \frac{1}{x} - 4, x \in \mathbb{R}, x \neq 0$

(g) $f(x) = \frac{1}{(x+1)^2 - 2x}, x \in \mathbb{R}, x \neq \pm 1.$

2. Use a graphic calculator to sketch the following functions. Use the sketch to superimpose the graph of the inverse function in each case.

(a) $f(x) = x^2 + 4, x \in \mathbb{R}, x > 0$

(b) $f(x) = \frac{1}{x-2} + 1, x \in \mathbb{R}, x \neq 2$

(c) $f(x) = 4x - 1, x \in \mathbb{R}$.

3. Copy the graph and superimpose the graph of the inverse function.

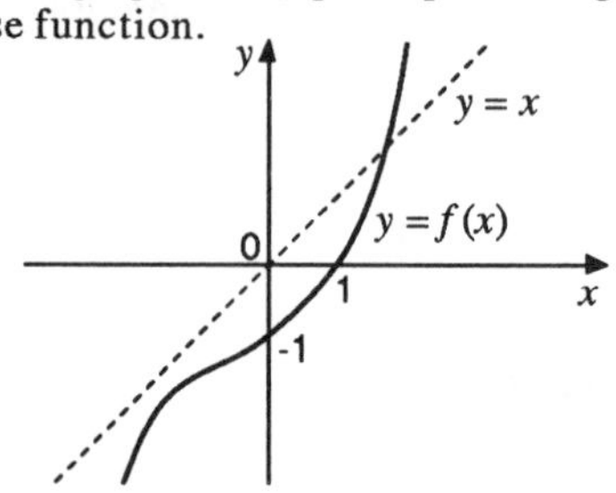

Show where the graph of $f^{-1}(x)$ cuts the x and y axes.

4. Copy the graph below, and superimpose the graph of $f(x-2)$. Hence sketch the inverse of this function.

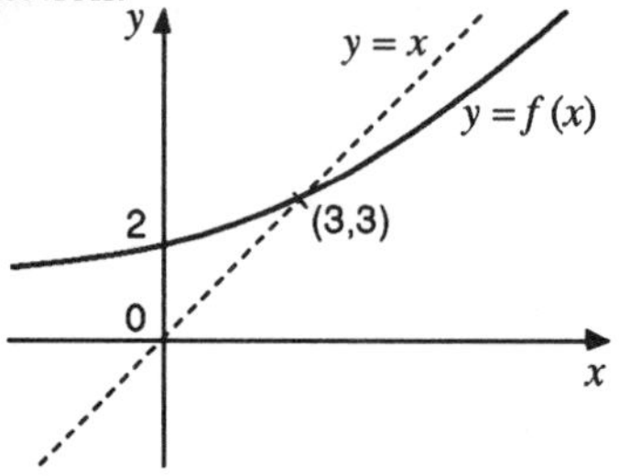

5. Plot and draw the following periodic functions, showing two full periods for each.

(a) $f(x)=\begin{cases} x & \text{for } 0 \le x \le 2 \\ 4-x & \text{for } 2 \le x \le 4 \end{cases}$

(b) $f(x)=\begin{cases} x^2 & \text{for } 0 \le x \le 1 \\ 1 & \text{for } 1 \le x \le 2 \end{cases}$

(c) $f(x)=2-\frac{x}{2}$ for $0 \le x \le 2$

(d) $f(x)=x^5$ for $0 \le x \le 1$.

4 GRAPH TRANSFORMS

Objectives

After studying this chapter you should

- be able to use appropriate technology to investigate graphical transformations;
- understand how complicated functions can be built up from transformations of simple functions;
- be able to predict the graph of functions after various transformations.

4.0 Introduction

You have already seen that the ability to illustrate a function graphically is a very useful one. Graphs can easily be used to explain or predict, so it is important to be able to sketch quickly the main features of a graph of a function. New technology, particularly graphic calculators, provides very useful tools for finding shapes but as a mathematician you will still need to gain the ability to understand what effect various transformations have on the graph of a function. First try the activity below **without** using a graphic calculator or computer.

Activity 1

You should be familiar with the graph of

$$y = x^2.$$

It is shown on the right. Without using any detailed calculations or technology, predict the shape of the graphs of the following

(a) $y = x^2 + 1$ (b) $y = 2x^2$ (c) $y = 3x^2$

(d) $y = (x-1)^2$ (e) $y = (x+1)^2$ (f) $y = \frac{1}{x^2}$ $(x \neq 0)$.

Now check your answers using a graphic calculator or computer.

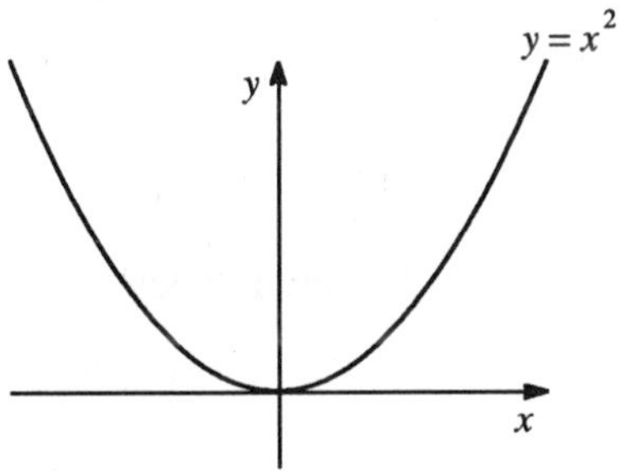

4.1 Transformation of axes

Suppose $y = x^2$, then the graph of $y = x^2 + 2$ moves the curve up by two units as is shown in the figure opposite. For any x value, the y value will be increased by two units.

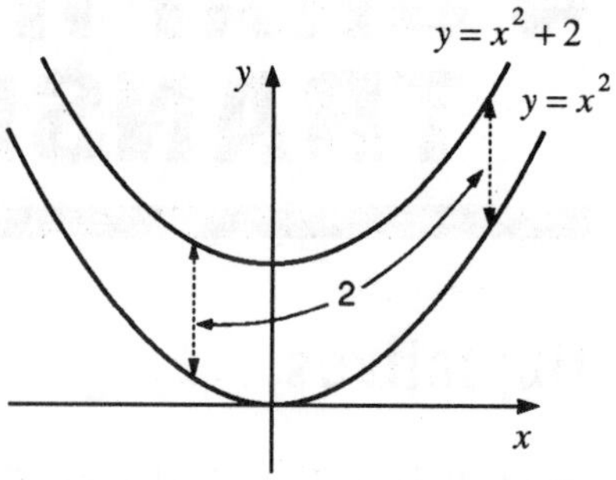

What does the graph of $y = x^2 + a$ look like?

What you are doing in the example above is equivalent to moving the x axes down by 2 units, which you can see by defining

$$Y = y - 2.$$

Then $Y = x^2$ and you are back to the original equation.

Describe the graph of $y = x^3 + 1$

> This type of transformation
>
> $$f(x) \mapsto f(x) + a$$
>
> is called a **translation** of the graph by a units along the y-axis.

Example

Find the value of a so that

$$y = x^2 - 2x + a$$

just touches the x-axis.

Solution

The graph of $y = x^2 - 2x$ is shown opposite. From this, you can see that it needs to be raised one unit, since its minimum value of -1 is obtained at $x = 1$. So the new equation will be

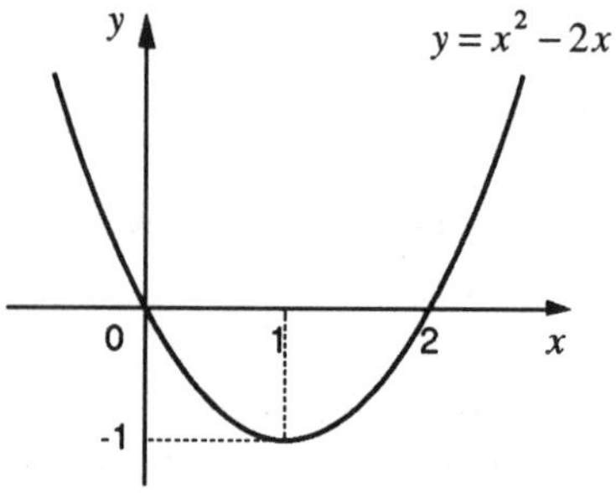

$$Y = x^2 - 2x + 1.$$

Note that the new Y function can be written as

$$Y = (x - 1)^2 \geq 0 \text{ for all } x$$

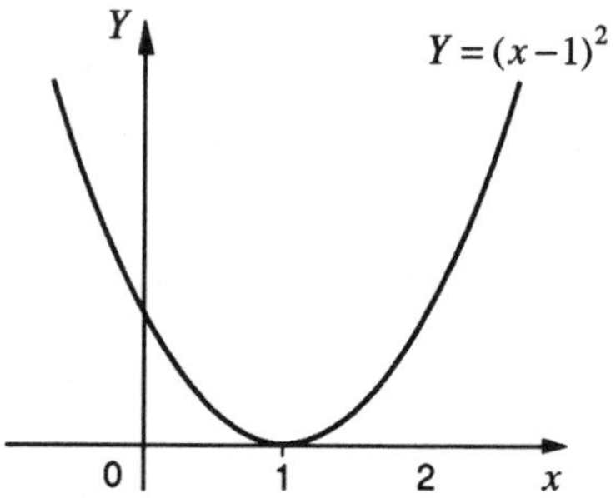

and equality only occurs when $x = 1$ (as illustrated).

As well as translations along the y-axis, you can perform similar operations along the x-axis.

Activity 2 Translations parallel to the x-axis

Again use the familiar $y = x^2$ curve, but this time write it as

$$f(x) = x^2.$$

Evaluate $f(x-2)$. Sketch the graph of $y = f(x-2)$.

What is the relationship between this curve and the original.

If you know the shape of $y = f(x)$, what does the graph of $y = f(x-a)$ look like?

> The transformation
>
> $$f(x) \mapsto f(x-a)$$
>
> is a translation by a units along the x-axis.

Example

The function $f(x)$ is defined by

$$f(x) = x^3 - 3x^2 + 3x - 1.$$

By considering $y = f(x+1)$, deduce the shape of the graph of $f(x)$.

Solution

$$f(x+1) = (x+1)^3 - 3(x+1)^2 + 3(x+1) - 1$$

$$(x+1)^2 = (x+1)(x+1) = x^2 + 2x + 1$$

$$(x+1)^3 = (x+1)(x+1)^2$$

$$= (x+1)(x^2 + 2x + 1)$$

$$= x^3 + 3x^2 + 3x + 1$$

$$f(x+1) = x^3 + 3x^2 + 3x + 1$$

$$- 3(x^2 + 2x + 1) + 3(x+1) - 1$$

$$= x^3 + x^2(+3-3) + x(3-6+3) + 1 - 3 + 3 - 1$$

$$= x^3$$

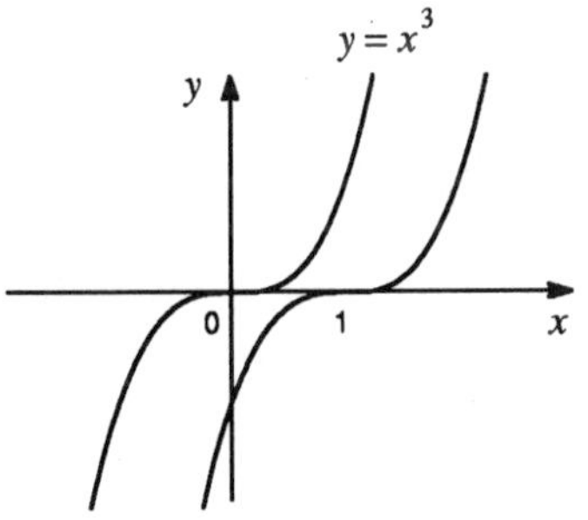

Hence $y = f(x+1) = x^3$ and this is illustrated opposite.

This means that $f(x)$ must also have this shape, but moved one unit along the x-axis.

Activity 3

Using a graphic calculator or computer,

(a) illustrate the curves

$$y = x^3 \text{ and } y = x^3 - 3x^2 + 3x - 1$$

and hence verify the result in the sketch on the previous page;

(b) illustrate the curves

$$y = x^4 \text{ and } y = x^4 - 8x^3 + 24x^2 - 32x + 16$$

and deduce a simpler form to write the second function.

Use x range –2 to 4 and y range 0 to 10.

Exercise 4A

1. Without using a graph plotting device, draw sketches of

   $f(x), f(x+5), f(x)+5$

   for the following functions

   (a) $f(x)=2x-1$

   (b) $f(x)=x^2-1$

   (c) $f(x)=(x-1)^2$.

2. Use a graph plotting device to illustrate the graphs of

   $f(x)=x^2, \; g(x)=x^2+2x+2$.

   Hence or otherwise write $g(x)$ in the form

   $f(x+a)+b$

   by finding the constants a and b.

3. If $f(x)=\frac{1}{x}$, sketch the graphs of

   (a) $f(x)$ (b) $f(x-1)$ (c) $f(x-1)+1$.

4.2 Stretches

In this section you will be investigating the effect of stretching either the y- or x-axis.

Example

For the function

$$y = f(x) = x + 1$$

draw the graphs of

(a) $f(2x)$ (b) $f\left(\frac{1}{2}x\right)$ (c) $2f(x)$ (d) $\frac{1}{2}f(x)$.

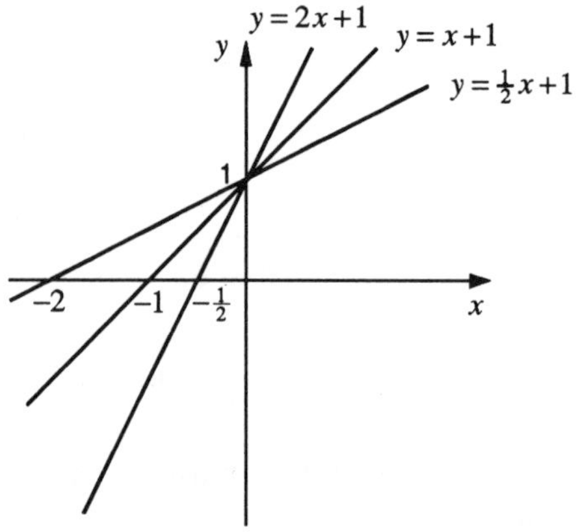

Solution

(a) $f(2x)=2x+1$

(b) $f(\frac{1}{2}x)=\frac{1}{2}x+1$

these are illustrated opposite

(c) $\quad 2f(x)=2(x+1)$
(d) $\quad \frac{1}{2}f(x)=\frac{1}{2}(x+1)$ } again illustrated opposite

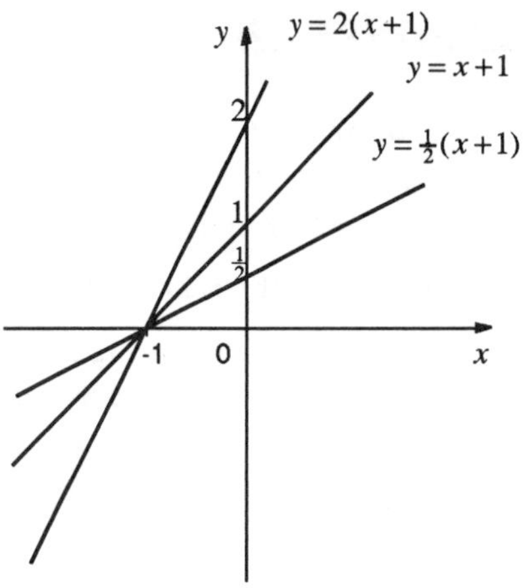

You should be beginning to get a feel for what the various types of transformations do, and the next activity will help you to clarify your ideas.

Activity 4 Stretches

For the function

$$y=f(x)=x^2+1$$

draw the graphs of

(a) $2f(x)$ (b) $\frac{1}{2}f(x)$ (c) $f(2x)$ (d) $f(\frac{1}{2}x)$.

Use a graph plotting device to help you if you are not sure of what the graphs look like.

The example and the activity have shown you that

> $y=\alpha f(x)$ is a stretch, parallel to the y-axis, by a factor α
>
> $y=f(\alpha x)$ is a stretch, parallel to the x-axis, by a factor $\dfrac{1}{\alpha}$

Example

If $f(x)=\dfrac{1}{x}$, illustrate (a) $2f(x)$ (b) $f(\frac{1}{2}x)$.

Solution

(a) $2f(x)=\dfrac{2}{x}$; this is illustrated opposite.

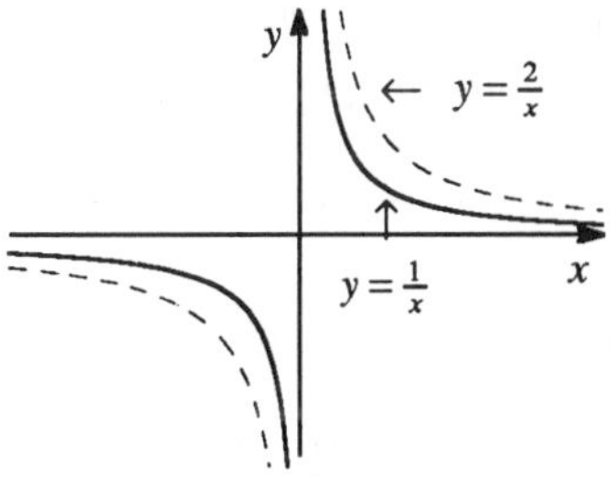

(b) $f(\frac{1}{2}x)=\dfrac{1}{(\frac{1}{2}x)}=\dfrac{2}{x}$, which is identical to $2f(x)$.

For this rather special function, a stretch of factor α parallel to the y-axis is identical to a stretch of factor α parallel to the x-axis.

Why are the two transformations identical for the function $y=\dfrac{1}{x}$?

Exercise 4B

1. For the function

   $f(x)=2x-1$

   illustrate the graphs of

   (a) $f(\frac{1}{2}x)$ (b) $f(2x)$ (c) $2f(x)$ (d) $\frac{1}{2}f(x)$.

2. For which of the following does the function $y=f(x)$ remain unaltered by the transformation $y=\frac{1}{\alpha}f(\alpha x)$?

   (a) $f(x)=x$ (b) $f(x)=x+1$

   (c) $f(x)=x^2$ (d) $f(x)=\frac{2}{x}$.

3. For the function $y=f(x)$, shown below, sketch the curves defined by

   (a) $y=f(\frac{1}{2}x)$ (b) $y=2f(x)$.

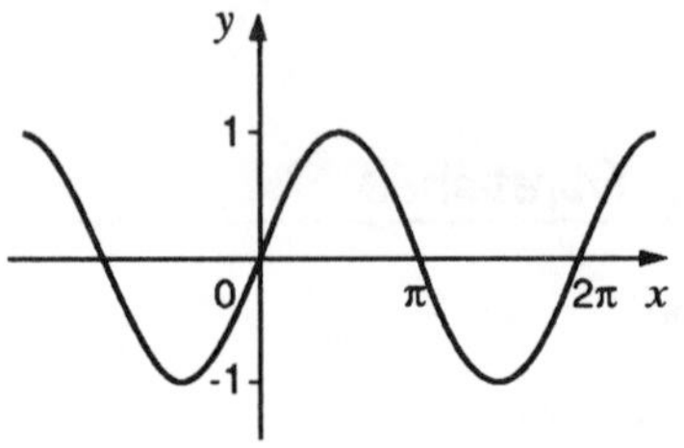

4.3 Reflections

If $f(x)=x+1$, then the graph of $-f(x)=-(x+1)$ is seen to be a **reflection** in the x-axis.

On the other hand

$$f(-x)=-x+1$$

can be seen to be a **reflection** in the y-axis.

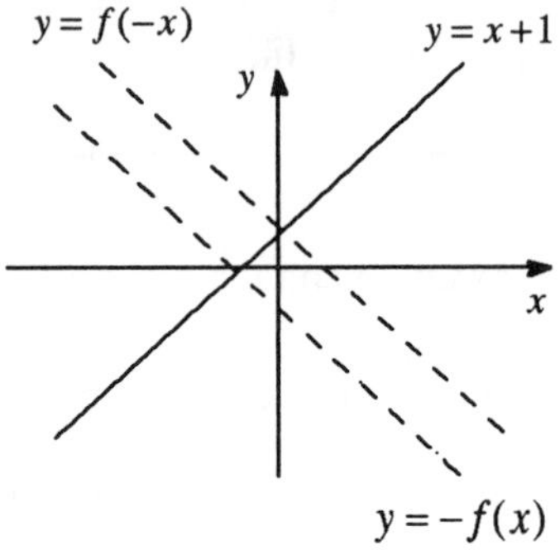

Activity 5 Reflections

For each of the functions below sketch (i) $-f(x)$ (ii) $f(-x)$:

(a) $f(x)=x^2$ (b) $f(x)=2x+1$ (c) $f(x)=x^3$ (d) $f(x)=\dfrac{1}{x}$.

Use a graphic calculator or computer to check your answers if you have any doubt.

You have seen that

$f(-x)$ is a reflection in the y-axis
$-f(x)$ is a reflection in the x-axis

It is now possible to combine various transformations.

Example

If the graph of $y=f(x)$ is shown opposite, illustrate the shape of

$$y=2f(-x)+3.$$

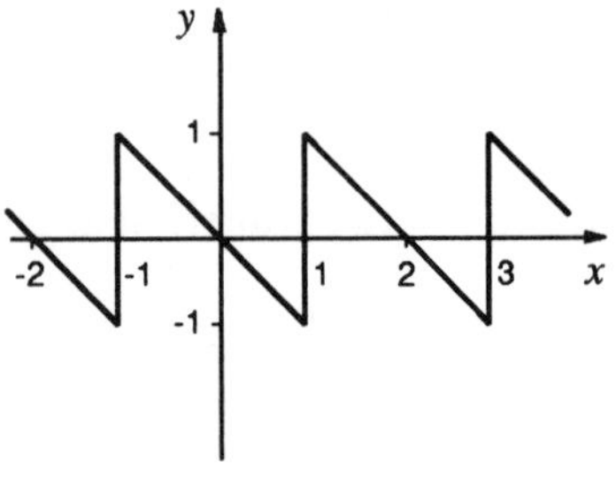

Solution

To find $f(-x)$, you reflect in the y-axis to give the graph opposite.

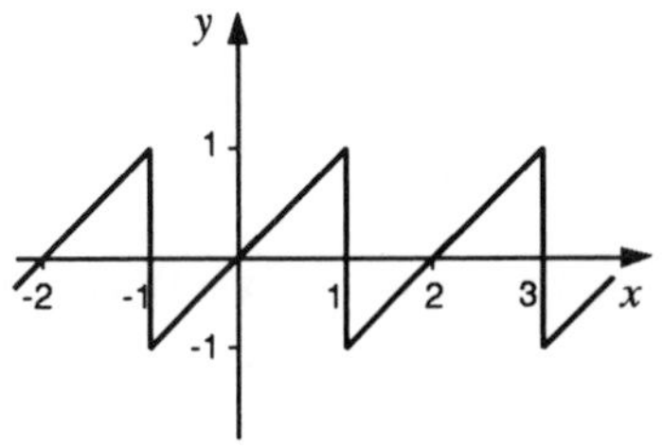

The sketch of $2f(-x)$ is shown opposite.

This is a stretch of factor 2 along the y-axis.

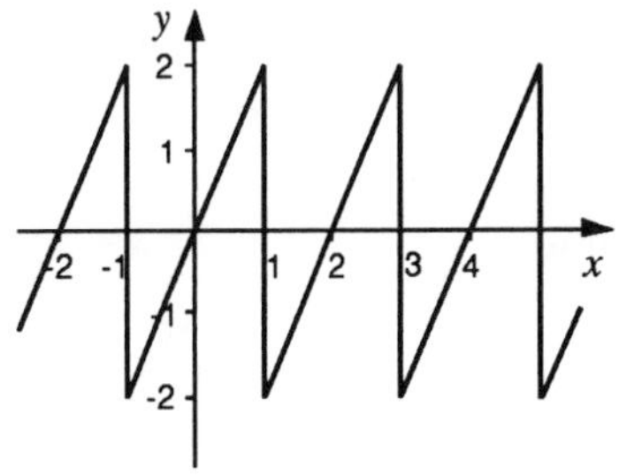

Finally adding 3 to each value gives the graph shown opposite,

$$y = 2f(-x) + 3.$$

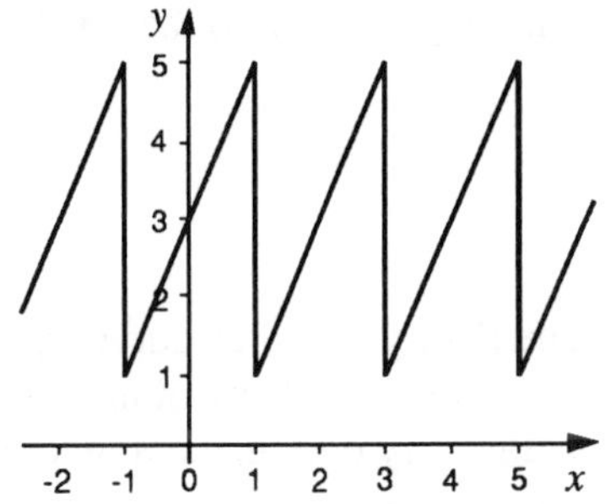

Example

Sketch the graph of $y = \dfrac{2}{x-1} + 2.$

Solution

Of course, you could find its graph very quickly using a graphic calculator or computer. It is, though, instructive to build up the sketch starting from a simple function, say

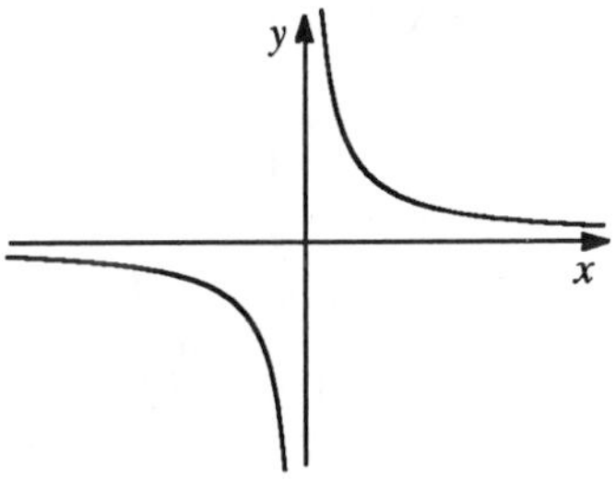

$$f(x) = \frac{1}{x}$$

and performing transformations to obtain the required function.

In terms of f, you can write

$$y = 2f(x-1) + 2.$$

So you must first sketch $y = f(x-1)$ as shown opposite.

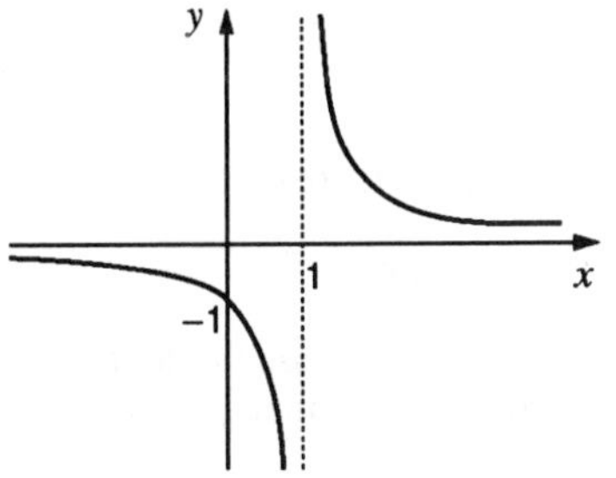

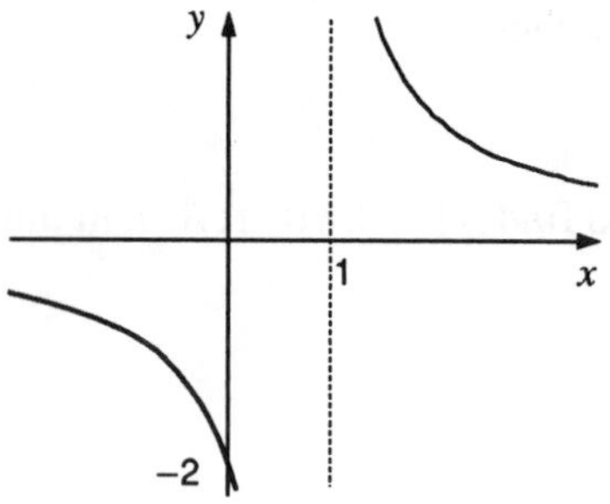

Now sketch $y = 2f(x-1)$ as shown opposite.

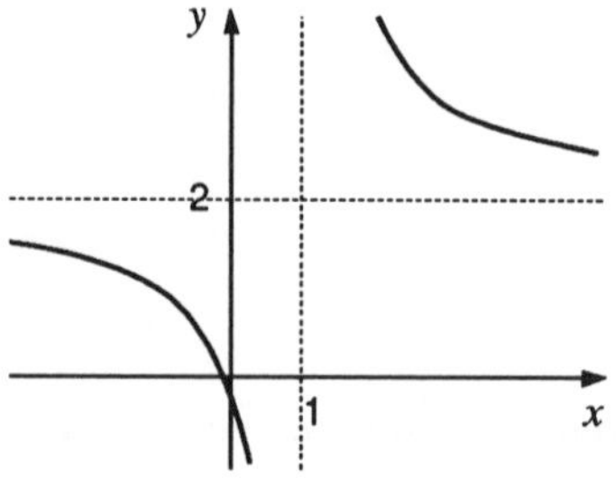

Finally you add 2 to the function to give the sketch opposite.

The ability to sketch curves quickly will be very useful throughout your course of study of mathematics. Although modern technology does make it much easier to find graphs, the process of **understanding** both what various transformations do and how more complex functions can be built up from a simple function is crucial for becoming a competent mathematician.

Exercise 4C

1. The graph below is a sketch of $y = f(x)$, showing three points A, B and C.

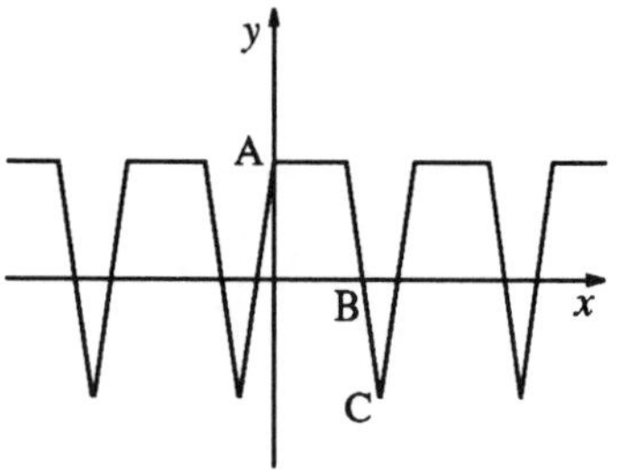

Sketch a graph of the following functions:

(a) $f(-x)$ (b) $2f(x)$ (c) $f\left(\frac{x}{3}\right)$

(d) $-\frac{1}{2}f(x)$ (e) $f(x+3)$ (f) $2f(x+1)$

(g) $f(x)+5$.

In each case indicate the position of A, B and C on the transformed graphs.

2. Using the functions $f(x) = x^2$, $g(x) = \frac{1}{x}$

show how each of the following functions can be expressed in terms of f or g. Hence sketch these graphs.

(a) $y = 2x^2 + 1$ (b) $y = 4 - x^2$

(c) $y = \frac{1}{(x+4)} + 2 \ (x \neq -4)$ (d) $y = -\frac{2}{x} + 1 \ (x \neq 0)$

(e) $y = x^2 + 2x + 42$.

4.4 Miscellaneous Exercises

1. The function $y = f(x)$ is illustrated below.

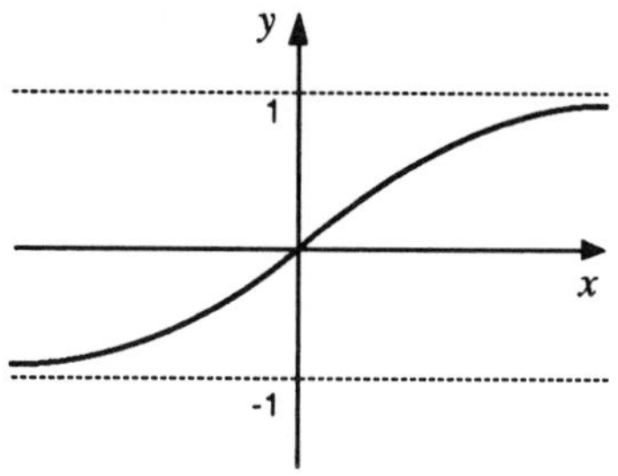

Sketch the following functions:

(a) $y = -f(x)$ (b) $y = f(-x)$

(c) $y = f(x)+1$ (d) $y = 2f(x)$.

2. Express each of the following functions in terms of either $f(x) = x^2$ or $g(x) = \frac{1}{x}$.

(a) $y(x) = 4x^2 + 1$

(b) $y(x) = 1 - \frac{1}{(x+1)}$ $(x \neq -1)$.

3. Sketch the graph of

$$f(x) = \frac{1}{x^3} \quad (x \neq 0).$$

Show that

$$f(-x) = -f(x).$$

What does this tell you about the function?

5 SOLVING PROBLEMS

Objectives

After studying this chapter you should

- have gained experience in formulating several types of problem in mathematical terms;
- appreciate how algebra can be used to solve problems;
- have improved your fluency in handling a variety of algebraic expressions;
- be able to solve several types of equations and inequalities.

5.0 Introduction

A more traditional title for this chapter might have been 'Elementary Algebraic Techniques', however, this would not tell the whole story. It is certainly true that you will have the opportunity to practice and develop your algebraic skills here, but perhaps the more important aim is to emphasise algebra as an effective problem-solving aid.

Algebra cannot solve every problem. Even where it can, there are sometimes alternatives. Nevertheless, algebra is an efficient way of communicating ideas and formulating problems; once a problem has been expressed in algebraic form, finding the answer to the problem is often much simpler.

5.1 Setting up and solving linear problems

Do not be put off by the simplicity of this problem.

> A coal merchant charges £8 per tonne of coal plus a fixed delivery charge of £5. How much coal can be delivered for £50?
>
> What is the answer if the merchant delivers only in 100 kg bags?

The purpose of beginning with such an easy problem is to demonstrate the general method of solving problems algebraically. Algebraic problem solving normally falls into three stages:

Stage 1 Translate the problem into a mathematical problem.

Stage 2 Solve the mathematical problem.

Stage 3 Translate the answer back into the terms of the original problem.

The simple problem above could be solved algebraically like this:

Let the number of tonnes delivered be x.
Total cost of x tonnes $= £(5+8x)$.
But the total cost $= £50$,
} **Stage 1**

so $5+8x=50$.

$$\left.\begin{aligned} &5+8x=50 \\ \Rightarrow\quad &8x=45 \\ \Rightarrow\quad &x=5.625 \end{aligned}\right\} \textbf{Stage 2}$$

$x=5.625$,
so the amount of coal that can be delivered is
5.625 tonnes or 5 tonnes 625kg.
} **Stage 3**

(Check the answer : $5+(8\times5.625)=5+45=50$.)

The last part of the problem could be put slightly differently. If the merchant delivered only in 100 kg bags then an answer of 5.625 tonnes is inadmissible, and clearly the required answer, by common sense, is 5.6 tonnes.

For the mathematics to come up with the proper answer the problem needs to be set up as an inequation, or inequality, rather than as equation.

Let the number of bags delivered be x.

Total cost of x bags $= £(5+0.8x)$

Total cost must not exceed £50, and x must be a natural number (i.e. a positive whole number):

$$5 + 0.8x \le 50, \ \ x \in \mathbb{N} \quad \text{(the set of natural numbers)}$$

$$\Rightarrow \quad 0.8x \le 45, \ \ x \in \mathbb{N}$$

$$\Rightarrow \quad x \le 56.25, \ \ x \in \mathbb{N}$$

The last line suggests directly that the largest possible value of x must be 56.

Since x represents the number of 100 kg bags the answer to the problem must now be **5.6 tonnes.**

Note also the importance of choosing the right domain for x. The inequality combined with the condition '$x \in \mathbb{N}$' yields the correct solution.

Below are three further examples. Before reading the solutions you should try to solve the problems by yourself, or in a group; then compare your solutions to the versions given in the text.

Make sure you set out each solution clearly. Try to follow the format of the worked examples given above.

Example

A coach travels along the M3 from Winchester to London. It sets off at 10.30 am and travels at a constant 65 mph. A car makes the same journey, travelling 10 mph faster but leaving 5 minutes later. When does the car overtake the coach?

Solution

Let t represent the number of minutes since the coach left Winchester, and let T be the number of minutes since the car left Winchester.

$$\text{Distance travelled by coach} = \frac{65t}{60} \text{ miles.}$$

$$\text{Distance travelled by car} = \frac{75T}{60} \text{ miles.}$$

The car left 5 minutes later than the coach, so when $T = 0$, $t = 5$. Hence $T = t - 5$.

The car overtakes the coach when they have travelled the same distance.

$$\frac{65}{60}t = \frac{75}{60}T$$

$$\Rightarrow \quad 65t = 75(t-5)$$

$$\Rightarrow \quad 13t = 15(t-5)$$

$$\Rightarrow \quad 13t = 15t - 75$$

$$\Rightarrow \quad 2t = 75$$

$$\Rightarrow \quad t = 37.5$$

So the car overtakes the coach $37\frac{1}{2}$ minutes after the coach's departure, i.e. at $11.07\frac{1}{2}$ am.

Example

Tickets for a pantomime cost £8 for adults and £5 for children. A party of 25 pays £143 in total. How many adults were there in the party?

Solution

Let the number of adults be x. Then the number of children must be $25-x$.

Cost of x adult tickets and $(25-x)$ children tickets

$$= £[8x + 5(25-x)]$$

But the total cost was £143, so

$$8x + 5(25-x) = 143$$

$$\Rightarrow \quad 3x + 125 = 143$$

$$\Rightarrow \quad 3x = 18$$

$$\Rightarrow \quad x = 6$$

Hence there were **6 adults** in the party.

(Check: 6 adult tickets and 19 child tickets cost $6 \times 8 + 19 \times 5 = 143$.)

Example

Alan has a non-interest current account at his bank from which mortgage repayments of £250 are made monthly. At the beginning of the year the account contains £3000. Barbara has a similar account: her monthly payments are £370 and her account contains £4150 at the start of the year. After how many payments does Alan's account contain more money than Barbara's?

Solution

Let the number of payments be n. After n payments:

Alan's account contains £$(3000-250n)$

Barbara's account contains £$(4150-370n)$

Alan's account has more money than Barbara's.

$$\Rightarrow \quad 3000-250n > 4150-370n, n \in \mathbb{N}$$
$$\Rightarrow \quad -250n > 1150-370n, n \in \mathbb{N}$$
$$\Rightarrow \quad 120n > 1150, n \in \mathbb{N}$$
$$\Rightarrow \quad n > 9.583, n \in \mathbb{N}$$

The last line suggests that the lowest possible value of n is 10. Hence Alan's account first has more money than Barbara's after **10 payments.**

Activity 1 Using simultaneous equations

The solution to the second example might have begun like this: Let the party consist of x adults and y children.

$$\text{Total cost} = 8x + 5y = 143$$
$$\text{Total number of people} = x + y = 25$$

Solve these simultaneous equations and check that the answer is the same as before.

(If you need to, revise how to solve simultaneous equations.)

Similarly the first example might have been solved as the answer to these simultaneous equations.

$$\left.\begin{aligned} 13t &= 15T \\ t-5 &= T \end{aligned}\right\}$$

Check that the answers obtained satisfy these questions.

All the equations in this section are called **linear** as they contain terms in x and y but not in x^2, y^2, xy, etc.

Exercise 5A below contains some more examples for you to try. The exercise begins with a brief opportunity to revise the solution of linear equations and inequalities.

Exercise 5A

1. Solve these equations. If the answers are not exact, give them to 3 s.f.

   (a) $1400-3a=638$ (b) $\dfrac{4(b+45)}{5}=24$

   (c) $16c+24=21c-481$ (d) $6(35-d)=d+19$

   (e) $\dfrac{13.2e-10.7}{4}=6.1$ (f) $\frac{1}{2}(3f+11)=6f-47$

2. Solve the following pairs of simultaneous equations

   (a) $\begin{cases}5p+3q=612\\ p+q=150\end{cases}$ (b) $\begin{cases}13m-5n=434\\ m-n=50\end{cases}$

   (c) $\begin{cases}9k+6l=306\\ 5k-2l=154\end{cases}$ (d) $\begin{cases}y=2x-4\\ y=5x+11\end{cases}$

   (e) $\begin{cases}p=2q-30\\ q=6p+16\end{cases}$ (f) $\begin{cases}u+3v+10=0\\ 3u=2v+1\end{cases}$

3. Solve these inequalities

   (a) $15a+365\le 560$

   (b) $61000-103b<62648$

   (c) $\frac{2}{3}(11c-76)\ge 8,\ \ c\in\mathbb{N}$

   (d) $5(d+6.3)>2d+3.2$

   (e) $-\left(\dfrac{187+65e}{3}\right)\le 12e-500$

   (f) $16.3(f-5)\ge 4(7.9-3.2f),\ f\in\mathbb{N}$

4. A school is looking to furnish two new classrooms. Tables cost £11 each and chairs £6. Each table will have two chairs except the two teachers' tables which will have one chair each. The total budget is £770.

   Assuming the budget is spent exactly, how many chairs and tables will the school buy?

5. An amateur operatic society needs to buy 20 vocal scores for their latest show. Hardback copies cost £14.50, paperback copies £9.20. £250 has been put aside to buy these scores. What is the maximum number of hardback copies they can buy and satisfy their needs?

6. At 6.00 pm a house's hot water tank contains only 10 litres of water, while the cold tank contains 100 litres. The cold water tank is emptying at a rate of 12 litres/min, half of this amount flowing into the hot tank. Water from the mains supply flows into the cold water tank at 3 litres/min. After how many minutes will the two tanks contain equal amounts of water?

7. Andrea is trying to save money on electricity bills. At present she estimates her family uses 8000 units of electricity per year at 6.59 pence per unit. They also have to pay an annual standing charge of £36.28.

   She is told that installing an 'Economy 7' system might save money. This means that off-peak units are charged at 2.63 pence per unit and the rest at 6.59p, but there is an additional annual standing charge of £10.04. She wants to know how many of the 8000 units would have to be off-peak units in order to save at least £50 per year. Solve her problem.

5.2 Revision

Section 5.1 concentrated more on the process of formulating problems in algebraic terms than on the algebra itself. Hence the algebra was uncomplicated. However, this is often not true, so this section is intended as an opportunity to revise some algebraic techniques you may have studied before. The worked examples should serve as a reminder of them before you tackle Exercise 5B.

Example

Multiply out (i.e. write without brackets):

(a) $p(p-7q)$ (b) $2mn(m^2-3n^2)$

(c) $(x+3)(x-5)$ (d) $(k^2-2l)(k+l)$.

Solution

(a) $p(p-7q)=p^2-7pq$

(b) $2mn(m^2-3n^2)=2m^3n-6mn^3$

(c)
$$\begin{aligned}(x+3)(x-5) &= x(x-5)+3(x-5)\\ &= x^2-5x+3x-15\\ &= x^2-2x-15\end{aligned}$$

(d)
$$\begin{aligned}(k^2-2l)(k+l) &= k^2(k+l)-2l(k+l)\\ &= k^3+k^2l-2kl-2l^2.\end{aligned}$$

Example

Factorise (i.e. simplify using brackets) :

(a) $2u^2+6u$ (b) ab^2-3a^3b.

Solution

(a) $2u^2+6u=2u(u+3)$

(b) $ab^2-3a^3b=ab(b-3a^2)$.

Example

Simplify the expression

$$(p+3)(p-1)-(p+2)(p-3).$$

Solution

$$\begin{aligned}&(p+3)(p-1)-(p+2)(p-3)\\ &\quad=(p^2+2p-3)-(p^2-p-6)\\ &\quad=p^2+2p-3-p^2+p+6\\ &\quad=3p+3\\ &\quad=3(p+1).\end{aligned}$$

Example

Factorise these :

(a) x^2+5x+6 (b) $x^2-9x+20$

(c) $x^2-3x-40$ (d) $x^2+2x-99$.

Solution

All these expressions are quadratic and will factorise to the form $(x+m)(x+n)$. Now

$$(x+m)(x+n)=x^2+(m+n)x+mn,$$

so to find the appropriate values of m and n compare $x^2+(m+n)x+mn$ with the quadratic required.

(a) x^2+5x+6:

$m+n=5$ and $mn=6$, so m and n must be 2 and 3, and

$$x^2+5x+6=(x+2)(x+3)$$

(b) $x^2-9x+20$:

Two numbers are required whose **product** is +20 and whose **sum** is -9. From the list on the right the required numbers are clearly −4 and -5, and

$$x^2-9x+20=(x-4)(x-5)$$

$$20=1\times 20=(-1)\times(-20)$$
$$=2\times 10=(-2)\times(-10)$$
$$=4\times 5=(-4)\times(-5)$$

(c) $x^2-3x-40$

Similarly from the list of factors of 40 the factorisation must be $(x-8)(x+5)$

(d) $x^2+2x-99=(x+11)(x-9)$.

Example

Factorise

(a) x^2-9 (b) $4a^2-9b^2$

(c) $2x^2-9x+4$ (d) $3x^2-2x-16$

(e) $3x^2+6x-24$.

Solution

(a) and (b) are the difference of two squares. You may recall that

$$p^2-q^2=(p+q)(p-q)$$

and so, by comparison,

(a) $x^2-9=(x+3)(x-3)$

(b) $4a^2-9b^2=(2a)^2-(3b)^2$

$$=(2a+3b)(2a-3b)$$

(c) and (d) are more difficult. Some methods are given below, but the technique is still best learned through experience.

(c) $2x^2 - 9x + 4$ must factorise to the form $(2x+m)(x+n)$. Now $(2x+m)(x+n) = 2x^2 + (m+2n)x + mn$. So the product of m and n must be 4, but notice that the n is doubled in the $(m+2n)x$ term. Looking at the list opposite the factorisation will be $(2x-1)(x-4)$.

$$4 = 1\times 4 = (-1)\times(-4)$$
$$= 2\times 2 = (-2)\times(-2)$$

(d) $3x^2 - 2x - 16$.

Similar techniques as before, but note that in multiplying out $(3x+m)(x+n)$ the 'n' is multiplied by '$3x$' to help give a term $(m+3n)x$.

$3x^2 - 2x - 16 = (3x-8)(x+2)$

(e) looks similar to (d), but notice that all the terms have a factor of 3, so

$$3x^2 + 6x - 24 = 3(x^2 + 2x - 8)$$
$$= 3(x+4)(x-2).$$

Exercise 5B

1. Multiply out :

   (a) $2(5x+7y)$ (b) $a(a-b)$

   (c) $3lm(6l-5m)$ (d) $p^2(2p-3q^2+1)$

   (e) $h^3k^3(2hk+3hk^2)$.

2. Multiply out :

   (a) $(x+1)(x+2)$ (b) $(x+3)(x-5)$

   (c) $(x-8)(x-2)$ (d) $(x+6)(x-5)$

   (e) $(x-10)(x+7)$.

3. Multiply out :

   (a) $(2x-7)(x-3)$ (b) $(2x+3)(x+1)$

   (c) $(3x+20)(x-8)$ (d) $(a-2b)(2a+b)$

   (e) $(2m^2-n)(m+5n^2)$.

4. Multiply out :

   (a) $(x+1)^2$ (this is not x^2+1)

   (b) $(p-3)^2$ (c) $(x-10)^2$

   (d) $(x+a)^2$ (a is any number)

   (e) $(2x-5)^2$.

5. Simplify these :

   (a) $2a(a-b)+b(2a-b)$

   (b) $(y-2)(y+3)+(2y+5)(y+1)$

   (c) $(n+4)^2-(n-1)(n+7)$

   (d) $5(m-6)(m+2)-2(2m+3)(m-7)$

   (e) $(u+2v)(u-v)-(4u-v)(u+3v)$.

6. Factorise these expressions :

   (a) $6x+15$ (b) u^2-3u

   (c) $3p^2+24p$ (d) $12a^2b^3-6ab^2$

   (e) $5x^2y+15y-35$.

7. Factorise these :

   (a) x^2+6x+8 (b) x^2+x-30

   (c) $x^2-7x+10$ (d) x^2+5x+4

   (e) $x^2-3x-70$ (f) $x^2-10x+9$

   (g) $x^2+6x-16$ (h) $x^2-5x-84$.

8. Factorise these :

   (a) x^2-16 (b) x^2-25x

   (c) $2x^2+7x+3$ (d) $2x^2-7x-4$

   (e) $3x^2-11x-20$ (f) $2x^2-4x-6$

   (g) $3x^2-4x-20$ (h) $100x^2-64$.

9. Factorise these :

   (a) $5x^2+3x-2$ (b) $4x^2+5x-6$

   (c) $4x^2-4x-3$ (d) $6x^2+15x-36$

   (e) $6x^2+5x-25$ (f) $12x^2-7x-10$.

5.3 Setting up and solving quadratic equations

Activity 2 A problem of surface area

The diagram shows an open-topped box with a square base. The sides of the box are 3 cm high.

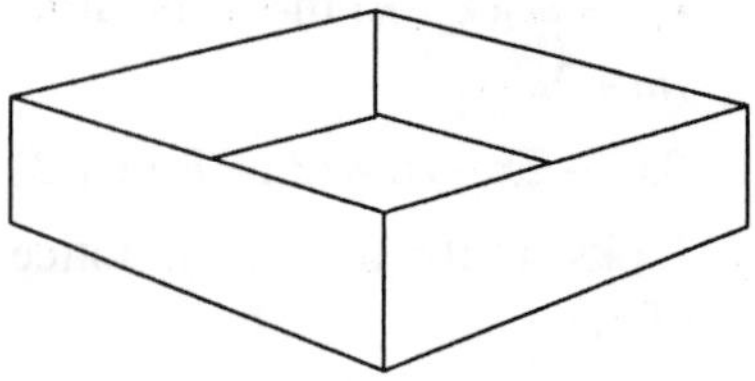

The box is to be made from a total of 160 cm^2 of card. What size must the square base be to maximise the volume contained? Try to set out an algebraic solution as in the previous section.

Solving the above problem algebraically leads to a quadratic equation, that is, an equation involving a quadratic function. You may have already covered how to solve this type of equation. The following worked example and activities should help to refresh your memory.

Example

Solve the equation $x(x+6)=16$.

Solution

$$x(x+6)=16$$

$$\Rightarrow \quad x^2+6x=16$$

$$\Rightarrow \quad x^2+6x-16=0.$$

$x^2+6x-16$ can be factorised to give $(x+8)(x-2)$. Hence the equation becomes

$$(x+8)(x-2)=0$$

$$\Rightarrow \quad x=-8 \text{ or } 2.$$

Example

Solve the equation $3x^2+10x=25$.

Solution

The procedure is exactly the same, though the factorisation is more difficult.

$$3x^2 + 10x = 25$$
$$\Rightarrow \quad 3x^2 + 10x - 25 = 0$$
$$\Rightarrow \quad (3x - 5)(x + 5) = 0$$
$$\Rightarrow \quad x = \tfrac{5}{3} \text{ or } -5.$$

Activity 3 Solutions and graphs

(a) Sketch the graph of $y = (x+9)(x-3)$
At what points does the curve cross the horizontal axis?

(b) At what point will the graph of $y = (x+m)(x+n)$ cross the horizontal axis?

(c) Sketch the graph of $y = (2x-1)(x+2)$. Explain why the curve crosses the x – axis where it does.

(d) Sketch the graphs of these functions all on one diagram, without using any electronic aids.

$$y = (x-6)(x+2)$$
$$y = 2(x-6)(x+2)$$
$$y = \tfrac{1}{3}(x-6)(x+2)$$
$$y = -(x-6)(x+2)$$

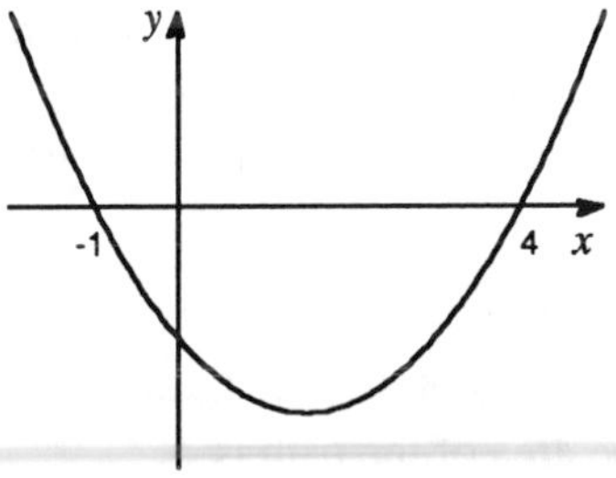

(e) Give a possible equation for the quadratic graph on the right. How many possibilities are there? What else would you need to know to narrow these possibilities down to one?

Activity 4 Match the graphs to the functions

Shown are eight quadratic functions, numbered 1 to 8, and five graphs, lettered A to E. Each graph corresponds to one of the functions. Decide which function goes with which graph. Draw sketches of the graphs of the functions that are not used.

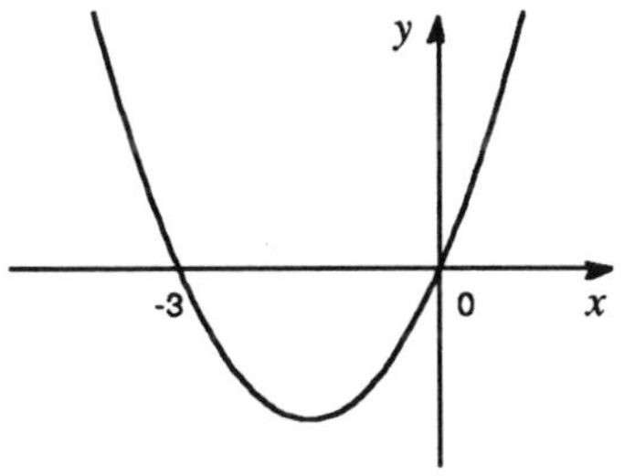

A.

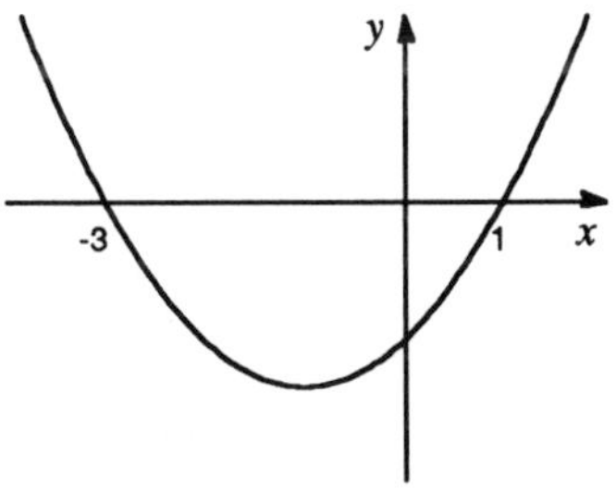

B.

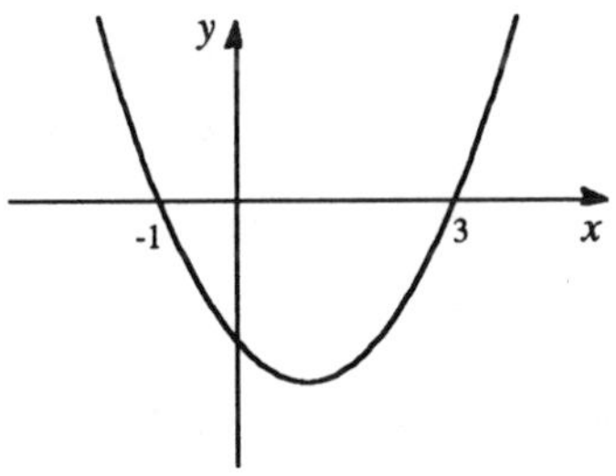

C.

1. $x^2 + 3x$
2. $(x-1)(x+3)$
3. $(x+17)(x-15)$
4. $(x+2)(x+3)$
5. $(x-17)(x+15)$
6. $x^2 - 5x + 6$
7. $(x+1)(x-3)$
8. $x(x-3)$.

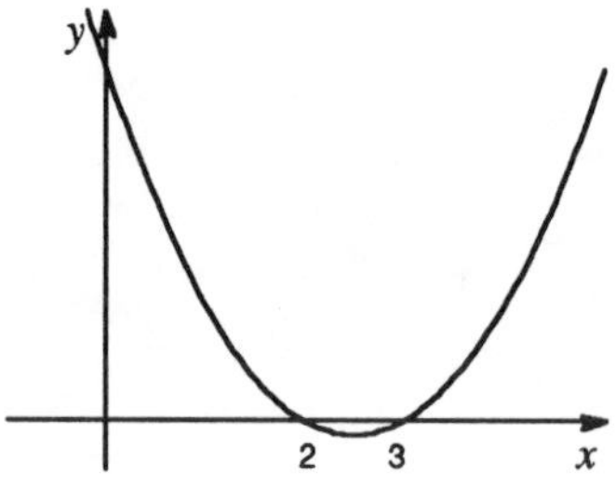

D.

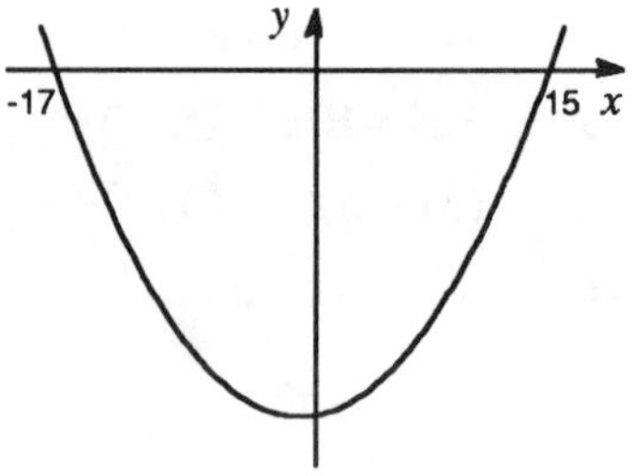

E.

Quadratic equations often arise when solving problems connected with area. (Can you think why?) When a quadratic equation does present itself, it is important to bear in mind the domain of the variable concerned: in general, quadratic equations have two solutions, but it is not necessarily true that both of them are solutions to the original problem, as you will see in the next example.

Example

Joe wishes to make a gravel path around his rectangular pond. The path must be the same width all the way round, as shown in the diagram. The pond measures 4 m by 9 m and he has enough gravel to cover an area of 48 m². How wide should the path be?

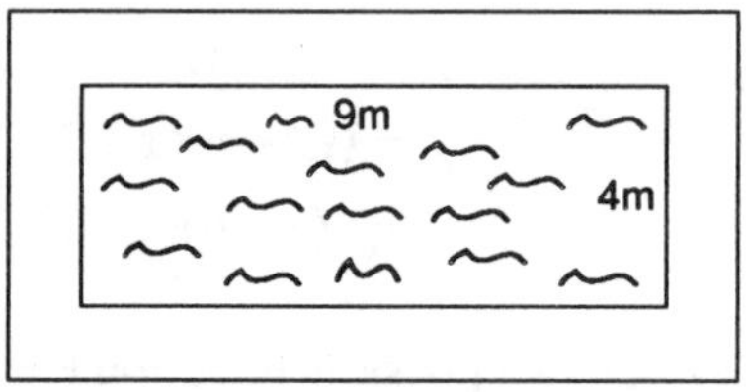

Solution

Let the width of the footpath be x metres. The diagram shows that the area of the path is

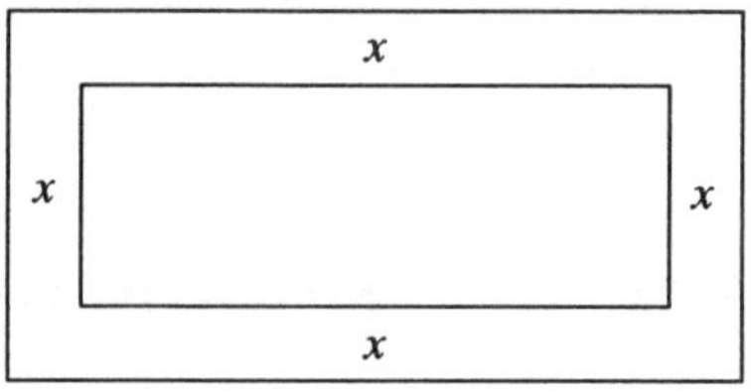

$$
\begin{aligned}
&(9+2x)(4+2x)-36 \\
&= 36 + 26x + 4x^2 - 36 \\
&= 4x^2 + 26x.
\end{aligned}
$$

Since the required area is 48 m², then $4x^2 + 26x = 48$.

To this equation must be added the condition that $x > 0$.

$$
\begin{aligned}
& 4x^2 + 26x = 48, && x > 0 \\
\Rightarrow\ & 2x^2 + 13x - 24 = 0, && x > 0 \\
\Rightarrow\ & (2x-3)(x+8) = 0, && x > 0 \\
\Rightarrow\ & x = \tfrac{3}{2} \text{ or } -8, && x > 0 \\
\Rightarrow\ & x = \tfrac{3}{2}.
\end{aligned}
$$

Hence the width of the path must be 1.5m, since the other value, $x = -8$m, is unrealistic, and does not satisfy the condition $x > 0$.

Exercise 5C

1. Solve these quadratic equations by factorising

   (a) $x(x+3)=4$ (b) $x(x+5)=50$

   (c) $x^2=x+72$ (d) $x^2+77=18x$

   (e) $x^2+50x+96=0$ (f) $x^2-50x+600=0$

   (g) $2x^2-13x+15=0$ (h) $x(2x-1)=21$

   (i) $3x^2-6x=45$ (j) $3x^2-14=x$.

2. A triangular flowerbed is to be dug in the corner of a rectangular garden. The area is to be 65 m^2.

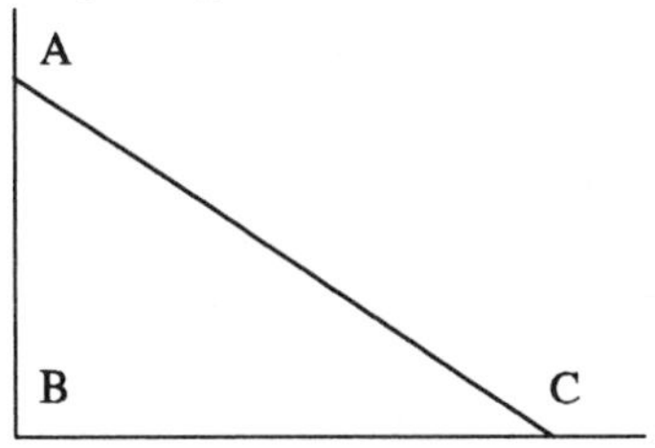

   The owner wants the length BC of the bed to be 3 m longer than the width AB. Find what the length and width should be.

3. A window is designed to be twice as wide as it is high. It is to be made up of three parts: a central, fixed part and two identical rectangles on either side of width 0.5 metres.

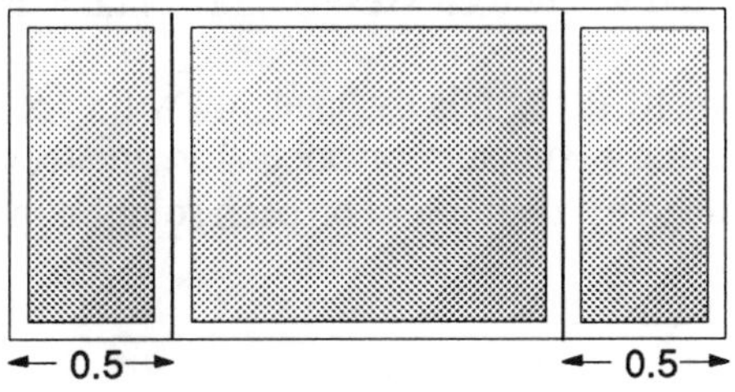

   Find the height of the window, if the central part is to have an area of 3 m^2.

5.4 Approximate solutions

In practical problems which lead to solving quadratic equations, it is not always possible to factorise the equation.

Activity 5 A fencing problem

50 m of fencing is being used to enclose a rectangular area, with a long straight wall as one of the sides of the rectangle. What dimensions give an area of 150 m^2?

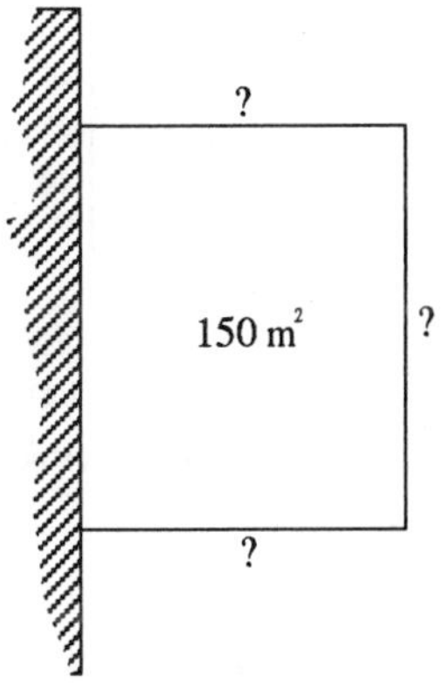

As Activity 5 will have illustrated, not all quadratic equations can be solved by factorisation. Another example is the equation

$$x^2-15x+40=0$$

which cannot be factorised.

You may know how to deal with such equations already - an algebraic method will be discussed in Section 5.5 - but you can use a combination of graphical or trial and improvement methods to find approximate solutions.

The **graphical method** can be undertaken with the help of a graphic calculator or with pencil and graph paper. Either way, draw the graph of

$$y = x^2 - 15x + 40$$

and find where it crosses the horizontal axis.

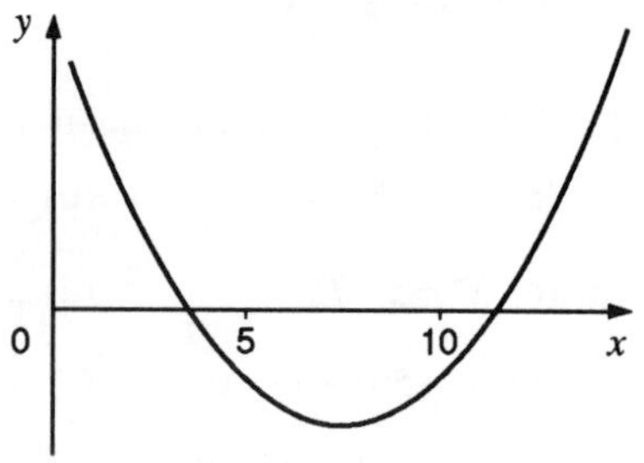

If you are doing this by hand you will need to be accurate; if you are using a computer or calculator, greater accuracy can be obtained by zooming in on each solution in turn.

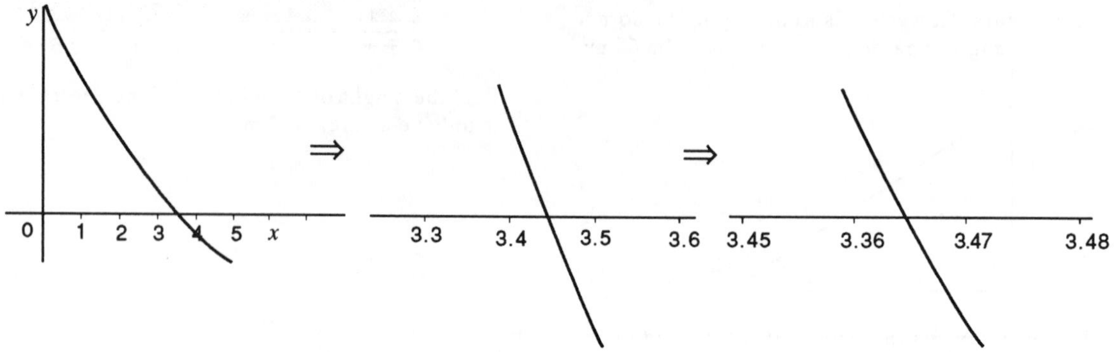

You may be familiar with the **trial and improvement** technique. It is best explained by example. The results of successive trials can be set out in a table.

x	$x^2 - 15x + 40$
0	40
1	26
2	14
3	4
4	–4

This shows that there must be a solution between $x = 3$ and $x = 4$, probably near 3.5. Now look more closely between $x = 3$ and $x = 4$.

3.4	0.56	root between $x = 3.4$ and 3.5
3.5	–0.25	
3.46	0.0716	root between $x = 3.46$ and 3.47 being closer to 3.47
3.47	–0.0091	

The solution is 3.47 to 3 s.f. Greater accuracy can be achieved by continuing the process as long as necessary. This, of course, is only one solution. The process must be repeated to find the other. (Try it yourself.)

Activity 6

The quadratic $x^2+10x-20$ cannot be factorised using whole numbers but can be factorised approximately using decimals. Find its factors correct to 2 d.p.'s.

Does a quadratic equation always have precisely two solutions?

Activity 7 Computer program

Devise a computer program to solve a quadratic equation by trial and improvement.

Exercise 5D

1. Use a graphical approach to solve these equations to 3 s.f.

   (a) $x(2x-3)=9$ (b) $x^2+x=14$

   (c) $2x(20-x)=195$ (d) $300-x^2=6x$.

2. Solve these equations to 3 s.f. using trial and improvement.

   (a) $x(x+3)=8$ (b) $7x-x^2=5$

   (c) $x^2+8x+11=0$ (d) $x(x+25)=8000$.

3. The distance across the diagonal of a square field is 50 m shorter than going round the perimeter. To the nearest metre, find the length of the side of the field.

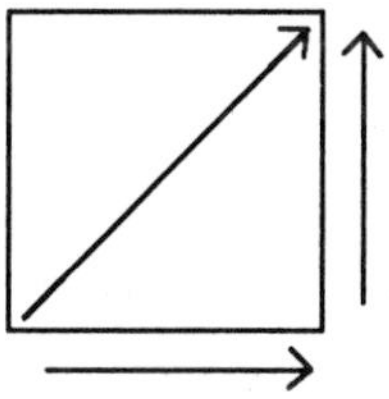

4. An architect decides that the smallest room in the house needs a window with area 4000 cm^2.

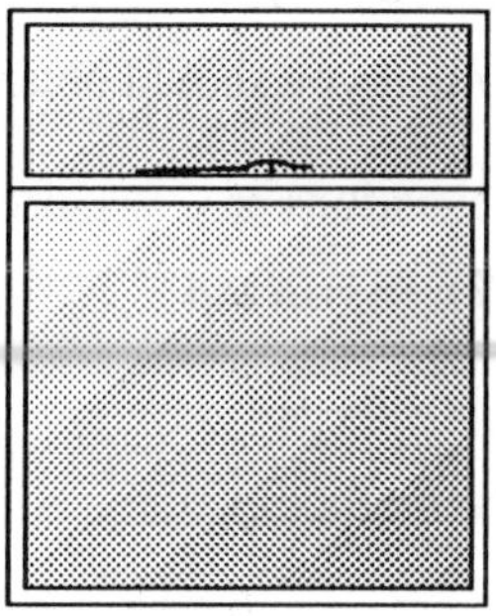

The window will be in two parts: a square part at the bottom, and a rectangular part above it hinged at the top and with height 25 cm. Find the width the window must be to satisfy these requirements. Answer to the degree of accuracy you think is appropriate to the problem.

5.5 Investigating quadratic functions

Graphical and numerical methods are of great importance in solving equations. Their big advantages are that they can be used to solve practically any equation, and solve them to any degree of accuracy. However it can be a slow process, and where quadratic equations cannot be solved by factorising there is another method of solution that is often faster.

Consider the equation $x^2 - 4x - 3 = 0$.

Activity 8 Completing the square

(a) Another way of expressing the function $x^2 - 4x - 3$ is to write it in the form

$$(x-p)^2 - q.$$

Multiply out this expression and equate it to $x^2 - 4x - 3$ to find the values of p and q.

(b) Having put the function in this new form, now solve the equation $x^2 - 4x - 3 = 0$.

Remember that you should obtain two solutions.

(c) Solve the equations

(i) $x^2 - 2x - 1 = 0$, and

(ii) $x^2 - 3x - 5 = 0$

by a similar method.

The method used in the activity above is called **completing the square**. Any quadratic can be written in this form. For example,

$$\begin{aligned} 2x^2 - 12x + 15 &= 2\left(x^2 - 6x + \tfrac{15}{2}\right) \\ &= 2\left((x-3)^2 - 9 + \tfrac{15}{2}\right) \\ &= 2\left((x-3)^2 - \tfrac{3}{2}\right). \end{aligned}$$

$(x-3)^2$: the 3 comes from half 'x' coefficient

-9 : introduced to cancel out 3^2

This quadratic $2x^2 - 12x + 15 = 0$ can now be solved since

$$2\left((x-3)^2 - \tfrac{3}{2}\right) = 0$$

$$\Rightarrow \quad (x-3)^2 - \frac{3}{2} = 0$$

$$(x-3)^2 = \frac{3}{2}$$

$$x-3 = \pm\sqrt{\frac{3}{2}}$$

$$x = 3\pm\sqrt{\frac{3}{2}}.$$

Example

By completing the square, solve

(a) $x^2+6x+4=0$ (b) $x^2-3x+1=0$

(c) $5x^2-6x-9=0.$

Solution

(a) $x^2+6x+4=(x+3)^2-9+4$

$$=(x+3)^2-5.$$

Hence the equation $x^2+6x+4=0$ can be rewritten

$$(x+3)^2-5=0$$

$\Rightarrow$ $(x+3)^2=5$

$\Rightarrow$ $x+3=\pm\sqrt{5}$

$\Rightarrow$ $x=-3\pm\sqrt{5}$

$=-5.24$ or -0.764 to 3 s.f.

(b) $x^2-3x+1=(x-1.5)^2-(1.5)^2+1$

$$=(x-1.5)^2-1.25.$$

Hence $x^2-3x+1=0$ can be re-written

$$(x-1.5)^2-1.25=0$$

$\Rightarrow$ $(x-1.5)^2=1.25$

$\Rightarrow$ $x-1.5=\pm\sqrt{1.25}$

$\Rightarrow$ $x=1.5\pm\sqrt{1.25}$

$=0.382$ or 2.62 to 3 s.f.

(c) $5x^2-6x-9=5[x^2-1.2x-1.8]$

$$=5[(x-0.6)^2-(0.6)^2-1.8]$$

$$=5[(x-0.6)^2-2.16].$$

Hence $5x^2-6x-9=0$ can be re-written

$$(x-0.6)^2-2.16=0$$

$$\Rightarrow \quad x=0.6\pm\sqrt{2.16}$$

$$=-0.870 \text{ or } 2.07 \text{ to } 3\text{ s.f.}$$

The technique of completing the square has wider applications than just solving equations. It is, for example, useful in helping to sketch curves of quadratic functions.

Look, for example, at the function $5x^2-6x-9$ (see (c) above). Completing the square, as suggested by Activity 8, can be seen as the splitting up of a quadratic function into several simpler ones. In this case, $f(x)=5x^2-6x-9$ is equivalent to the transformation

$$a: x \mapsto x-0.6$$

followed by $b: x \mapsto x^2$

followed by $c: x \mapsto x-2.16$

followed by $d: x \mapsto 5x.$

These four functions gradually build up the expression required:

$$a(x)=x-0.6$$
$$ba(x)=(x-0.6)^2$$
$$cba(x)=(x-0.6)^2-2.16$$
$$dcba(x)=5[(x-0.6)^2-2.16]$$
$$=5x^2-6x-9.$$

Activity 9

In earlier chapters you found out how simple graphs were affected by simple transformations. Explain why the graph of $y=5x^2-6x-9$ looks like the sketch opposite.

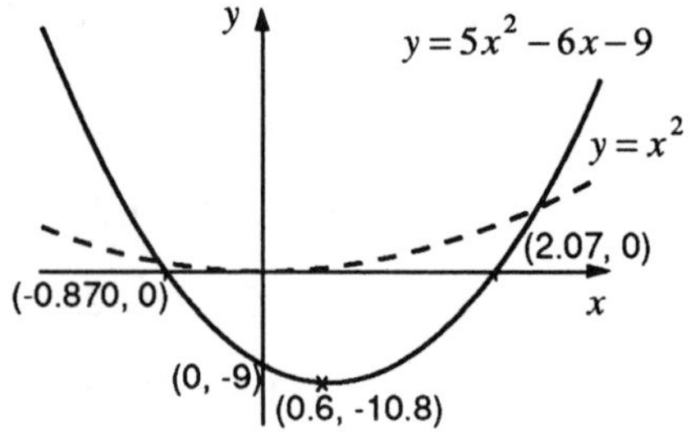

Activity 10 Transformations of $y=x^2$

(a) Using the graph of $y=x^2$, sketch the graphs of these functions, to the same scale.

(i) $y=(x-3)^2+2$ (ii) $y=(x+5)^2-8$

(iii) $y=3[(x-1)^2+1]$ (iv) $y=x^2-8x+10$

(v) $y=2x^2+5x-3.$

Do not use any graph-plotting package except to check your answers. Label the crucial points in the same way as the sketch above.

(b) Explain how the minimum point of the quadratic curve $y = x^2 - 10x + 20$ can be found without having to draw the curve itself.

Activity 11

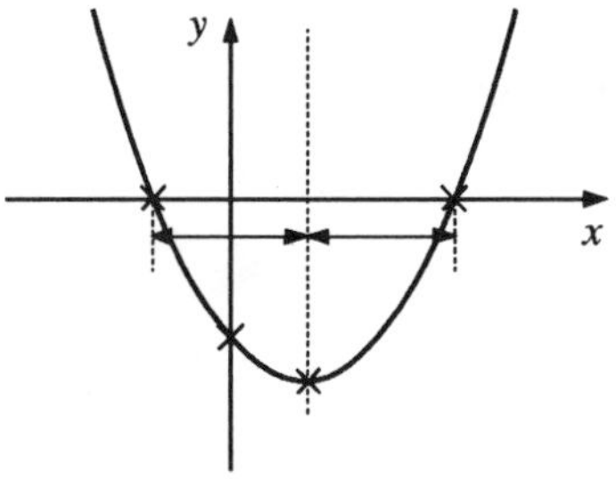

On the right is a sketch of the graph of

$$y = (x - p)^2 - q.$$

Copy it and mark on

(a) the co-ordinates of the points marked with crosses;

(b) the line of symmetry of the graph, with its equation;

(c) the distances marked with arrows, $\longleftrightarrow$.

Activity 12 Maximum values

(a) Plot the graphs of the functions

$$y = 4 + 2x - x^2$$

$$y = 10 - 5x - 2x^2$$

and give an explanation for their general shape.

(b) Show that

$$4 + 2x - x^2 = 5 - (x - 1)^2$$

and rewrite $10 - 5x - 2x^2$ in a similar way.

(c) What are the maximum values of these two functions? How can you tell without drawing a graph?

As you can see another application of completing the square is that of finding the maximum or minimum values of quadratic functions.

Example

Find the minimum value of the function $x^2 + 3x + 7$.

Solution

$$x^2 + 3x + 7 = (x + 1.5)^2 + 4.75$$

So the minimum value must be 4.75, which occurs when $x = -1.5$.

Example

Find the value of x that maximises the function $100 + 50x - 2x^2$ and find this maximum value.

Solution

$$\begin{aligned} 100 + 50x - 2x^2 &= -2\left[x^2 - 25x - 50\right] \\ &= -2\left[(x - 12.5)^2 - 206.25\right] \\ &= 412.5 - 2(x - 12.5)^2. \end{aligned}$$

Thus the maximum value is 412.5 achieved when $x = 12.5$.

Exercise 5E

1. Solve the quadratic equations to 3 s.f.

   (a) $a^2 - 4a - 7 = 0$ (b) $b^2 - 12b + 30 = 0$

   (c) $c^2 - c - 1 = 0$ (d) $2d^2 + 20d = 615$

   (e) $2e^2 - 8e + 1 = 0$ (f) $5f^2 + 4f = 13$

   (g) $53 + 30g - g^2 = 0$ (h) $1225 + 46h - 2h^2 = 0$.

2. (a) What value of x maximises the function $x^2 + 40x + 25$?

   (b) What is the minimum value taken by the function $x^2 + 9x + 14$?

   (c) What is the maximum value of $46 - 24x - x^2$?

   (d) What is the maximum value of $25 - 60x - 2x^2$ and what value of x makes this function a maximum?

3. 100 m of fencing is used to make an enclosure as shown in the diagram, jutting out from the corner of a rectangular building.

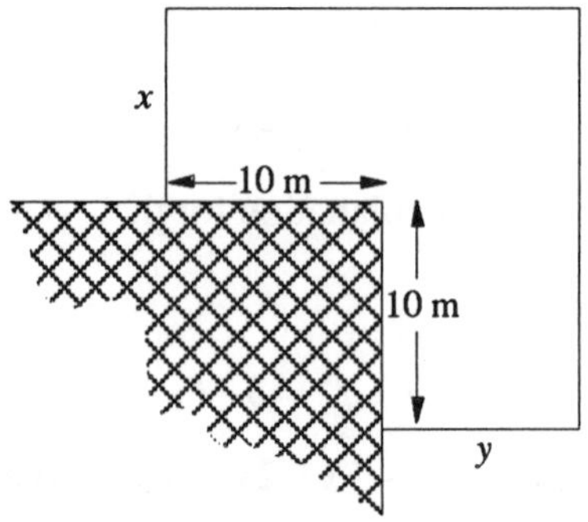

If x and y are as marked, show that $y = 40 - x$ and hence

(a) find x if the area of the enclosure is to be 600 m^2;

(b) find the maximum area that can be enclosed.

5.6 Quadratic solution formula

Completing the square is a technique that can be used to solve any quadratic equation. In many cases it is easy to use. However, in practice quadratic equations can sometimes have awkward coefficients and 'completing the square' leads to some unhappy arithmetic; for example,

$$7.8x^2 - 11.2x - 4.9 = 0$$

$$\Rightarrow \quad 7.8\,[x^2 - 1.4359x - 0.6282] = 0 \quad \text{(working to 4 d.p.'s)}$$

$$\Rightarrow \quad (x - 0.7179)^2 - 1.1437 = 0$$

$$\Rightarrow \quad x = 0.7179 \pm \sqrt{1.1437}$$

$$= -0.351 \text{ or } 1.79 \text{ to 3 s.f.}$$

For cases like this there is a formula which will enable you to calculate the answer more quickly.

Activity 13 Finding a formula

(a) If $x^2 + bx + c = 0$, show that $\left(x + \frac{b}{2}\right)^2 + c - \left(\frac{b}{2}\right)^2 = 0$ and

hence that

$$x = -\frac{b}{2} \pm \sqrt{\frac{b^2}{4} - c}\,.$$

Can you see why this formula is the same as

$$x = \frac{-b \pm \sqrt{b^2 - 4c}}{2}\ ?$$

(b) Now extend this process to solve the general quadratic equation

$$ax^2 + bx + c = 0.$$

The two solutions to $ax^2+bx+c=0$ can be shown to be given by

$$x=\frac{-b\pm\sqrt{b^2-4ac}}{2a}$$

Example

Solve the equation $7.8x^2-11.2x-4.9=0$.

Solution

Use the formula with $\begin{cases} a=7.8 \\ b=-11.2 \\ c=-4.9 \end{cases}$

Solutions are $x=\dfrac{11.2\pm\sqrt{(-11.2)^2-4\times(7.8)\times(-4.9)}}{2\times7.8}$

$$=\frac{11.2\pm\sqrt{278.32}}{15.6}$$

$$=-0.351 \text{ or } 1.79 \text{ to 3 s.f.}$$

Activity 14

(a) Complete the square for the function $x^2-6x+10$. Sketch its graph, labelling the minimum point clearly.

(b) Try to solve the equation $x^2-6x+10=0$ using the formula.

What happens? Explain your answer graphically.

(c) Try to solve the equation $x^2-12x+36=0$ using the formula.

Use a graph to explain what happens.

(d) What general statements can you make about quadratic equations?

The quantity (b^2-4ac) is clearly of importance in the behaviour of quadratics. It is referred to as the **discriminant** of the function.

What happens if $b^2-4ac=0$ or $b^2-4ac<0$?

Exercise 5F

1. Use the formula $\dfrac{-b \pm \sqrt{b^2 - 4ac}}{2a}$ to solve these equations to 3 s.f.:

   (a) $0.7a^2 - 0.2a - 0.8 = 0$

   (b) $17b^2 + 12b - 1 = 0$

   (c) $2.05c^2 = 4.79c + 12.26$

   (d) $1500d^2 - 17000d = 100000$

   (e) $\frac{1}{2}e^2 - \frac{1}{4}e + \frac{1}{45} = 0$

   (f) $2\pi f^2 = 150f - 400$.

2. Find the discriminant of each of the following equations. How many solutions does each have? (You are not expected to find the solutions.)

   (a) $x^2 + x + 10 = 0$

   (b) $x^2 + 10x - 1 = 0$

   (c) $3x^2 - x - 15 = 0$

   (d) $4x^2 - 36x + 81 = 0$

   (e) $1.72x^2 + 5.71x + 4.68 = 0$

   (f) $9x^2 + 60x + 100 = 0$.

3. A stone is hurled vertically upwards at a speed of 21 metres per second. Its height above the ground in metres is given by the formula

   $$2 + 21t - 5t^2.$$

   (a) After how many seconds does the stone hit the ground?

   (b) What is the maximum height reached by the stone?

4. The surface area of a circular cylinder of radius r and height h is $2\pi r(r+h)$. What radius, to 3 s.f., will give a cylinder of height 15 cm a surface area of 600 cm^2?

5.7 Equations with fractions

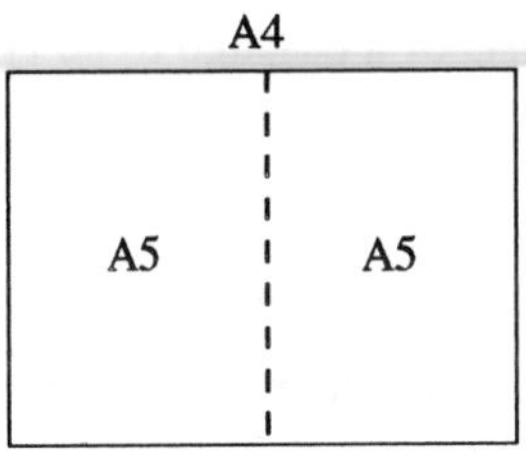

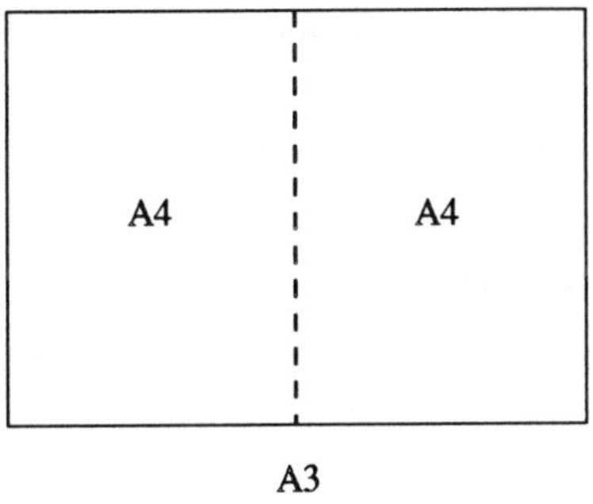

You may at this moment be using A4 paper. Paper sizes in the 'A' series have a special property.

If you fold a piece of A4 paper in half you get two pieces of size A5 (see diagram).

If you put two A4 sheet together side by side, then the resulting size is A3.

Two A3 sheets side by side make an A2 sheet and so on.

All the rectangles in the 'A' series are similar, that is, the ratio

$$\frac{\text{shortest side}}{\text{longest side}}$$

is the same for each size. But what is this ratio?

The problem can be solved algebraically. Let r denote the required ratio, and let l stand for the length of a sheet of A4 paper. The width is therefore rl.

Cutting the sheet in half makes an A5 sheet, with the same ratio. For the A5 sheet:

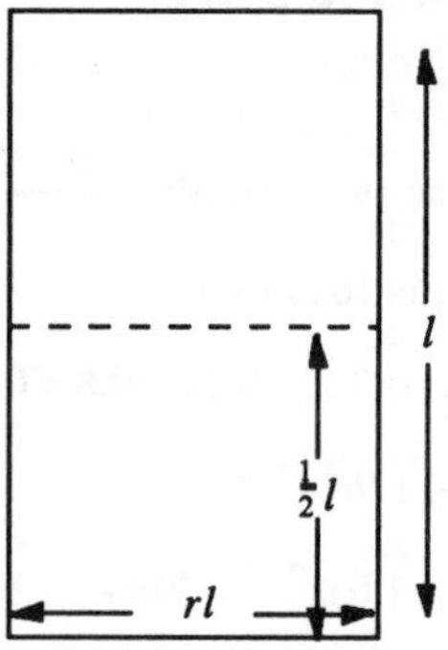

shortest side = $\frac{1}{2}l$ longest side $= rl$.

Hence $$\frac{\frac{1}{2}l}{rl} = r, \quad 0 < r < 1.$$

This is an equation involving an algebraic fraction. The best way to solve it is to multiply both sides by rl, the denominator of the fraction, so that the fraction disappears. This leaves

$$\frac{1}{2}l = r^2 l, \quad 0 < r < 1$$

$$\Rightarrow \quad \frac{1}{2} = r^2, \quad 0 < r < 1$$

$$\Rightarrow \quad r = +\sqrt{\tfrac{1}{2}} = 0.707 \text{ to 3 s.f.}$$

The answer must now be validated.

Measure a piece of A4 paper to check this answer.

Algebraic fractions often turn up when solving problems connected with ratio or rates. Here is another example.

Example

Two tests for a typing certificate are being designed. Each test consists of a passage to be typed as quickly and accurately as possible. The tests will follow on, one after the other, without a break. The following criteria should also be used:

- between them the tests should last 25 minutes;
- the anticipated typing speed for test 1 is 36 words per minute and for test 2, 45 words per minute;
- both tests should contain the same number of words.

How many words should each test contain?

Solution

Let W stand for the number of words in each test. The total time is 25 minutes, so

$$\frac{W}{45} + \frac{W}{36} = 25,$$

which must be solved to find W.

In any equation involving fractions an efficient way to start is to multiply through by the denominators so that no fractions are left. In doing this, take care to multiply each separate term by the same number. So to solve the equation above you first multiply the equation by 45, to give

$$45\times\frac{W}{45}+45\times\frac{W}{36}=45\times 25$$

$$\Rightarrow \quad W+\frac{45}{36}W=1125$$

$$\Rightarrow \quad W+\frac{5}{4}W=1125.$$

Now multiply both sides by 4:

$$4W+5W=4500$$

$$\Rightarrow \quad 9W=4500$$

$$\Rightarrow \quad W=500.$$

Example

Solve the equation $\frac{x}{2}=\frac{10}{x+1}$.

Solution

$$\frac{x}{2}=\frac{10}{x+1}$$

$$\Rightarrow \quad x=\frac{20}{x+1} \qquad \text{(multiply both sides by 2)}$$

$$\Rightarrow \quad x(x+1)=20 \qquad \text{(multiply both sides by } (x+1)\text{)}$$

$$\Rightarrow \quad x^2+x-20=0$$

$$\Rightarrow \quad (x+5)(x-4)=0$$

$$\Rightarrow \quad x=-5 \text{ or } 4.$$

Example

If $\frac{24}{x}+\frac{30}{x-1}=10$, find x.

Solution

$$\frac{24}{x}+\frac{30}{x-1}=10$$

$\Rightarrow \quad 24+\dfrac{30x}{x-1}=10x$ (multiply both sides by x)

$\Rightarrow \quad 24(x-1)+30x=10x(x-1)$ (multiply both sides by $(x-1)$)

$\Rightarrow \quad 24x-24+30x=10x^2-10x$

$\Rightarrow \quad 10x^2-64x+24=0$

$\Rightarrow \quad 5x^2-32x+12=0$

$\Rightarrow \quad (5x-2)(x-6)=0$

$\Rightarrow \quad x=\frac{2}{5}$ or 6.

Activity 15 Spot the deliberate mistakes

These two solutions contain deliberate errors; spot them, correct them, and find the right answers.

(a) $\dfrac{24}{x+1}=\dfrac{x}{6}$

$\Rightarrow \quad \dfrac{24}{1}=\dfrac{x^2}{6}$

$\Rightarrow \quad 6\times 24=x^2$

$\Rightarrow \quad 144=x^2$

$\Rightarrow \quad x=\pm 12.$

(b) $\dfrac{8}{x}+\dfrac{10}{x-3}=3$

$\Rightarrow \quad 8+\dfrac{10x}{x-3}=3$

$\Rightarrow \quad 8(x-3)+10x=3$

$\Rightarrow \quad 18x-24=3$

$\Rightarrow \quad x=1.5.$

Exercise 5G

1. Solve the equations

(a) $\frac{x}{7}+\frac{2x}{3}=17$ (b) $\frac{x}{9}-\frac{x}{12}=1$

(c) $\frac{x}{8}=\frac{18}{x}$ (d) $\frac{3}{x+1}=\frac{1}{2}$

(e) $\frac{7}{x+1}=\frac{8}{x-2}$ (f) $\frac{2x-3}{5}=\frac{27}{x}$

(g) $\frac{x+1}{3}=\frac{18}{x-2}$ (h) $\frac{6}{x+2}+\frac{4}{x-2}=1$

(i) $\frac{18}{2x-1}-\frac{15}{x}+1=0$ (j) $\frac{x+1}{4}-\frac{20}{x-5}=0$.

2. Foolscap paper obeys the following property. If the sheet is folded to make a square and a rectangle, the rectangular part is similar to the foolscap sheet itself, that is, for both rectangles the ratio $\frac{\text{longest side}}{\text{shortest side}}$ is the same. Find this ratio.

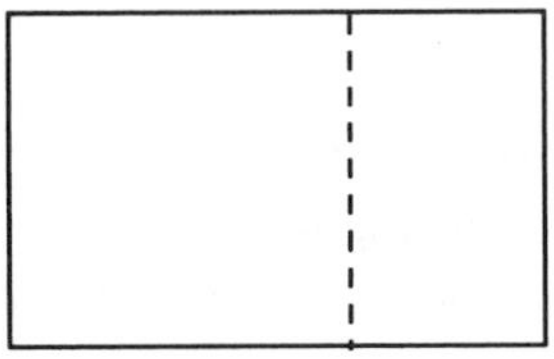

3. 'Petrol is 75p per gallon more expensive now than it was in 1981. You can buy as much petrol now for £132 as you could for £87 in 1981'. Assuming these statements are true, find the cost of petrol in 1981.

4. Sandra buys some 'fun sized' chocolate bars as prizes for her son's birthday party. She spends £16.80 on them in total.

   She recalls that she spent exactly the same amount of money on them for last year's party, but this year the same amount bought 20 bars fewer, since the price had gone up by 2p a bar.

   What is the current cost of a 'fun-sized' chocolate bar?

5.8 Inequalities

Here is a variation on a problem posed in Activity 5 of Section 5.4

Activity 16 A quadratic inequality

A farmer uses 50 m of fencing to form a rectangular enclosure with one side against a wall as shown opposite. The area of the enclosure must be at least 250 m^2.

Show that $x^2-25x+125\le 0$, where x metres is the width of the enclosure.

Find the range of values of x that satisfy this inequality. (You might find it helpful to draw a graph of the function)

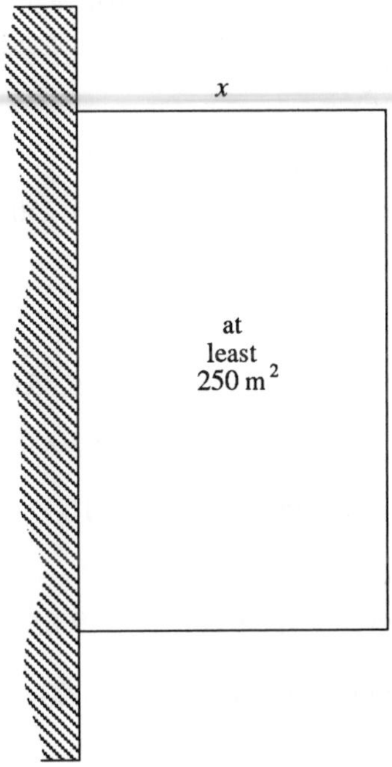

Quadratic inequalities can be solved by a mixture of algebraic and graphical means. For example, to solve $2x^2+7x-5>0$, you might first consider the graph of the function $y=2x^2+7x-5$, shown on the right. The solution to the inequality is clearly the two regions $x<a$ and $x>b$, where a and b are the two solutions to the quadratic equation $2x^2+7x-5=0$.

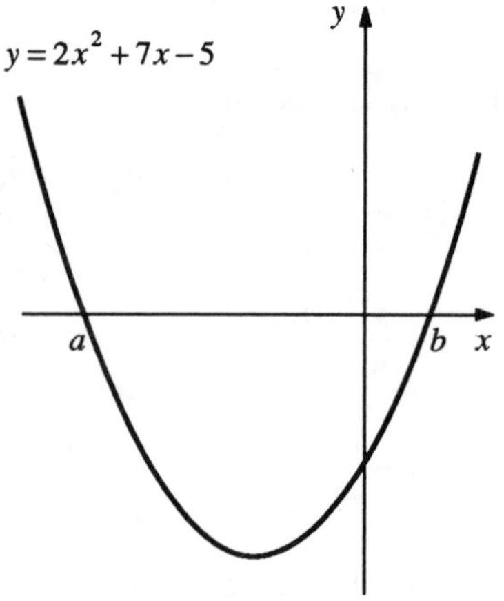

The values of a and b can be found either by completing the square or by using the formula. This gives $a=4.11$ and $b=0.608$. Hence the solution to the equality is $x<-4.11$ or $x>0.608$.

This solution could have been found without drawing a graph at all. Once you know where the quadratic function is zero there are two possibilities.

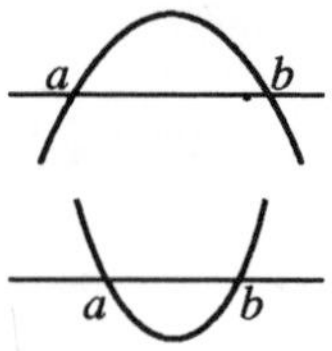

Either - the function is positive between these two values, negative elsewhere;

Or - the function is negative between these two values, positive elsewhere.

You can quickly discover which of these is true by choosing a number between a and b and seeing whether the function is positive or negative. In the example above, look to see what happens at $x=0$:

$$x=0 \Rightarrow y=2x^2+7x-5=-5$$

so function is negative between $x=-4.11$ and $x=0.608$ and the required solution is either side of these values.

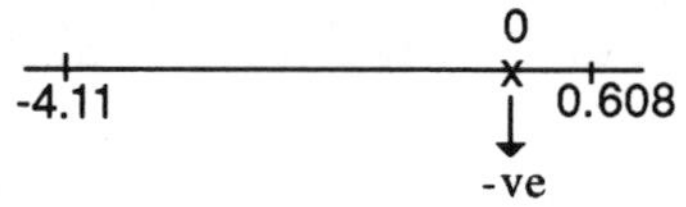

Example

Solve the inequality $4(x^2-250)\le 65x$

Solution

$$4(x^2-250)\le 65x$$

$$\Rightarrow \quad 4x^2-65x-1000\le 0.$$

The function $4x^2-65x-1000$ is zero at $x=-9.65$ and 25.9 to 3 s.f.

Choose a value between -9.65 and 25.9, say $x=0$.

When $x=0$, $4x^2-65x-1000=-1000$ so the function is negative between -9.65 and 25.9.

The required solution is between these two values:

$$-9.65\le x\le 25.9.$$

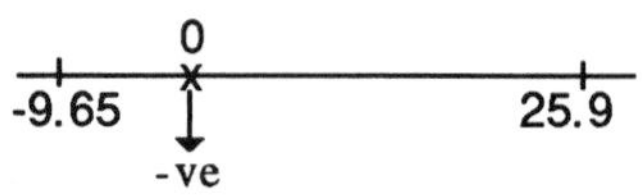

Two alternative methods are illustrated in the next two activities.

Activity 17

(a) Consider the inequality $x^2 > 9$. Why is the answer $x > 3$ incomplete? What is the full solution?

(b) Now consider the inequality

$$x^2 - 6x - 11 \geq 0.$$

Complete the square and use this form of the function to solve the inequality directly.

Activity 18

In the inequality $2x^2 - 7x - 39 < 0$ the quadratic function can be factorised. Rewrite the inequality in the form

$$(\quad)(\quad) < 0.$$

If the product of two brackets is negative, as required by this inequality, what can you say about the two factors?

Hence solve the inequality.

Two further worked examples are given below, one for each of these alternative methods. After that there follows an exercise for you to practice these techniques.

Example

Solve $x^2 + 8x + 9 < 0$.

Solution

$x^2 + 8x + 9$ cannot be factorised, but it is easy to complete the square.

$$
\begin{aligned}
& x^2 + 8x + 9 < 0 \\
\Rightarrow \quad & (x+4)^2 - 7 < 0 \\
\Rightarrow \quad & (x+4)^2 < 7 \\
\Rightarrow \quad & -\sqrt{7} < x + 4 < +\sqrt{7} \\
\Rightarrow \quad & -\sqrt{7} - 4 < x < +\sqrt{7} - 4.
\end{aligned}
$$

Example

Solve $x^2 - 3x - 28 \geq 0$.

Solution

$x^2 - 3x - 28$ can be factorised

$$x^2 - 3x - 28 \geq 0$$
$$\Rightarrow \quad (x-7)(x+4) \geq 0.$$

The two factors can be either both positive or both negative, as the diagram suggests, so the solution must be

$$x \leq -4, x \geq 7.$$

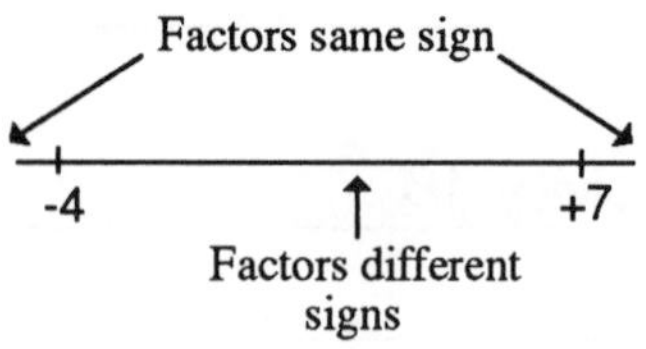

Exercise 5H

1. Solve these by factorising
   (a) $x^2 - 5x - 66 \geq 0$
   (b) $3x^2 + 1 < 4x$
   (c) $(x-7)(x+5) \geq 28$
   (d) $x^2 + 110x + 3000 > 0$.
2. Solve these inequalities by completing the square.
   (a) $x^2 + 2x > 4$
   (b) $x^2 - 8x + 10 \leq 0$
   (c) $x^2 + 24x + 100 < 0$
   (d) $x(x-100) \geq 2000$.
3. Solve these inequalities by whatever method you choose.
   (a) $x^2 - 7x \leq 60$
   (b) $x^2 + 12x + 28 > 0$
   (c) $x(50-3x) < 200$
   (d) $6x^2 + 11x \leq 350$
   (e) $\dfrac{14x - 3x^2}{9} \geq 1$
   (f) $0.7x^2 - 3.9x + 2.5 < 0$.
4. In a right-angled triangle the hypotenuse is more than double the shortest side. The third side of the triangle is 2 cm longer than the shortest side. What values can the shortest side take? (Remember the domain when setting up the problem).

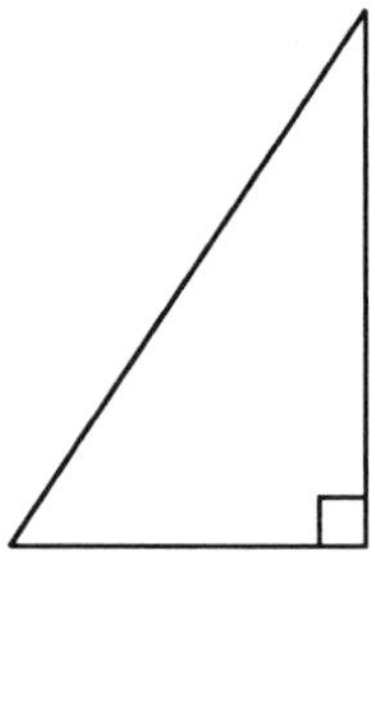

5.9 Modulus sign

The use of the modulus sign will be introduced through this problem.

> Two cars are driving in opposite directions on the motorway. One starts from London at a constant speed of 75 mph; the other starts at the same time from Leeds, 198 miles away, at a constant 60 mph.
>
> Both cars are equipped with two-way radios but need to be within 10 miles of each other to make contact. When can they contact one another?

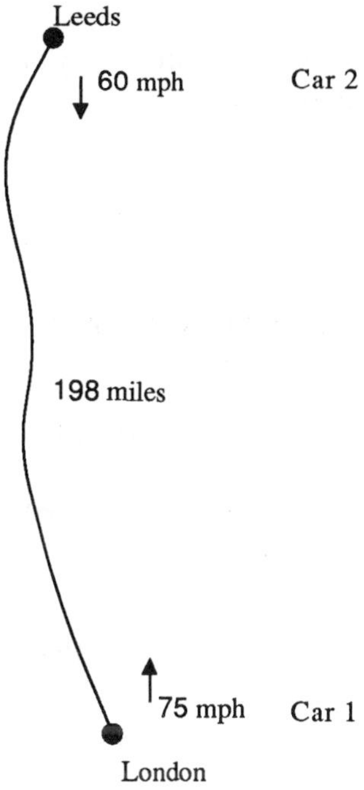

If t is the number of minutes after the journeys start then

distance of car 1 from London

$$= \frac{75t}{60} \text{ miles}$$
$$= \frac{5t}{4} \text{ miles.}$$

Distance of car 2 from Leeds $= \frac{60t}{60} = t$ miles, so distance of car 2 from London $= (198 - t)$ miles.

Their distance apart is found by subtracting one distance from the other, i.e. distance apart in miles is

$$= 198 - t - \frac{5t}{4}$$
$$= 198 - \frac{9t}{4}.$$

So, for example, after one hour ($t = 60$) the cars are 63 miles apart. But when $t = 120$, the formula gives -72. This means that the cars are 72 miles apart, but that car 2 is now closer to London than car 1, i.e. the cars have crossed.

There is an agreed convention for getting round this problem, and that is to write

$$\text{distance apart} = \left| 198 - \frac{9t}{4} \right|$$

where the two vertical lines mean 'the **modulus** of ' or 'the **absolute value** of '.

The modulus sign causes any minus sign to be disregarded. So,

when $t = 60$, distance apart $= |\ 63\ | = 63$ miles,

when $t = 120$, distance apart $= |\ -72\ | = 72$ miles.

The mathematical way of expressing the original problem is to find t when

$$\left| 198 - \frac{9t}{4} \right| < 10.$$

This can be solved by regarding it as short for two separate inequalities.

$$-10 < 198 - \frac{9t}{4} < 10.$$

Writing it in this form enables two inequalities to be solved at the same time;

$$-10 < 198 - \frac{9t}{4} < 10$$

$$\Rightarrow \quad 10 > \frac{9t}{4} - 198 > -10$$

$$\Rightarrow \quad 208 > \frac{9t}{4} > 188$$

$$\Rightarrow \quad 92\frac{4}{9} > t > 83\frac{5}{9}.$$

Hence the two cars are within 10 miles of one another between $83\frac{5}{9}$ and $92\frac{4}{9}$ minutes after the start of their journeys.

Example

Solve

(a) $\left| 40\left(1 - \frac{x}{7}\right) \right| < 5$

(b) $|\ 8t - 11|\ \geq 13.$

Solution

(a) $\left| 40\left(1 - \frac{x}{7}\right) \right| < 5$

$$\Rightarrow \quad -5 < 40\left(1 - \frac{x}{7}\right) < 5$$

$$\Rightarrow \quad -\frac{1}{8} < 1 - \frac{x}{7} < \frac{1}{8}$$

$$\Rightarrow \quad \frac{1}{8} > \frac{x}{7} - 1 > -\frac{1}{8}$$ (multiplying by –1 changes the inequality round)

$$\Rightarrow \quad \frac{9}{8} > \frac{x}{7} > \frac{7}{8}$$

$$\Rightarrow \quad \frac{63}{8} > x > \frac{49}{8} \quad \text{or} \quad 7.875 > x > 6.125.$$

(b) $|8t - 11| \geq 13$

$$\Rightarrow \quad 8t - 11 \geq 13 \quad \text{or} \quad 8t - 11 \leq -13$$

$$\Rightarrow \quad 8t \geq 24 \quad \text{or} \quad 8t \leq -2$$

$$\Rightarrow \quad t \geq 3 \quad \text{or} \quad t \leq -\tfrac{1}{4}.$$

Example

Laila wants some leaflets printed. She gets two quotes:

> 'Bulkfast' say they will charge a fixed charge of £60 plus 5p per copy. 'Smallorder' printers quote a £25 fixed charge plus 8p per copy.

Find a formula for the difference in price if Laila decides to have n copies printed. She decides that a difference of £5 or less is 'negligible' and, if this is the case, that quality of product will be the deciding factor between the two firms. For what values of n is the difference 'negligible'?

Solution

For n copies 'Bulkfast' will charge £$(60 + 0.05n)$ and 'Smallorder' £$(25 + 0.08n)$.

$$\text{Difference in price } = |(60 + 0.05n) - (25 + 0.08n)|$$

$$= |\,35 - 0.03n\,|.$$

For the difference to be negligible

$$\begin{aligned} & |35 - 0.03n| \le 5, && n \in \mathrm{N} \\ \Rightarrow\quad & -5 \le 35 - 0.03n \le 5, && n \in \mathrm{N} \\ \Rightarrow\quad & 5 \ge 0.03n - 35 \ge -5, && n \in \mathrm{N} \\ \Rightarrow\quad & 40 \ge 0.03n \ge 30, && n \in \mathrm{N} \\ \Rightarrow\quad & 1333.33 \ge n \ge 1000, && n \in \mathrm{N}. \end{aligned}$$

So the difference is negligible when n is between 1000 and 1333 copies inclusive.

Example

Solve $\left| x^2 + 4x - 1 \right| < 2.$

Solution

$\left| x^2 + 4x - 1 \right| < 2 \Rightarrow -2 < x^2 + 4x - 1 < 2.$

This can be solved as two separate inequalities $x^2 + 4x - 3 < 0$ and $x^2 + 4x + 1 > 0$ and the results combined.

A quicker technique is to complete the square;

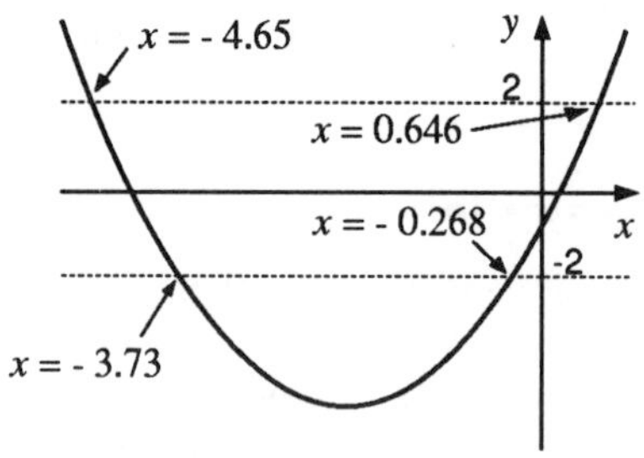

$$\begin{aligned} & -2 < (x+2)^2 - 5 < 2 \\ \Rightarrow\quad & 3 < (x+2)^2 < 7 \\ \Rightarrow\quad & \sqrt{3} < x + 2 < \sqrt{7} \quad \text{or} \quad -\sqrt{3} > x + 2 > -\sqrt{7} \\ \Rightarrow\quad & \sqrt{3} - 2 < x < \sqrt{7} - 2 \quad \text{or} \quad -\sqrt{3} - 2 > x > -\sqrt{7} - 2 \\ \Rightarrow\quad & -0.268 < x < 0.646 \quad \text{or} \quad -3.73 > x > -4.65. \end{aligned}$$

Activity 19 Properties of the modulus function

Which of these statements below are true? x and y stand for any numbers.

(a) $|x + y| = |x| + |y|$ (b) $|x - y| = |x| - |y|$

(c) $|xy| = |x|\,|y|$

(d) $\left| \dfrac{x}{y} \right| = \dfrac{|x|}{|y|}$ (e) $(|x|)^2 = x^2.$

Activity 20 Graphs involving the modulus function

(a) Sketch the graph of $y = x$. What will the graph of $y = |x|$ look like?

(b) Sketch the graph of $y = 2x - 5$ and hence the graph of $y = |2x - 5|$

(c) Sketch the graph of $y = x^2 - 7x + 5$ and $y = \left|x^2 - 7x + 5\right|$.

(d) The graph of $y = f(x)$ is shown on the right.

Sketch $y = |f(x)|$ and $y = f(|x|)$.

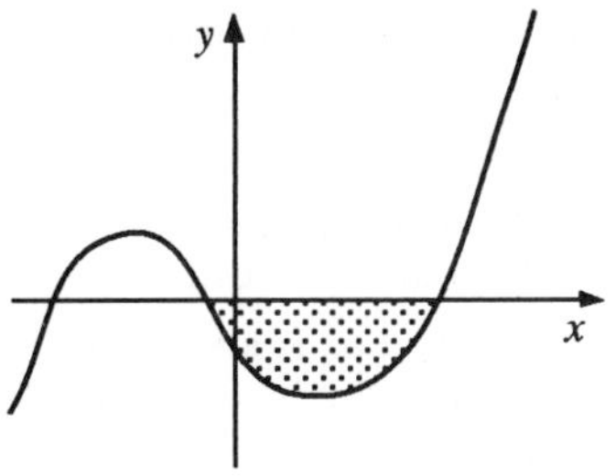

Exercise 5I

1. Solve these inequalities :

(a) $|5a+3| \le 2$ (b) $|10-b| < 6$

(c) $|15-4c| \ge 3$ (d) $\left|\frac{2d}{3}+7\right| \le 11$

(e) $\left|2(5+\frac{12e}{5})\right| < 16$ (f) $\left|\frac{4-9f}{13}\right| \le 10$

2. Use a graph to solve :

(a) $\left|12x^2+7x-10\right| < 20, x \in \mathbb{N}$

(b) $\left|100-5x-x^2\right| < 50, x \in \mathbb{N}$

3. Solve

(a) $\left|x^2-8x+10\right| < 3$ (b) $\left|x^2+2x-6\right| > 6$

(c) $\left|x^2+10x+18\right| < 8$.

4. The formula $F = \frac{9}{5}C + 32$ is used to convert degrees Celsius (C) into degrees Fahrenheit (F). Often, however, the formula $F = 2C + 30$ is used to make the arithmetic easier. Over what temperature range (in °C) is the approximate formula correct

(a) to within 5°F (b) to within 2°F.

5. Di and Vi decide to race each other over 100 metres. Vi is a faster sprinter than Di. Vi's average time for the 100 metres is 12.5 seconds whilst Di's is 16 seconds. It is agreed that, while Vi will run the full distance, Di will be given a head start of d metres.

(a) Suppose they run the race at the same speed as their average times suggest. How many seconds apart will they cross the finishing line?

(b) They decide to set d so that no more than 1 second is expected between them at the finish. Find over what values d could range.

5.10 Miscellaneous Exercises

1. In setting an exam paper, it is agreed that short questions will carry 4 marks each and long questions 13 marks. The paper must contain 16 questions altogether and must be out of 100 marks in total.

   How many of the two types of question must there be?

   (You should assume that candidates have to answer all the questions.)

2. This question is about taxation. At the time of writing tax is calculated like this:

   - first £3005 earned in a year is not taxed.
   - income between £3005 and £20 700 is taxed at 25%;
   - all income over £20 700 is taxed at 40%.

   Two brothers compare their 1990/91 tax bills. Peter notices that, although his income was twice as much as Jonathan's, he paid 2.8 times as much tax. How much money did Peter earn? (Assume that neither brother receives any allowance other than the £3005 mentioned above.)

3. Staff at a factory are working overtime to get a job finished quickly. It is decided that continuous supervision is needed. Six supervisors are chosen, each to work a 6-hour shift, with an equal overlap time between each shift. The job will not take less than 32 hours and must be finished within 35 hours. How long could the overlap between shifts be?

4. (a) Clair needs to get to work by 9.00 am. She finds that if she leaves home at 7.00 am, the journey takes 1 hour, but that every two minutes after 7 o'clock adds another minute to her travelling time. At what time must she leave home in order to get to work exactly on time?

   (b) Her journey home takes 1 hour if she leaves at 4.30 pm. Every 4 minutes later than this adds 3 minutes to her travelling time. To the nearest minute, when must she leave work to arrive home at 6.00 pm?

5. Economists often talk about a firm's total cost function. This function relates the total cost C to the level of output Q units.

   Suppose a firm's total cost function is

   $$C = 4Q^2 + 100Q + 16000,$$

   find the values of $Q (\in \mathbb{N})$ for the total cost to be less than £70 000.

6. An office manager employs the following method of buying Christmas presents for staff. He buys a consignment of turkeys, all at the same price. 15 of them are reserved for his colleagues and the rest are resold when the price has risen by £2 per turkey above what he paid. He then sells the reserved turkeys at whatever price he needs to break even.

   This year he had to pay £1200 for the original consignment, and his colleagues paid exactly half the original price for their birds. How many turkeys did he buy?

7. A light plane travels from London to Inverness, a distance of 450 miles, at an average speed of 200 mph. Another plane travels the same route but gets there half an hour quicker. How fast was the second plane travelling?

8. Two cars travel 150 miles along the motorway. On average, one car travels 10 mph faster than the other, and completes the journey 15 minutes before the other one. What speed was the slower one doing, to the nearest mile per hour?

9. In a cycle race the contestants ride from A to B and back. Both outward and return journeys are the same distance, but the return journey is mostly downhill; average speeds on the return leg are 8 km/h faster than on the outward.

   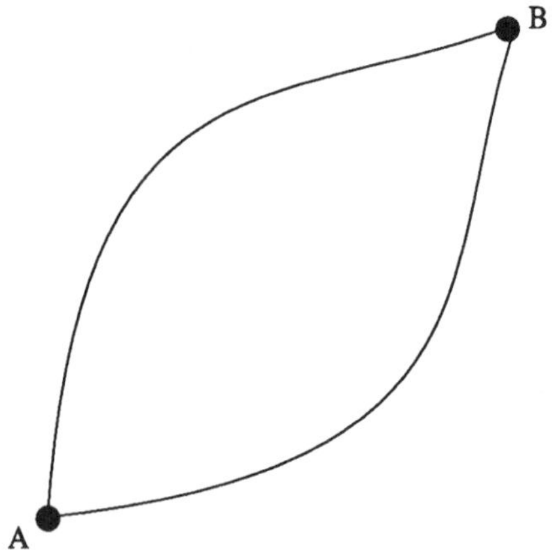

   Neville covers the 60 km course in $2\frac{1}{2}$ hours. Work out his average speed for the first half of the course, to the nearest km/h.

10.

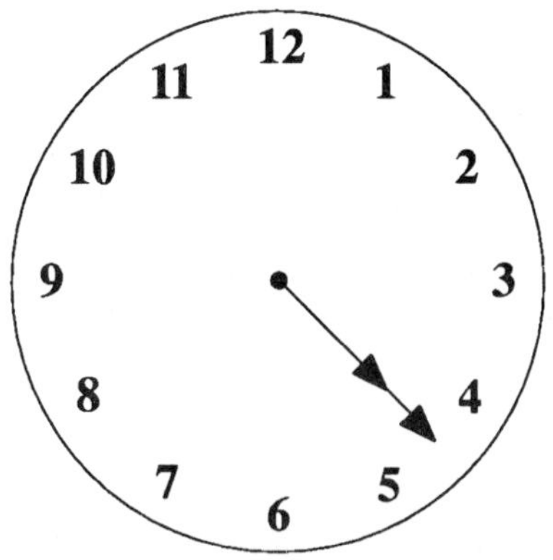

The hands on the clock move smoothly and continually. In the above picture the minute hand is exactly covering the hour hand. What time is it? (NOT 4.20)

11. The shape below is known as a pentagram. Find x.

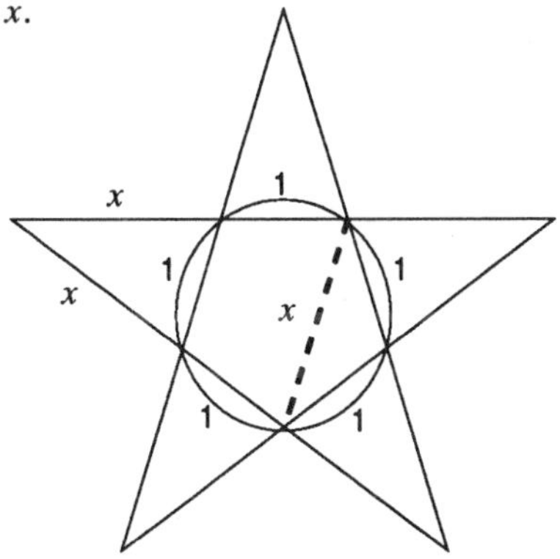

12. The diagram shows the elevation of a garden shed, the roof of which overhangs to the level of the top of the window. The distance AB is 30 cm longer than the length of the overhang, marked x in the diagram. Find x.

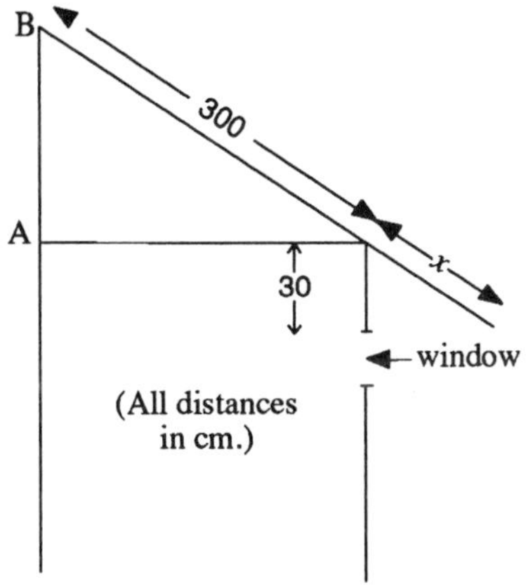

13. A fighter and a spy plane are travelling on perpendicular paths that cross at the point C. At 1.10 pm the fighter is 100 miles due west of C and travelling east at 400 mph. At the same time the spy plane is 60 miles due south of C and travelling north at 300 mph.

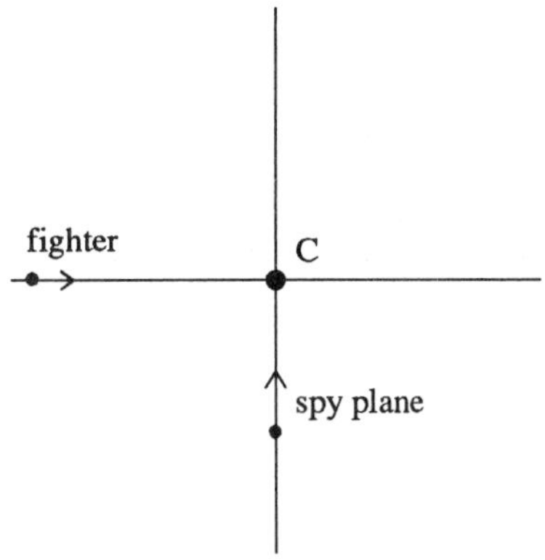

(a) If t is the time in hours after 1.10 pm, write down formulae for the distances of both planes from C at time t.

(b) For how many minutes are the two planes within 50 miles of each other?

14. A rectangular paddock is 3 times longer than it is wide. The width is increased by 20 m. This has the effect of doubling the area. Find the original dimensions of the paddock.

15. Solve these:

(a) $|x| = |x+1|$ (b) $\frac{12}{x+1} > \frac{x}{6}$

(c) $x^4 - 13x^2 + 36 = 0$ (d) $x - 6\sqrt{x} + 8 = 0$

(e) $x^3 + 2x^2 - 48x = 0$ (f) $x^2 - |x| - 2 = 0$.

6 EXTENDING ALGEBRA

Objectives

After studying this chapter you should

- understand techniques whereby equations of cubic degree and higher can be solved;
- be able to factorise polynomials;
- be able to use the remainder theorem.

6.0 Introduction

This chapter is different from the others in this book; although it begins with a realistic example, much of the rest does not have any immediate relevance to the outside world. Its purpose is to extend the algebra you already know.

This does not make it a dull chapter. On the contrary, there are many people who enjoy abstract mathematics as being interesting in its own right. Over the centuries mathematical techniques have developed partly in response to problems that needed to be solved, but there have always been those who have pondered on the less applicable side of the subject purely out of interest and curiosity.

6.1 The cubic equation

How can an open-topped box with volume 500 cm^3 be made from a square piece of card 20 cm by 20 cm?

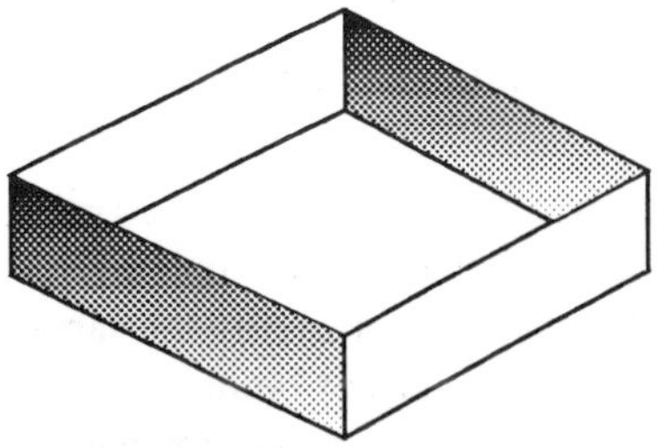

To make such a box, a net can be made by cutting off equal squares from each corner, as shown in the diagram.

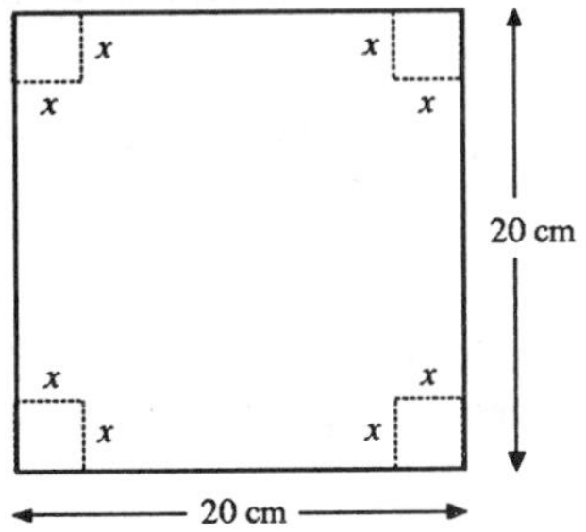

Suppose each smaller square has side x cm. The dimensions of the box will then be x by $(20-2x)$ by $(20-2x)$. For the volume to be 500 cm^3, x must satisfy the equation

$$x(20-2x)^2 = 500, \quad 0 \le x \le 10$$

When the expression has been multiplied out, the highest power of x in this equation is x^3; accordingly this equation is called a **cubic equation.**

As with a quadratic equation, it is good practice to reduce this equation to the form $f(x)=0$.

$$x(400-80x+4x^2)=500$$

$$\Rightarrow \quad 4x^3-80x^2+400x-500=0$$

$$\Rightarrow \quad x^3-20x^2+100x-125=0, \; 0\le x\le 10$$

Again by comparison with quadratic equations, the next thing you might want to do would be to try to factorise it. With a cubic function, however, this is not easy.

Fortunately one solution to the problem can be seen 'by inspection'. A little experimentation reveals that $x=5$ will fit the bill. Is this the only solution? Remember that for quadratic equations where there was one answer there was almost always another.

One method of solution is to draw the graph of the cubic function $x^3-20x^2+100x-125$ and see where it crosses the x-axis.

Activity 1 Using a graph

Sketch the graph of the function

$$f(x)=x^3-20x^2+100x-125$$

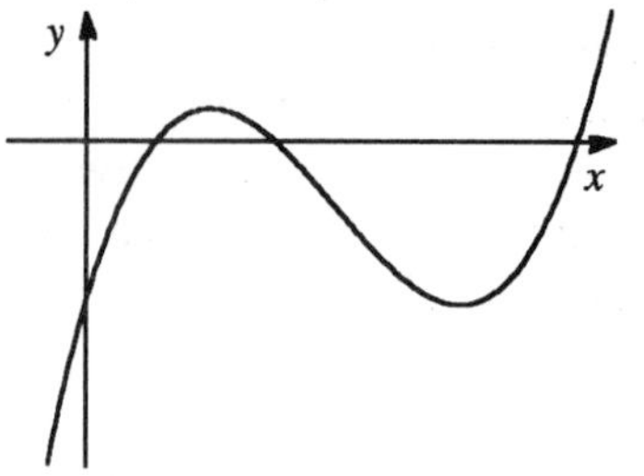

Verify that $f(5)=0$ and find any other values of x where the curve crosses the horizontal axis.

Bearing in mind the domain of x, solve the original problem to the nearest millimetre.

The solutions of an equation are called the **roots** of an equation.

Hence 5 is a root of $x^3-20x^2+100x-125=0$ and Activity 1 should have revealed that there are two other roots as well. Another way of saying the same thing is to refer to 5 and the two other solutions as being **zeros** of the function; in other words, these values make that function equal to zero.

α is a root of $f(x)=0 \Longleftrightarrow f(\alpha)=0$

How could the cubic equation have been solved without the need to draw the graph? Activity 2 gives a clue.

Activity 2 Zeros and factors

You may find it useful to use a graphic calculator.

(a) Sketch the graph of the function $x^2+2x-143$. What is the factorised form of this function? How can you tell by looking at the graph?

(b) Now sketch the graph of the cubic function $(x+4)(x-1)(x-3)$. How does the form of the function correspond to its zeros?

(c) Sketch the graph of the function $x^3-79x+210$. Hence write this function as the product of three linear factors.

(d) Can you factorise x^3-5x^2+3x+4 by looking at its graph?

(e) Suggest a possible equation for the curve on the right.

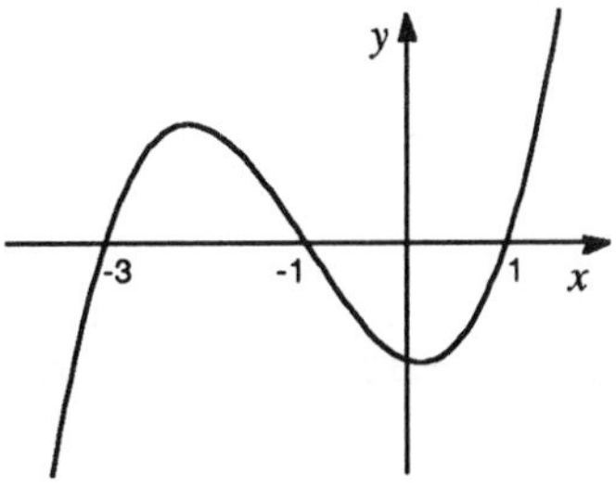

Now look again at the equation

$$x^3-20x^2+100x-125=0$$

$x=5$ is known to be a zero of the function $x^3-20x^2+100x-125$ and so it can be deduced, from your work on Activity 2 that $(x-5)$ is a factor.

If $(x-5)$ is a factor, how does the rest of the factorisation go? It is evident that $x^3-20x^2+100x-125=(x-5)\times$(quadratic function). Moreover, the quadratic must be of the form

$$x^2+bx+25$$

Finding b is not quite so obvious but can be done as follows :

$$x^3-20x^2+100x-125=(x-5)(x^2+bx+25)$$

To make $-20x^2$ in the cubic equation:

$$-20=-5+b \Rightarrow b=-15$$

To make $+100x$ in the cubic equation:

$$100=25-5b \Rightarrow b=-15$$

Hence $x^3-20x^2+100x-125=(x-5)(x^2-15x+25)$

The solution to the cubic equation is as follows

$$x^3-20x^2+100x-125=0$$

$$\Rightarrow \quad (x-5)(x^2-15x+25)=0$$

$$\Rightarrow \quad \text{either } x-5=0 \text{ or } \quad x^2-15x+25=0$$

$$\Rightarrow \quad x=1.9, 5 \text{ or } 13.1 \text{ to } 1 \text{ d.p.}$$

Example

Find all solutions of $x^3-3x^2-33x+35=0$

Solution

A bit of searching reveals that $x=1$ is a root of this equation, since $f(1)=0$. Hence $(x-1)$ must be a factor, and you can write

$$x^3-3x^2-33x+35=(x-1)(x^2+bx-35)$$

To find b : the cubic equation contains $-33x$, so

$$-33=-b-35$$

$$\Rightarrow \quad b=-2$$

$$\Rightarrow \quad x^3-3x^2-33x+35=(x-1)(x^2-2x-35)$$

In this case, the quadratic factor itself factorises to

$$(x-7)(x+5)$$

so

$$x^3-3x^2-33x+35=(x-1)(x-7)(x+5)$$

The original equation can thus be re-written

$$(x-1)(x-7)(x+5)=0$$

$$\Rightarrow \quad x=-5, 1 \text{ or } 7$$

Example

Solve $x^3-14x-15=0$

Solution

$x=-3$ is a root of this equation. Hence $(x+3)$ is a factor.

$$x^3-14x-15=(x+3)(x^2+bx-5)$$

To find b: cubic equation has $0x^2$, so

$$0=b+3$$

$$\Rightarrow \quad b=-3$$

$$\Rightarrow \quad x^3-14x-15=(x+3)(x^2-3x-5)$$

The original equation thus reads

$$(x+3)(x^2-3x-5)=0$$

$$\Rightarrow \quad \text{either } x+3=0 \text{ or } x^2-3x-5=0$$

$$\Rightarrow \quad x=-3, -1.19, \text{ or } 4.19, \text{ to 3 s.f.}$$

Activity 3 Missing roots

(a) Find a linear factor of $x^3-4x^2-2x+20$ and the corresponding quadratic factor. Hence find all the solutions of $x^3-4x^2-2x+20=0$.

(b) Illustrate your answer by means of a sketch graph.

Exercise 6A

1. (a) Work out the missing quadratic factors
   (i) $x^3-3x^2-6x+8=(x-4)(\quad)$
   (ii) $x^3+8x^2+12x-9=(x+3)(\quad)$
   (iii) $2x^3-x^2-117x-324=(2x+9)(\quad)$

   (b) Use your answers to (a) to find all the roots of
   (i) $x^3-3x^2-6x+8=0$
   (ii) $x^3+8x^2+12x-9=0$
   (iii) $2x^3-x^2-117x-324=0$

2. Explain how you know that
   (a) $(x-3)$ is a factor of x^3-2x^2+x-12
   (b) $(x+5)$ is a factor of $2x^3+6x^2-23x-15$
   (c) $(2x-1)$ is a factor of $4x^3+2x^2+8x-5$.

3. Find all the roots of these equations
   (a) $x^3-5x^2+6x-2=0$
   (b) $x^3+3x^2-46x=48$
   (c) $2x^3-x^2-18x+9=0$

4. Four identical 'square corners' are cut from a square piece of card measuring 10 cm by 10 cm. The resulting net will make an open topped box with volume 64 cm^3. Find the size of the squares that must be removed.

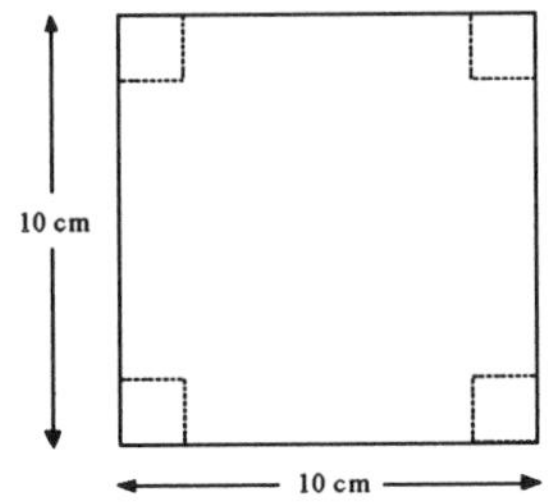

6.2 No simple solution

You should by now have asked the question : "What happens if no simple solution can be found?" The process you have used depends crucially on first being able to find a root. You may wonder whether, as with quadratic equations that cannot be factorised, there is a formula that will give all the roots automatically.

The answer is that a systematic method of finding roots of cubics does exist. The bad news, however, is that

(a) it is a long-winded method which is seldom used;

(b) it involves complicated maths.

A practical solution is to use either a graphical method or trial and improvement. Both methods can be time-consuming and both depend on first knowing approximately where the roots are.

For example, to solve the equation $x^3 - 100x^2 + 2000x - 1500 = 0$ it is a help to work out a few values of the function first. Let the function be labelled $f(x)$.

A table of values is shown on the right. The arrows show where $f(x)$ changes from positive to negative or vice versa. Hence the zeros of $f(x)$ must occur

between 0 and 10

between 20 and 30

between 70 and 80

Trial and improvement, or graphs drawn in the correct regions, eventually give answers of 0.78, 26.40 and 72.82 to 2 d.p.

x	$f(x)$
−30	−178500
−20	−89500
−10	−32500
0	−1500 ←
10	9500
20	6500 ←
30	−4500
40	−17500
50	−26500
60	−25500
70	−8500 ←
80	30500

Exercise 6B

1. (a) Explain how you can tell that the function $f(x) = x^3 + x^2 - x + 5$ has a zero between $x = -3$ and $x = -2$.

   (b) Find this value to 3 s.f.

2. Solve these cubic equations to 3 s.f.

   (a) $2x^3 - 150x^2 + 75000 = 0$

   (b) $x^3 + 4x^2 - 32x - 100 = 0$

6.3 Factor theorem

Quadratics and cubics are particular examples of **polynomial functions** : a quadratic function is a polynomial of degree 2 : a cubic has degree 3. In general a **polynomial of degree** n has the form

$$a_n x^n + a_{n-1}x^{n-1} + \dots + a_2 x^2 + a_1 x + a_0$$

where a_0, a_1, ... a_n are real numbers, and $a_n \neq 0$. When solving cubic equations, the spotting of a root leads immediately to a simple linear factor : e.g.

$$\begin{aligned} & 3 \text{ is a zero of } x^3 - 5x^2 + 11x - 15 \\ \Rightarrow \quad & (x-3) \text{ is a factor of } x^3 - 5x^2 + 11x - 15 \\ \Rightarrow \quad & x^3 + 5x^2 + 11x - 15 = (x-3) \times (\text{quadratic}) \end{aligned}$$

The same technique can be applied to polynomials of any degree. For example,

$$\begin{aligned} & 2 \text{ is a zero of } x^4 + 3x^2 - 17x + 6 \\ \Rightarrow \quad & (x-2) \text{ is a factor of } x^4 + 3x^2 - 17x + 6 \\ \Rightarrow \quad & x^4 + 3x^2 - 17x + 6 = (x-2) \times (\text{cubic}) \end{aligned}$$

In general

> If $P(x)$ is a polynomial of degree n and has a zero at $x = \alpha$, that is $P(\alpha) = 0$, then $(x - \alpha)$ is a factor of $P(x)$ and
>
> $$P(x) = (x - \alpha)Q(x)$$
>
> where $Q(x)$ is a polynomial of degree $(n-1)$

This is known as the **factor theorem.**

Example

Show that $(x-5)$ is a factor of the polynomial

$$x^5 - 4x^4 - x^3 - 21x^2 + 25.$$

Solution

Denote the polynomial by $P(x)$.

$$\begin{aligned} P(5) &= 5^5 - 4\times 5^4 - 5^3 - 21\times 5^2 + 25 \\ &= 3125 - 2500 - 125 - 525 + 25 \\ &= 0 \end{aligned}$$

Hence 5 is a zero of $P(x)$ and so by the factor theorem, $(x-5)$ is a factor.

Activity 4 Fractions as roots

(a) Show that $x = \frac{1}{2}$ is a zero of $2x^3 - 3x^2 - 3x + 2$.

(b) $2x^3 - 3x^2 - 3x + 2$ has two linear factors other than $x = \frac{1}{2}$. Find them. Check that all three factors multiply together to give the original cubic.

(c) Find the quadratic expression missing from this statement :

$$2x^3 - 3x^2 - 3x + 2 = (2x-1)(\qquad)$$

(d) Suppose the fraction $\frac{p}{q}$ is a root of a polynomial. What could the associated factor be?

Activity 5 Tips for root-spotting

(a) Just by looking at the equation $x^3 + 3x^2 + 3x + 2 = 0$ it is possible to deduce that, if there is an integer root, it can only be ± 1 or ± 2. Why? What is the root?

(b) If there is an integer root of $x^4 + 3x^3 + x^2 + 2x - 3 = 0$ then what could it be? For example, how can you tell that neither +2 nor -2 could be a root?

You have now met the main techniques to find factors, but you should always remember that some polynomials will not have any **real** roots, whilst others will have real roots, but they will not be integers or even rational numbers.

Exercise 6C

1. Show that

   (a) $(x-1)$ is a factor of $x^4+3x^3-2x^2+5x-7$

   (b) $(x+1)$ is a factor of $x^5-7x^4-8x^3+2x^2+x-1$

   (c) $(x-3)$ is a factor of x^4-2x^3-7x-6

   (d) $(x-2)$ is a factor of $2x^6+5x^4-27x^3+8$

   (e) $(x+10)$ is a factor of $5x^5+23x^4-269x^3-90x+100$

   (f) $(x-8)$ is a factor of $x^{10}-9x^9+8x^8-x^2+x+56$

2. Three of the polynomials below have a linear factor from the list on the right. Match the factors to the polynomials. The 'odd one out' does have a simple linear factor, but not one in the list. Find the factor.

A: x^4-5x^2+3x-2	1: $x+1$
B: $x^5-4x^4+2x^3-8x^2-x+4$	2: $x-2$
C: x^3-4x^2-6x-1	3: $x+3$
D: $x^3+12x^2-43x+6$	

3. Find a linear factor for each of these polynomials.

   (a) x^3+4x^2+x-6

   (b) x^4-6x-4

   (c) $x^4-6x^3-8x^2+6x+7$

   (d) $2x^4+x^3-6x^2-x+1$

   (e) $3x^3+10x^2-11x+2$

6.4 Solving higher order equations

The next activity shows how you can tackle higher order equations using the factor theorem.

Activity 6 Solving a quartic equation

The equation $x^4-4x^3-13x^2+4x+12=0$ is an example of a **quartic** equation, a polynomial equation of degree 4.

Find a simple linear factor of the quartic, and use this factor to complete a statement of this type :

$$x^4-4x^3-13x^2+4x+12=(x-\alpha)\times(\text{cubic})$$

Hence find all the solutions of the quartic equation and sketch the graph of $y=x^4-4x^3-13x^2+4x+12$ without the help of a calculator or computer.

Activity 6 shows how the factor theorem can help solve higher order equations. However, it may have taken you some time! Probably the longest part was finding the cubic factor. When the same process is applied to, say,

$$x^6 - x^4 + 17x - 14 = (x+2)\text{ (polynomial of degree 5)}$$

it will take longer still.

Fortunately there are ways of finding the polynomial factor which are more efficient. Two methods will be introduced here. You may, later on, like to reflect on how they are essentially the same method expressed differently.

The first method involves juggling with coefficients, and is best demonstrated by example.

Consider the quartic $x^4 + 5x^3 + 7x^2 + 6x + 8$. $x = -2$ is a zero of this function and hence $(x+2)$ is a factor. The cubic factor can be found thus :

$$x^4 + 5x^3 + 7x^2 + 6x + 8$$

$$= x^3(x+2) + 3x^3 + 7x^2 + 6x + 8$$

$$= x^3(x+2) + 3x^2(x+2) + x^2 + 6x + 8$$

$$= (x^3 + 3x^2)(x+2) + x(x+2) + 4x + 8$$

$$= (x^3 + 3x^2 + x)(x+2) + 4(x+2)$$

$$= (x^3 + 3x^2 + x + 4)(x+2)$$

Hence the cubic factor is $x^3 + 3x^2 + x + 4$.

Example

Find the missing expression here :

$$x^4 - 3x^3 + 5x^2 + x - 4 = (x-1)(\quad)$$

Solution

$$x^4 - 3x^3 + 5x^2 + x - 4$$

$$= x^3(x-1) - 2x^3 + 5x^2 + x - 4$$

$$= x^3(x-1) - 2x^2(x-1) + 3x^2 + x - 4$$

$$= (x^3 - 2x^2)(x-1) + 3x(x-1) + 4x - 4$$

$$= (x^3 - 2x^2 + 3x)(x-1) + 4(x-1)$$

$$= (x^3 - 2x^2 + 3x + 4)(x-1)$$

so the missing expression is $x^3 - 2x^2 + 3x + 4$.

The second method is sometimes called 'long division of polynomials'. The statement

$$x^4 + 5x^3 + 7x^2 + 6x + 8 = (x+2)(\text{cubic})$$

can be written instead in this form

$$\frac{x^4 + 5x^3 + 7x^2 + 6x + 8}{x+2} = \text{cubic polynomial}$$

The cubic polynomial is thus the result of dividing the quartic by $(x+2)$. This division can be accomplished in a manner very similar to long division of numbers.

$$
\begin{array}{llllll}
 & & x^3 & +3x^2 & +\ x & +4 \\ \cline{3-6}
x+2 & \big) & x^4 & +5x^3 & +7x^2 & +6x+8 \\
 & & \underline{x^4} & \underline{+2x^3} & & \\
 & & & 3x^3 & +7x^2 & \\
 & & & \underline{3x^3} & \underline{+6x^2} & \\
 & & & & x^2 & +6x \\
 & & & & \underline{x^2} & \underline{+2x} \\
 & & & & & 4x+8 \\
 & & & & & \underline{4x+8} \\
 & & & & & \quad 0
\end{array}
$$

So $x^4 + 5x^5 + 7x^2 + 6x + 8 = (x+2)\left(x^3 + 3x^2 + x + 4\right)$,

the same answer is obtained as on the previous page by the 'juggling' method.

Activity 7 Long division

When $x = 10$, the quotient $\dfrac{x^4 + 5x^3 + 7x^2 + 6x + 8}{x+2}$ becomes the division sum $15\ 768 \div 12$. Evaluate this by long division (**not** short division). Discuss the resemblance between your sum and the algebraic long division above. Try putting other values of x into the quotient (e.g. $x = 9, x = -5$).

Example

Evaluate the quotient $\dfrac{x^4-5x^3-2x^2+25x-3}{x-3}$.

Solution

$$
\begin{array}{r}
x^3-2x^2-8x+1 \\
x-3\overline{)\,x^4-5x^3-2x^2+25x-3} \\
\underline{x^4-3x^3} \qquad\qquad\qquad\quad \\
-2x^3-2x^2 \qquad\qquad\quad \\
\underline{-2x^3+6x^2} \qquad\qquad\quad \\
-8x^2+25x \qquad\quad \\
\underline{-8x^2+24x} \qquad\quad \\
x-3 \\
\underline{x-3} \\
0
\end{array}
$$

The quotient is therefore x^3-2x^2-8x+1.

Example

Work out the missing cubic factor in this statement:

$$4x^4-11x^2+15x-18=(2x-3)(......)$$

Solution

Note that there are no terms in x^3. To simplify the division, a term $0x^3$ is included.

$$
\begin{array}{r}
2x^3+3x^2-x+6 \\
2x-3\overline{)\,4x^4+0x^3-11x^2+15x-18} \\
\underline{4x^4-6x^3} \qquad\qquad\qquad\qquad \\
6x^3-11x^2 \qquad\qquad\qquad \\
\underline{6x^3-9x^2} \qquad\qquad\qquad \\
-2x^2+15x \qquad\quad \\
\underline{-2x^2+3x} \qquad\quad \\
12x-18 \\
\underline{12x-18} \\
0
\end{array}
$$

The missing cubic factor is therefore $2x^3+3x^2-x+6$.

Exercise 6D

1. Find these quotients by long division

   (a) $7982 \div 26$

   (b) $22149 \div 69$

   (c) $45694 \div 134$

   (d) $55438 \div 106$

2. Use the 'juggling' method to find the missing factors

   (a) $x^4 + 8x^3 + 17x^2 + 12x + 18 = (x+3)(\ldots\ldots)$

   (b) $x^4 - 5x^3 - x^2 + 25 = (x-5)(\ldots\ldots)$

   (c) $x^3 + 4x^2 - 8 = (x+2)(\ldots\ldots)$

3. Use long division to find the missing factors

   (a) $x^4 + 6x^3 + 9x^2 + 5x + 1 = (x+1)(\ldots\ldots)$

   (b) $x^4 + 7x^3 - 39x - 18 = (x+6)(\ldots\ldots)$

   (c) $2x^3 - 4x^2 - 7x + 14 = (x-2)(\ldots\ldots)$

   (d) $9x^5 + 9x^4 - 16x^3 + 11x + 2 = (3x+2)(\ldots\ldots)$

4. Evaluate these quotients

   (a) $\dfrac{x^3 + 6x^2 - 6x + 7}{x^2 - x + 1}$ (b) $\dfrac{2x^4 + 5x^3 - 5x - 2}{x^2 + 3x + 2}$

   (c) $\dfrac{x^4 - 6x^3 + 4x^2 - 6x + 3}{x^2 + 1}$ (d) $\dfrac{x^4 + 2x^3 - 2x - 4}{x^3 - 2}$

6.5 Factorising polynomials

In the next examples, you will see how to factorise polynomials of degrees higher than two.

Example

Factorise the quartic $x^4 - 4x^3 - 7x^2 + 34x - 24$ as fully as possible and hence solve the equation $x^4 - 4x^3 - 7x^2 + 34x - 24 = 0$.

Solution

$x = 1$ is a zero of the quartic, so $(x-1)$ is a factor.

Long division yields

$$x^4 - 4x^3 - 7x^2 + 34x - 24 = (x-1)(x^3 - 3x^2 - 10x + 24)$$

Now factorise the cubic; since $x = 2$ is a zero of the cubic, $(x-2)$ is a factor.

Long division gives

$$x^3 - 3x^2 - 10x + 24 = (x-2)(x^2 - x - 12)$$

The quadratic $x^2 - x - 12$ factorises easily to give $(x-4)(x+3)$

The full factorisation of the original quartic is therefore

$$(x-1)(x-2)(x-4)(x+3)$$

and the solutions to the equation are thus

$$x = -3, 1, 2 \text{ and } 4.$$

Example

Solve the equation $x^4 + 3x^3 - 11x^2 - 19x - 6 = 0$.

Solution

First, factorise the quartic as far as possible.

$x = -1$ is a zero so $(x+1)$ is a factor.

By long division

$$x^4 + 3x^3 - 11x^2 - 19x - 6 = (x+1)(x^3 + 2x^2 - 13x - 6)$$

$x = 3$ is a zero of the cubic so $(x-3)$ is a factor.

$$x^3 + 2x^2 - 13x - 6 = (x-3)(x^2 + 5x + 2)$$

The quadratic $x^2 + 5x + 2$ has no straightforward linear factors, but the equation $x^2 + 5x + 2 = 0$ does have solutions, namely -4.56 and -0.438.

The quartic thus factorises to $(x+1)(x-3)(x^2 + 5x + 2)$ yielding solutions $x = -4.56, -1, -0.438$ and 3.

Exercise 6E

1. Solve the following quartic equations :

   (a) $x^4 + 8x^3 + 14x^2 - 8x - 15 = 0$

   (b) $x^4 + 8x^3 - 13x^2 - 32x + 36 = 0$

2. Solve the quintic equation

   $x^5 - 8x^3 + 6x^2 + 7x - 6 = 0$

6.6 Remainders

In the previous section you saw how to divide a polynomial by a factor. These ideas will be extended now to cover division of a polynomial by an expression of the form $(x - \alpha)$.

If $(x - \alpha)$ is not a factor, there will be a remainder.

Activity 8

(a) Carry out the long division $\dfrac{x^3+5x^2-2x+1}{x+1}$

(b) If you substitute $x=9$ in this quotient it becomes $1117 \div 10$. Carry out the division. Repeat with $x=10, 11, 12$. Do not use a calculator. Comment on your answers and how they correspond to part (a).

As with numbers, long divisions of polynomials often leave remainders. For example $(x+3)$ is **not** a factor of x^3+6x^2+7x-4, and so long division will yield a remainder.

$$
\begin{array}{r}
x^2+3x-2 \\
x+3\overline{)\,x^3+6x^2+7x-4} \\
\underline{x^3+3x^2} \\
3x^2+7x \\
\underline{3x^2+9x} \\
-2x-4 \\
\underline{-2x-6} \\
2
\end{array}
$$

One way of expressing this might be to write

$$\frac{x^3+6x^2+7x-4}{x+3}=x^2+3x-2,\text{ rem } 2$$

but the normal method is to write either

$$x^3+6x^2+7x-4=(x^2+3x-2)(x+3)+2$$

or

$$\frac{x^3+6x^2+7x-4}{x+3}=x^2+3x-2+\frac{2}{x+3}$$

Activity 9 Remainders

(a) Substitute any positive integer for x in the quotient

$\dfrac{x^3+6x^2+7x-4}{x+3}$. Verify by division that the remainder is 2.

Try some negative values of x (except -3) and comment.

(b) Find the remainder when x^3+6x^2+x-7 is divided by $x+1$.

(c) Find the remainder for the division

$(x^3+x^2-4x+8)\div(x-2)$.

Exercise 6F

1. Find the remainders

(a) when $x^2-15x+10$ is divided by $(x-5)$

(b) when $x^3+4x^2-7x+10$ is divided by $(x+3)$

2. Use Question 1 to complete these statements

(a) $\dfrac{x^3+4x^2-7x+10}{x+3}=(......)+\dfrac{......}{x+3}$

(b) $x^2-15x+10=(......)(x-5)+.....$

6.7 Extending the factor theorem

Activity 10

(a) How can you tell that $(x-1)$ is not a factor of $x^3-7x+10$?

(b) When the division is carried out a statement of the form

$$x^3-7x+10=(x-1)Q(x)+R$$

will result, where $Q(x)$ is a quadratic function and R the remainder. Without doing the division, calculate R. (Hint : choose a suitable value of x to substitute in the equation above.)

(c) Without doing the division, calculate the remainder when $x^4+3x^3-5x+10$ is divided by $x+2$.

Activity 10 illustrates the result known as the **remainder theorem.**

> If $P(x)$ is a polynomial of degree n then
>
> $$P(x)=(x-\alpha)Q(x)+R$$
>
> where $Q(x)$ is a polynomial of degree $n-1$ and $R=P(\alpha)$.

The useful fact that $R=P(\alpha)$ can be demonstrated simply by considering what happens to the equation $P(x)=(x-\alpha)Q(x)+R$ when $x=\alpha$ is substituted into it.

Does this provide a proof of the remainder theorem?

*Activity 11 Division by quadratics

Carry out the algebraic division

$$\frac{x^4+3x^3-10x^2-26x+28}{x^2+2x-3}$$

Can you suggest a remainder theorem for division by quadratics? Can you generalise to division by any polynomial?

Exercise 6G

1. Work out the remainder when

   (a) x^2+5x-7 is divided by $(x-2)$;

   (b) x^4-3x^2+7 is divided by $(x+3)$;

   (c) $5x^3+6x^2+2x-3$ is divided by $(x+5)$.

2. When the quadratic x^2+px+1 is divided by $(x-1)$ the remainder is 5. Find p.

3. x^2+px+q divides exactly by $(x-5)$ and leaves remainder -6 when divided by $(x+1)$.

   Find p and q.

4. Find the linear expressions which yield a remainder of 6 when divided into $x^2+10x+22$.

6.8 Rationals and irrationals

Until about the 5th century AD it was firmly believed that whole numbers and their ratios could be used to describe any quantity imaginable. In other words, that the set Q of rational numbers contained every number possible. Gradually, though, mathematicians became aware of 'incommensurable quantities', quantities that could not be expressed as the ratio of two integers. Such numbers are called **irrational numbers.**

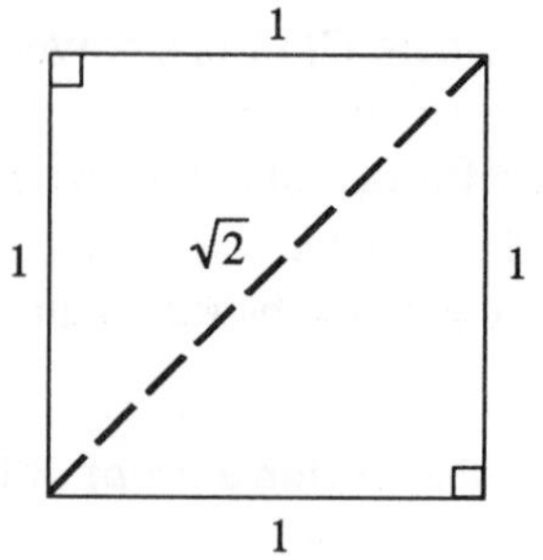

The origin of this concept is uncertain, but one of the simplest examples of an irrational number arises from Pythagoras' Theorem. This theorem gives the length of the diagonal of the unit square as $\sqrt{2}$.

The proof that $\sqrt{2}$ is irrational is one of the most famous proofs in all mathematics. It employs a technique called '*reductio ad absurdum*' (reduction to the absurd) the proof begins by assuming that $\sqrt{2}$ is rational and then shows that this assumption leads to something impossible (absurd). See if you can follow the reasoning:

Suppose $\sqrt{2}$ is rational.

This means that $\sqrt{2} = \frac{p}{q}$, where p and q are integers with no common factor, and $q \neq 0$.

$$\sqrt{2} = \frac{p}{q} \Rightarrow \frac{p^2}{q^2} = 2 \Rightarrow p^2 = 2q^2$$

$\Rightarrow \quad p^2$ is even $\quad \Rightarrow p$ is even.

Hence p can be written as $2r$, where r is an integer.

Since p is even, q must be odd as they have no common factors.

$$p^2 = 2q^2 \Rightarrow 4r^2 = 2q^2 \Rightarrow q^2 = 2r^2$$

$\Rightarrow \quad q^2$ is even $\quad \Rightarrow q$ is even.

q is thus seen to be both odd **and** even, which is impossible. The original assumption that $\sqrt{2}$ is rational must therefore be false.

Hence $\sqrt{2}$ is irrational.

Other examples of irrationals are π and any square root like $\sqrt{5}$. Still more examples can be constructed from these, e.g. $\sqrt{2}+1, 6\pi$, etc. The set of rational **and** irrational numbers is called the set of real numbers, denoted by $\mathbb{R}$.

Activity 12 True or false?

Decide whether these statements are true or false

(a) (i) rational + rational = rational

(ii) rational + irrational = irrational

(iii) irrational + irrational = irrational

(b) (i) rational × rational = rational

(ii) rational × irrational = rational

(iii) irrational × irrational = rational

(c) 'Between any two rational numbers there is another rational number'.

(d) 'Between any two irrational numbers, there is another irrational number'.

A different way of looking at rational and irrational numbers comes from considering equations.

To solve any linear equation involving integer coefficients, the set of rationals is sufficient.

e.g. $71x+1021=317 \Rightarrow x=-\dfrac{704}{71}$

However, Q is **not** sufficient to solve every polynomial of degree 2 and higher. While some do have rational solutions,

e.g. $x^2-7x+12=0 \Rightarrow x=3$ or 4

in general, they do not.

e.g. $x^2-3x+1=0 \Rightarrow x=\frac{1}{2}(3\pm\sqrt{5})$.

In fact, there is still a further class of numbers; these are the **transcendental** numbers. If you are interested, find out what these are by consulting a mathematical dictionary.

Irrational expressions like $\sqrt{5}$ are called **surds.** Surds cannot be expressed as ratios of natural numbers.

Activity 13 Handling surds

(a) Use a calculator to verify that $\sqrt{8} = 2\sqrt{2}$. Explain why this is true.

(b) What surd can be written as $3\sqrt{2}$?

(c) Express $\sqrt{12}$ as a multiple of $\sqrt{3}$.
Use a calculator to check your answer.

A method of manipulating surds is used to 'rationalise' the denominators in expressions like

$$\frac{1}{\sqrt{5}+1}$$

To rationalise a denominator means literally to turn an irrational denominator into a rational one.

Activity 14 How to rationalise a denominator

(a) What is $(\sqrt{5}+1)(\sqrt{5}-1)$?

(b) Multiply the fraction $\left(\frac{1}{\sqrt{5}+1}\right)$ by $\left(\frac{\sqrt{5}-1}{\sqrt{5}-1}\right)$.

(c) Explain why $\frac{1}{\sqrt{5}+1} = \frac{\sqrt{5}-1}{4}$.

(d) What is $(\sqrt{10}-2)(\sqrt{10}+2)$?

(e) Write $\frac{3}{(\sqrt{10}-2)}$ as a fraction with a rational denominator.

Example

(a) $\sqrt{20} = \sqrt{4\times 5} = \sqrt{4}\times\sqrt{5} = 2\sqrt{5}$

(b) $\sqrt{216} = \sqrt{4\times 54} = 2\sqrt{54}$

But $\sqrt{54}$ can itself be simplified :
$2\sqrt{54} = 2\sqrt{9\times 6} = 2\sqrt{9}\times\sqrt{6} = 6\sqrt{6}$

Example

(a) $\frac{5}{\sqrt{6}-1} = \left(\frac{5}{\sqrt{6}-1}\right)\left(\frac{\sqrt{6}+1}{\sqrt{6}+1}\right) = \frac{5(\sqrt{6}+1)}{5} = \sqrt{6}+1$

(b) $\frac{1}{\sqrt{11}+\sqrt{7}} = \left(\frac{1}{\sqrt{11}+\sqrt{7}}\right)\left(\frac{\sqrt{11}-\sqrt{7}}{\sqrt{11}-\sqrt{7}}\right) = \frac{\sqrt{11}-\sqrt{7}}{4}$

Activity 15 Fence posts

The diagram shows a circular field cut in half by the diameter AB. The owner of the field wants to build two fences, one round the circumference of the circle, the other across the diameter. Fence posts are placed at A and B and further posts spaced equally along the diameter.

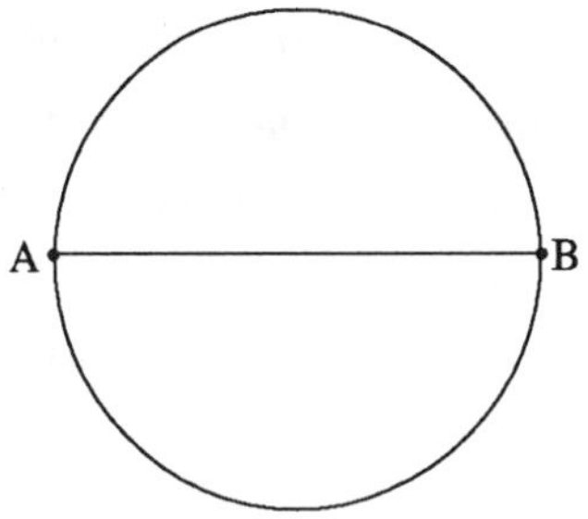

Explain why the owner must use a different measure of equal spacing when fence posts are put around the circumference. ('Spacing' is to be taken to mean 'distance apart round the circumference').

Activity 16 $\sqrt{3}$

Prove that $\sqrt{3}$ is irrational, using the same method of proof as was used for $\sqrt{2}$.

Can the same method be used to 'prove' that $\sqrt{4}$ is irrational?

Exercise 6H

1. Write down an irrational number
   (a) between 3 and 4;
   (b) between 26 and 27;
   (c) between -6 and -5.
2. Simplify the surds
   (a) $\sqrt{52}$ (b) $\sqrt{75}$ (c) $\sqrt{120}$ (d) $\sqrt{245}$
3. Use a similar technique to simplify
   (a) $\sqrt[3]{16}$ (b) $\sqrt[3]{54}$ (c) $\sqrt[4]{48}$
4. Rationalise the denominators in these expressions
   (a) $\frac{1}{\sqrt{2}-1}$ (b) $\frac{3}{\sqrt{21}-3}$ (c) $\frac{2}{\sqrt{5}-\sqrt{2}}$
   (d) $\frac{3}{\sqrt{2}}$ (e) $\frac{5}{\sqrt{14}-2}$

6.9 Miscellaneous Exercises

1. Find a linear factor for each of these polynomials :

   (a) $x^4-3x^3-10x^2-x+5$

   (b) $x^5+3x^4+x^3+5x^2+12x-4$

2. Solve these equations :

   (a) $x^4-3x^3-10x^2-x+5=0$

   (b) $x^4+2x^3-67x^2-128x+192=0$

3. Copy and complete these identities :

   (a) $x^3-7x^2-x-6=(x-7)(\quad)+(\quad)$

   (b) $\dfrac{x^5+5x^4-3x^2+2x+1}{x+2}=(\quad)+\dfrac{(\quad)}{x+2}$

4. What is the remainder when

   (a) $x^4-5x^2+12x-15$ is divided by $x+3$;

   (b) $x^3-5x^2-21x+7$ is divided by $x-10$?

5. $x^3+ax^2+5x-10$ leaves remainder 4 when divided by $x+2$. Find a.

6. Find the linear expressions which leave remainder 14 when divided into $x^2-5x-10$.

7. A quadratic function is exactly divisible by $x-2$, leaves remainder 12 when divided by $x+1$ and remainder 8 when divided by $x-3$. What is the quadratic function?

8. Find the linear expressions which leave remainder –8 when divided into

   $x^3-12x^2+17x+22$.

9. Simplify these, where possible

   (a) $\dfrac{x^2-1}{2(x+1)}$ (b) $\dfrac{6a^3}{2a+a^2}$

   (c) $\dfrac{m^2-4}{2m}$ (d) $\dfrac{3x^2+5x-2}{3x+6}$

   (e) $\dfrac{x^3-1}{x-1}$

10. Find the remainder when

    $p(x)=2x^3-x^2-2x+1$

    is divided by

    (a) $x-2$ (b) $x+1$

    Factorise $p(x)$ completely. (AEB)

11. The polynomial $p(x)\equiv 2x^3-9x^2+kx-13$, when k is a constant, has $(2x-1)$ as a factor.

    Determine the value of k. (AEB)

12. An equilateral triangle has sides of length a.

    Show that the area is $\dfrac{a^2\sqrt{3}}{4}$.

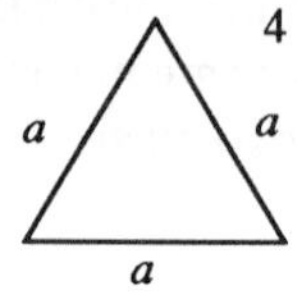

13. (a) Show that

    (i) $(p+4q)$ is a factor of $p^2+2pq-8q^2$ and find the other linear factor;

    (ii) $(x-2y)$ is a factor of $x^3+x^2y-7xy^2+2y^3$ and find the quadratic factor;

    (iii) $(a+3b)$ is a factor of $2a^3+7a^2b-9b^3$ and find the two other linear factors.

    (b) Factorise these expressions completely

    (i) $x^2-2ax-3a^2$

    (ii) $p^2+10pq-24q^2$

    (iii) $a^3-2a^2b-11ab^2+12b^3$

14. Factorise the expression

    $16x^5-81x$

    as completely as possible.

7 STRAIGHT LINES

Objectives

After studying this chapter you should

- be familiar with the equation of a straight line;
- understand what information is needed to define a straight line;
- appreciate the significance of the gradient of a straight line;
- be able to solve simple linear inequality problems;
- be able to find the distance between two points in the xy-plane and the coordinates of the midpoint.

7.0 Introduction

In solving problems, a great deal of effort is often made to find and use a function which 'models' the situation being studied. The easiest type of functions to use and work with are those whose graphs are straight lines. These are called **linear** functions.

You will see how linear models can be constructed and then used for predicting in the following activity. For this activity you will need:

spring, stand and set of weights.

Activity 1 Spring extensions

The extension of a spring held vertically depends on the weight fixed on the free end. Measure the extension, x, in cm, of the spring beyond its natural length for a variety of weights, w, in grams.

(a) Plot the data points on a graph of x against w.

(b) Draw a straight line as accurately as possible through the data points.

(c) Assuming that the straight line has an equation of the form

$$x = \alpha w$$

for some constant α, find a point on your line and use it to find the value of α.

(d) Use your model to predict the extension for various weights; test your model by obtaining further experimental data.

7.1 Gradients

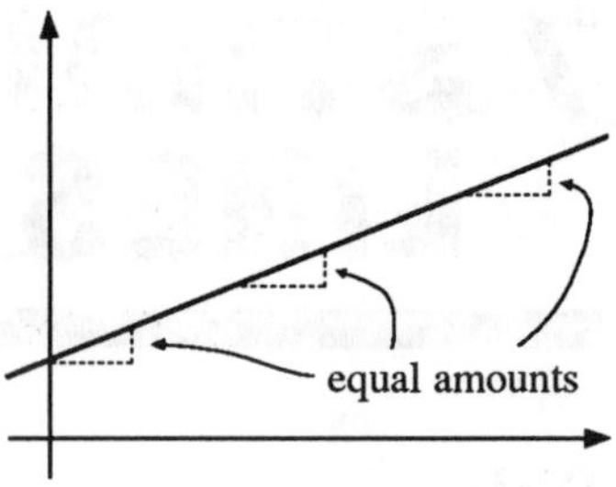

The figure shows a straight line - the graph increases its 'heights' by equal amounts for equal increases of the horizontal variable. This is because the slope or gradient is constant. Remember the gradient is defined as

$$\text{gradient} = \frac{\text{increase in } y}{\text{increase in } x}$$

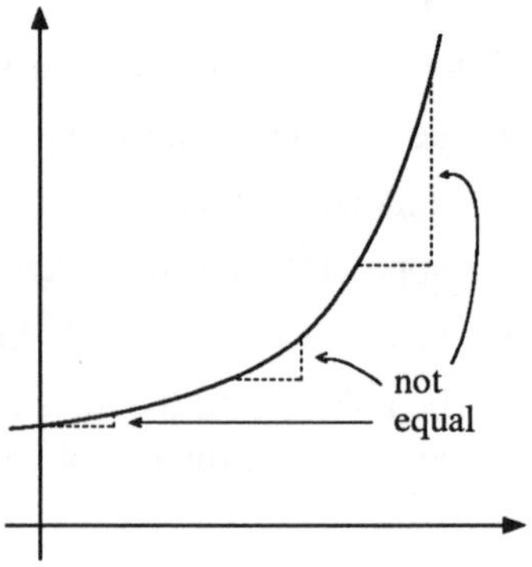

When the graph is curved as shown in the figure opposite, then the gradient is no longer constant.

Example

A company offers a personal life insurance so that your life is insured against accidental death for

£250 000 for a payment of £50 per year

or

£100 000 for a payment of £25 per year.

If other rates are 'pro-rata' (in proportion) determine

(a) the amount of life insurance that can be obtained for a yearly payment of
(i) £10 (ii) £80

(b) the yearly payment for life insurance of amount
(i) £160 000 (ii) £550 000

Solution

Define

x = yearly payment in £'s

y = amount of insurance in £1000's

The two pieces of information can now be written as

$y = 250$ when $x = 50$,

$y = 100$ when $x = 25$.

These are illustrated on the graph opposite.

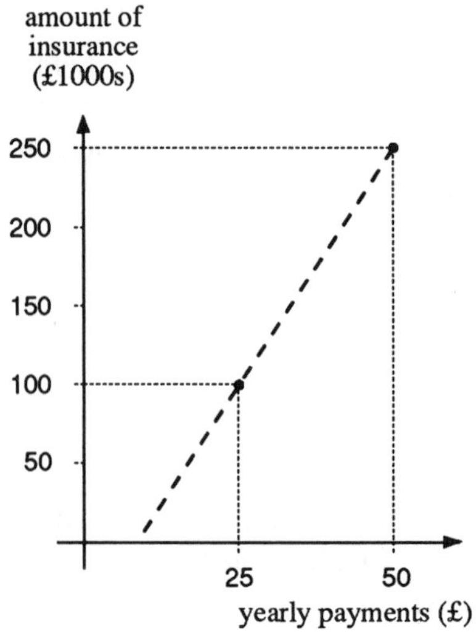

A graphical approach would be to draw the straight line between the two data points, extending in each direction beyond the points. The line could then be used to find corresponding values of yearly payment and amount of insurance.

Algebraically, the relationship between x and y can be written as

$$y = mx + c.$$

Since the two points, (25, 100) and (50, 250), satisfy this equation

$$250 = 50\,m + c \qquad (1)$$

$$100 = 25\,m + c. \qquad (2)$$

You can solve these equations for m and c by first subtracting (2) from (1).

$$\begin{aligned} 250 - 100 &= 50m + c - (25m + c) \\ &= 50m - 25m + (c - c) \\ \Rightarrow \quad 150 &= 25m \\ \Rightarrow \quad m &= 6. \end{aligned}$$

Substituting m in (1) now gives

$$c = 250 - 50 \times 6 = -50.$$

(You should now check that (2) is in fact satisfied by $m = 6$ and $c = -50$)

So the life insurance system can be modelled by the equation

$$\boxed{y = 6x - 50} \qquad (3)$$

(a) (i) $x = 10 \Rightarrow y = 6 \times 10 - 50 = 10$ or £10 000 life insurance.

(ii) $x = 80 \Rightarrow y = 6 \times 80 - 50 = 430$ or £430 000 life insurance.

(b) It is easier to first make x the subject of equation (3).

Now $6x = y + 50$

$$\Rightarrow \quad x = \frac{1}{6}(y + 50).$$

(i) $y = 160 \Rightarrow x = \frac{1}{6}(160 + 50) = 35$

(ii) $y = 550 \Rightarrow x = \frac{1}{6}(550 + 50) = 100.$

In the example above, it is worth noting that the value of m, namely 6, represents the gradient of the line. It shows that any increase of £1 in the yearly payment results in an extra insurance cover of £6000.

Can you suggest why $x \neq 0$ when $y = 0$?

The real bonus of this algebraic approach is that the model equation, $y = 6x - 50$, can be used to solve any problem related to this life insurance system.

Activity 2 Ski-passes

At a particular ski resort in Switzerland, ski-passes are advertised at the following two rates:

6 day pass for 38 Swiss Francs
13 day pass for 80 Swiss Francs.

Assuming that other days are charged at the pro-rata rate, find using algebraic methods a linear model to describe this situation. Use the model to find the cost of a ski pass for

(a) 3 days (b) 30 days.

Exercise 7A

1. The volume of 20 g of the metal Lithium was measured by a chemist and was found to be 37 cm^3. Use the fact that 0 g of Lithium must have a volume of 0 cm^3 to draw a graph of weight on the vertical axis against volume on the horizontal axis. Find the gradient of the graph, and hence state the density of Lithium in g cm^{-3}.

2. A car overtakes a lorry. At the start of the manoeuvre, the car is travelling at a speed of 13.4 ms^{-1} (30 mph). Five seconds later, after passing the lorry, it is travelling at a speed of 22 ms^{-1} (50 mph). Draw a graph of the speed, v, of the car against the time, t. Put v on the vertical axis, using metres per second, and t on the horizontal axis, using seconds. You may assume the graph is a straight line. Find the gradient of the graph, and so find the rate at which the speed of the car has increased, in metres per second per second.

3. The speed of a train pulling into a station decreases from 11.2 ms^{-1} to 0 ms^{-1} in 15 seconds. Draw a straight line graph showing this information, with the speed on the vertical axis. By finding the gradient of the line, find the rate at which the train decelerates, in ms^{-2}.

4. A petrol pump works at a rate of 20 litres per minute. Draw a graph showing the volume of petrol pumped on the vertical axis against the time taken in seconds on the horizontal axis. You should choose scales from 0 to 40 litres and from 0 to 2 minutes. Use your graph to find the time required to pump 35 litres.

5. Boats are hired at the following rates

   2 hours for £11 5 hours for £20

   Assuming charges for other times are pro-rata, develop a linear model to describe this relationship and use it to find the hire charges for

   (a) $1\frac{1}{2}$ hours (b) 3 hours (c) 12 hours.

7.2 Equation of a straight line

One of the advantages that linear functions have is that their equations can all be written in a simple form. When the equation of a straight line is known, it is possible to find its gradient and the point it crosses the vertical axis immediately, without drawing. Also, it is possible to write down the equation of the line once the gradient and any single point on the line is known.

Remember that the equation of any straight line can be written in the form

$$\boxed{y = mx + c}$$

where m and c are constant.

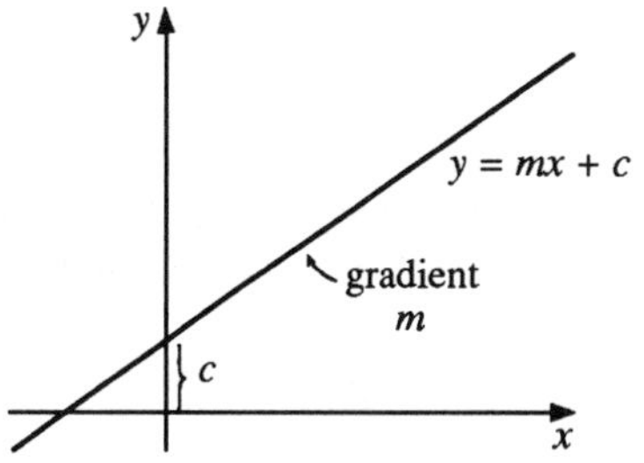

This is illustrated opposite; m is the value of the gradient of the line, whilst c is the length of the intercept on the y-axis (since when $x = 0$, $y = m \times 0 + c = c$).

Example

A straight line with a gradient of -2 passes through the point $(4, \ -1)$. Find the equation of the line, and draw its graph.

Solution

As the graph is a straight line, its equation can be written in the form

$$y = mx + c.$$

As the gradient is -2, m in this equation must be -2, and

$$y = -2x + c.$$

The point $(4, -1)$ lies on this line, so its x and y coordinates must satisfy the equation. That is, the coordinates $x = 4$ and $y = -1$ can be substituted to make the equation true.
So

$$-1 = -2 \times 4 + c$$

$$-1 = -8 + c$$

$$\Rightarrow \quad 7 = c$$

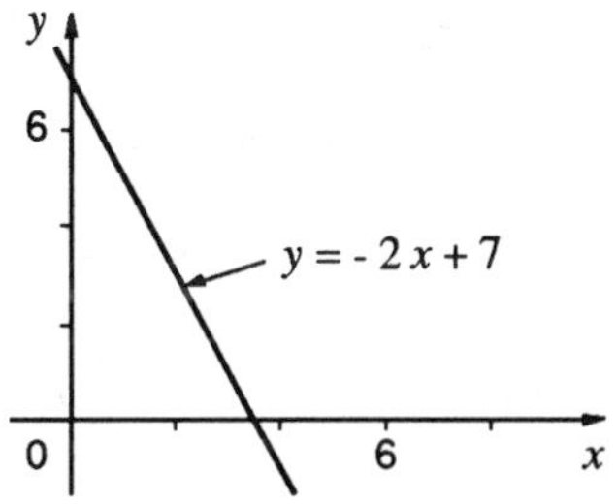

So the equation is given by

$$y = -2x + 7.$$

Example

A straight line passes through the points A, (1, 0) and B, (3, 6). Find the gradient of the line, and its equation.

Solution

The figure opposite shows a sketch of the line. The gradient can be calculated using this formula:

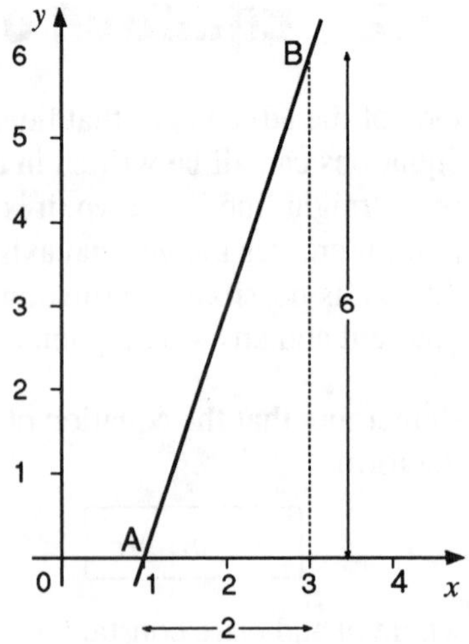

$$\text{gradient} = \frac{y_B - y_A}{x_B - x_A} \quad \left(\frac{\text{differences in } y\text{'s}}{\text{differences in } x\text{'s}}\right)$$

$$= \frac{6-0}{3-1} \quad \text{since } y_B = 6,\ y_A = 0,\ x_B = 3 \text{ and } x_A = 1$$

$$= \frac{6}{2} = 3$$

As the graph is a straight line, the equation can be written in the form $y = mx + c$. The gradient is 3, so this is the value of m :

$$y = 3x + c.$$

To find c, the coordinates of a point on the line must be substituted into the equation. The coordinates of point A $(x = 1,\ y = 0)$ are used here ;

$$0 = 3 \times 1 + c$$

$$0 = 3 + c$$

$$\Rightarrow \quad c = -3.$$

The equation is $y = 3x - 3$.

Example

The graph $4x + 3y - 6 = 0$ is a straight line. Find its gradient, and the intercept with the y-axis.

Solution

To read the gradient and intercept of a line from its equation it must be written in the form $y = mx + c$ first. Now

$$4x + 3y = 6$$

$$\Rightarrow \quad 3y = -4x + 6$$

$$\Rightarrow \quad y = -\frac{4}{3}x + \frac{6}{3}$$

$$= -\frac{4}{3}x + 2$$

If this equation is compared with $y = mx + c$, it can be seen that the gradient is $-\frac{4}{3}$ and the intercept with the y-axis is 2.

Activity 3

Draw the following lines on the same axes

(a) $2y+x=0$ (b) $4y=1-2x$ (c) $6y+3x=1$.

What do you notice about these lines?

Exercise 7B

1. Write down the gradient and its intercept with the y-axis of each of these lines

   (a) $y=3x-1$ (b) $y=-4x-3$

   (c) $y=\frac{1}{2}x+5$ (d) $y=-\frac{6}{5}x-\frac{1}{2}$

   (e) $y=4x$ (f) $y=x$

   (g) $y=-x$ (h) $y=5$.

2. Find the gradient and intercept with the y-axis of each of the lines without drawing the graphs.

   (a) $4x+y=9$ (b) $x+2y=6$

   (c) $3x-2y=4$ (d) $4y-2x+6=0$

3. A line passes through the point (5, 1) and has a gradient of 3. Find the equation of the line.

4. A line with gradient $-\frac{1}{3}$ passes through the point (4, 6). Find the equation of the line, leaving fractions in your answer.

5. Find the equation of the straight line which passes through the points (2, −1) and (6, 7).

6. A line which is parallel to $y=2x$ passes through the point (3, −2). Find the equation of this line.

7. A line which is parallel to $4x+3y-6=0$ passes through the origin. Find its equation.

7.3 Perpendicular lines

There is an important result that connects the gradients of perpendicular lines.

Activity 4

(a) Accurately construct a number of pairs of perpendicular lines. Measure the gradients of each pair of lines. What do you notice?

(b) Draw on the same graph

   (i) $y=2x, \quad y=-\dfrac{1}{2}x$

   (ii) $y+x=1, \quad y=1+x$

What can you conjecture about the gradients of perpendicular lines?

Suppose you have two lines with gradients m_1 and m_2 - remember that the gradient can be positive or negative. Then the two lines are **perpendicular** if and only if

$$\boxed{m_1 m_2 = -1}$$

You can easily see this from the geometry of the situation. Take, for example, a line with gradient 2, as shown opposite. This means that for a unit increase in the x direction, there will be an increase of 2 in the y direction.

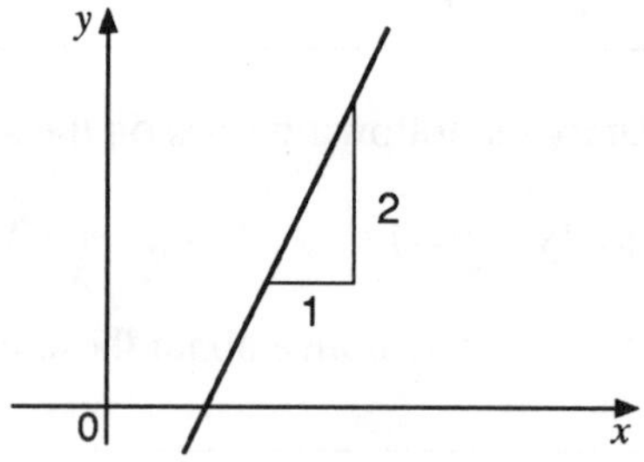

Now consider a line perpendicular to this line as llustrated opposite.

Since the angle between them is 90°, then the triangles shown are congruent, and it can be seen that the gradient of the perpendicular line is given by

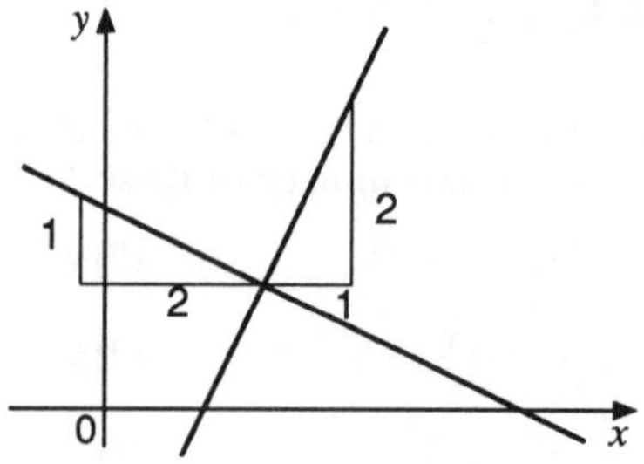

$$\frac{1}{-2}=-\frac{1}{2}$$

So in this case $m_1 = 2,\quad m_2 = -\frac{1}{2}$ and

$$m_1\, m_2 = -1$$

This is of course not a proof of this result only a verification.

Activity 5

Prove the result, $m_1\, m_2 = -1$, for perpendicular lines by generalising the method above.

Example

Find the equation of the line that passes through the point (1,2) and is perpendicular to $y = 1 + x$.

Solution

Since the gradient of $y = 1 + x$ is 1, the gradient of the perpendicular line is -1. Hence its equation is of the form

$$y = -x + c$$

To pass through the point (1,2) requires

$$2 = -1 + c$$

$$\Rightarrow \quad c = 3$$

$$\Rightarrow \quad y = 3 - x$$

Exercise 7C

1. Find the equation of the straight line which passes through the point (1,1) and is perpendicular to the line $2y+x=1$.
2. Find the equation of the straight line which passes through the origin, and is perpendicular to the line joining the points (1,4) and (4,1).
3. Show that the lines $y+2x=3$ and $2y-x=1$ are perpendicular. At what point do they intersect?
4. A straight line passes through the intersection of the two lines with equation

$$y+x=2$$

$$2y-x=7$$

and is perpendicular to the line with equation $y=2x$. Find its equation.

7.4 Linear inequalities

Often real life problems can have more than one solution, but some solutions may be better than others.

Activity 6

A club is organising a trip, and needs to transport at least 210 people using mini buses, coaches or some of each. A coach holds 45 people and costs £120 to hire, whilst a minibus holds 15 and costs £60. The club only has £600 to spend on the transport. Find a possible solution to this problem. Is it unique?

Find the most economic way to arrange the transport.

To solve the problem in Activity 6 in a logical and precise way requires the use of inequalities. Another similar problem is given below.

A farmer has 100 hectares available on which to sow 2 crops, wheat and sugar beet. Each hectare of wheat is expected to produce a profit of £20, whilst each hectare of sugar beet should produce a profit of £30. However EEC quota regulations will not allow the farmers to grow more than 50 acres of sugar beet and 70 hectares of wheat. The time taken in soil preparation, seeding and tendering is estimated to be 5 man hours per hectare of wheat and 10 man hours per hectare of sugar beet. The available man power is up to 700 hours.

Can you find the optimum solution - that is a solution which satifies all the conditions and maximises the profit?

You can use intelligent trial and error methods, but an algebraic approach is ideal.

Let $x =$ no. of hectares sown with wheat

$y =$ no. of hectares sown with sugar beet.

The land restriction can be written as

$$x + y \leq 100.$$

It should also be noted that

$$x \geq 0$$

and $y \geq 0.$

These three inequalities can be illustrated on a graph.

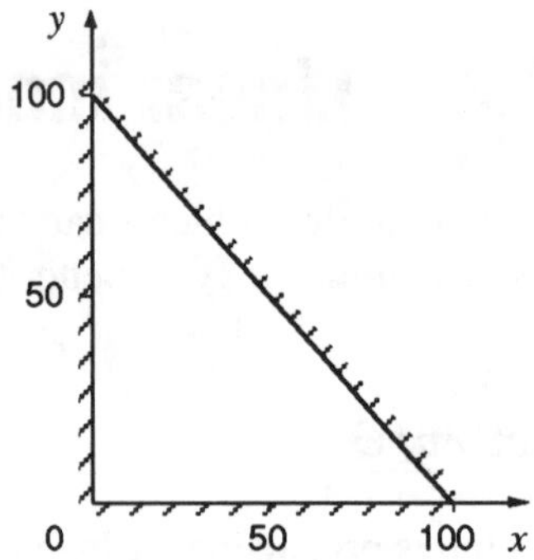

Note that the actual lines shown are $x + y = 100$, $x = 0$, $y = 0$ and that, for example, all the region to the left of the line $x + y = 100$ satisfies the inequality

$$x + y \leq 100$$

(for example, the point $x = y = 0$ satisfies this inequality).

So to find the 'solution' of an inequality, you first draw the equality, and then identify the allowable region.

The region to be excluded, is shown partially shaded.

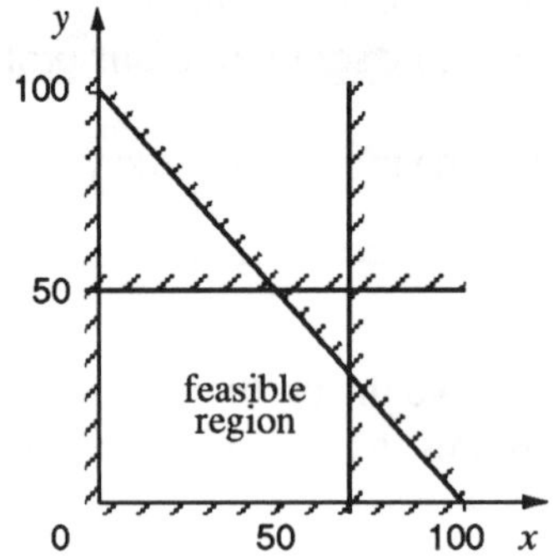

There are further inequalities to be satisfied, because of the regulations; namely

$$x \leq 70$$
$$y \leq 50$$

These can be shown on the graph so that the allowable (or feasible) region is further restricted.

There is yet one more inequality to consider; that is the available number of man-hours. This gives

$$5x + 10y \leq 700.$$

This is added to the graph as shown opposite.

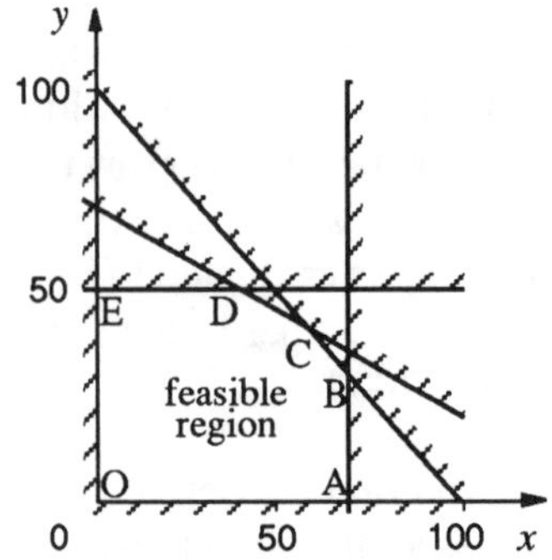

The feasible region, which contains all possible solutions, is a convex polygon with vertices at O, A, B, C, D, and E.

Any point inside this polygon is a possible solution, but the optimum solution is the one which gives rise to a maximum value of

$$P = 20x + 30y$$

Why should P obtain its maximum value at a vertex of the polygon?

In this case the optimum solution will occur at one of the vertices, and the table below evaluates P at each vertex.

Point	Coordinates	Profit	
0	$x=0,\ y=0$	$P=0$	
A	$x=70,\ y=0$	$P=20\times70+30\times0=1400$	
B	$x=70,\ y=30$	$P=20\times70+30\times30=2300$	
C	$x=60,\ y=40$	$P=20\times60+30\times40=2400\leftarrow$	maximum value
D	$x=40,\ y=50$	$P=20\times40+30\times50=2300$	
E	$x=0,\ y=50$	$P=20\times0+30\times50=1500$	

So the optimum solution occurs at $x=60,\ y=40$ showing that the farmer should sow 60 hectares of wheat and 40 hectares of sugar beet.

This example illustrates the technique of **linear programming**, which has been used extensively in business and commerce.

The complete theory is beyond the scope of this text (it is, in fact, dealt with in detail in the Decision Mathematics text), but it does indicate the importance of being able to illustrate inequalities.

Activity 7

Return to the problem in Activity 6 and use graphical analysis of the type shown above to find the most economic way of organising the transport.

Exercise 7D

1. Show graphically the region defined by

   $x+y\le 2,\ y-2x\le 0,\ y\ge -1$

2. Show that the region defined by

   $x+y\le 1,\ x-y\le 1,\ y\le 1$

   is finite.

3. Determine the region defined by

   $x+2y\le 4,\ y\ge x,\ y\le 2x$

   If, in addition, $x\le\frac{1}{2}$, are there any values of x and y which satisfy all the inequalities?

7.5 Cartesian coordinates

The x and y axes frequently used in mathematics form part of a system called Cartesian coordinates, named after a French mathematician and philosopher, *René Descartes*. It has been found to be one of the most convenient ways of describing how things are related in space.

As an example of the usefulness of such a system, consider the grid reference system which in effect is a set of Cartesian coordinates, each 100 m standing for a unit on a typical OS (Ordnance Survey) map.

Example

A helicopter pilot is told to fly from grid reference (115, 208) to (205, 088) (Luton Airport to Hatfield Aerodrome). The figure opposite illustrates the journey.

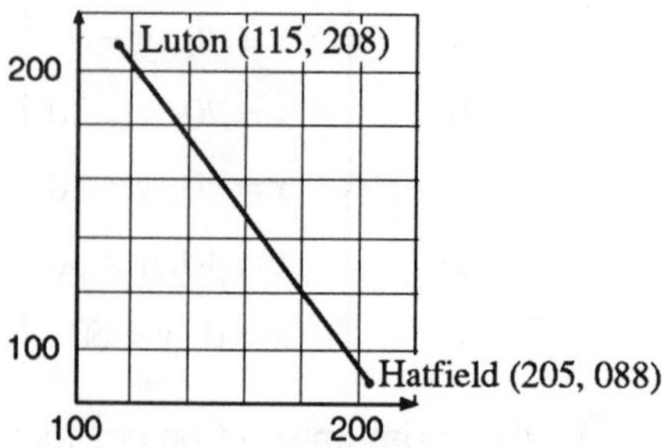

The pilot needs to know the distance in order to estimate his time of arrival. Using Pythagoras' theorem, calculate the distance to be flown.

Solution

The figure shows the right angled triangle to be used. Note that the coordinates are given in 100 m units. By Pythagoras' theorem, the distance d in metres can be calculated from

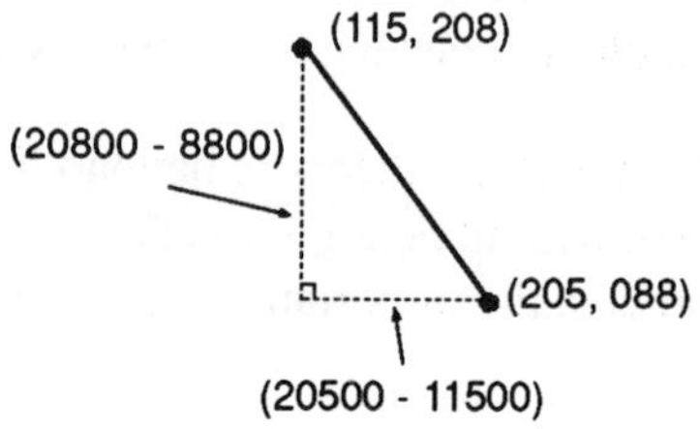

$$d^2 = (20800 - 8800)^2 + (20500 - 11500)^2$$

$$\Rightarrow \quad d^2 = 12000^2 + 9000^2$$

$$\Rightarrow \quad d^2 = 225000000.$$

Hence $\quad d = \sqrt{225000000}$

$$\Rightarrow \quad = 15000 \text{ m}$$

$$= 15 \text{ km}.$$

This example illustrates the method for calculating the distance between any two points on a Cartesian coordinate grid.

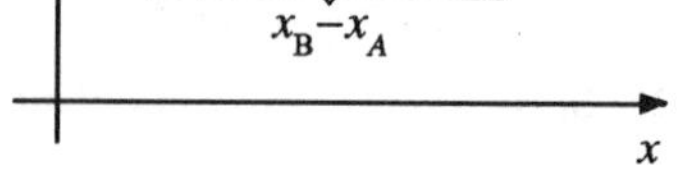

If a point A has coordinates (x_A, y_A), and point B is (x_B, y_B), then, using Pythagoras' theorem, the distance AB is given by

$$\boxed{AB = \sqrt{(y_B - y_A)^2 + (x_B - x_A)^2}}$$

The formula applies even when coordinates are negative.

Example

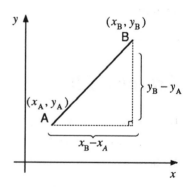

The points A(1, 1), B(–3, 3), C(–1, 7) and D(3, 5) form a square. Find the area of the square and the point P at which its diagonals cross.

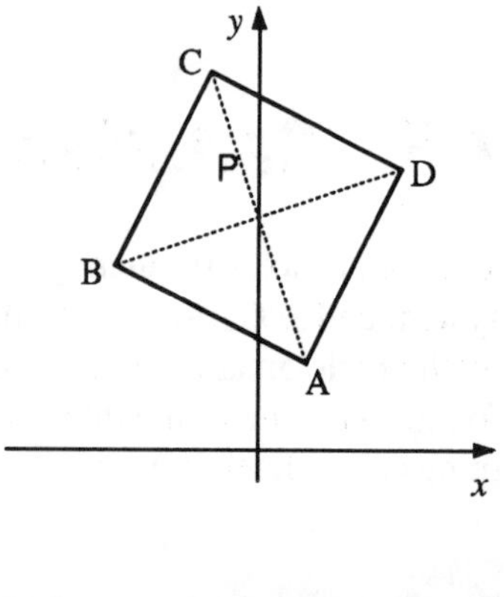

Solution

The figure opposite shows the square ABCD. The area of ABCD is simply the square of the length of one of its sides. The length of any of the four sides can be found using Pythagoras' theorem, as above.

For example

$$\begin{aligned} AB &= \sqrt{(y_A - y_B)^2 + (x_A - x_B)^2} \\ &= \sqrt{(1-3)^2 + (1-(-3))^2} \\ &= \sqrt{(-2)^2 + (4)^2} \\ &= \sqrt{4+16} \\ &= \sqrt{20} \end{aligned}$$

So the area of ABCD $= (AB)^2 = \left(\sqrt{20}\right)^2 = 20$ units^2.

Now P is the midpoint of either diagonal. One of the diagonals, BD, is shown opposite. Since P is the midpoint, its coordinates will be the average of those of B and D.

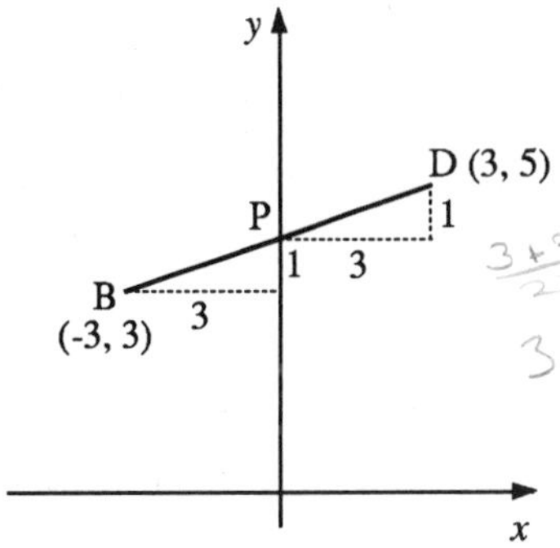

$$x: \quad \frac{1}{2}(-3+3) = \frac{1}{2} \times 0 = 0$$

$$y: \quad \frac{1}{2}(3+5) = \frac{1}{2} \times 8 = 4$$

So P has coordinates (0, 4), which can be verified from the figure.

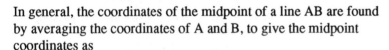

In general, the coordinates of the midpoint of a line AB are found by averaging the coordinates of A and B, to give the midpoint coordinates as

$$\left(\frac{x_A + x_B}{2}, \frac{y_A + y_B}{2} \right).$$

Exercise 7E

1. Find the distances between these pairs of points using Pythagoras's theorem

   (a) (0, 0) and (3, 4) (b) (−1, 3) and (11, 2)

   (c) (4, 1) and (−2, −5) (d)(0, 6) and (3, −8)

   Give answers to three significant figures where necessary.

2. Find the midpoints of the lines joining the pairs of points in Question 1.

3. Calculate the area of the right angled triangle formed by the points A(1, 3), B(2, 5) and C(5, 1). The right angle is formed at the point A.

4. Show that the quadrilateral PQRS is a square, where P is the point (−2, 5), Q is (−5, 1), R is

7.6 Miscellaneous Exercises

1. A bank charges £10 for 850Fr and £20 for 1900Fr. Plot these data on a graph, with pounds on the horizontal axis, and draw a straight line graph through the points. Find the gradient of the graph, stating its units and its meaning.

2. A car entering a town decelerates from 26.8 ms^{-1} to 13.4 ms^{-1}s in 8 seconds. Draw a graph showing the velocity, v, on the vertical axis and time t, on the horizontal. Find the gradient of the line joining the points, stating the units and the meaning of the gradient.

3. Find the gradient of the lines joining these pairs of points :

   (a) (2, 1) and (8, 7) (b) (–3, 6) and (1, 12)

   (c) (1, 9) and (5, 3) (d) (3, –6) and (12, –20)

4. Without drawing any of the graphs for the equations below, state the gradient and intercept with the y-axis for each of these lines :

   (a) $y = 5x + 3$ (b) $y = -x + 1$

   (c) $y = \frac{1}{2}x$ (d) $3y = x + 6$

   (e) $5x - 2y - 11 = 0$ (f) $3x + 4y + 1 = 0$

5. A line has a gradient of 2 and passes through the point (5, –1) Find its equation.

6. Find the equation of the line parallel to the line $y = 4x - 1$ which passes through the point (–3, 9)

7. Find the equation of the straight line which passes through (0, 5) and (3, 1).

8. An experiment was carried out to see the extension, e cm, produced when different weights were hung from a spring. The results are shown in this table.

Weight, w (grams)	0	100	200	300	400
Extension, e (cm)	0	5	11	14.5	21

   Plot these data on a graph, with e on the vertical axis, and draw a line of best fit. Find the gradient of the line and the intercept with the vertical axis, and hence find an equation relating e to w. Use your equation to estimate the extension produced when the weight on the spring is 1 kg.

9. Find the equation of the line which crosses the line $y = 4x + 2$ at the point (3, 14) at right angles.

10. Find the equation of the line which is perpendicular to the line $3y - 2x + 5 = 0$ and which passes through the point (1, 1).

11. Find the equation of the line parallel to $y = 5x - 1$ which passes through the point (4, 0).

12. Two sides of a square are formed by the lines $y = 3x$ and $3y + x - 6 = 0$. Find the coordinates of the corner of the square at which these sides meet using an algebraic method.

13. Find the equation of the straight line passing through the point (2, 3) which is perpendicular to the line with equation $5x + 3y = 0$. (AEB)

14. The points P, Q and R have coordinates (2, 4), (7, –2) and (6, 2) respectively. Find the equation of the straight line l which is perpendicular to the line PQ and which passes through the midpoint of PR. (AEB)

8 RATES OF CHANGE

Objectives

After studying this chapter you should

- appreciate the connection between gradients of curves and rates of change;
- know how to find the gradient at any point on a curve;
- be able to find the maximum and minimum points;
- understand and know how to find equations of tangents and normals to curves.

8.0 Introduction

Most things change: the thickness of the ozone layer is changing with time; the diameter of a metal ring changes with temperature; the air pressure up a mountain changes with altitude. In many cases, however, what is important is not whether things change, but how fast they change.

The study of rates of change has an important application, namely the process of **optimisation**. An example of an optimisation problem that you have already met is deciding what proportions a metal can should have in order to use the least material to enclose a given volume.

You may have seen a sign like the one opposite before. They are often put by the roadside to discourage drivers on main roads from driving too fast through small towns or villages; it is in such places that the police often set up 'speed traps' to catch drivers who are exceeding the speed limit.

Activity 1

The town of Dorchester in Dorset is 2 km from end to end, and a 30 mph speed limit is in force throughout. Although the A35 road now by-passes the town, many drivers consider it quicker, late at night when traffic is light, to drive through the centre.

A driver takes 2 minutes 40 seconds to drive through the town. Was the speed limit broken?

1 km $= 0.6214$ miles

1 mile $= 1.6093$ km

What is the shortest time a driver can take to drive through Dorchester and not break the speed limit?

In reality cars do not travel at a constant speed. Suppose the driver's progress through the town was described by the distance-time graph in Activity 2.

Activity 2 When was the driver speeding?

(a) Travelling through Dorchester one encounters a major roundabout. Where do you think it is, and how can you tell?

(b) What was the driver's average speed between

- (i) Grey's Bridge and the Night Club;
- (ii) the Night Club and the Hospital;
- (iii) Cornhill and Glyde Path Road;
- (iv) the Military Museum and St. Thomas Road
- (v) Wessex Road and Damers Road?

(c) Cut out a right-angled triangle as shown in the diagram below.

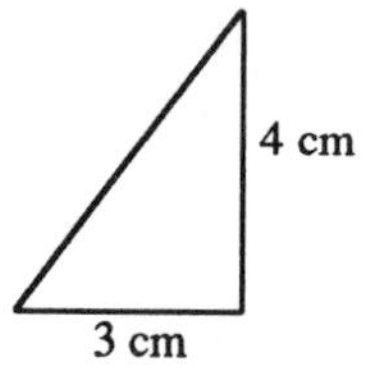

It represents a speed of 30 mph, or $13\frac{1}{3}\ \mathrm{ms}^{-1}$. Use this to determine when the instantaneous speed of the car was greater than 30 mph.

(d) Suppose the police set up a speed-trap somewhere in Dorchester. They decide to stop any vehicle going faster than 40 mph. Use a similar method to (c) to determine where along the route the car's speed exceeds 40 mph.

(e) Assuming it was working accurately, what would the car's speedometer have shown as the car passed

- (i) the Night Club;
- (ii) Wessex Road?

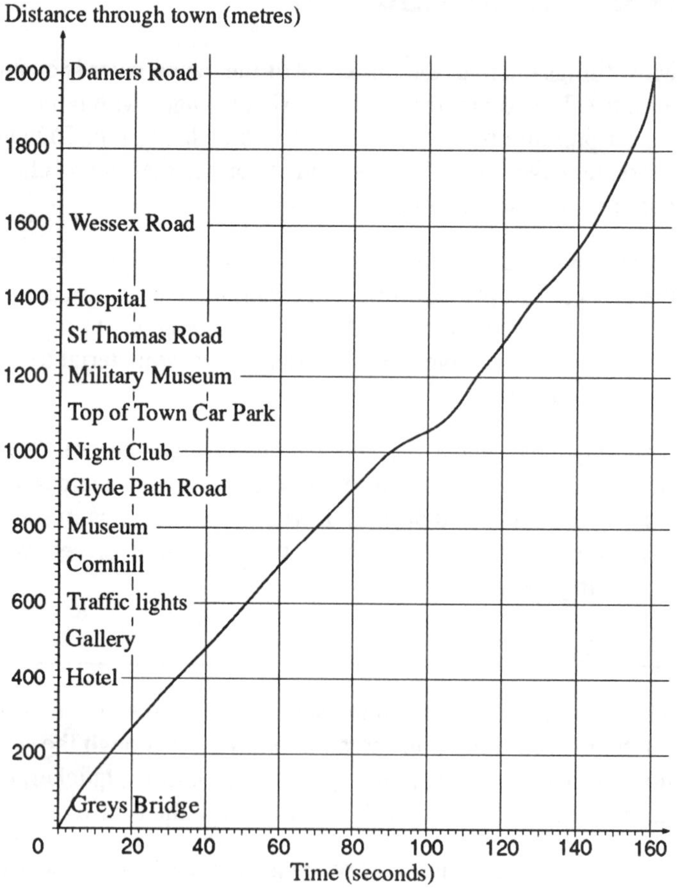

8.1 Instantaneous speed

One method the police use to discover whether or not a car is speeding is to use video cameras to time it between two fixed points. In the above example, suppose the car was timed between Glyde Path Road and the Hospital; then the speed would have been calculated like this

$$\frac{\text{distance travelled}}{\text{time taken}} = \frac{500}{50} = 10 \text{ ms}^{-1} \left(\text{about } 22\tfrac{1}{2} \text{ mph}\right)$$

This figure is only an average speed. However the car's actual speed varied between these two points, and it may have gone faster than 30 mph and then slowed down.

Another method of finding the speed is to use a 'radar gun', which is focussed on the car as it passes. This gives the **instantaneous** speed of the vehicle, as shown on the speedometer.

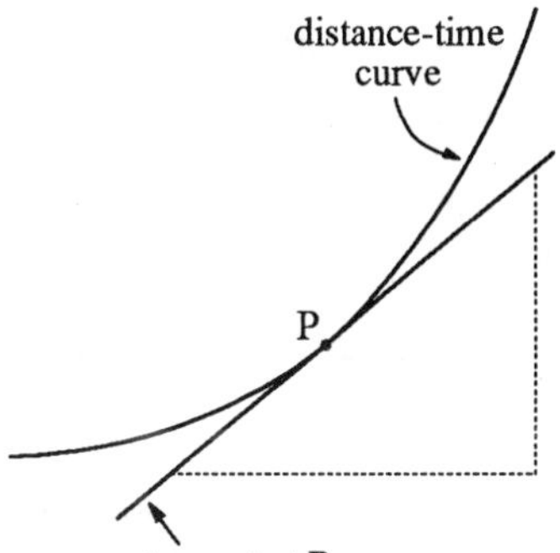

On a distance-time graph, the instantaneous speed is indicated by the steepness, or gradient, but when the graph is a complicated curve the gradient is difficult to pin down accurately. One way is to draw a tangent to the curve and to work out the gradient as you saw in Activity 2.

Activity 3 Unemployment Statistics

The table below shows the number of people unemployed in the two years between August 1989 and July 1991. Draw a graph to represent these figures.

Month	Thousands	Month	Thousands
Aug 1989	1741.1	Aug 1990	1657.8
Sept	1702.9	Sept	1673.9
Oct	1635.8	Oct	1670.9
Nov	1612.4	Nov	1728.1
Dec	1639.0	Dec	1850.4
Jan 1990	1687.0	Jan 1991	1959.7
Feb	1675.7	Feb	2045.4
Mar	1646.6	Mar	2142.1
Apr	1626.3	Apr	2198.5
May	1578.5	May	2213.8
June	1555.6	June	2241.0
July	1623.6	July	2367.5

(a) What figures are missing from these political press releases?

Labour Party	**Conservative Party**
In the 12 months following Jan. 1990 unemployment rose at an average rate of ? per month.	In the 3 months following Jan. 1990 unemployment fell at an average rate of ? per month.

(b) Which of these statements gives a truer impression of:
   (i) the rate of change of unemployment at the start of 1990;
   (ii) the unemployment trend during 1990 as a whole?

(c) Use your graph to find the rate of change of unemployment
   (i) at January 1991
   (ii) at October 1989.

Discuss the meaning, relevance and accuracy of your answers.

Activity 3 gave another example of a graph where the **gradient**, or steepness, had an important significance. It gave the rate of change of unemployment. This property of the gradient has important applications to all kinds of graphs.

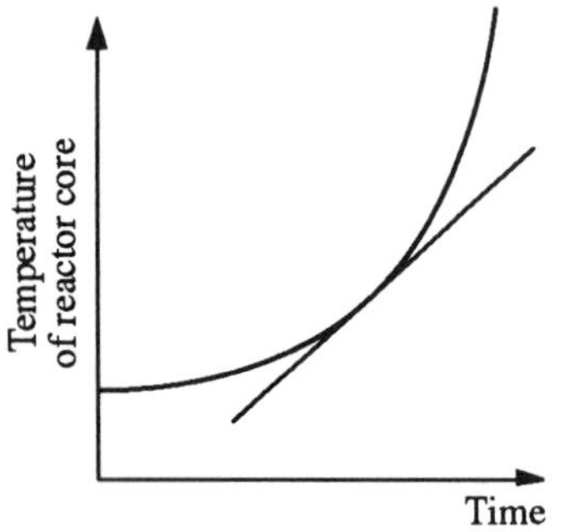

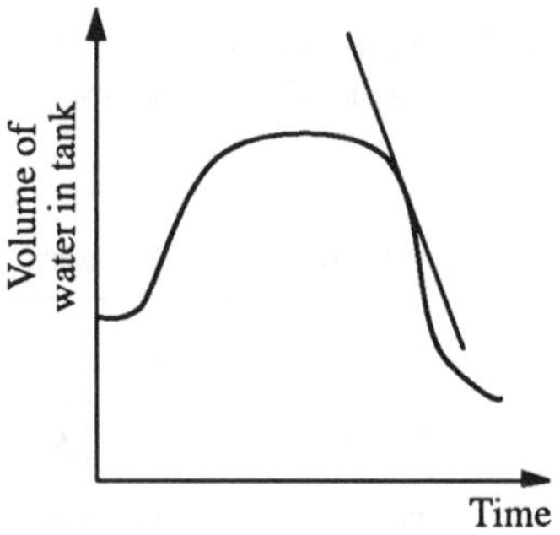

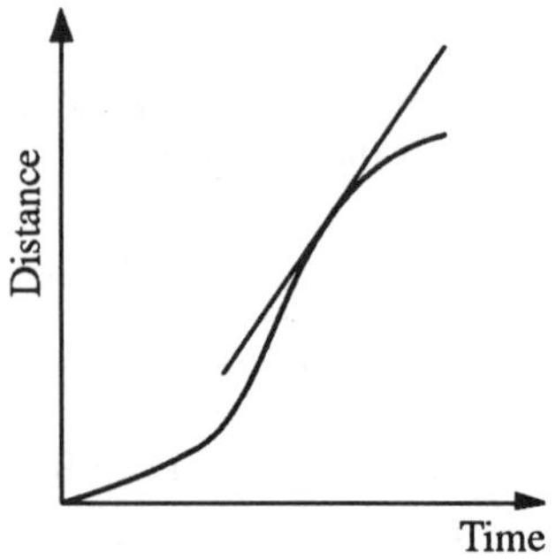

Rates of change have meaning even when neither of the variables is time. For example, the graph opposite shows how the temperature changes with height above sea level. The gradient of the **tangent** at P is 3°C / km. This indicates that, 1 km above P, the temperature will be approximately 3°C higher. The rate of change of temperature with distance is sometimes called the **temperature gradient**.

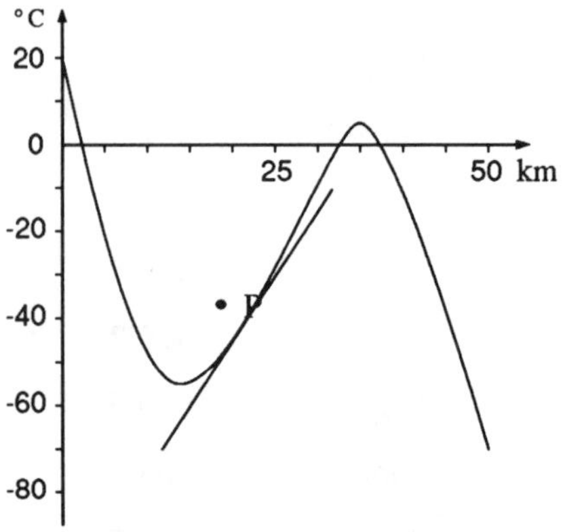

In **rugby union** a try, worth 5 points, is scored by touching the ball down behind the line of the goal-posts. An extra 2 points can be scored by subsequently kicking the ball between the posts, over the cross-bar. This is known as a 'conversion': 4 points is converted into 6 points. The conversion kick must be taken as shown in the diagram, from somewhere on the line perpendicular to the goal line through the point where the ball was touched down.

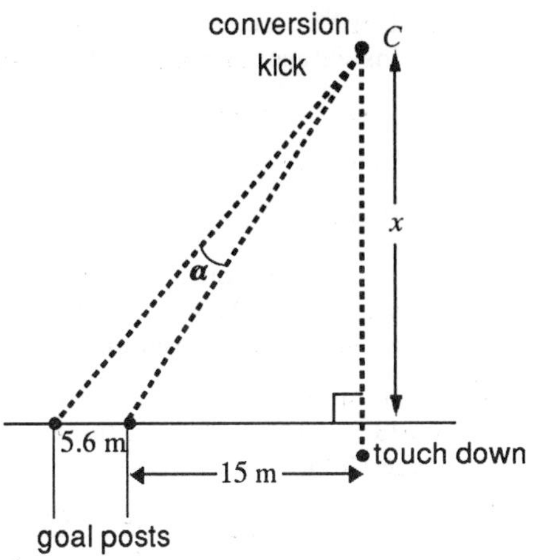

Activity 4 Optimum kicking point

Imagine that a try has been scored 15 m to one side of the goal. The angle in which the ball must be propelled is marked α; the smaller the angle, the trickier the kick. The angle depends on how far back the kick is taken. The way it changes is shown in the table.

Distance (x)	0	5	10	15	20	25	30	35	40	45	50
Angle (α)	0	4.8	7.8	8.9	9.0	8.5	7.9	7.3	6.7	6.2	5.7

(a) Draw a graph of angle against distance.

(b) Estimate the gradient of the graph at $x = 5$ and $x = 15$.

(c) What connection do the figures in (b) have with rates of change? What do these figures tell you?

(d) Estimate the gradient of the curve when $x = 40$. Interpret your answer.

(e) What is the best point from which to take the kick? What is the gradient at this point?

What assumptions have been made about taking the 'conversion' in this activity?

Exercise 8A

1. Harriet is a passenger in a car being driven along a motorway. She monitors the progress of the journey by counting the distance markers by the roadside. She writes down the distance travelled from the start every 5 minutes.

Time (minutes)	0	5	10	15	20	25	30	35	40	45	50	55	60
Distance travelled (miles)	0	6.4	13.1	20.0	26.2	31.3	35.5	39.2	43.4	47.9	53.1	59.8	67.0

(a) Draw a distance-time graph. Estimate the instantaneous speed of the car in mph after

(i) 20 mins.

(ii) 40 mins.

(iii) 55 mins.

(b) The speed limit is 70 mph. Estimate from your graph the times at which the car was exceeding the speed limit.

2. The table below shows approximately how the world's population in millions has increased since 1700.

Year	1700	1720	1740	1760	1780	1800	1820	1840
Pop.	560	610	670	730	790	850	940	1050

Year	1860	1880	1900	1920	1940	1960	1980
Pop.	1170	1330	1550	1870	2270	3040	4480

(a) Draw a graph to represent these data. Draw tangents at the years 1750, 1800, 1850, 1900 and 1950 and measure their gradients.

(b) Explain what meaning can be attached to the gradients in (a) and write a brief account of what they show.

(c) Find the gradient at the year 1880 and use your answer to estimate the population in 1881.

3. The height h of a stone above the ground is given by the formula $h = 2 + 21t - 5t^2$, where h was measured in metres and t in seconds.

(a) Draw a graph of h against t, for values of t between 0 and 5.

(b) Estimate the velocity of the stone after 1, 2, 3 and 4 seconds. Make sure your method is clear.

(c) Use one of your answers to (b) to estimate the value of h when $t = 1.1$. Check the accuracy by substituting $t = 1.1$ into the original formula.

4. The time taken to travel 120 miles depends on the average velocity v, according to the formula $t = 120/v$,

where t is in hours and v is in miles per hour. This relationship is shown in the graph below.

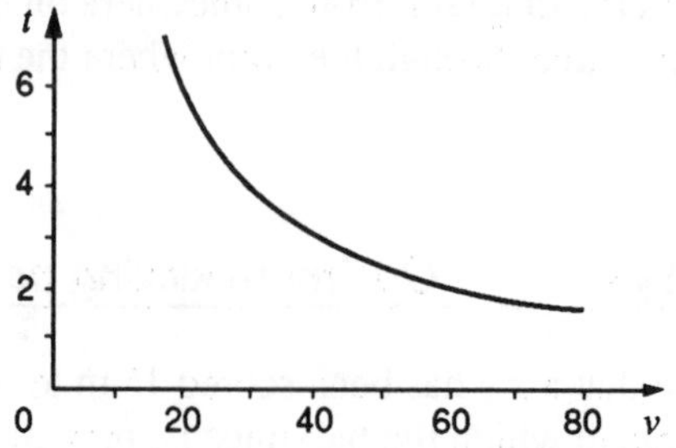

(a) The gradient of the graph when $v = 20$ is -0.3. What does this figure mean?

(b) The gradient when $v = 50$ is -0.048. Given that $t = 2.4$ at this point, estimate t when $v = 51$. How accurate is this estimate?

(c) Describe briefly how the gradient changes as v increases. Explain in everyday terms what this means.

8.2 Finding the gradient

Question 3 of the last exercise required you to draw the graph of the function $h = 2 + 21t - 5t^2$ and to find the gradient at certain points. If you compare your answers to someone else's you may well find that they do not agree precisely; this is because the process of drawing tangents is not a precise art - different people's tangents will have slightly different slopes. Moreover, the process of drawing and measuring tangents can become tiresome if repeated too often - you may well agree!

If the function had been $2 + 21t$ then finding the gradient would have been easy. The function $2 + 21t - 5t^2$ is not linear but there is more than one way of getting an accurate value for the gradient at any point, as you will see in the next activity.

Activity 5 Finding the gradient

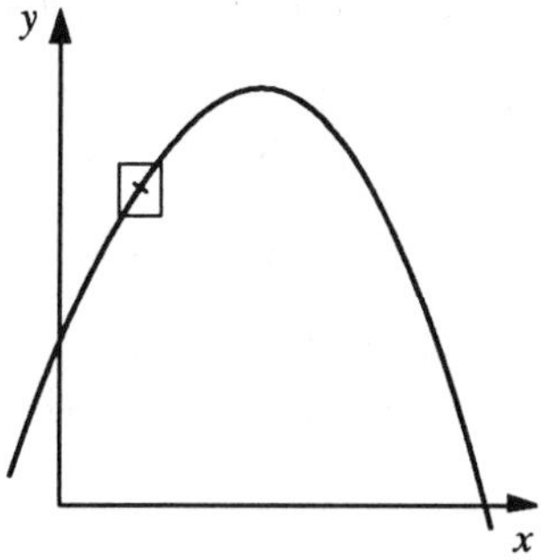

(a) Plot the graph of $y = 2 + 21x - 5x^2$ using a graph-plotting facility. Zoom in on the curve in the region of $x = 1$. The further in you go, the more the curve will resemble a straight line.

Use the calculator or computer to give the coordinates of two points very close to (1, 18). Use these coordinates to give an estimate of the gradient.

What do you think the exact gradient is?

Repeat this process for the point (2, 24).

(b) Consider the point A (1, 18). A nearby point on the curve, B, has coordinates (1.1, 19.05). What is the gradient of the line AB?

Find the y-coordinates when $x = 1.01$ and $x = 1.001$.

Label these points B_1 and B_2. Find the gradients of AB_1 and AB_2. Can you infer the exact value of the gradient of the curve at A?

Repeat this process for the point (3, 21).

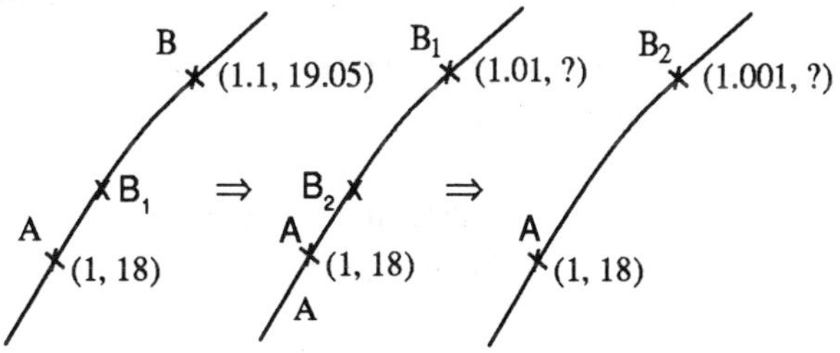

The methods developed in Activity 5 have the advantage of accuracy, but they still take time. A more efficient method is desirable, and the next two Activities examine the simplest non-linear function of all with a view to finding one.

Activity 6 Gradient of x^2

Use the methods above to find the gradient of $y = x^2$ at different points. (Do not forget negative values of x). Make a table of your results and describe anything you notice.

Activity 7 General approach

The diagram shows $y = x^2$ near the point (1, 1), labelled A. The point B is a horizontal distance h along from A.

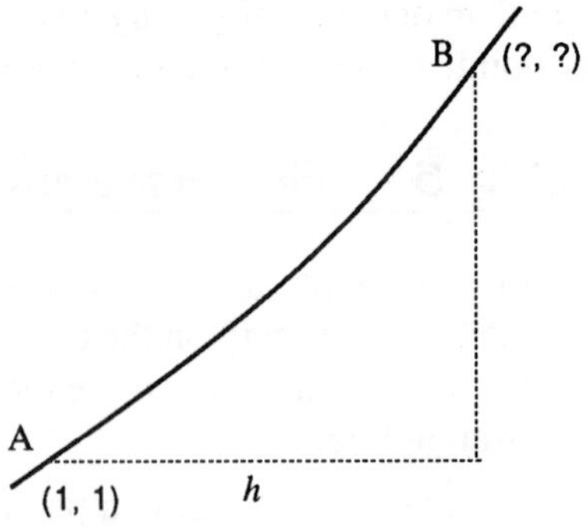

(a) In terms of h, what are the coordinates of B?

(b) Find, and simplify as far as possible, a formula for the gradient of AB in terms of h.

(c) What happens to this formula as B gets closer to A?

(d) Repeat steps (a) to (c) for different positions of the point A, e.g. (2, 4), (5, 25), (–3, 9). Generalise as far as you can.

Activity 6 should have convinced you that at any point of $y = x^2$ the gradient is double the x–coordinate. For example, at the point (3, 9) the gradient is 6.

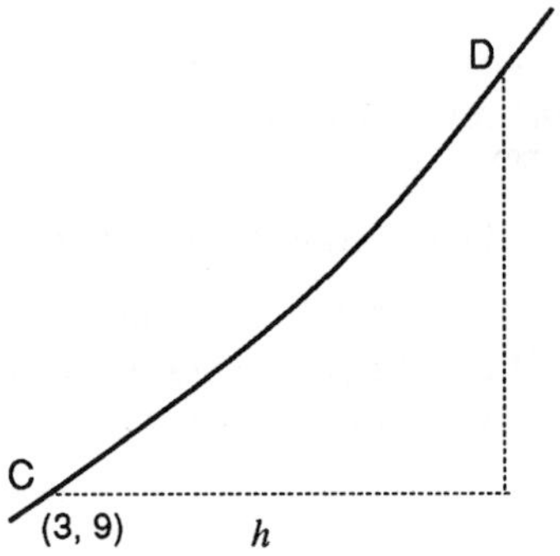

Activity 7 gives an algebraic way of getting the same answer. In the second diagram, D has coordinates $(3+h, (3+h)^2)$. Thus the gradient of CD is

$$\frac{\text{change in } y}{\text{change in } x} = \frac{(3+h)^2 - 9}{h}$$

Expanding the brackets in the numerator gives

$$\frac{9+6h+h^2-9}{h} = \frac{6h+h^2}{h}$$

$$= \frac{h(6+h)}{h}$$

$$= 6+h$$

Hence, as D gets closer to C (i.e. as $h \to 0$), the gradient of CD gets closer to 6.

This procedure can be generalised. Suppose the point (3, 9) is replaced by the general point (x, x^2). In the diagram this point is denoted P, and Q has coordinates $(x+h, (x+h)^2)$.

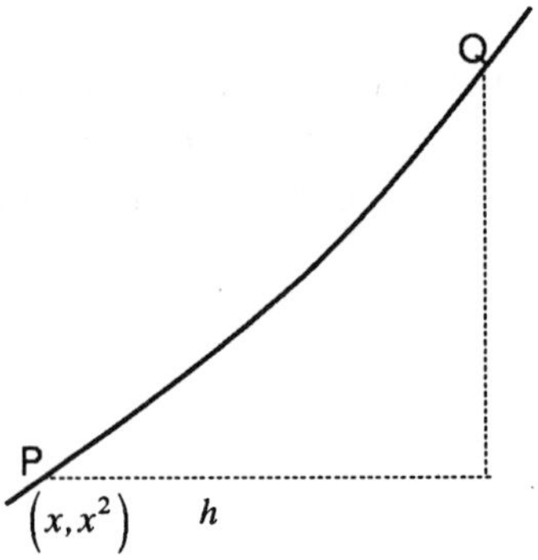

The gradient of PQ is

$$\frac{(x+h)^2 - x^2}{h} = \frac{x^2 + 2hx + h^2 - x^2}{h}$$
$$= \frac{2hx + h^2}{h}$$
$$= \frac{h(2x+h)}{h}$$
$$= 2x + h \text{ (dividing by } h\text{)}$$

This suggests that the gradient at (x, x^2) is $2x$, that is, double the x-coordinate.

Activity 8 Alternative derivations

The above approach is based on considering a point B 'further along' the curve from A.

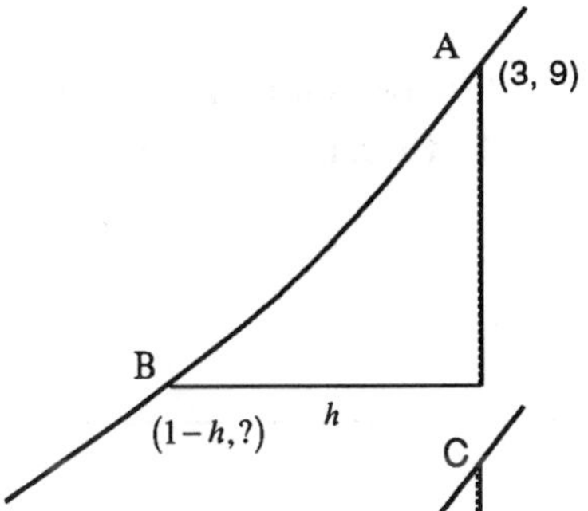

(a) Suppose A is the point (3, 9) and B is a distance h along the x-axis in the negative direction. Find a formula for the gradient of AB and see whether it gets closer to 6 as B gets closer to A.

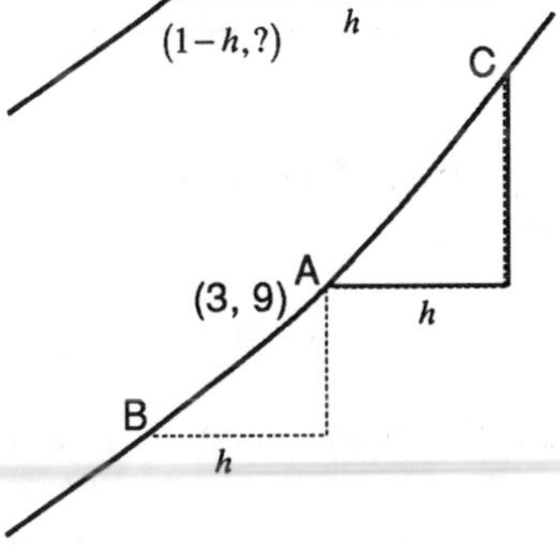

(b) Now, suppose B is one side of A and C is the other. Find a formula for the gradient of BC and comment on anything of interest.

(c) Generalise (a) and (b) to the point (x, x^2).

8.3 Gradient of quadratics

You should now be familiar with three methods of finding gradients of curves :

- using a graphic calculator to zoom in;
- calculating gradients of chords;
- using algebra.

The next activity may take some time, according to the method you choose. Its purpose is to establish a formula for the gradient of any quadratic curve, that is, any curve with an equation of the form $y = ax^2 + bx + c$. The method you use, out of the three above, is up to you.

Activity 9 Gradient of any quadratic

(a) Find formulas for the gradients of

$$y=2x^2,\ y=\tfrac{1}{2}x^2,\ y=3x^2,\ y=\tfrac{1}{3}x^2.$$

What is the formula for the gradient of $y=ax^2$?

(b) Find formulas for the gradients of

$$y=x^2+3,\ y=x^2-8,\ y=x^2+1.$$

What is the formula for the gradient of $y=x^2+c$? Explain why this is true.

(c) Repeat for equations of the form $y=x^2+bx$, where b is any number.

(d) Propose a formula for the gradient of $y=ax^2+bx+c$. Does the formula work for

$$y=2+21x-5x^2,$$

the function you used in Activity 5?

At any point of the curve $y=ax^2+bx+c$ the gradient is given by the function

$$2ax+b.$$

A useful way to remember this rule is as follows :

- the gradient of $y=x^2$ is given by $2x$, so the gradient of $y=ax^2$ is $a\times 2x$
- the gradient of $y=bx$, a straight line, is just b;
- adding a constant, c, merely moves the curve up or down and does **not** alter the gradient;
- the formula $2ax+b$ comes from combining these properties.

Example

Find formulas for the gradients of these curves :

(a) $y=5x^2-7x+10$

(b) $s=\frac{5}{8}t-\frac{1}{6}t^2$

(c) $q=\dfrac{2p^2-7p+8}{3}$.

Solution

(a) gradient $= 5\times(2x)-7 = 10x-7$

(b) gradient $= \frac{5}{8} - \frac{1}{6}\times(2t) = \frac{5}{8} - \frac{1}{3}t$

(c) gradient $= \frac{2\times(2p)-7}{3}$

$= \frac{4}{3}p - \frac{7}{3}.$

Can you see why the denominator of 3 is 'untouched' in part (c)?

Example

If $y = \frac{x^2-7x}{10} + 17$, what is the gradient when $x = 15$?

Solution

To answer this question, find the gradient function and then substitute the value 15 for x. Now

$$\text{gradient} = \frac{2x-7}{10}.$$

When $x = 15$, gradient $= \frac{2\times15-7}{10} = \frac{23}{10} = 2.3$

Exercise 8B

1. Find formulas that give the gradients of these curves

   (a) $y = 2x^2$
   (b) $y = x^2 + x$
   (c) $s = t^2 + 4t - 8$
   (d) $y = x^2 - x + 10$
   (e) $h = 6l^2 - 7$
   (f) $y = 10x - \frac{x^2}{5}$
   (g) $T = \frac{1}{9}Y^2 + 3Y - 1$
   (h) $A = \frac{n^2 - 5n + 10}{2}$
   (i) $u = v - 6v^2 + \frac{1}{15}$
   (j) $y = \frac{3}{4}x^2 + \frac{x}{5} + 2$

2. Find the gradients of

   (a) $y = 10 + 5x - 3x^2$ when $x = 2$
   (b) $p = \frac{T^2}{2} + 8T - 16$ when $T = -3$
   (c) $y = 3u^2 - \frac{u}{6}$ when $u = 4$
   (d) $y = \frac{x^2 + 7x - 3}{12}$ when $x = 10$
   (e) $m = 100 + 65N - \frac{N^2}{5}$ when $N = -15$.

3. The gradient of the graph of $h = 2 + 21t - 5t^2$ gives the speed of a stone where h is the height in metres and t the time in seconds. Find the speed

   (a) when $t = 0.5$

   (b) when $t = 2.8$.

8.4 Differentiation

The process of finding 'gradient functions' is called **differentiation.** Another name for the gradient function is the derivative or derived function. Hence the function

$3x^2 - 12x + 5$ is **differentiated** to give $6x - 12$

$6x - 12$ is the **derivative** of $3x^2 - 12x + 5$.

The inventor of this technique is generally thought to have been *Sir Isaac Newton*, who developed it in order to explain the movement of stars and planets. However, the German mathematician *Gottfried Wilhelm Leibniz* ran him close, and it was Leibniz who was the first actually to publish the idea, in the year 1684. Much vigorous and acrimonious discussion ensued as to who discovered the technique first. Today both are saluted for their genius.

The notation used by Leibniz is still used today. The gradient of a straight line is

$$\frac{\text{change in } y}{\text{change in } x}$$

which he shortened to $\frac{dy}{dx}$ (read as 'dy by dx').

The above example could be written thus :

$$y = 3x^2 - 12x + 5 \Rightarrow \frac{dy}{dx} = 6x - 12$$

or alternatively

$$\frac{d}{dx}(3x^2 - 12x + 5) = 6x - 12,$$

the symbol $\frac{'d'}{dx}$ standing for the derivative with respect to x.

Another way of denoting a derived function is to use the symbol f', as follows:

$$f(x) = 3x^2 - 12x + 5 \qquad \text{(function)}$$

$$f'(x) = 6x - 12 \qquad \text{(derived function)}$$

Activity 10 Differentiating $y = x^3$

The aim of this Activity is to find the derivative of the function $y = x^3$. There is more than one way to accomplish this; it can be done numerically by finding gradients at different points; or it can be done algebraically. You should attempt at least one of (a) or (b) in the Activity.

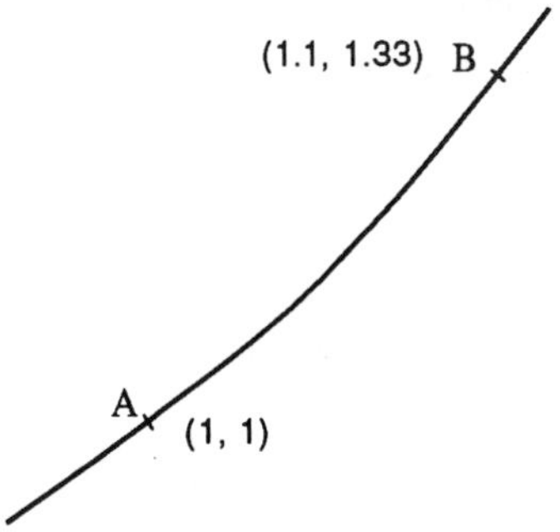

(a) Either by using a graphic calculator or by considering a nearby point, find the gradient of the curve $y = x^3$ at the point (1, 1). Repeat for the points (2, 8), (3, 27), (4, 64), and for negative values of x. Can you establish a formula for the gradient?

(b) In the second diagram, C is the point with x-coordinate $1 + h$ and A is the point (1, 1). Explain why the gradient of AC is

$$\frac{(1+h)^3 - 1}{h}$$

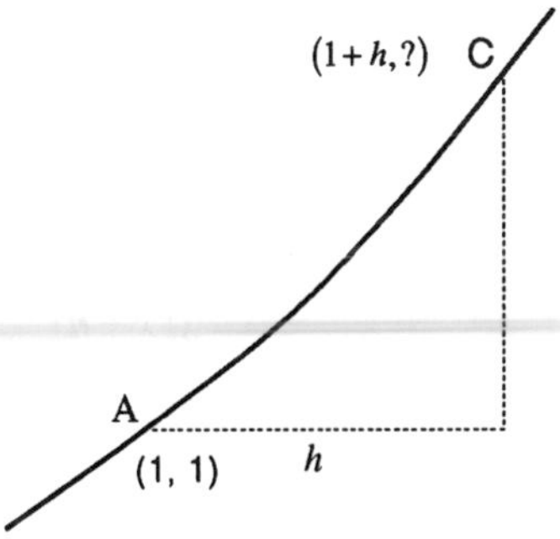

Expand $(1+h)^3$ by treating it as

$$(1+h)(1+h)^2 = (1+h)(1+2h+h^2).$$

Hence simplify the formula for the gradient and deduce the gradient of the graph at (1, 1).

Repeat this process for the points (2, 8), (3, 27), (4, 64). Generalise to any point on the curve.

You may have established the derivative of the function x^3. In case you didn't the details are given below.

With reference to the diagram opposite, the gradient of PQ is given by

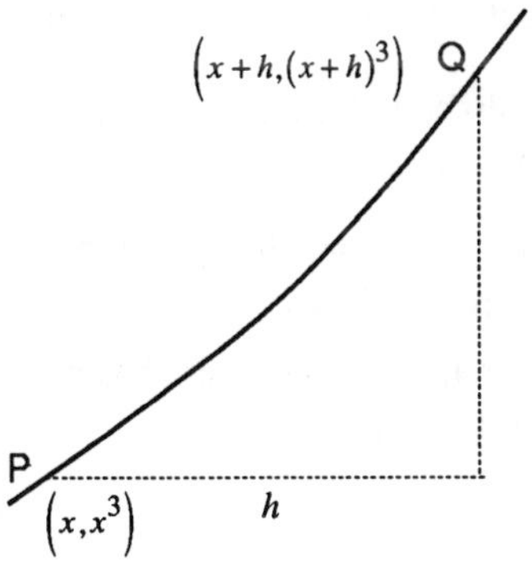

$$\frac{(x+h)^3 - x^3}{h}$$

$$= \frac{x^3 + 3x^2h + 3xh^2 + h^3 - x^3}{h}$$

$$= 3x^2 + 3xh + h^2$$

Whatever the value of x, this gradient gets closer and closer to $3x^2$ as $h \to 0$, so

$$\frac{dy}{dx} = 3x^2$$

Example

Find the derivative of $y = \frac{1}{x}$ $(x \neq 0)$

Solution

In this case the gradient of AB is

$$\left(\frac{1}{x+h} - \frac{1}{x}\right)\frac{1}{h}$$

$$= \left(\frac{x-(x+h)}{(x+h)x}\right)\frac{1}{h}$$

$$= \left(\frac{-h}{x(x+h)}\right)\frac{1}{h}$$

$$= \frac{-1}{x(x+h)}$$

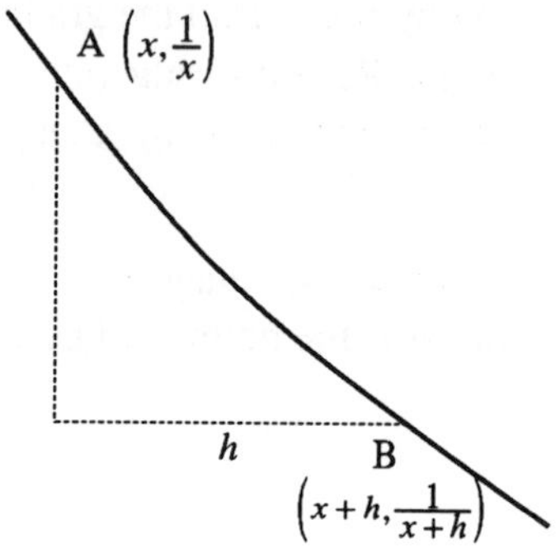

As h gets closer to zero, this formula gets closer to $\frac{-1}{x^2}$. Hence

$$\frac{dy}{dx} = -\frac{1}{x^2} \, (x \neq 0)$$

The derivatives of the functions x^2, x^3 and $\frac{1}{x}$ have now been established. Two other functions can be added to those, for completeness :

- the line $y = x$ has gradient 1, and so the derivative of the function x is 1;
- the line $y =$ constant has zero gradient, and so the derivative of a constant is 0.

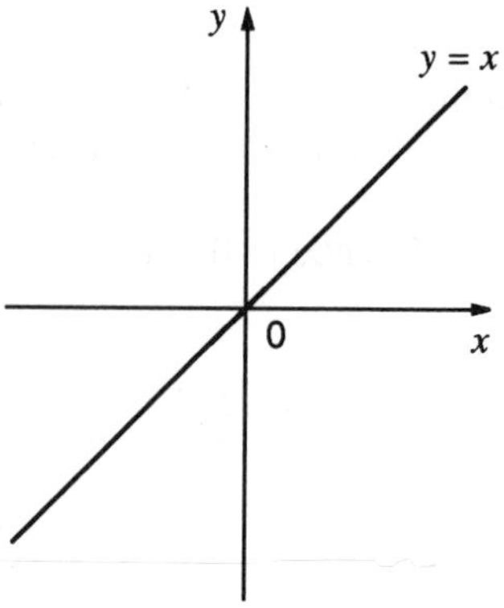

A summary of the results obtained so far is as follows :

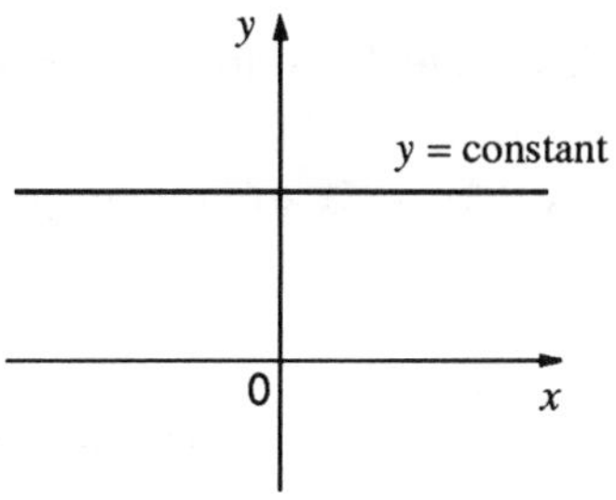

Function	Derivative
constant	0
x	1
x^2	$2x$
x^3	$3x^2$
$\frac{1}{x}$	$-\frac{1}{x^2}$

You may be able to guess the derivatives of higher powers of x; this and other matters will be covered in the last section of this chapter.

In Section 8.2, it was observed that the derivative of, for example, $5x^2$ was 5 times the derivative of x^2.

Similarly, the derivative of $5x^3$ is 5 times the derivative of x^3 :

$$\begin{aligned}\frac{d}{dx}(5x^3) &= 5\times\frac{d}{dx}\left(x^3\right)\\ &= 5\times 3x^2\\ &= 15x^2\end{aligned}$$

Another assumption to make is that functions such as $x^2+\frac{1}{x}$ can be differentiated by adding together the derivatives of x^2 and $\frac{1}{x}$:

e.g. $\frac{d}{dx}\left(x^2+\frac{1}{x}\right)=\frac{d}{dx}(x^2)+\frac{d}{dx}\left(\frac{1}{x}\right)=2x-\frac{1}{x^2}$

Justification for this assumption will be considered later on.

Example

Differentiate the following functions :

(a) $y = 3x^3 - 5x + 6$ with respect to x

(b) $y = x(x-3)(x+4)$ with respect to x

(c) $A = 10q^3 - \dfrac{5}{q}$ with respect to q

(d) $P = \dfrac{(h^3+3)}{2h}$ with respect to h

Solution

(a) $\dfrac{dy}{dx} = 3\dfrac{d}{dx}\left(x^3\right) - 5\dfrac{d}{dx}(x) + \dfrac{d}{dx}(6) = 3(3x^2) - 5 = 9x^2 - 5$

(b) $y = x^3 + x^2 - 12x$ (brackets must first be multiplied out)

$\dfrac{dy}{dx} = 3x^2 + 2x - 12$

(c) $\dfrac{dA}{dq} = 10(3q^2) - 5(-\dfrac{1}{q^2})$ (note $\dfrac{dA}{dq}$ instead of $\dfrac{dy}{dx}$ as the derivation is of A with respect to q)

$= 30q^2 + \dfrac{5}{q^2}$

(d) $P = \dfrac{h^2}{2} + \dfrac{3}{2h}$ (function must be divided out)

$\dfrac{dP}{dh} = \dfrac{2h}{2} + \dfrac{3}{2}(-\dfrac{1}{h^2}) = h - \dfrac{3}{2h^2}$

Exercise 8C

1. Find the derivative of the following functions :

(a) $y = x^3 + 5x^2 + 3x$ with respect to x

(b) $r = 6t^3 - 10t^2 + 2t$ with respect to t

(c) $f(x) = 5x^2 + \dfrac{1}{x}$ with respect to x

(d) $g(x) = x^2(x - \dfrac{1}{x})$ with respect to x

(e) $f(t) = \dfrac{t^3 + 3t}{5}$ with respect to t

2. Differentiate these functions :

(a) $(x+2)^2$

(b) $x(x+1)(x-1)$

(c) $s(s+\frac{1}{3})^2$

(d) $\dfrac{8y^3 + 3y^2}{9} + 3$

(e) $\dfrac{x^4 - 5x^2 - 1}{x}$

3. (a) What is the gradient of the curve

   $y = x^3 - 3x^2 + 6$ at the point (3, 6)?

   (b) What is the gradient of the curve

   $$y = 2x - \frac{5}{x}$$

   at the point (2, 1)?

   (c) At what point is the gradient of

   $y = x^2 + 6x + 3$ equal to 10?

   (d) When is the tangent to the curve

   $y = 3x^2 - 5x + 10$ parallel to the line

   $y = 20 - 11x$?

   (e) At what two points is the gradient of

   $y = 2x^3 - 9x^2 + 36x - 11$ equal to 24?

4. A student suggests that the height of the average male (beyond the age of 3) can be modelled according to the formula

   $$h = 6 - \frac{12}{y}$$

   where h is the height in feet and y is the age in years.

   Use this model to find the rate of growth of the average male (in feet per year) at the ages of

   (a) 6 (b) 8

8.5 Optimisation

Here is a problem similar to that at the start of Chapter 6. A piece of card 20 cm by 20 cm has four identical square pieces of side x removed from the corners so that it forms a net for an open-topped box. The problem this time is not to make a specific volume but to find the dimension of a box with the largest volume.

Activity 11 Maximising the volume

(a) Write down a formula for the volume V in terms of x.

(b) Sketch a graph of V against x for all the allowable values of x.

(c) Find the gradient of the graph when $x = 1$, 2 and 3. Interpret these figures, in terms of rates of change.

(d) What is the gradient when $x = 4$? Interpret your answer.

(e) Find the coordinates (x, V) where the gradient is zero. What is the significance of this?

Activity 12 Stationary points

The graph opposite shows a function $f(x)$. Copy the graph and underneath sketch a graph of the derivative $f'(x)$.

(The graph of $f(x)$ should not attempt to be accurate. It should be made clear where the gradient is positive, where it is negative, and where it is zero.)

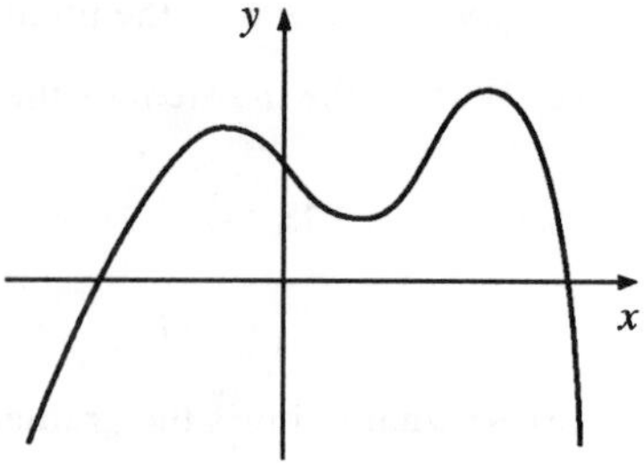

The graph in the last Activity contained three examples of stationary points. This is the general term used to describe maximum and minimum points. At a stationary point the gradient of the graph is zero; the tangent is exactly horizontal.

Activity 11 showed how useful this fact is. The **maximum** and **minimum** points of any function can be found by working out where the gradient is zero. The process of finding maximum and minimum points is sometimes called **optimisation**. It should also be noted that stationary points can also turn out to be points of inflection, as illustrated opposite.

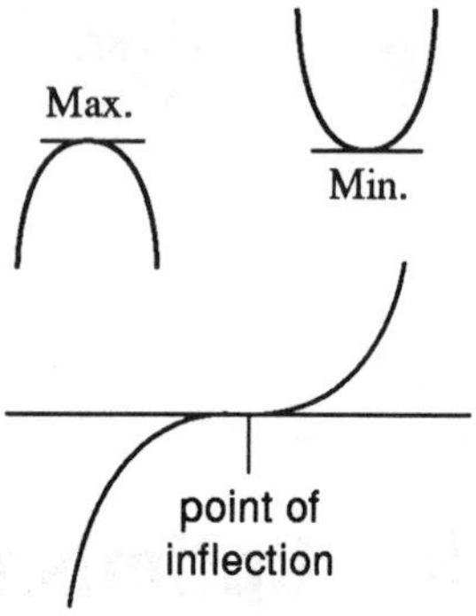

Example

Find the largest volume of an open top box that can be made from a piece of A4 paper (20.9 cm by 29.6 cm).

Solution

Suppose squares of side x are cut from each corner. Then the volume is given by

$$\begin{aligned} V &= x(20.9-2x)(29.6-2x) \\ &= 618.64x - 101x^2 + 4x^3 \end{aligned}$$

(Remember: brackets must be multiplied out before differentiation).

The volume is a maximum when the gradient is zero.

$$\frac{dV}{dx} = 618.64 - 202x + 12x^2$$

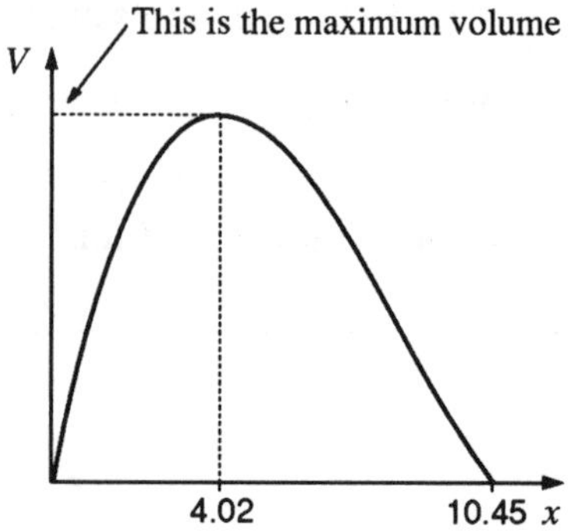

The required value of x can be obtained by solving the quadratic equation

$$12x^2 - 202x + 618.64 = 0$$

Hence $$x = \frac{202 \pm \sqrt{202^2 - 4\times 12\times 618.64}}{24}$$

$$= 4.02 \text{ cm or } 12.8 \text{ cm}.$$

12.8 cm is clearly inappropriate to this problem. Hence $x = 4.02$ cm is the size of square that maximises the volume. The largest volume is therefore the value of V when $x = 4.02$:

$$V_{max} = 4.02(20.9 - 2\times 4.02)(29.6 - 2\times 4.02)$$

$$= 1115 \text{ cm}^3 \text{ (to the nearest whole number)}$$

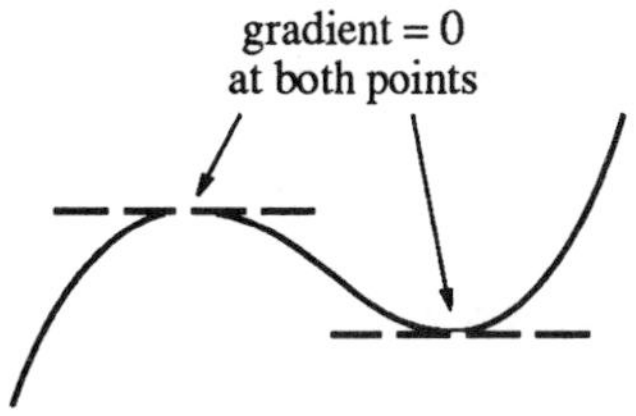

A potential snag with this method is that it only tells you where the stationary points are, but does not distinguish between maxima and minima. There are two simple ways round this problem.

Activity 13 Maximum or minimum?

(a) Show that the graph of $y = 2x^3 + 3x^2 - 72x + 15$ has stationary points at (–4, 223) and (3, –120).

(b) Copy and complete these tables :

x	– 4.1	– 4	– 3.9
y		223	

x	2.9	3	3.1
y		–120	

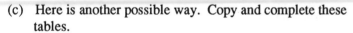

Use these answers to infer which point is a maximum and which is a minimum.

(c) Here is another possible way. Copy and complete these tables.

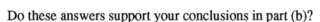

x	– 4.1	– 4	–3.9
gradient		0	

x	2.9	3	3.1
gradient		0	

Do these answers support your conclusions in part (b)?

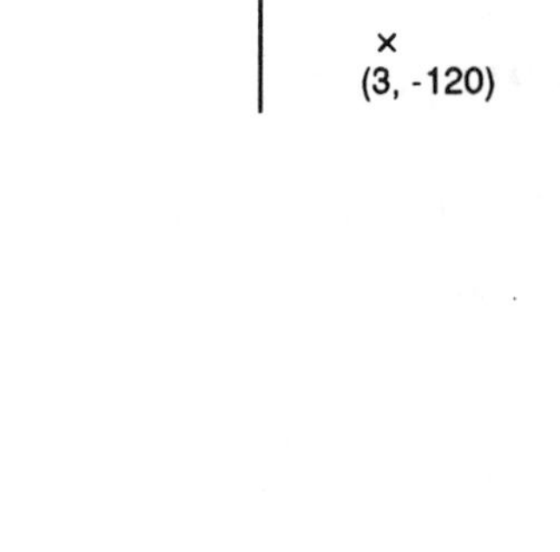

(d) Spot the flaw in this argument :

"(– 4, 223) is higher than (+3, – 120). Therefore (– 4, 223) must be the maximum and (3, –120) the minimum."

Example

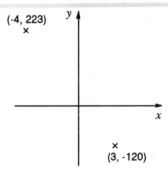

Find the two stationary points of the function

$$T = 2k + \frac{8}{k}$$

and determine which is a maximum and which is a minimum.

Solution

Now $\frac{dT}{dk} = 0$ for stationary point,

and $\frac{dT}{dk} = 2 - \frac{8}{k^2}$

$\Rightarrow \quad 2 - \frac{8}{k^2} = 0$

$\Rightarrow \quad 2 = \frac{8}{k^2}$

$\Rightarrow \quad k^2 = 4$

$\Rightarrow \quad k = 2$ or -2.

When $k = 2, T = 8$, and when $k = -2, T = -8$

k	-2.1	-2	-1.9
T	-8.01	-8	-8.01

maximum

k	1.9	2	2.1
T	8.01	8	8.01

minimum

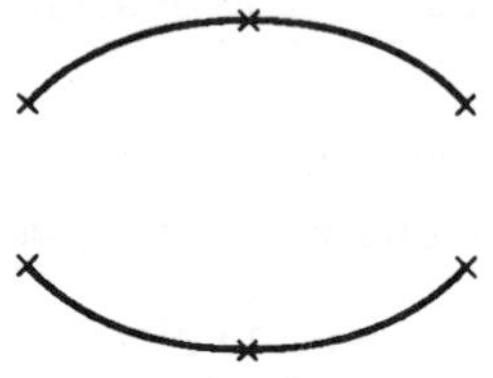

Hence the function has a

maximum at (–2, –8)

minimum at (2, 8).

Two important points arise from the last worked example :

1. Note that the maximum point is lower than the minimum.
2. The word 'maximum' is always taken to mean 'local maximum'. In the diagram, P is higher than any neighbouring point, but there are other points on the curve that are higher. Similarly, the word 'minimum' is taken to mean 'local minimum'.

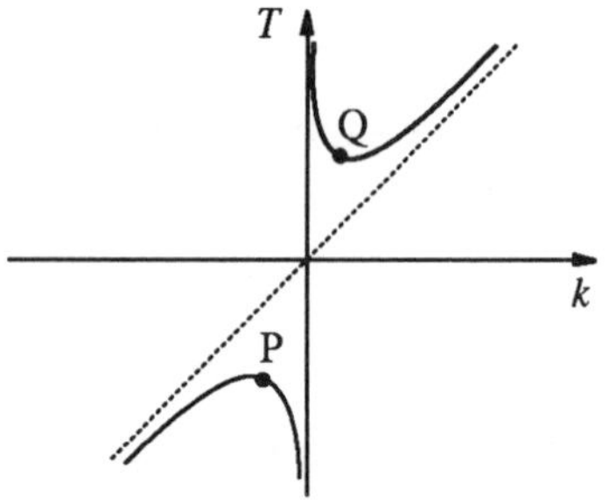

Exercise 8D

1. A function $f(x)$ is defined as follows :

   $$f(x) = x^3 - 6x^2 - 36x + 15$$

   Show that $f'(-2) = f'(6) = 0$, and hence find the co-ordinates of the maximum and minimum points.

2. Find the maximum and minimum points of these curves :

   (a) $y = 2x^2 - 6x + 7$ (b) $y = 3x + \frac{27}{x}$

   (c) $y = 70 + 105x - 3x^2 - x^3$

   (d) $y = x^2 + \frac{16}{x}$.

3. A manufacturing company has a total cost function

$$C = 5Q^2 + 180Q + 12500$$

This gives the total cost of producing Q units.

(a) Find a formula for the unit cost U, in terms of Q, where $U = C/Q$.

(b) Find the value of Q that minimises the unit cost. Find this minimum unit cost.

4. The makers of a car use the following polynomial model to express the petrol consumption M miles per gallon in terms of the speed v miles per hour,

$$M = \frac{v^3 - 230v^2 + 15100v - 145000}{4000}$$

(a) Find the speed that maximises the petrol consumption, M.

(b) The manufacturers only use this model for $30 < v < 90$. Give two reasons why this restriction is sensible.

8.6 Real problems

Activity 14 Maximising subject to a constraint

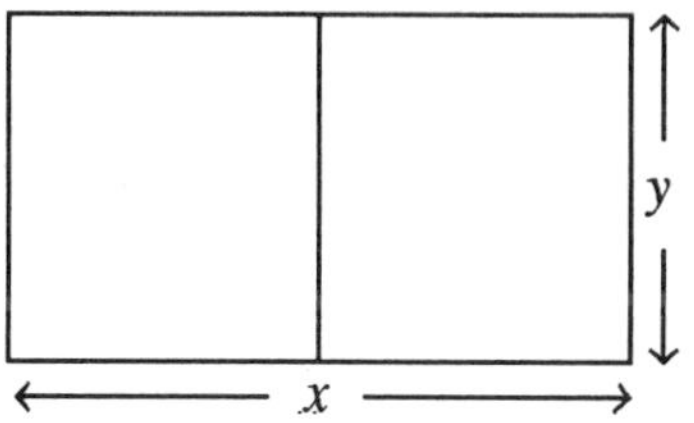

You have 120 m of fencing and want to make two enclosures as shown in the diagram. The problem is to maximise the area enclosed.

Let A be the area in square metres. Clearly $A = xy$.

(a) To find the maximum area, differentiate the expression for A and put it equal to zero. What is the problem with doing this?

(b) Use the fact that the total length of fencing is 120 m to write an equation connecting x and y.

(c) Make y the subject of this equation. Hence write a formula for A in terms only of x. Now differentiate with respect to x to solve the original problem.

(d) Try doing (c) the other way round. That is, make x the subject, express A in terms of y alone, and see if you get the same answer.

The problem posed in the Activity above was different to those earlier in this section. The quantity that needed maximising was first expressed in terms of two quantities, x and y. However, x and y were connected by the condition that the total length of fencing had to be 120 m. This sort of condition is known as a constraint. It allowed A to be expressed in terms of one quantity only, and thus the problem could be solved.

Example

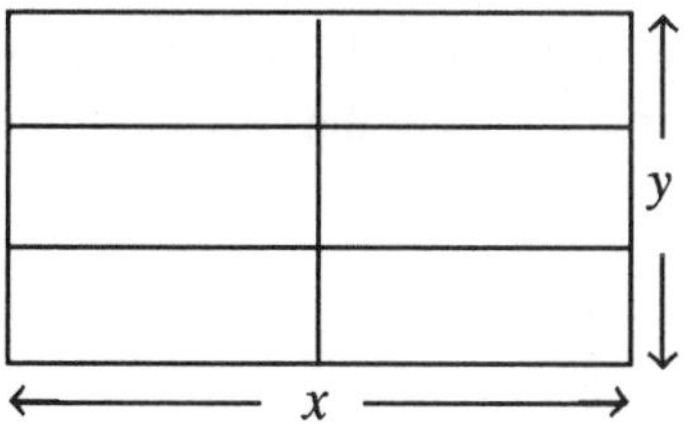

Find the maximum area that can be enclosed by 120 m of fencing arranged in the configuration on the right.

Solution

Let the overall dimensions be x metres and y metres and the area be A square metres.

$$A = xy \quad \text{(the quantity to be minimised)}$$

$$4x + 3y = 120 \quad \text{(constraint from total length of fencing)}$$

$$y = \frac{120 - 4x}{3} \quad (\text{make } y \text{ the subject})$$

$$A = \frac{x(120 - 4x)}{3}$$

$$= 40x - \frac{4}{3}x^2$$

$$\frac{dA}{dx} = 40 - \frac{8}{3}x$$

At a stationary point $\frac{dA}{dx}$ must be zero; this gives

$$40 - \frac{8}{3}x = 0$$

$$\Rightarrow \qquad x = 15$$

The question asked for the maximum area. From the equation for y

$$y = \frac{120 - 4 \times 15}{3} = 20$$

So maximum area $= 20 \times 15 = 300 \text{ m}^2$.

How do you know that the area is actually a maximum?

The worked example below is identical to the problem in Activity8 of Chapter 1. However, whereas before you solved the problem approximately, using a graph, it is now possible to obtain an accurate solution.

Example

A closed cylindrical can has a volume of 350 cm^3. Find the dimensions of the can that minimise the surface area.

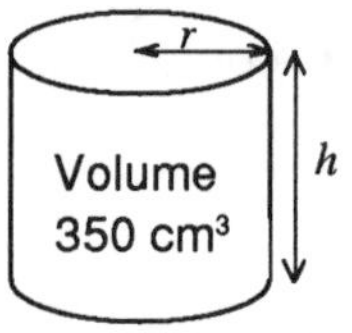

Solution

Let the radius be r cm and the height h cm. Let the surface area be S cm^2; then

$$S = 2\pi r^2 + 2\pi rh \quad \text{(the quantity to be minimised)}$$

At present, S involves two variables, r and h. The fact that the volume has to be 350 cm^3 gives a connection between r and h; namely

$$\pi r^2 h = 350 \quad \text{(constraint).}$$

So $$h = \frac{350}{\pi r^2} \quad \text{(make } h \text{ the subject)}$$

and $$S = 2\pi r^2 + 2\pi r\left(\frac{350}{\pi r^2}\right) \quad \text{(substitute for } h \text{ in the } S \text{ formula)}$$

$$= 2\pi r^2 + \frac{700}{r}$$

giving $$\frac{dS}{dr} = 4\pi r - \frac{700}{r^2}.$$

At a stationary point, $\frac{dS}{dr} = 0$,

giving

$$4\pi r - \frac{700}{r^2} = 0$$

$$\Rightarrow \quad 4\pi r = \frac{700}{r^2}$$

$$\Rightarrow \quad r^3 = \frac{700}{4\pi} \approx 55.7$$

$$\Rightarrow \quad r = 3.82 \text{ cm to 3 s.f.}$$

$$\Rightarrow \quad h = \frac{350}{\pi r^2} = 7.64 \text{ cm to 3 s.f. (from equation above)}$$

Could the problem have been solved by making r the subject of the constraint instead of h?

Exercise 8E

1. The rectangular window frame in the diagram uses 20 m of window frame altogether. What is the maximum area the window can have?

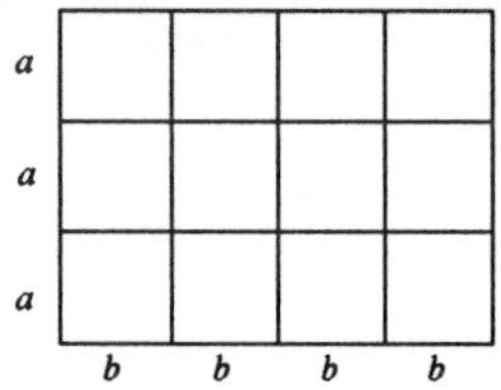

2. Repeat Question 1 for these window designs.

(a)

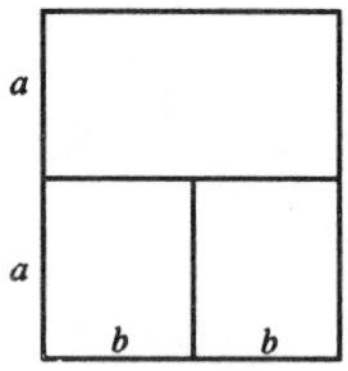

(b)

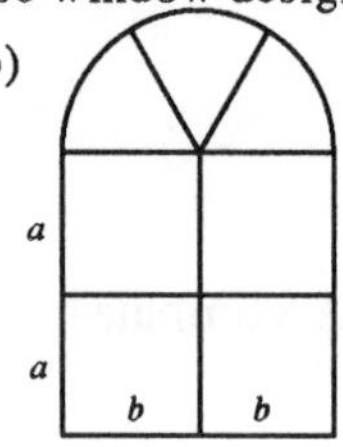

3. A rectangular paddock is to have an area of 50 m². One side of the rectangle is a straight wall; the remaining three sides are to be made from wire fencing.

   What is the least amount of fencing required?

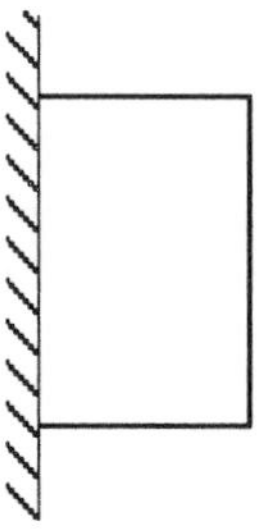

4. The enclosure shown has a total area of 300 m². Find the minimum amount of fencing required.

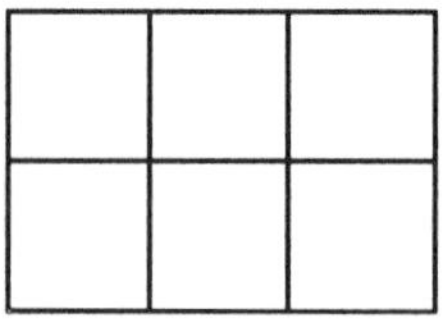

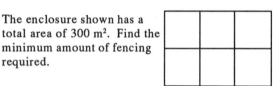

5. A small closed water tank is in the shape of a cuboid with a square base. The total surface area is 15000 cm². The problem here is to maximise the volume.

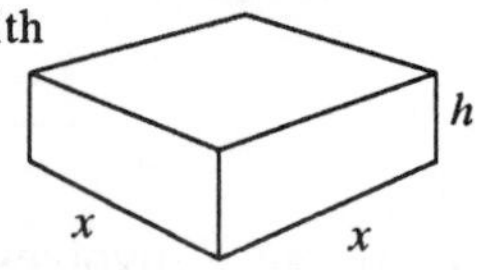

   (a) Let x cm be the side of the square and h cm be the height. Write down an expression for the volume V.

   (b) Show that $h = \frac{3750}{x} - \frac{x}{2}$

   (c) Show that the maximum volume is 125 litres.

6. An emergency petrol tank is designed to carry 1 gallon of petrol (4546 cm³). Its shape can be considered to be a cuboid.

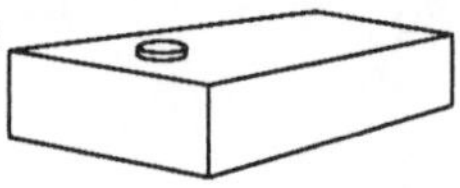

   The base of the cuboid is a rectangle with the length double the width.

   Find the dimensions of the tank that minimise the surface area required. Give the answers to the nearest millimetre.

7. The solution to the last worked example was such that the diameter and the height were equal. Show that this is true for any fixed volume of a cylinder when the surface area is to be minimised.

8.7 Differentiating other functions

From the work done so far, you should be able to differentiate any function involving sums and differences of $x^3, x^2, x, \frac{1}{x}$ and constants. This section extends this to other powers of x.

Activity 15 Continuing the pattern.

(a) The table opposite shows some of the derivatives you already know. Guess the derivatives lower down the table and conjecture a formula for the derivative of x^n, where n is any positive integer.

(b) Use the techniques of earlier sections to see whether your guess for x^4 is correct. You may wish to restrict yourself to numerical evaluation of gradients at particular points but, if you can, use algebra.

Function	Derivative
x	1
x^2	$2x$
x^3	$3x^2$
x^4	
x^5	
.	
.	
.	
x^n	

You can now differentiate any polynomial function. For example :

$$y = x^6 - 3x^5 + 8x^3 + 2x - 6$$

$$\Rightarrow \quad \frac{dy}{dx} = 6x^5 - 3\times(5x^4) + 8\times(3x^2) + 2$$

$$= 6x^5 - 15x^4 + 24x^2 + 2$$

Another function which you know how to differentiate is $\frac{1}{x}$. The next activity suggests how functions such as $\frac{1}{x^2}$, can be differentiated.

Activity 16 Differentiation of $1/x^n$

(a) Another way of writing $\frac{1}{x}$ is x^{-1}. In the activity above you found that the derivative of x^n is nx^{n-1}. What happens if you put $n = -1$ in this formula? Does it give the right answer?

(b) Extend this to find the derivatives of $\frac{1}{x^2}$, $\frac{1}{x^3}$, and $\frac{1}{x^{10}}$.

---

*Activity 17 Differentiating $1/x^2$ using algebra.

In the activity above you found that the derivative of $\frac{1}{x^2}$ was $-\frac{2}{x^3}$.

The objective here is to prove this result formally.

(a) Show that the gradient of the chord AB is

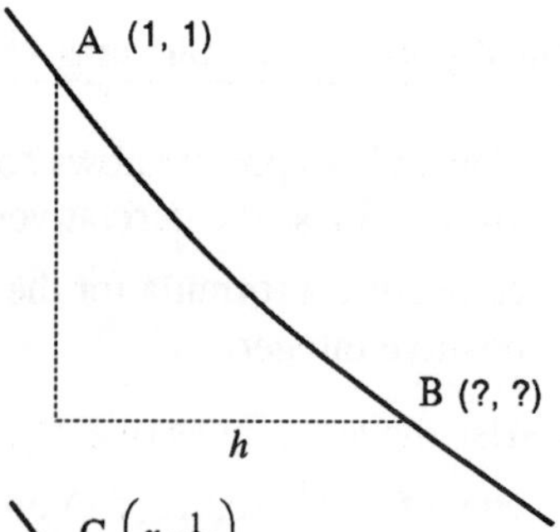

$$\frac{1}{h}\left\{\frac{1}{(1+h)^2}-1\right\}$$

and show that this simplifies to

$$-\frac{(2+h)}{(1+h)^2}$$

What is the gradient of the tangent at (1,1)?

(b) Now consider finding the tangent at $\left(x, \frac{1}{x^2}\right)$

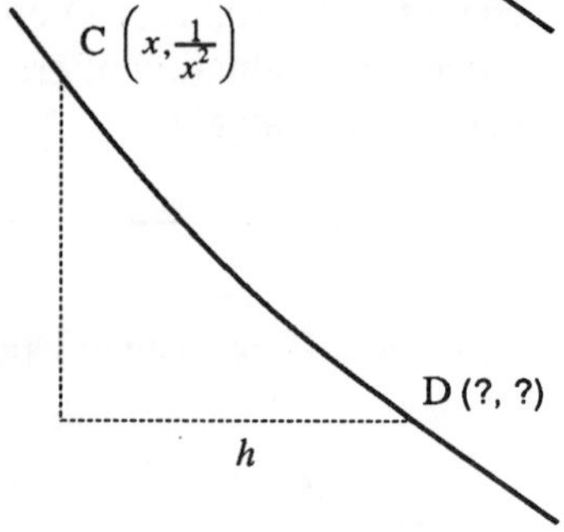

The overall summary of these results is as follows :

If $y = x^n$, then $\frac{dy}{dx} = nx^{n-1}$ for n any integer.

Is this result true for $n = 0$?

Example

If $y = \frac{7}{x^5}$, find $\frac{dy}{dx}$.

Solution

$\frac{7}{x^5}$ can be written as $7x^{-5}$,

so $$\frac{dy}{dx} = 7 \times (-5x^{-6}) = -35x^{-6} = -\frac{35}{x^6}.$$

Example

If $A = 5t^3 + \frac{2}{t^3}$, find $\frac{dA}{dt}$.

Solution

Re-write the function as $A = 5t^3 + 2t^{-3}$

So $$\frac{dA}{dt} = 5\times(3t^2) + 2\times(-3t^{-4})$$

$$= 15t^2 - 6t^{-4}$$

$$= 15t^2 - \frac{6}{t^4}.$$

Example

Differentiate $T = 6p^5 - 8p^4 + 10p - \dfrac{4}{p^2}$

Solution

Since $$T = 6p^5 - 8p^4 + 10p - 4p^{-2}$$

$$\Rightarrow \quad \frac{dT}{dp} = 6\times(5p^4) - 8\times(4p^3) + 10 - 4\times(-2p^{-3})$$

$$= 30p^4 - 32p^3 + 10 + \frac{8}{p^3}$$

Example

If $f(x) = (x^2-2)^2$ find $f'(2)$

Solution

$$f(x) = x^4 - 4x^2 + 4$$

$$\Rightarrow \quad f'(x) = 4x^3 - 8x$$

$$\Rightarrow \quad f'(2) = 4\times 2^3 - 8\times 2 = 16$$

Exercise 8F

1. Differentiate

(a) $y=\frac{1}{x^6}$

(b) $y=3x^3+\frac{2}{x^2}$

(c) $C=5q^4+6q^2+15-\frac{3}{q^3}$

(d) $G=t^8-\frac{3}{t^6}$

(e) $y=\frac{1}{2x^4}$

(f) $L=\frac{3}{5x^2}$

(g) $S=\frac{2}{t}-\frac{7}{2t^4}$

(h) $y=\frac{x^5-3}{4x^3}$

2. (a) $f(x)=6-\frac{10}{x^2}$ find $f'(2)$

(b) $g(t)=15t+\frac{4}{t}$ find $g'(-1)$

(c) If $h(w)=w^7-\frac{8}{w^3}$ find $h'(-2)$

3. Find the gradients of :

(a) $y=x^2-\frac{1}{x^2}$ at the point (1, 0);

(b) $y=4x^5+3x^2$ at the point (–2, –116);

(c) $y=\frac{54}{x^2}-\frac{81}{x^3}$ at the point (3, 3).

8.8 Linearity

In this chapter the assumption has been made that differentiation is a **linear** process. This means for example that the function x^3+x^5 can be differentiated as follows :

$$\frac{d}{dx}(x^3+x^5)=\frac{d}{dx}(x^3)+\frac{d}{dx}(x^5)$$

(Differentiate x^3 and x^5 separately, then add).

Similarly, to differentiate $6x^3$:

$$\frac{d}{dx}\left(6x^3\right)=6\frac{d}{dx}(x^3)$$

(Differentiate x^3 and multiply by 6).

In general, given two functions f and g and two constants a and b, linearity means that

$$\frac{d}{dx}(af(x)+bg(x))$$

$$=a\frac{d}{dx}(f(x))+b\frac{d}{dx}(g(x))$$

or $$(af(x)+bg(x))'=af'(x)+bg'(x)$$

Is this assumption valid?

The only evidence in favour of it, is that obtained in Section 8.2 when quadratic functions were being investigated. To prove that differentiation is indeed linear, first of all a more formal definition of the derivative is needed. This is found as follows :

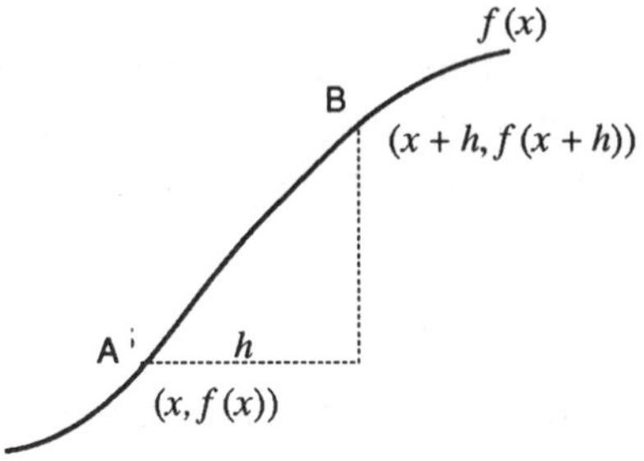

In the diagram, A and B are nearby points on the general curve $y = f(x)$. A is the general point $(x, f(x))$. B is at a horizontal distance h further along and has co-ordinates $(x+h, f(x+h))$.

(Compare this to the way derivatives were established for functions like x^2, x^3 etc.)

The gradient of AB is given by

$$\frac{f(x+h)-f(x)}{h}$$

The gradient at A is defined as the tangent at A to the curve, which is the limit of the gradient of AB as $h \to 0$. This is written

$$\boxed{f'(x) = \lim_{h\to 0}\left\{\frac{f(x+h)-f(x)}{h}\right\}}$$

Before tackling the final Activity, make sure you clearly understand the above definition and how it was formulated.

Activity 18 Proving linearity

(a) Suppose $p(x) = f(x) + g(x)$. Then

$$p'(x) = \lim_{h\to 0}\left\{\frac{p(x+h)-p(x)}{h}\right\}$$

Show that

$$p'(x) = \lim_{h\to 0}\left\{\frac{f(x+h)-f(x)}{h} + \frac{g(x+h)-g(x)}{h}\right\}$$

What conclusion can be inferred about $p'(x)$?

(b) Suppose $q(x) = kf(x)$, where k is a constant. Find an expression for $q'(x)$ in terms of k, h, $f(x+h)$ and $f(x)$ and explain why $q'(x) = kf'(x)$

(c) Suppose $r(x) = f(x)\,g(x)$. Show that $r'(x) = f'(x)\,g'(x)$ is **not** in general true.

8.9 Using the results

This chapter ends with practice in some traditional problems involving differentiation. Follow through these worked examples and then attempt Exercise 8G.

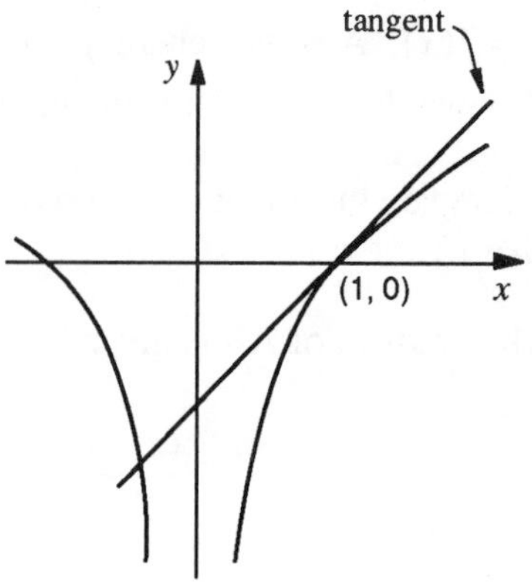

Example

Find the equation of the tangent to the curve

$$y = x^2 - \frac{1}{x^2}$$

at the point (1, 0)

Solution

The gradient is first found when $x = 1$.

$$\frac{dy}{dx} = 2x + \frac{2}{x^3} \text{ and when } x = 1, \frac{dy}{dx} = 4.$$

The tangent is thus a straight line with gradient 4 passing through (1, 0).

Equation must be of the form $y = 4x + c$, where the constant c can be found by substituting (1, 0) for (x, y) :

$$0 = 4 + c \Rightarrow c = -4$$

So the equation is $y = 4x - 4$.

Example

Find the equation of the normal to the curve $y = x^3 - 3x + 2$ when $x = 2$.

(The normal is the line perpendicular to the tangent.)

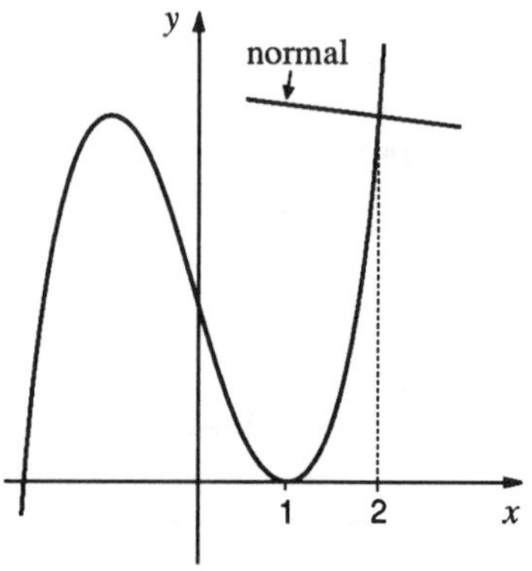

Solution

$$\frac{dy}{dx} = 3x^2 - 3 \text{ and when } x = 2, \frac{dy}{dx} = 9.$$

When $x = 2$ the gradient of the tangent is 9. The gradient of the normal is therefore $-\frac{1}{9}$. Also when $x = 2$,

$$y = 2^3 - 3 \times 2 + 2 = 4.$$

To find the equation of the normal, one point that lies on the normal needs to be found. The one point known is (2, 4), the point on the curve through which the normal passes.

So the equation is given by

$$y = -\frac{1}{9}x + c$$

and substituting (2, 4) gives

$$4 = -\frac{1}{9} \times 2 + c$$

$$\Rightarrow \quad c = \frac{38}{9}.$$

Hence the equation is

$$y = -\frac{1}{9}x + \frac{38}{9}$$

or $\quad 9y + x = 38.$

Exercise 8G

1. Find the equation of the tangent to :

   (a) $y = x^2 + 4x - 3$ at $(3, 18)$

   (b) $y = 5x^3 - 7x^2 + x$ at $(1, -1)$

   (c) $y = 2x - \dfrac{16}{x^2}$ when $x = -2$

2. Find the equation of the normal to :

   (a) $y = 3x^2 - 5x + 10$ at $(1, 8)$

   (b) $y = 2(1 - \dfrac{1}{x^2})$ when $x = -4$

   (c) $y = x^4 - 4x^3 + 7x + 9$ when $x = 3$

3. You are given that

   $f'(3) = 2 \qquad f'(5) = -1$

   $g'(3) = -6 \qquad g'(5) = 8$

   Find the following, where possible :

   (a) $p'(3)$ where $p(x) = 2f(x)$

   (b) $q'(5)$ where $q(x) = f(x)\,g(x)$

   (c) $r'(5)$ where $r(x) = 5f(x) + g(x)$

   (d) $f'(8)$

8.10 Miscellaneous Exercises

1. Differentiate with respect to x

   (a) x^2+4x-3 (b) $x^3-4x^2+17x+10$

   (c) $x(x+1)^2$ (d) $x^2+\frac{2}{x}$

   (e) $x(x-\frac{1}{x})^2$.

2 Find the derived function for :

   (a) $f(x)=5x^4+\frac{3}{x^2}$ (b) $f(t)=\frac{9}{2t^4}$

   (c) $f(y)=y^2(y^4-\frac{5}{y^4})$ (d) $f(p)=\frac{(p+1)^2}{p^2}$

   (e) $f(x)=\left(\frac{3+2x^2}{5x}\right)^2$.

3. (a) Find the equation of the tangent to the curve

   $y=2x^2-7$ at the point (2, 1).

   (b) Find the equation of the normal to the curve

   $y=2x-\frac{1}{x}$ when $x=-1$.

4. The definition of the derived function is :

$$f'(x)=\lim_{h\to 0}\left\{\frac{f(x+h)-f(x)}{h}\right\}$$

   (a) Use this definition to show that the derivative of x^2+3x is $2x+3$. (This is known as differentiating from first principles.)

   (b) Differentiate the function $5x^2-2x+4$ from first principles.

5. Wire from a construction kit is used to make a skeleton for a cuboid, which has a square base. The total length of wire is 300 cm. What is the maximum volume enclosed?

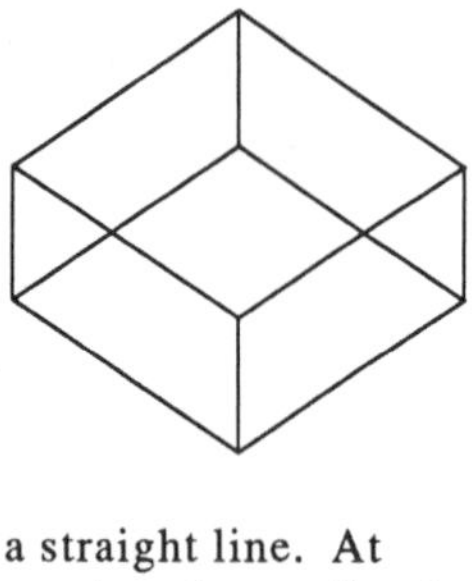

6. A particle is moving along a straight line. At time t seconds its distance s metres from a fixed point F is given by

$$s=t^3-12t^2+45t+10$$

   (a) Its velocity v in ms^{-1} can be obtained by differentiating s with respect to t. Find v in terms of t.

   (b) Find the two values of t for which the particle is stationary.

   (c) The acceleration of the particle can be obtained by differentiating v with respect to t. When is the particle's acceleration zero?

7. Another particle moves along the line so that its distance from F is given by :

$$s=25+40t-8t^2.$$

   (a) Find s when the particle is stationary.

   (b) Show that the particle's acceleration is constant.

8. (a) If $y=x^4-8x^3-62x^2+144x+300$, show that

$$\frac{dy}{dx}=4(x^3-6x^2-31x+36)$$

   (b) Show that there is a stationary point where $x=1$ and find the two other points

   where $\frac{dy}{dx}=0$.

   (c) Sketch the curve, showing clearly the co-ordinates of the three stationary points.

9. A enclosure $PQRS$ is to be made as shown in the diagram.

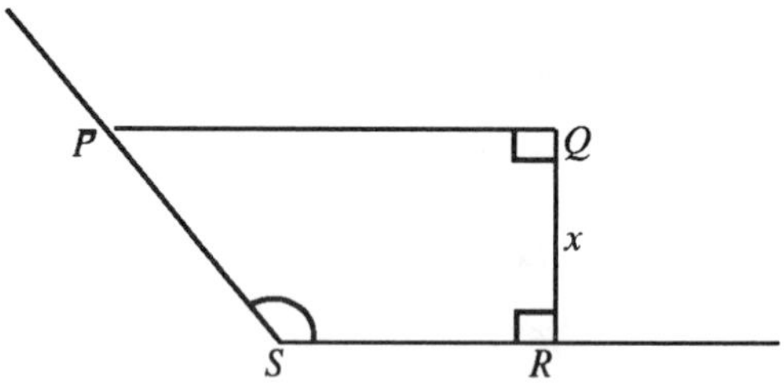

PQ and QR are fences of total length 300 m. The other two sides are hedges. The angles at Q and R are right angles and angle S is 135°. The length of QR is x m.

   (a) Show that the area, $A\ \text{m}^2$ of the enclosure is

   given by $A=300x-\frac{3x^2}{2}$.

   (b) Show that A can be written as

$$-\frac{3}{2}\left[(x-a)^2-b\right],$$

   where a and b are constants whose values you should determine. Hence show that A cannot exceed 15000. (AEB)

10. The diagram below shows a 24 cm by 15 cm sheet of cardboard from which a square of side x cm has been removed from each corner.

The cardboard is then folded to form an open rectangular box of depth x cm and volume V cm^3. Show that

$$V = 4x^3 - 78x^2 + 360x.$$

Find the value of x for which V is a maximum, showing clearly that this value gives a maximum and not a minimum value for V.

(AEB)

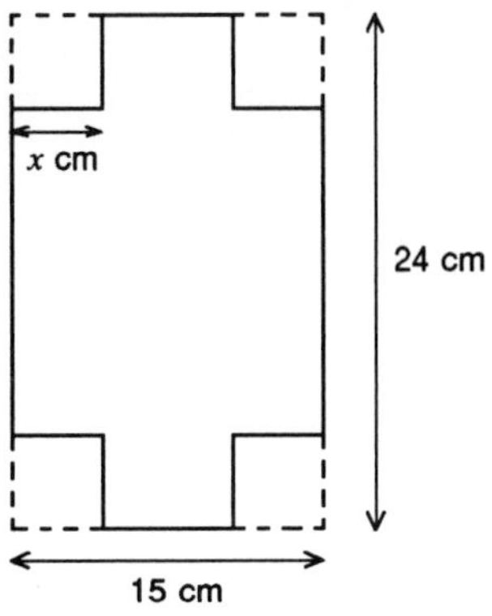

9 POWERS

Objectives

After studying this chapter you should

- understand fractional indices;
- know how to use the binomial theorem for any positive integers;
- be able to answer simple combinational problems.

9.0 Introduction

You are already familiar with expressions like $3^2, 4^{10}$ and 10^{-6}, all of which involve **powers** (or **indices**). But can any meaning be attached to an expression like $2^{0.6}$? If so, does it have any relevance? This chapter starts off by answering these questions. The rest of the chapter is concerned with a famous and important piece of mathematics known as the **binomial theorem**.

The topic is introduced through a case study on bacterial growth. Bacteria perform the roles of friend and foe at the same time. They are micro-organisms that perform a crucial function in nature by causing plant and animal debris to decay in the soil, but at the same time they can cause disease. Under favourable conditions they reproduce freely. Lone bacterium will first split into two bacteria, then both of these bacteria will themselves split into two and so on.

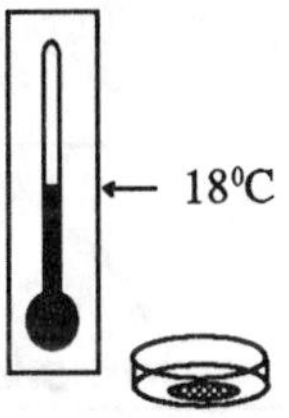

Petri dish with jelly

This growth can be observed by placing a lone bacterium onto a petri dish and positioning the dish in a warm environment. The splitting process under these sorts of conditions will take place twice per hour; hence after one hour there will be 4 bacteria, after two hours 16 bacteria and so on.

Activity 1 Bacterial growth

(a) Copy and complete the table shown. Write a formula for the number of bacteria after t hours.

Time (hours)	0	1	2	3	4	...
Number of bacteria	1	4	16	...	...	...

(b) Interpret this formula when $t = \frac{1}{2}, 1\frac{1}{2}, 2\frac{1}{2}, 3\frac{1}{2}$.

9.1 Fractional indices

Before continuing, you will find it useful to revise your knowledge of how integer indices work.

Activity 2 Revision

Complete these general statements :

For any non-zero number x, and any integers m and n :

(a) $x^m x^n =$ (b) $\dfrac{x^m}{x^n} =$ (c) $\left(x^m\right)^n =$

(d) $x^0 =$ (e) $x^{-n} =$

Activity 3

(a) You have already seen that $2^0 = 1, 2^1 = 2, 2^2 = 4$ and $2^3 = 8$. Draw an accurate graph of $y = 2^x$ by joining together these points with as smooth a curve as you can.

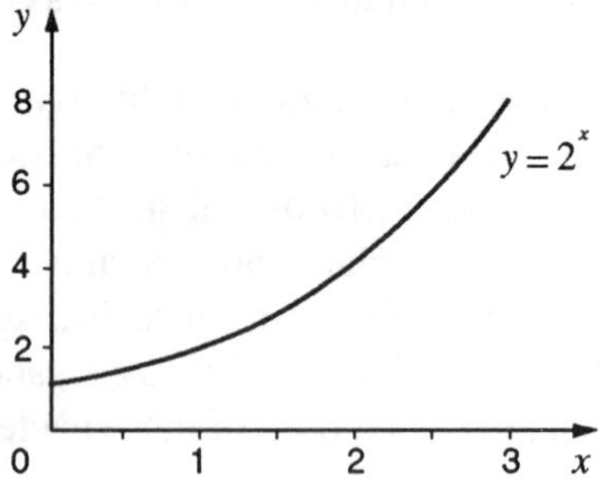

(b) The value of $2^{1\frac{1}{2}}$ must be double that of $2^{\frac{1}{2}}$. Why? Make a similar statement about $2^{2\frac{1}{2}}$. Are these statements supported by your graph?

(c) What is your interpretation of $2^{\frac{1}{2}}$?

Activity 4 Some logical deductions

(a) Let p stand for the value of $2^{\frac{1}{2}}$. What can you say about p^2? What rule of indices did you use?

(b) What is the meaning of $x^{\frac{1}{2}}$?

(c) Suppose q stands for the value of $2^{\frac{1}{3}}$. What is q^3?

(d) What does $x^{\frac{1}{3}}$ mean?

In general :

$x^{\frac{1}{2}}$ is another way of writing $\sqrt{x}$

$x^{\frac{1}{3}}$ is another way of writing $\sqrt[3]{x}$

$x^{\frac{1}{n}}$ is another way of writing $\sqrt[n]{x}$.

This alternative notation is often used on calculators. Your calculator may have a function $x^{\frac{1}{y}}$. If so, it can be used to find *n*th roots as follows.

To find $\sqrt[10]{2}$ or $2^{\frac{1}{10}}$ press [2] [$x^{\frac{1}{y}}$] [10] [=] The answer should be 1.071773463.

Activity 5 *n*th root

Find $\sqrt[10]{100}$ to 3 s.f. without using the $x^{\frac{1}{y}}$ or $\sqrt[x]{\ }$ function on your calculator. You **may** use the x^y function.

(Try simpler examples like $\sqrt{100}$ or $\sqrt[3]{100}$ first if you're not sure how to do this.)

Repeat for $\sqrt[100]{1\ 000\ 000\ 000}$ and $\sqrt[10]{0.1}$.

The problem at the beginning of this chapter is an example of 'exponential' growth. This will be dealt with in more detail in Chapter 11 but for the present it can be defined as a growth whereby the number of bacteria present is multiplied by 4 every hour.

Fractional indices are useful in many situations. A good example concerns credit card accounts where any unpaid debt grows exponentially by a certain percentage each month. Credit cards quote a monthly interest rate and the equivalent APR (annual percentage rate).

A typical APR is 29.84%. This means that a debt of £100 at the start of the year becomes one of £129.84 by the end. However, the interest is worked out monthly at a monthly rate of 2.2%. This figure arises because

$$(1.022)^{12} = 1.2984$$

giving an APR of (1.2984–1)100%.

Another way of writing this is to say

$$1.2984^{\frac{1}{12}} = 1.022.$$

Example

What is the monthly interest rate if the APR is 34.45%?

Solution

Since $(1.3445)^{\frac{1}{12}} = 1.02498...,$

monthly interest rate = 2.5%.

Example

Joel has an outstanding credit card bill of £162. The APR is 30.23%. He leaves it two months before paying. How much does he have to pay?

Solution

2 months is $\frac{1}{6}$ of a year.

But $(1.3023)^{\frac{1}{6}} = 1.045$

and $1.045 \times 162 = £169.29$

Exercise 9A

1. Calculate these without a calculator:

   (a) $16^{\frac{1}{2}}$ (b) $8^{\frac{1}{3}}$ (c) $81^{\frac{1}{3}}$

   (d) $\left(\frac{1}{4}\right)^{\frac{1}{2}}$ (e) $\left(\frac{16}{625}\right)^{\frac{1}{4}}$ (f) $(-1)^{\frac{1}{3}}$

2. Use a calculator to work these out to 3 s.f.

   (a) $6^{\frac{1}{2}}$ (b) $10^{\frac{1}{3}}$ (c) $56^{\frac{1}{3}}$

   (d) $(0.03)^{\frac{1}{20}}$ (e) $(0.5)^{\frac{1}{2}}$

3. Solve these equations:

   (a) $4^x = 2$ (b) $125^x = 5$

   (c) $100\,000^x = 10$ (d) $81^x = \frac{1}{3}$

4. The APR on a credit card is 26.08%.

   (a) Jan has an outstanding bill of £365. To how much does this grow in 6 months, assuming no other transactions take place?

   (b) Mark has a bill of £218. What is his bill a month later?

5. Water lilies on a pond grow exponentially so that the area they cover doubles every week. On Sunday they cover 13% of the surface. What percentage do they cover on Monday?

6. An investment policy boasts exponential growth and guarantees to treble your investment, at least, over 20 years. Work out the minimum guaranteed value, to the nearest pound, of

   (a) a £1000 investment after 10 years;

   (b) a £600 investment after 5 years;

   (c) a £2400 investment after 4 years.

9.2 Further problems

Piano tuners also deal with exponential growth. When tuning a piano to 'concert pitch' the first thing to do is to make sure the note A in the middle of the piano is in tune. A properly tuned 'middle A' has a vibrating frequency of 440 Hz (Hz is short for Hertz and means cycles per second).

There are lots of notes called A on the piano. The distance between consecutive As is called an octave. Every octave up, the frequency doubles, as follows :

two As above	1760
one A above	880
middle A	440
one A below	220
two As below	110

Activity 6 Finding the frequency

(a) Write down a formula for the frequency of the note p octaves above middle A.

(b) Use this to find the frequency of the note half an octave above A.

(c) An octave actually consists of 12 notes, so 'half an octave higher' means '6 notes higher'. Find the frequency of the note

(i) 3 notes above middle A

(ii) 5 notes above middle A

(iii) 6 notes below middle A

(iv) 11 notes below middle A

(d) Adapt your formula in (a) to find the frequency of the note n above middle A. Does this formula apply to notes below middle A?

Activity 7

Before reading on, discuss the meaning of these numbers and hence find their numerical value to 3 s.f., explaining your method clearly. Can you find more than one method for some of them?

$$2^{\frac{5}{12}} \quad 5^{\frac{3}{2}} \quad 10^{1.2} \quad 2^{-\frac{11}{12}} \quad 3^{-0.4}$$

There are always at least two ways of thinking about expressions like $3^{\frac{2}{5}}$.

Remembering that $\left(x^m\right)^n = x^{mn}$,

$$3^{\frac{2}{5}} = \left(3^2\right)^{\frac{1}{5}} \quad \text{or} \quad 3^{\frac{2}{5}} = \left(3^{\frac{1}{5}}\right)^2$$

$$= \left(\sqrt[5]{3^2}\right) \qquad\qquad = \left(\sqrt[5]{3}\right)^2$$

$$= \left(\sqrt[5]{9}\right).$$

In general,

$$x^{\frac{p}{q}} = \sqrt[q]{x^p} \text{ or } \left(\sqrt[q]{x}\right)^p.$$

Since $\frac{2}{5} = 2 \times \frac{1}{5}$ or $\frac{1}{5} \times 2$,

the order of the root and the power does not matter.

Does this extend to negative indices?

Examples are

$$3^{-2} = \frac{1}{3^2} = \frac{1}{9}$$

and $$3^{-\frac{2}{5}} = \frac{1}{3^{\frac{2}{5}}}.$$

Example

Calculate the numerical values of

(a) $2^{\frac{4}{7}}$ (b) $10^{\frac{3}{2}}$ (c) $6^{-\frac{3}{8}}$ (d) $(0.6)^{-\frac{7}{3}}$

Solution

There is always more than one method of working these out. Only one method is shown for each one here. Pay particular regard to the methods in (b) and (d).

(a) $2^{\frac{4}{7}} = \left(2^4\right)^{\frac{1}{7}} = \sqrt[7]{16} = 1.49$ to 3 s.f.

(b) $10^{\frac{3}{2}} = 10^1 \times 10^{\frac{1}{2}} = 10\sqrt{10} = 31.6$ to 3 s.f.

(c) $6^{\frac{3}{8}} = \left(6^{\frac{1}{8}}\right)^3 = (1.251033...)^3 = 1.9579731...$

$$6^{-\frac{3}{8}} = \frac{1}{6^{\frac{3}{8}}} = \frac{1}{1.9579731...} = 0.511 \text{ to 3 s.f.}$$

(d) $(0.6)^{\frac{7}{3}} = (0.6)^{2\frac{1}{3}} = (0.6)^2 \times (0.6)^{\frac{1}{3}}$

$= 0.36 \times \sqrt[3]{0.6} = 0.3036358...$

$(0.6)^{-\frac{7}{3}} = \dfrac{1}{0.3036358...} = 3.29$ to 3 s.f.

(Calculator note : always carry through as many figures as you can until the end of the calculation.)

Exercise 9B

1. Work these out without a calculator.

   (a) $4^{1\frac{1}{2}}$ (b) $27^{\frac{2}{3}}$ (c) $100^{\frac{5}{2}}$

   (d) $1000^{1\frac{1}{3}}$ (e) $16^{\frac{5}{4}}$ (f) $32^{0.4}$

2. Use a calculator to work these out to 3 s.f.

   (a) $120^{\frac{3}{2}}$ (b) $(0.7)^{\frac{5}{3}}$ (c) $5^{3.25}$

   (d) $1000^{\frac{2}{9}}$ (e) $\left(\frac{1}{4}\right)^{\frac{3}{7}}$ (f) $(0.36)^{3.1}$

3. Write these as fractions.

   (a) $16^{-\frac{1}{2}}$ (b) $4^{-1\frac{1}{2}}$ (c) $32^{-0.4}$ (d) $125^{-\frac{4}{3}}$

4. Calculate these to 3 s.f.

   (a) $10^{-\frac{1}{2}}$ (b) $15^{-\frac{1}{3}}$ (c) $(0.2)^{-\frac{5}{2}}$ (d) $(3.5)^{-\frac{4}{3}}$

5. Solve these equations. A calculator is not required.

   (a) $100^x = 100$ (b) $4^x = 32$

   (c) $9^x = \frac{1}{3}$ (d) $8^x = \frac{1}{2}$

   (e) $64^x = 16$ (f) $16^x = \frac{1}{8}$

6. Rewrite these formulas without using fractional or negative indices.

   (e.g. $x^{-1} = \frac{1}{x}$; $x^{\frac{3}{2}} = x\sqrt{x}$ or $\sqrt{x^3}$.)

   (a) $5p^{\frac{1}{2}}$ (b) $6q^{-1}$

   (c) $10x^{-\frac{1}{2}}$ (d) $\frac{3}{4}y^{-\frac{1}{2}}$

   (e) $\frac{1}{2}m^{\frac{3}{2}}$ (f) $12t^{-\frac{5}{2}}$

7. The population of a city is expected to grow exponentially and to double in 15 years. By what percentage would you expect the population to have risen after

   (a) 4 years; (b) 10 years.

9.3 Binomial expansions

'Binomial' is a word meaning 'two terms', and is used in algebra to mean expressions such as $a+2$ and $2x-y$. (Compare with the word 'polynomial').

Binomial expressions were used extensively in Chapter 8; for example the gradient of the chord in this diagram is

$$\frac{(2+h)^2-4}{h}$$

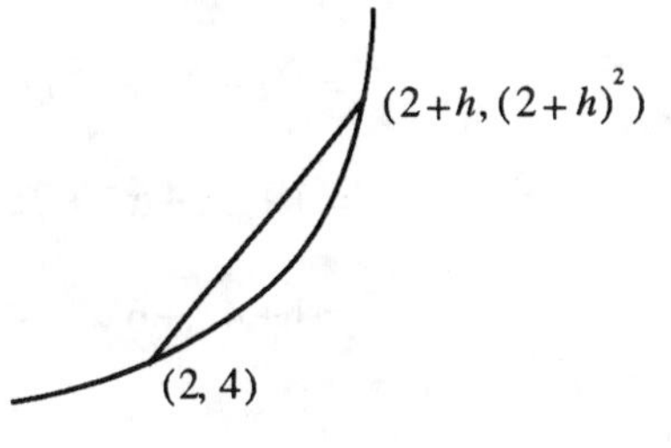

At the heart of this is the binomial $2+h$, raised to a power. For a more complicated curve the gradient might be

$$\frac{(2+h)^7-128}{h},$$

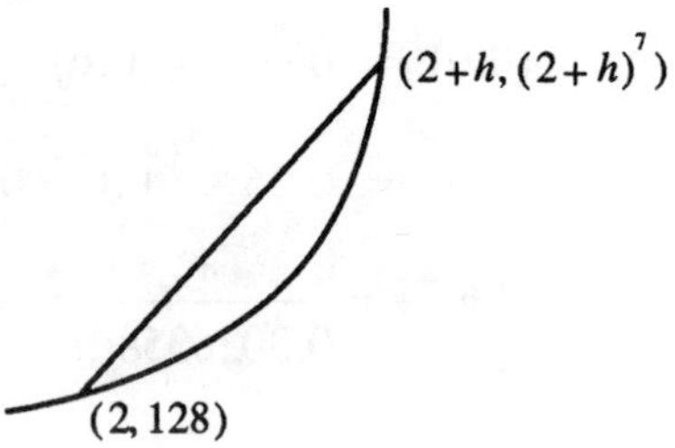

which is not so easily simplified because the binomial is raised to a high power. Dealing with expressions like $(2+h)^7$ is the focus of the next sections.

Activity 8 True or False?

Here are six statements about binomials. Which of these are true, and which false?

(a) $2(a+b)=2a+2b$ (b) $(a+b)\div 2=(a\div 2)+(b\div 2)$

(c) $(a+b)^2=a^2+b^2$ (d) $(a+b)^3=a^3+b^3$

(e) $\sqrt{(a+b)}=\sqrt{a}+\sqrt{b}$ (f) $2^{(a+b)}=2^a+2^b$

Writing $(a+b)^2$ for a^2+b^2 is a common mistake (though hopefully one you no longer make!). During Chapter 8 you should have got used to handling expansions like

$$(a+b)^2=a^2+2ab+b^2$$

$$(a+b)^3=a^3+3a^2b+3ab^2+b^3$$

These are simple examples of **binominal expansions.**

Example

Expand $(1+x)^4$

Solution

$$\begin{aligned}(1+x)^4 &= (1+x)^2(1+x)^2\\ &= (1+2x+x^2)(1+2x+x^2)\\ &= 1(1+2x+x^2)+2x(1+2x+x^2)+x^2(1+2x+x^2)\\ &= 1+2x+x^2+2x+4x^2+2x^3+x^2+2x^3+x^4\\ &= 1+4x+6x^2+4x^3+x^4\end{aligned}$$

Exercise 9C

1. Write out the expansion of these :

   (a) $(1+x)^2$ (b) $(1+x)^3$

   (c) $(1+x)^4$ (d) $(1+x)^5$

2. Repeat for these :

   (a) $(a+x)^2$ (b) $(a+x)^3$

   (c) $(a+x)^4$ (d) $(a+x)^5$

3. Write out the expansions of

   (a) $(3-2x)^2$ (b) $(2+5p)^3$ (c) $(\frac{1}{2}m-5)^4$

9.4 Binomial coefficients

You will be thankful that Exercise 9C was neither lengthy nor involved powers higher than the 5th power. As the index rises, so the expansions become more tedious. Expanding $(1+x)^{50}$ by this method, for example, would be somewhat daunting.

Activity 9

(a) Using your answers to Question 1 of Exercise 9C, complete this table :

Coefficients of

	1	x	x^2	x^3	x^4	x^5	x^6	x^7
$(1+x)^1$	1	1						
$(1+x)^2$	1	2	1					
$(1+x)^3$	1	3	3	1				
$(1+x)^4$								
$(1+x)^5$								

(b) What are the coefficients in the 6th and 7th rows?

(c) Write out the expansions of $(1+x)^6$ and $(1+x)^7$.

(d) How does the table above correspond to the expansions of $(a+x)^2, (a+x)^3$ etc.? What do all the terms in the expansion of, say $(a+x)^4$ have in common?

(e) Write out the expansions of $(a+x)^6$ and $(a+x)^7$.

(f) What is the **sum** of the numbers in the *n*th row?

The numbers in the table are called the **binomial coefficients**. It is evident that they obey a pattern, but finding the numbers in a particular row depends on knowing the numbers in the row before.

To expand $(1+x)^{50}$ you would need to know all the coefficients up to and including the 49th row first.

To get a formula for the binomial coefficients it is important to see how they arise. Look more closely at the expression $(a+x)^5$. Remember that it is short for

$$(a+x)(a+x)(a+x)(a+x)(a+x)$$

and that the expansion is

$$a^5+5a^4x+10a^3x^2+10a^2x^3+5ax^4+x^5.$$

In each term the two index numbers add up to 5. Moreover, the sum of the coefficients is 32. These two facts reflect what is going on here : each term is the product of a mixture of 'a's and 'x's, one letter from each of the 5 brackets. Each bracket can supply one of two letters, so the number of different combinations of 'a's and 'x's is $2\times2\times2\times2\times2$.

Only one such combination is all 'a's, hence the expansion starts with a single a^5 term. Five of the 32 possibilities give a^4x, 10 of them a^3x^2, and so on. It is the general method of finding the binomial coefficients 1, 5, 10, 10, 5, 1 that is being sought. That is the aim of the next section.

Activity 10 Bridge problem

Bridge is one of the best of all card games. In particular, it is one in which the skills of the player can overcome the luck of the deal. Here is a situation often faced by bridge players.

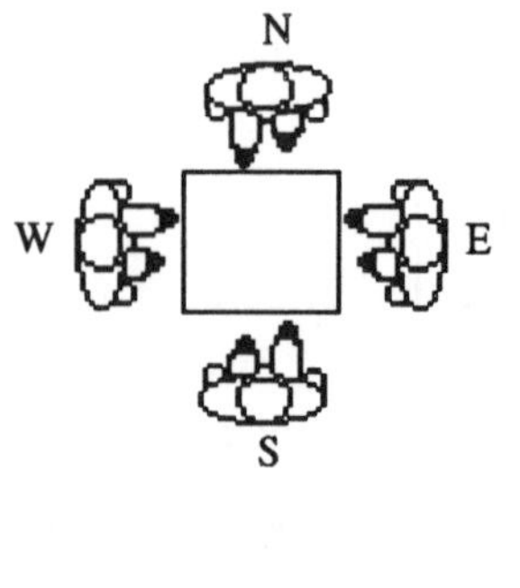

Suppose you are sitting at S (south). The opposing players are sitting either side of you at W (west) and E (east). You know that between them they have four cards in the heart suit. It is important to know the relative likelihood of various distributions of these four cards between W and E.

Each of the four cards can be in one of two places. Hence there are $2^4=16$ different arrangements.

(a) How many of these arrangements involve all four hearts being with W and none with E?

(b) How many of them involve E having only **one** heart?

(c) Complete the table below.

W	E	No. of ways
4	0	
3	1	
2	2	
1	3	
0	4	
	Total	16

(d) Bridge players sometimes claim that in these circumstances a '1-3 split' (either way) is more likely than an even split. Is this true? Explain.

(e) Extend this to the case where S knows that W and E have 5 hearts between them.

You should by now have realised that it could be dangerous to play bridge with a mathematician!

Activity 11 Streets of Manhattan

Many U.S. cities have a street layout based on a rectangular pattern. On Manhattan Island, for instance, more than 200 streets run across the island and ten avenues run at right angles to them.

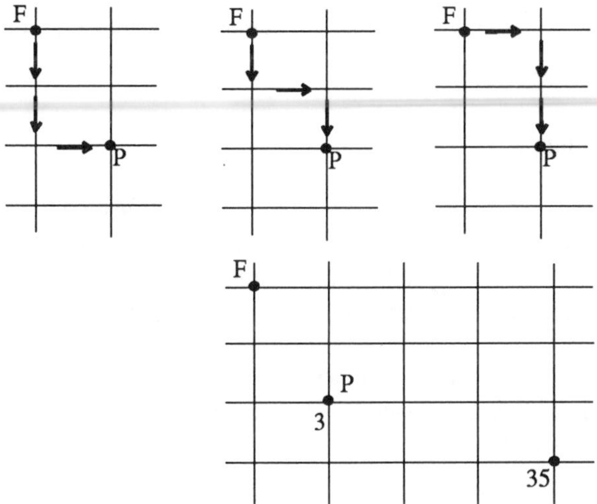

F represents a fire station. A fire is reported at junction P and the fire services need to take the shortest route from F to P. In fact, there are three equally short routes, as the three diagrams show.

Copy the street plan shown opposite and, by each crossroad, write the number of shortest routes there are from F. Some have been written in to help you.

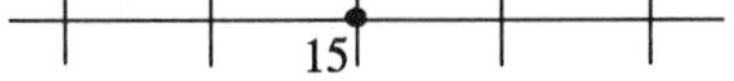

See if you can discover the link between this problem and the binomial coefficients.

Activities 10 and 11 give the same pattern as that of the binomial coefficients. This is because all three situations can be reduced essentially to the same thing. Here are specific questions and solutions from all three.

Bridge problem

How many ways can 5 cards be divided so that 3 are with E and 2 with W?

Solution

Imagine all five cards in a row. Each can be marked either E or W. There must be 3 Es and 2 Ws in any order. The answer to the question is, therefore, the number of different combinations possible with 3 Es and 2 Ws. As the list opposite shows, that number is 10.

EEEWW	EWWEE
EEWEW	WEEEW
EEWWE	WEEWE
EWEWE	WEWEE
EWEEW	WWEEE

Streets problem

In this plan, how many shortest routes are there from F to Q?

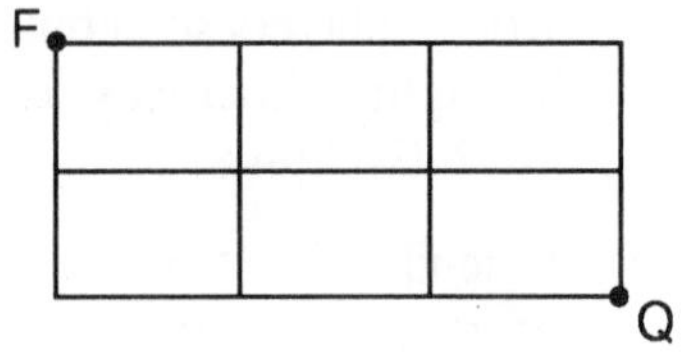

Solution

F and Q are 5 blocks away. To get to Q you must go across (A) 3 and down (D) 2, in any order. The number of such routes is therefore the number of different combinations of 3 As and 2 Ds. The answer is 10.

AAADD	ADDAA
AADAD	DAAAD
AADDA	DADAA
ADADA	DAADA
ADAAD	DDAAA

Binomial coefficients

In the expansion of $(a+x)^5$, what is the coefficient of the term a^3x^2?

Solution

$(a+x)^5$ is short for $(a+x)(a+x)(a+x)(a+x)(a+x)$. To get a^3x^2 three brackets must supply an 'a' and two of them an 'x'. The coefficient will be the number of ways this can be done. A list of the possible ways is shown on the right.

aaaxx	*axxaa*
aaxax	*xaaax*
aaxxa	*xaaxa*
axaax	*xaxaa*
axaxa	*xxaaa*

It should now be clear why three apparently unrelated problems give identical answers. The number of ways of arranging 3 As and 2 Ds is denoted

$$\binom{5}{3} \quad \text{or} \quad {}^5C_3.$$

The 'C' stands for COMBINATION.

To take another example.

$$\binom{7}{2} \quad \text{or} \quad {}^7C_2$$

means the number of different combinations of 7 objects, 2 of one type and 5 of another.

Exercise 9D

1. From what you have done in this section, write down the values of

   (a) $\binom{4}{2}$ (b) $\binom{5}{1}$ (c) $\binom{5}{2}$ (d) $\binom{6}{3}$ (e) $\binom{3}{1}$

2. How many different ways are there of arranging the letters of the words BOB and ANNA? Express your answers in terms of combinations,

   i.e $\binom{p}{q}$

*9.5 Factorials

Activity 12 Combinations of letters

(a) In the 8-letter word DOMINATE all the letters are different. Including the one given, how many arrangements are there of these letters.

(b) The word NOMINATE also has 8 letters, but two of them are the same. How many arrangements are there now?

(c) The word ADDITION has eight letters with two pairs of identical ones. How many different arrangements are there?

(d) How many arrangements are there of the word CALCULUS?

(e) The word DIVISION has one letter that appears three times. How many arrangements of these eight letters are there?

(f) How many arrangements are there of the words COCOONED and ASSESSES?

(g) Write down a general rule that finds the number of arrangements of the letters of an 8-letter word.

In general, the number of **arrangements** of an n-letter word with one letter repeated p times is given by the formula

$$\frac{n!}{p!}$$

$n!$ read as 'n factorial', is short for the product of all the natural numbers up to and including n; so for example

$$7! = 7\times6\times5\times4\times3\times2\times1 = 5040.$$

The number of different arrangements of letters in the word **SIMILAR** is therefore

$$\frac{7!}{2!} = \frac{7\times6\times5\times4\times3\times2\times1}{2\times1} = 2520.$$

This rule can be extended to cover the repetition of more than one letter. The number of arrangements of letters in the word **SENSES** is

$$\frac{6!}{3!2!}=\frac{6\times5\times4\times3\times2\times1}{3\times2\times1\times2\times1}=60.$$

This automatically provides a way of finding binomial coefficients.

$\binom{5}{3}$ is the number of arrangements of the letters AAADD

so $$\binom{5}{3}=\frac{5!}{2!3!}=\frac{5\times4\times3\times2\times1}{2\times1\times3\times2\times1}=\frac{5\times4}{2\times1}=10.$$

Similarly the binomial coefficient

$$\binom{10}{7}=\frac{10!}{3!7!}=\frac{10\times9\times8\times7\times6\times5\times4\times3\times2\times1}{(3\times2\times1)\times(7\times6\times5\times4\times3\times2\times1)}$$

$$=\frac{10\times9\times8}{3\times2\times1}=120.$$

Note also that

$$\binom{n}{n-r}=\frac{n!}{\left(n-(n-r)\right)!\,(n-r)!}=\frac{n!}{r!(n-r)!}=\binom{n}{r}.$$

Thus the general formula for binomial coefficients is given by

$$\binom{n}{r}=\frac{n!}{(n-r)!r!}$$

Your calculator probably has a factorial function on it. It may also have a function for working out binomial coefficients; consult your manual if you are not certain. In any case, it is often possible to work them out without a calculator; though the formula looks difficult there is always a good deal of cancelling that can be done, as the examples so far have shown.

Example

How many ways are there of selecting a tennis team of 5 from a squad of 9 players?

Solution

Imagine all 9 players in a line, 5 of them are in the team : label them T; 4 are not : label them N. The answer to the question is the number of arrangements of 5 Ts and 4 Ns, since each different arrangement gives a different team.

$$\binom{9}{5}=\frac{9!}{4!5!}=\frac{9\times8\times7\times6\times5\times4\times3\times2\times1}{(4\times3\times2\times1)(5\times4\times3\times2\times1)}=126$$

Activity 13

Compose a question to which the answer is $\binom{5}{5}$. Why does this mean that $0! = 1$?

*Exercise 9E

1. How many 'words' can be made from
   (a) 6 As and 3 Xs;
   (b) 7 Us and 5 Ws;
   (c) 10 Ys and 13 Zs?
2. How many different ways are there of arranging the letters in these names?
   SADIA
   WILLIAM
   BARBARA
   CHRISTOPHER
3. A committee of four is to be selected from a club of 25 people. How many different possibilities are there?
4. A florist puts ten pot plants in the window. Six of them are red, four green. How many different arrangements of the colours can be made?
5. Eleven hockey players are to be selected from a squad of 16. How many possible selections are there?
6. 12 people are to be split up into
   group A - four people;
   group B - six people;
   group C - two people.

9.6 Binomial theorem

First, there are some results concerning binomial coefficients which will be very useful later.

Activity 14

(a) Show that $\binom{n}{0}=1, \binom{n}{1}=n$ and $\binom{n}{2}=\frac{n(n-1)}{2}$.

(b) Write down corresponding formulas for $\binom{n}{3}$ and $\binom{n}{4}$.

(c) What is $\binom{n}{r}$?

Activity 15

$$\binom{21}{12} = 293\ 930 \text{ and } \binom{21}{13} = 203\ 490$$

Without using a calculator , write down the values of

$$\binom{21}{9} \text{ and } \binom{22}{13}$$

What properties of the binomial coefficients have you used? Express this symbolically.

The expansion of $(1+x)^5$ can now be written down as follows :

$$1+\binom{5}{1}x+\binom{5}{2}x^2+\binom{5}{3}x^3+\binom{5}{4}x^4+x^5$$

$$=1+5x+10x^2+10x^3+5x^4+x^5.$$

Similarly the expansion of $(a+x)^8$, where a is any number, can be found thus :

$$a^8+\binom{8}{1}a^7x+\binom{8}{2}a^6x^2+\binom{8}{3}a^5x^3+\binom{8}{4}a^4x^4+\binom{8}{5}a^3x^5$$
$$+\binom{8}{6}a^2x^6+\binom{8}{7}ax^7+x^8$$
$$=a^8+8a^7x+28a^6x^2+56a^5x^3+70a^4x^4+56a^3x^8$$
$$+28a^2x^6+8ax^7+x^8$$

The general result is known as the **binomial theorem** for a positive integer index.

> For $a, x \in \mathbb{R}$ and $n \in \mathbb{N}$
>
> $$(a+x)^n = a^n+\binom{n}{1}a^{n-1}x+\binom{n}{2}a^{n-2}x^2+\ldots$$
> $$\ldots+\binom{n}{r}a^{n-r}x^r+\ldots+x^n$$

Note the way this result is set out. Since n is unknown it is impossible to show the whole expansion. So the formula shows how the expansion starts and finishes, and gives a formula for the general term as

$$\binom{n}{r}a^{n-r}x^r.$$

One use of the binomial theorem is to give rough approximations to numbers like $(1.01)^8$. You can write

$$1.01 = 1 + 0.01$$

so that

$$\begin{aligned}(1.01)^8 &= 1 + \binom{8}{1}(0.01) + \binom{8}{2}(0.01)^2 + \binom{8}{3}(0.01)^3 + \ldots \\ &= 1 + 8 \times 0.01 + 28 \times 0.0001 + 56 \times 0.000001 + \ldots\end{aligned}$$

If 3 s.f. accuracy is required, clearly only the first three terms are needed at most:

$$(1.01)^8 = 1.0828\ldots = 1.08 \text{ to 3 s.f.}$$

The first four terms give an accuracy of at least 6 s.f.

$$\begin{aligned}(1.01)^8 &= 1 + 0.08 + 0.0028 + 0.000056 \\ &= 1.08286 \text{ to 6 s.f.}\end{aligned}$$

And all this without a calculator!

Example

Expand $(2x+3y)^4$.

Solution

$$\begin{aligned}(2x+3y)^4 &= (2x)^4 + \binom{4}{1}(2x)^3(3y) + \binom{4}{2}(2x)^2(3y)^2 \\ &\quad + \binom{4}{3}(2x)(3y)^3 + (3y)^4 \\ &= 16x^4 + 96x^3y + 216x^2y^2 + 216xy^3 + 81y^4\end{aligned}$$

Example

Expand $(3-\tfrac{1}{2}p)^5$

Solution

$$\begin{aligned}(3-\tfrac{1}{2}p)^5 &= 3^5 + \binom{5}{1}3^4(-\tfrac{1}{2}p) + \binom{5}{2}3^3(-\tfrac{1}{2}p)^2 + \binom{5}{3}3^2(-\tfrac{1}{2}p)^3 \\ &\quad + \binom{5}{4}3(-\tfrac{1}{2}p)^4 + (-\tfrac{1}{2}p)^5 \\ &= 243 - \frac{405}{2}p + \frac{135}{2}p^2 - \frac{45}{4}p^3 + \frac{15}{16}p^4 - \frac{1}{32}p^5.\end{aligned}$$

Example

Find the coefficient of x^5 in the expansion of $(4-3x)^9$.

Solution

The x^5 term must be $\binom{9}{5}4^4(-3x)^5$

$$=126\times256\times(-243)x^5$$

$$=-7\ 838\ 208x^5$$

So the coefficient of x^5 is $-7\ 838\ 208$.

Exercise 9F

1. Expand in full :

   (a) $(1+2x)^4$ (b) $(5-2p)^3$

   (c) $(6-\frac{1}{2}a)^6$ (d) $(2m+3n)^5$

   (e) $(2-\frac{1}{2}r)^4$

2. Find the coefficients of

   (a) x^3 in $(2+x)^{10}$ (b) a^5 in $(5-2a)^7$

   (c) q^6 in $(2p+5q)^9$ (d) k^4 in $(3k-2l)^{12}$

   (e) n^7 in $(5-\frac{5}{6}n)^{10}$

3. Find these to 3 s.f. without using a calculator.

   (a) $(1.01)^5$ (b) $(1.02)^{10}$

   (c) $(0.99)^7$ (d) $(2.01)^3$

   (e) $(99.5)^4$ (f) 11^6

9.7 Miscellaneous Exercises

1. Write these as fractions

   (a) $81^{-\frac{1}{4}}$ (b) $\left(\frac{9}{4}\right)^{\frac{1}{2}}$ (c) $\left(\frac{1}{8}\right)^{\frac{1}{3}}$ (d) $16^{-\frac{3}{4}}$

2. Solve these equations. A calculator is not needed.

   (a) $16^x=2$ (b) $100^x=0.1$ (c) $8^x=\frac{1}{4}$

   (d) $25^{2x+1}=0.04$

3. Given that $3^{2.524}=16$, solve these equations to 3 d.p.

   (a) $3^x=4$ (b) $3^x=\frac{1}{2}$ (c) $3^x=\frac{1}{256}$ (d) $9^x=32$

4. A class of 23 students selects a Year Council representative, four duty team members and two quiz team members. How many ways are there of doing this if

   (a) no-one is allowed to fill more than one of these roles;

   (b) there is no such restriction?

5. Use the binomial theorem to expand:

   (a) $(1+x)^5$ (b) $\left(3+\frac{x}{2}\right)^4$ (c) $(2-3p)^6$

6. Find the coefficient of

   (a) x^6 in $\left(x+x^2\right)^4$ (b) p^3 in $\left(p^2-\frac{3}{p}\right)^6$

   (c) n^4 in $(2+n)^3(1+2n)^4$

   (d) y^6 in $(5-2y)^4(y-1)^5$

7. Determine the coefficient of x^3 in the binomial expansion of $(1-2x)^7$. (AEB)

10 TRIGONOMETRY

Objectives

After studying this chapter you should

- know that radians are a unit for measuring angles;
- be able to convert from degrees to radians and vice versa;
- know and be able to use formulae for arc length and sector area in terms of radians;
- be familiar with basic properties of sine, cosine and tangent functions;
- be able to solve simple trigonometric equations.

10.0 Introduction

You are familiar with using degrees to measure angles, but this is not the only way to do it. In fact, as you see in some areas of mathematics, it is not even the most convenient way.

Activity 1 History of circular measure

(a) Your calculator will have settings for 'degrees', 'radians' and 'gradians'. Look up gradians in an encyclopaedia, and find out when these were first introduced. When did they last get used in Europe? How many gradians are there in a full turn, or in a right angle?

(b) Find out why 360 degrees make a full turn, and which civilizations invented them. What were the reasons for adopting 360? Why are 360 degrees still used?

Activity 2

The figure opposite shows a circle of radius r and arc PQ which is subtended by an angle of θ degrees.

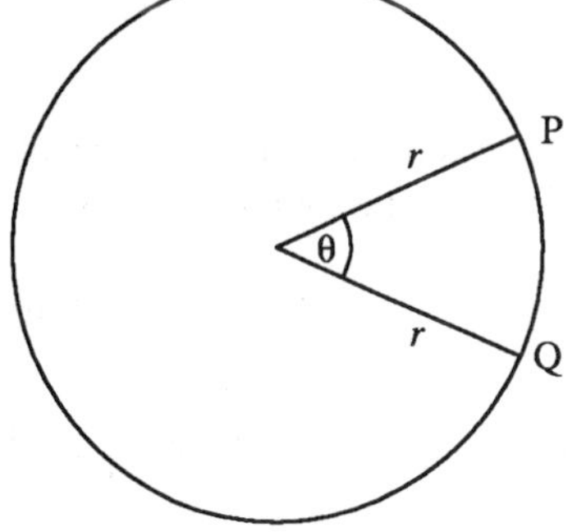

(a) What is the length of the complete circumference?

(b) What is the arc length PQ in terms of θ and r?

(c) If $PQ = r$, what is the value of θ?

10.1 Radian measure

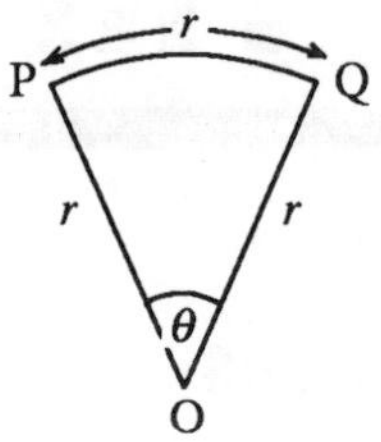

The second activity gives the clue as to how radians are defined. One **radian** corresponds to the angle which gives the same arc length as the radius. So if θ is the angle POQ in degrees.

$$\frac{\theta}{360} = \frac{r}{2\pi r} = \frac{1}{2\pi}$$

Thus $\theta = \frac{360}{2\pi} = \frac{180}{\pi}$ showing that

$$1 \text{ radian} \equiv \frac{180}{\pi} \text{ degrees}$$

This is not a very convenient definition, so it is usual to note that

$$\boxed{\pi \text{ radians} \equiv 180 \text{ degrees}}$$

Example

Convert the following angles in degrees to radians.

(a) 90° (b) 360° (c) 720° (d) 60°

Solution

Since $180° = \pi$ radians,

(a) $90° = \frac{\pi}{2}$ radians (b) $360° = 2\pi$ radians

(c) $720° = 4\pi$ radians (d) $60° = \frac{\pi}{3}$ radians

Activity 3 Conversion between degrees and radians

Copy the diagram opposite, putting in the equivalent radian measure for each angle given in degrees.

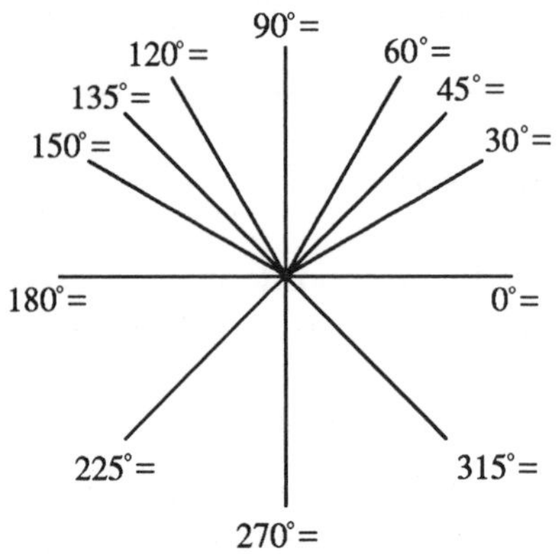

As you have seen, there is a one to one correspondence between degrees and radians so that

$$\theta° \equiv \theta \times \frac{\pi}{180} \text{ radians}$$

or

$$\theta \text{ radians} \equiv \left(\theta \times \frac{180}{\pi}\right)^{\circ}$$

Example

Use the formulae above to convert

(a) to radians (i) 45° (ii) 30° (iii) 150°

(b) to degrees (i) $\frac{2\pi}{3}$ radians (ii) $\frac{\pi}{12}$ radians.

Solution

(a) (i) $45° = 45 \times \frac{\pi}{180}$ radians $= \frac{\pi}{4}$ radians

(ii) $30° = 30 \times \frac{\pi}{180}$ radians $= \frac{\pi}{6}$ radians

(iii) $150° = 150 \times \frac{\pi}{180}$ radians $= \frac{5\pi}{6}$ radians.

(b) (i) $\frac{2\pi}{3}$ radians $= \left(\frac{2\pi}{3} \times \frac{180}{\pi}\right)^\circ = 120°$

(ii) $\frac{\pi}{12}$ radians $= \left(\frac{\pi}{12} \times \frac{180}{\pi}\right)^\circ = 15°$.

Exercise 10A

1. Convert these angles in radians to degrees:

   (a) $\frac{7\pi}{6}$ radians (b) 3π radians

   (c) 2 radians (d) $\frac{11\pi}{12}$ radians.

2. Convert these angles in degrees to radians:

   (a) $12\frac{1}{2}°$ (b) $72\frac{1}{2}°$

   (c) 210° (d) 20°.

10.2 Arc length and sector area

You may already have seen how to find the arc length. If θ is measured in degrees, then

$$\text{arc length PQ} = \frac{\theta}{360} \times 2\pi r = \frac{\pi r\theta}{180},$$

but if θ is measured in radians

$$\text{arc length PQ} = \frac{\theta}{2\pi} \times 2\pi r = r\theta.$$

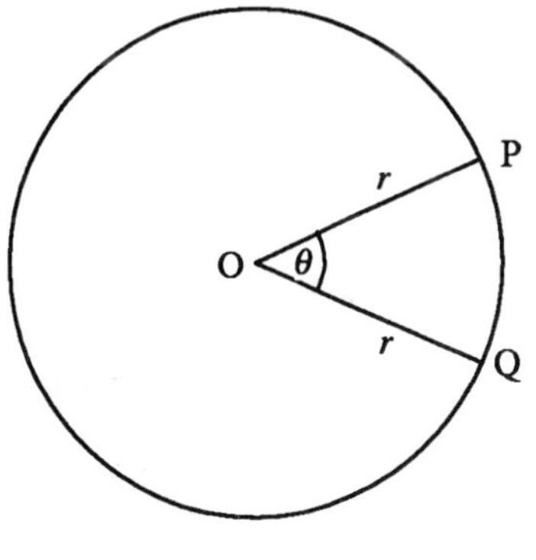

There is a simple formula for the area of a sector of a circle subtended by an angle.

Activity 4 Sector area

(a) What is the area of a circle, of radius r?

(b) The sector subtends an angle of θ radians at the centre of a circle. What proportion is the area of the sector to the area of the whole circle?

(c) Deduce the formula for the sector area?

So, using radian measure, the formula for both arc length and sector area take a simple form, namely

$$\text{arc length} = r\theta$$

$$\text{sector area} = \frac{1}{2}r^2\theta$$

You will see how these formulae are used in the following example.

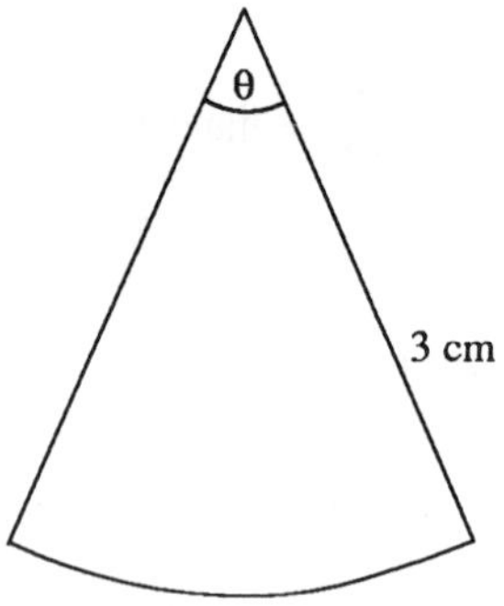

Example

(a) A silver pendant is made in the form of a sector of a circle as shown opposite. If the radius is 3 cm, what is the angle, θ, in radians so that the area is 6 cm^2 ?

(b) Another pendant has the same total perimeter, but with radius 2.5 cm. What is the required angle, θ, in radians?

Solution

(a) Sector area $= 6 = \frac{1}{2} \times 3^2 \times \theta$

$$\Rightarrow \quad \theta = \frac{4}{3} \text{ radians.}$$

(b) Total perimeter length $= 3 + 3 + 3 \times \frac{4}{3}$

$$= 10 \text{ cm.}$$

Hence, for the second pendant

$$10 = 2.5 + 2.5 + 2.5 \times \theta$$

$$\Rightarrow \quad \theta = 2 \text{ radians.}$$

Exercise 10B

1. An oil drum of diameter 60 cm is floating as shown in the diagram below :

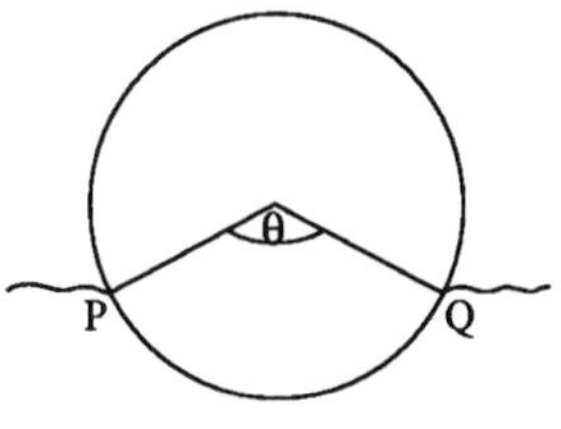

   (a) Given that the arc length PQ is 50 cm, find θ in radians.

   (b) The drum is 1 metre long, find the volume of the drum which lies below the surface level.

2. The length of the arc AB is 20 cm, and the area of the sector AOB is 100cm^2.

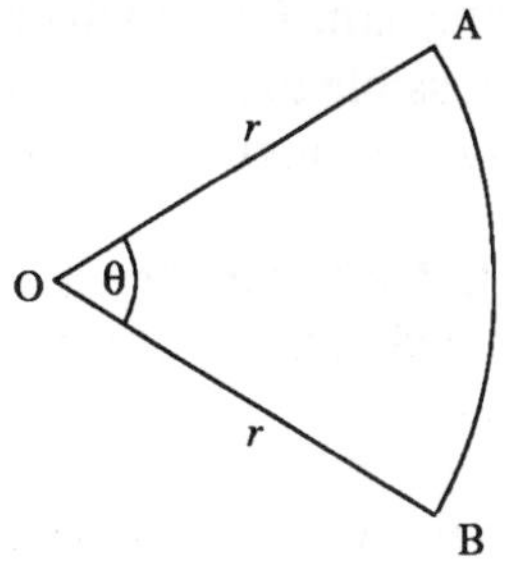

   Form two equations involving r and θ when θ is measured in radians. Solve these equations simultaneously to find r and θ.

3. A stone, swung round on the end of a 200 cm string, completes an arc subtending an angle at the centre of 2 radians every second. Find the speed at which the stone is moving.

10.3 Sine, cosine and tangent functions

You are probably familiar with the uses of sine, cosine and tangents in right angled triangles, but the following activities below will further revise the concepts.

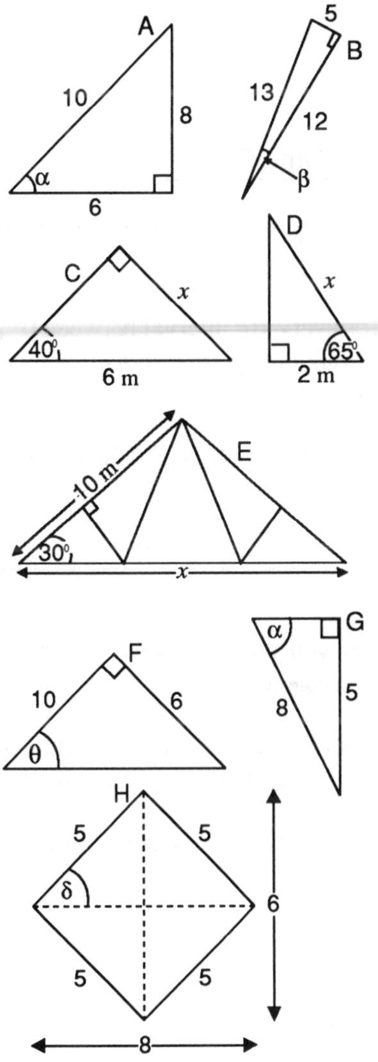

Activity 5

(a) Write down the sine, cosine and tangent of the angles marked in the triangles A and B.

(b) Find the lengths marked x to 2 d.p. in these triangles C and D.

(c) The sketch labelled E shows the frame of a roof. Find the width x.

(d) Find the angle marked, to 1 d.p., in each of the triangles, F and G.

(e) Find the angle δ in the rhombus shown opposite, as H.

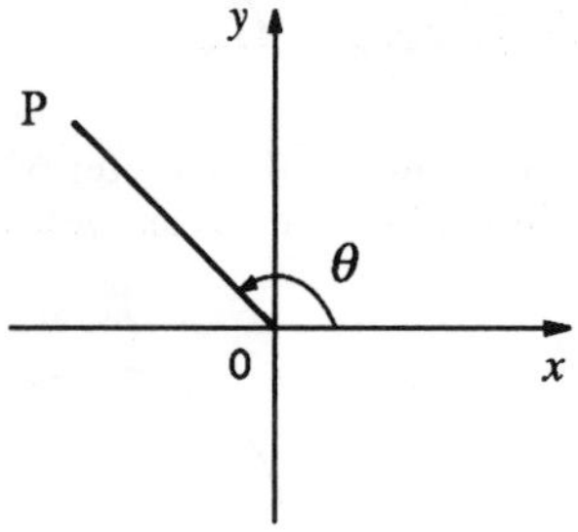

You have seen how sine, cosine and tangent are defined for angles between 0° and 90° but this can be extended to other angles.

Angles of more than 90° can be defined as the angle θ made between a rotating 'arm' OP and the positive x axis, as shown opposite. It is possible to define angles of more than 360° in this way, or even negative angles, as shown opposite.

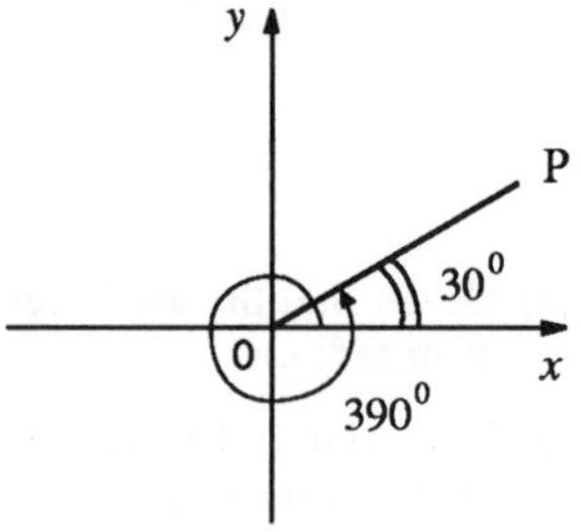

If the length of OP is 1 unit, then the sine, cosine and tangent of any angle is defined in terms of the x and y co-ordinates of the point P as follows;

$$\sin\theta = y \qquad \cos\theta = x \qquad \tan\theta = \frac{y}{x}$$

Note that $\sin\theta$, $\cos\theta$ and $\tan\theta$ may be negative for certain values of θ. For instance in the third figure opposite, y and x are negative, whilst $\tan\theta$ is positive.

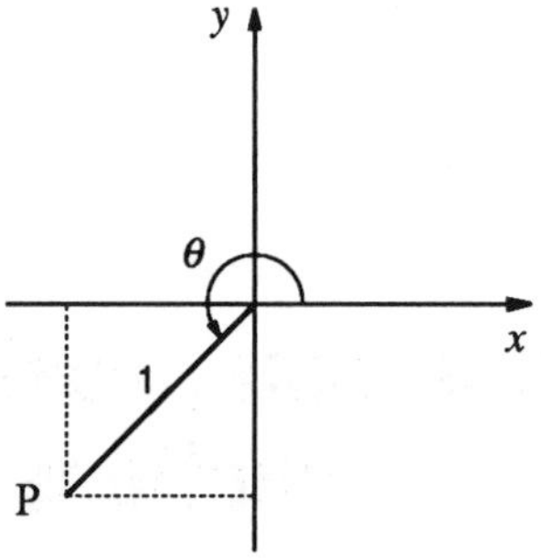

Scientific calculators give sine, cosine and tangent of any angle.

Activity 6

Using graph paper, plot the function

$$y = \sin x$$

for every 10° interval between 0° and 360°. Draw a smooth curve through the points. What are the maximum and minimum values of the function y?

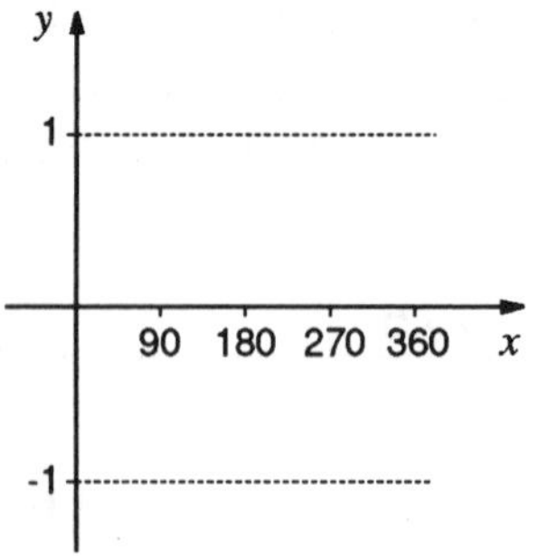

Repeat the process for the function

$$y = \cos x.$$

Can you explain why both functions, $\sin x$ and $\cos x$, lie between ± 1?

Whilst you have only plotted the functions for $0 \le x \le 360°$, it is easy to see how it can be extended.

What is the period of each function?

For the range $360° \le x \le 720°$, the pattern will repeat itself, and similarly for negative values. The graphs are illustrated below

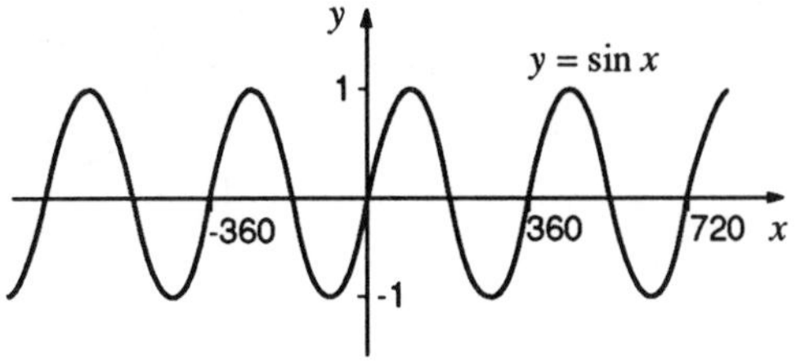

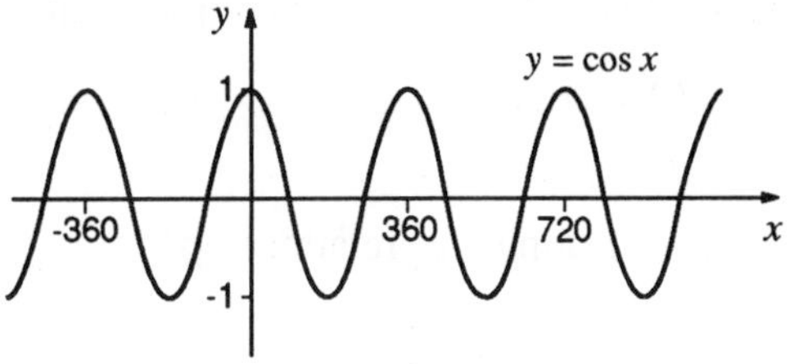

You can see from these graphs that $y = \sin x$ is an **odd** function $(y(-x) = -y(x))$, whilst $y = \cos x$ is an **even** function $(y(-x) = y(x))$.

You can always use your calculator to find values of sine and cosine of an angle, although sometimes it is easier to use the properties of the functions.

Example

Show that $\sin 30° = \frac{1}{2}$, and find the following without using tables:

(a) $\sin 150°$ (b) $\sin(-30°)$ (c) $\sin 210°$

(d) $\sin 390°$ (e) $\cos 60°$ (f) $\cos 120°$

(g) $\cos(-60°)$ (h) $\cos 240°$

Solution

From the sketch opposite of an equilateral triangle,

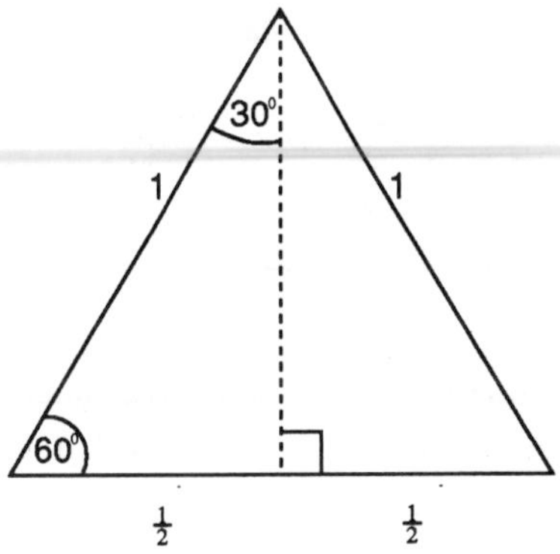

$$\sin 30° = \frac{\frac{1}{2}}{1} = \frac{1}{2}.$$

(a) $\sin 150° = \sin(180° - 30°) = \sin 30° = \frac{1}{2}$

(b) $\sin(-30°) = -\sin 30°$ (function is odd)

$$= -\frac{1}{2}$$

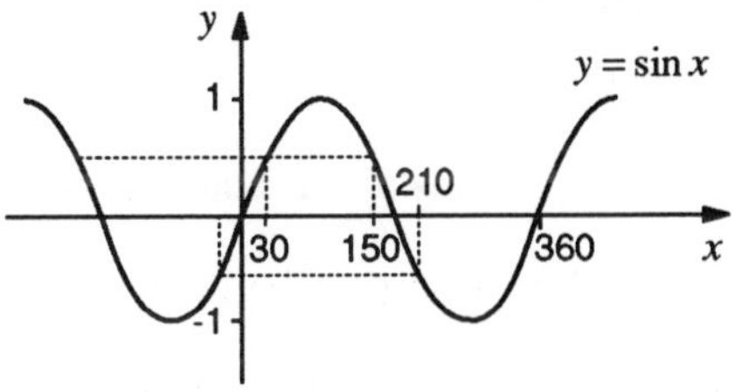

(c) $\sin 210° = -\frac{1}{2}$

(d) $\sin 390° = \sin 30° = \frac{1}{2}$

(e) Since $\cos\theta = \sin(90 - \theta°)$

$$\cos 60° = \sin(90 - 60°)$$

$$= \sin 30°$$

$$= \frac{1}{2}$$

(f) $\cos 120° = -\cos 60°$ (function is odd about $90°$)

$$= -\tfrac{1}{2}$$

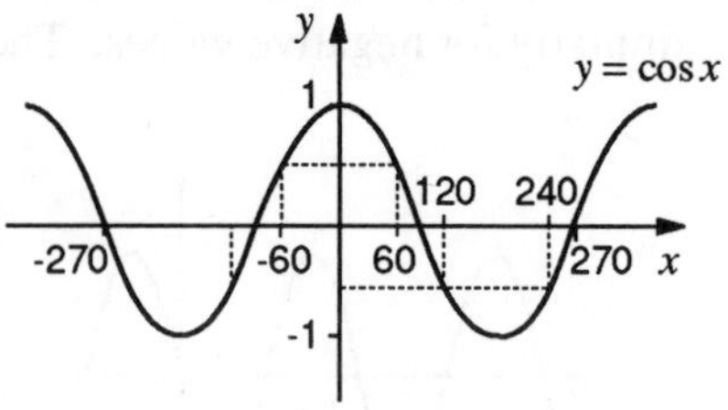

(g) $\cos(-60°) = \cos 60 = \tfrac{1}{2}$ (function is even)

(h) $\cos 240° = \cos 120° = -\tfrac{1}{2}$

In the above example, the relationship

$$\cos\theta = \sin(90 - \theta°)$$

was used.

Why is this result true?

Similarly, it should be noted that

$$\sin\theta = \cos(90 - \theta°)$$

The last function to consider here is $\tan x$, which has rather different properties from $\sin x$ and $\cos x$.

Activity 7 tan x

Using a graphic calculator or computer, sketch the function

$$y = \tan x$$

for x in the range $-360°$ to $360°$. What is the period of the function?

Unlike the sine and cosine functions, $\tan x$ is not bounded by ± 1. In fact, as x increases to $90°$, $\tan x$ increases without limit.

Example

Using the values

$$\tan 45° = 1 \quad \text{and} \quad \tan 30° = \frac{1}{\sqrt{3}}$$

find, without using a calculator,

(a) $\tan 135°$ (b) $\tan(-45°)$ (c) $\tan 315°$

(d) $\tan(-30°)$ (e) $\tan 150°$ (f) $\tan 60°$.

Solution

(a) $\tan 135° = \tan(180° - 45°) = -\tan 45° = -1.$

(b) $\tan(-45°) = -\tan 45°$

$= -1.$

(c) $\tan 315° = -\tan 45°$

$= -1.$

(d) $\tan(-30) = -\tan 30° = -\frac{1}{\sqrt{3}}.$

(e) $\tan 150° = -\tan 30° = -\frac{1}{\sqrt{3}}.$

(f) $\tan 60° = \frac{\sin 60°}{\cos 60°} = \frac{\cos 30°}{\sin 30°} = \frac{1}{\tan 30°}$

$= \frac{1}{(1/\sqrt{3})} = \sqrt{3}.$

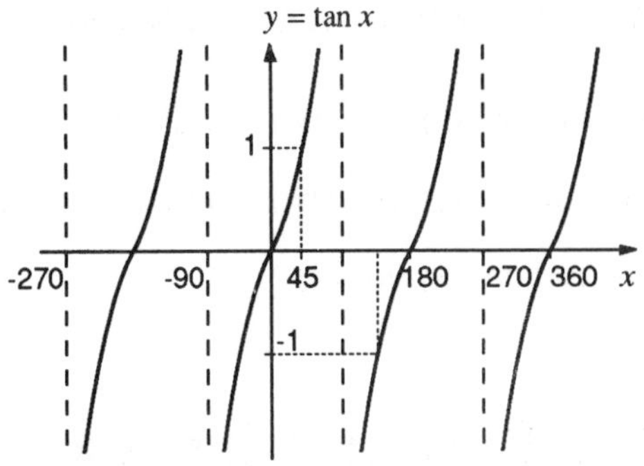

In (f), the result is equivalent to using

$$\tan\theta = \frac{1}{\tan(90-\theta)}$$

which is set in the exercise below.

The full results are summarised below.

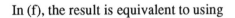

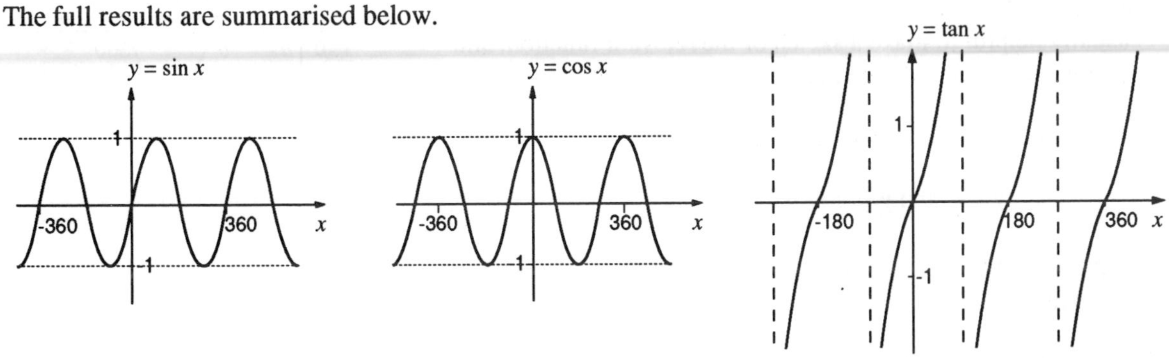

Exercise 10C

1. Find the length marked x to 2 d.p. for each of the figures below.

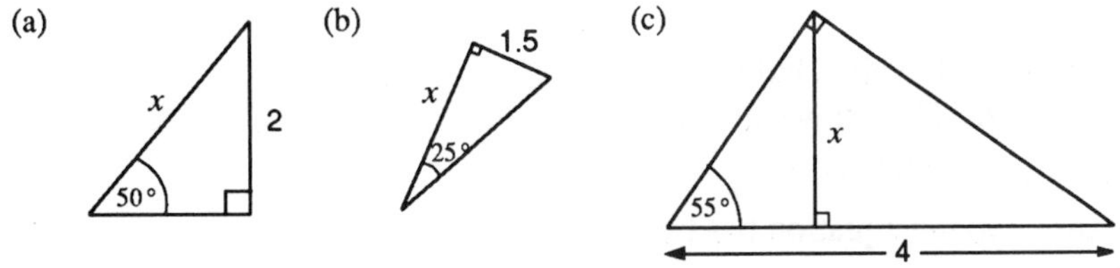

2. Given that $\sin 45° = \frac{1}{\sqrt{2}}$, find, without using tables

   (a) $\sin 135°$ (b) $\sin(-45°)$ (c) $\sin 315°$

   (d) $\cos 45°$ (e) $\cos(225°)$ (f) $\tan 45°$

   (g) $\tan 135°$ (h) $\tan(-45°)$

3. Prove that $\sin\theta = \cos(90-\theta)$.

4. Prove that $\tan\theta = \dfrac{1}{\tan(90-\theta)}$.

10.4 Solving trigonometrical equations

Trigonometric functions can be used to model physical phenomena but applying these functions to problems in the real world will often result in a trigonometric equation to solve. In this section, you will consider some simple equations to solve. These will highlight the difficulties that can occur.

Example

Solve $\sin x = \frac{1}{2}$ for $0° \le x \le 360°$

Solution

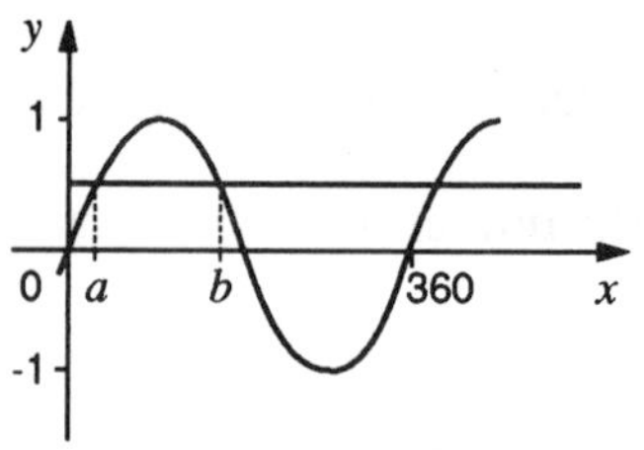

In solving equations of this sort it is **vital** to be aware that there may be **more than one** possible solution in the allowable domain - this possibility results from the periodic nature of this function. It is usually helpful to make a sketch of the relevant function, and this will help to identify the number of possible solutions.

In this case, the functions to plot are

$$y = \tfrac{1}{2} \text{ and } y = \sin x.$$

The points of intersection in the range $0° \le x \le 360°$ are solutions of the equation.

The figure shows that there are just **two** solutions, denoted by a and b, in the range. You can find the value of a by entering 0.5 in your calculators and using the 'inverse' sin or 'arc sin' buttons. This gives $a = 30°$ (or $\frac{\pi}{6} \approx 0.524$ radians, if you are using radians).

Your calculator will only give you this single value, but it is easy to find b provided you have used a sketch. This shows that the function $y = \sin x$ is **symmetrical** about $x = 90°$ and so $b = 90° + 60° = 150°$ (≈ 2.618 radians). So the equation has two solutions, namely $30°$ or $150°$.

Note: Even though your calculator cannot directly give you both solutions, it can be usefully used to check the answers. To do this enter $30°$ and press the sin button; similarly for $150°$.

If in the example above, the range had been $-360°$ to $360°$, how many solutions would there be?

Example

Solve $3\cos x = -0.6$ for $0° \le x \le 360°$, giving your answer to 1 d.p.

Solution

Rearranging the equation

$$\cos x = -\frac{0.6}{3} = -0.2.$$

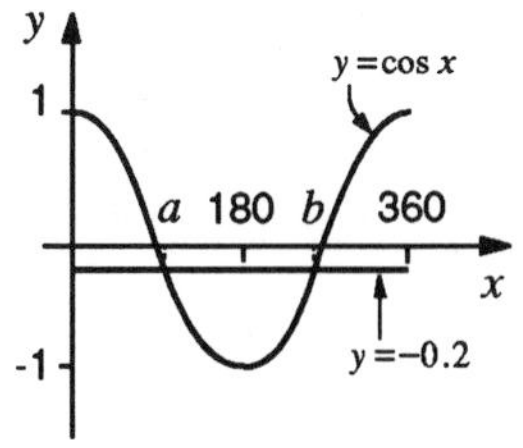

As before, you plot the functions

$$y = \cos x \text{ and } y = -0.2.$$

There are two solutions, a and b, with a between $90°$ and $180°$, and b between $180°$ and $270°$. Enter -0.2 into your calculator and use the 'inverse' cosine button - this will give you the answer

$$a = 101.5°.$$

From the graph the second solution b is given by

$$b - 180° = 180° - a \approx 78.5°$$

$$\Rightarrow \quad b = 258.5°.$$

and to 1 d.p. the solutions are $101.5°$ or $258.5°$.

(Remember to check the solutions on your calculator)

What would be the solutions to the previous problem if the range had been given as $-360° \le x \le 0°$?

Example

Solve the equation $\tan x = -2$ where x is measured in radians and $-2\pi \le x \le 2\pi$. Give your answers to 2 d.p. (Set your calculator to radian mode).

Solution

Note that x is given in radians rather than degrees here and remember that π radians $\equiv 180°$.

The graph of $y = \tan x$ and $y = -2$ are shown opposite.

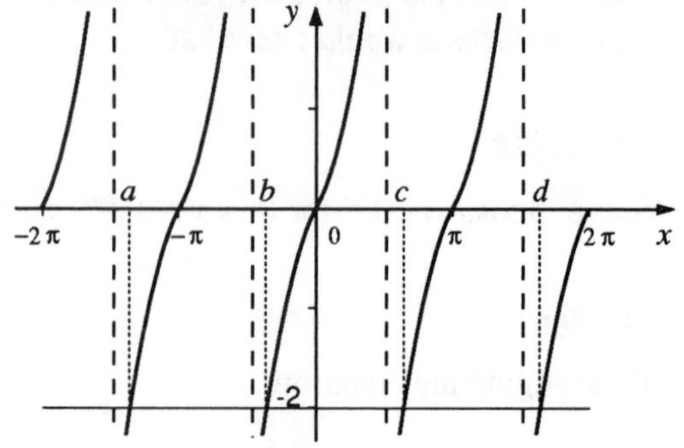

You can see that there are four solutions denoted by a, b, c, and d.

To find one of these solutions, enter -2 in your calculator and use the 'inverse tan' (or 'arctan')button. This should give -1.107 radians, so that $b = -1.107$. Since the function $\tan x$ has period π (or $180°$).

$$a = b - \pi = -4.249$$
$$c = b + \pi = 2.035$$
$$d = b + 2\pi = 5.177$$

To 2 d.p.'s, the solutions in radians are

$$-4.25, \quad -1.11, \quad 2.04 \text{ and } 5.18$$

Exercise 10D

Give all answers to 3 significant figures

1. Solve $\cos x = 0.5,\ 0° \le x \le 360°$
2. Solve $\tan x = 1, 0° \le x \le 360°$
3. Solve $\sin x = \frac{1}{4}, 0° \le x \le 180°$
4. Solve $\sin x = -0.5, 0° \le x \le 360°$
5. Solve $4\tan x = 1, 0° \le x \le 720°$
6. Solve $\sin x = -\frac{1}{3},\ -\pi \le x \le \pi$
7. Solve $3\cos x = 1 - \pi \le x \le \pi$
8. Which of these equations have no solutions?

   (a) $\sin x = 1,\ 0° \le x \le 360°$

   (b) $\cos x = -\frac{1}{4},\ 0° \le x \le 90°$

   (c) $\cos x = 2,\ 0° \le x \le 360°$

   (d) $\tan x = 2, 0° \le x \le 90°$

   (e) $4\sin x = -5,\ 0° \le x \le 360°$

10.5 Properties of trig functions

There are a number of important properties, which you have already been using. These are

	Degrees	Radians
1.	$\cos(x) = \sin(90° - x)$	$\cos(x) = \sin\left(\frac{\pi}{2} - x\right)$
2.	$\sin(x) = \cos(90° - x)$	$\sin(x) = \cos\left(\frac{\pi}{2} - x\right)$
3.	$\cos(180° - x) = -\cos(x)$	$\cos(\pi - x) = -\cos(x)$
4.	$\sin(180° - x) = +\sin(x)$	$\sin(\pi - x) = \sin(x)$
5.	$\tan x = \frac{\sin x}{\cos x}$	
6.	$\sin^2 x + \cos^2 x = 1$	

The last result is a very important one and is proved below for $0 < x < 90°$.

Theorem $\sin^2 x + \cos^2 x = 1$

Proof

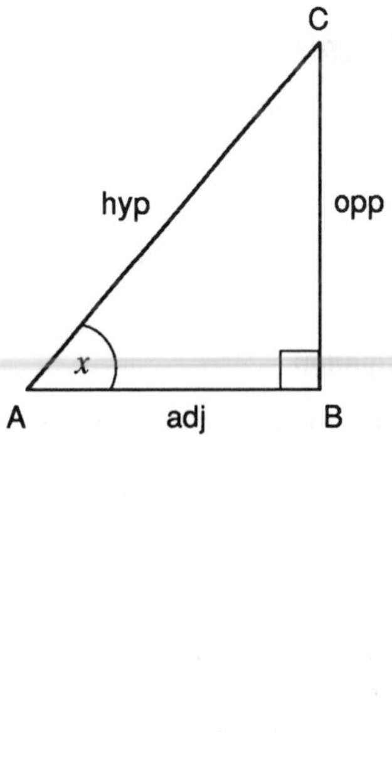

Using Pythagoras' Theorem,

$$BC^2 + AB^2 = AC^2.$$

Dividing by AC^2,

$$\left(\frac{BC}{AC}\right)^2 + \left(\frac{AB}{AC}\right)^2 = 1.$$

But $\sin x = \frac{\text{opp}}{\text{hyp}} = \frac{BC}{AC}$

$$\cos x = \frac{\text{adj}}{\text{hyp}} = \frac{AB}{AC}$$

giving $\sin^2 x + \cos^2 x = 1$.

Note $\sin^2 x$ is used for $(\sin x)^2$ so that there is no confusion between $(\sin x)^2$ and $\sin(x^2)$.

These properties can be used to solve more complex trig equations.

Example

Find all solutions between $0°$ and $360°$ of the equation

$$\sin x = 2\cos x \quad \text{to 2 d.p.}$$

Solution

Assuming $\cos x \neq 0$, you can divide both sides of the equation by $\cos x$ to give

$$\tan x = 2$$

(since $\frac{\sin x}{\cos x} = \tan x$).

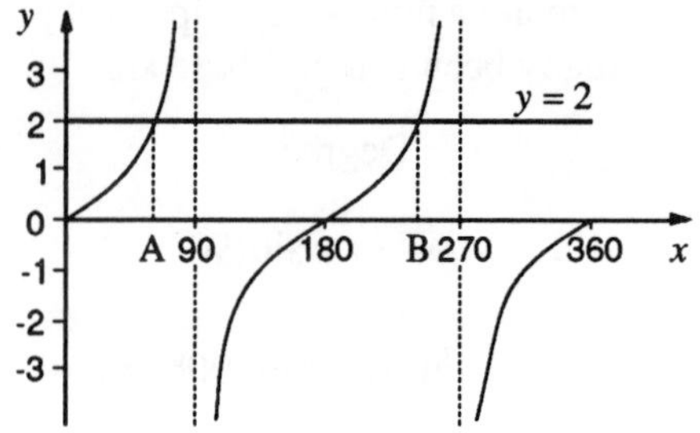

The graph of $y = \tan x$ and $y = 2$ is shown opposite. This shows that there are 2 solutions in the range $0°$ to $360°$.

Using a calculator, the inverse tangent of 2 is $63.4°$ (to 1d.p.). This is marked A on the graph. Since the tangent graph has a period of $180°$, B is given by

$$63.4° + 180° = 243.4°.$$

Note that at the start of the solution, $\cos x = 0$ was excluded.

When $\cos x = 0$, this gives $\sin x = 0$. These two equations are not both true for any value of x.

Example

Find all solutions between $0°$ and $360°$ of the equation

$$\cos x \sin x = 3\cos x$$

giving answers to 1 d.p.

Solution

The equation can be rewritten as

$$\cos x \sin x - 3\cos x = 0$$

or $$\cos x(\sin x - 3) = 0.$$

So either $\cos x = 0$ or $\sin x - 3 = 0 \Rightarrow \sin x = 3$.

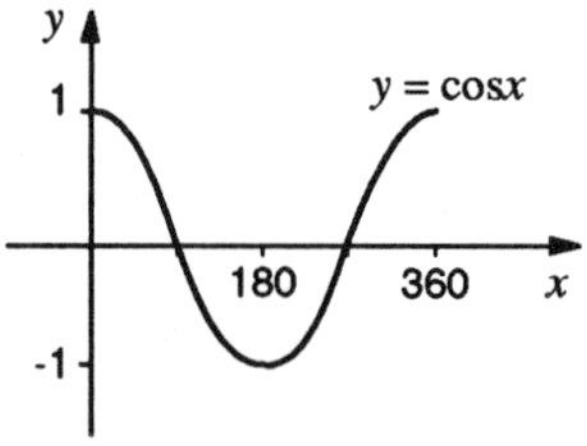

The graph of $y = \cos x$ is shown opposite for $0° \leq x \leq 360°$. The solutions are given by $\cos x = 0$, which gives

$$x = 90° \text{ or } 270°.$$

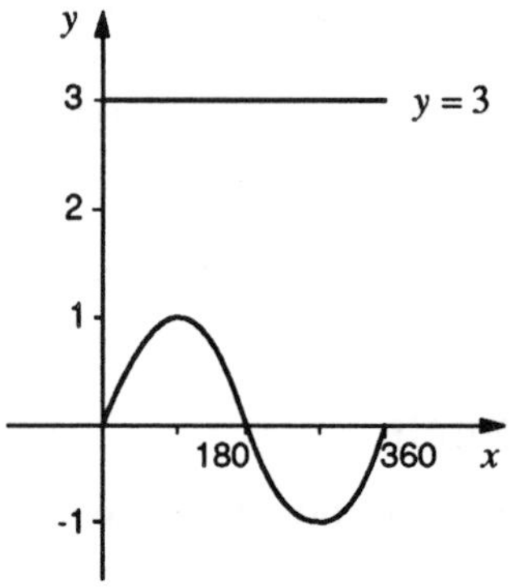

The other possibility is $\sin x = 3$. The graph of $y = \sin x$ and $y = 3$ are shown opposite. They do not intersect so there are no solutions.

The only solutions of the equation are therefore $x = 90°$ or $270°$.

The example above showed that algebraic techniques like factorising can be applied to equations involving trigonometric functions. The next example shows that **quadratics** in sines or cosines can also be solved.

Example

Find all solutions between $0°$ and $360°$ to the equation

$$3\cos x = 2\sin^2 x .$$

Solution

This equation contains a mixture of 'cos' and 'sin' terms, but using the identity

$$\cos^2 x + \sin^2 x = 1$$

will make it possible to express the equation in 'cos' terms only.

Now $\quad \sin^2 x = 1 - \cos^2 x$

so that the equation becomes

$$3\cos x = 2\left(1 - \cos^2 x\right)$$
$$= 2 - 2\cos^2 x$$

Hence $\quad 2\cos^2 x + 3\cos x - 2 = 0.$

(This is a quadratic equation in $\cos x$)

This can be factorised to give

$$(2\cos x - 1)(\cos x + 2) = 0$$

and either $\quad 2\cos x - 1 = 0$ or $\cos x + 2 = 0.$

The first equation gives

$$\cos x = \tfrac{1}{2}$$

and the graphs of $y = \cos x$ and $y = \tfrac{1}{2}$

are shown in the figure opposite.

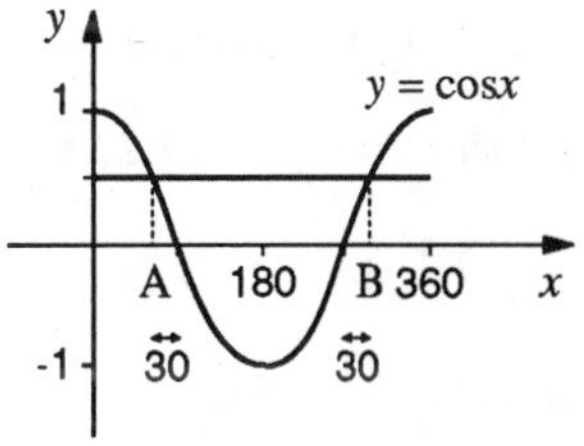

Using the inverse cosine function on a calculator gives $x = 60^0$, and this corresponds to A on the figure. Using symmetry about 180^0, gives B as

$$270° + 30° = 300° .$$

The second equation, $\cos x = -2$, has no solutions. The only possible solutions of the original equation are $60°$ and $300°$.

Exercise 10E

1. Find all the solutions to the equation $\sin x\cos x+\sin x=0$ for $0°\leq x\leq 360°$
2. Solve completely the equation $1-\sin x=2\cos^2 x$, $0°\leq x\leq 360°$. (Hint: there are three solutions).
3. Find all solutions between $0°$ and $360°$, to 1 d.p., of the equation $5-2\cos x=8\sin^2 x$.
4. Find all the solutions between 0 and 2π radians of the equation $\sin x=-\cos x$, leaving π in your answers.
5. Solve $3\sin x=\cos x$ for $0°\leq x\leq 360°$

10.6 Miscellaneous Exercises

1. Find in radians the angle subtended at the centre of a circle of circumference 36 cm by an arc of length 7.5 cm.
2. Find the length of the arc of a circle of radius 2 cm which subtends an angle of $\frac{\pi}{r}$ at the centre.
3. Find the radius of a circle if a chord of length 10 cm subtends an angle of 85° at the centre.
4. Change the following angles into radians.

   (a) 45° (b) 73.78° (c) 178.83°
5. Find the area of a sector of a circle of radius 2 cm which subtends an angle of $\frac{\pi}{4}$ at the centre.
6. Determine the angle in radians subtended by the sector of a circle of radius 5 cm such that the area of the sector is 10 cm^2.
7. Solve the following equations completely for the values of x shown, to 1 d.p.if necessary.

   (a) $\tan(x+90°)=1$, $0°\leq x\leq 360°$

   (b) $\cos 2x=\frac{1}{2}$, $0\leq x\leq 2\pi$

   (c) $3\cos\left(\frac{1}{2}x+45°\right)=-1$, $0°\leq x\leq 360°$

   (d) $\sin 3x=-\frac{1}{2}$, $0\leq x\leq 2\pi$
8. Solve these equations completely giving answers to 1 d.p. where necessary.

   (a) $\sin x=\cos x$, $0°\leq x\leq 360°$

   (b) $3\sin x+\cos x=0$, $0\leq x\leq 2\pi$

   (c) $3\sin^2 x-4\sin x+1=0$, $0°\leq x\leq 360°$

   (d) $2\sin^2 x+5\cos x+1=0$, $0°\leq x\leq 360°$
9. Solve these equations completely

   (a) $3\sin 2x=\cos 2x$, $0°\leq x\leq 180°$

   (b) $\cos^2 x-1=0$, $0°\leq x\leq 360°$

   (c) $\cos^2 3x+4\sin 3x=1$, $0°\leq x\leq 360°$

11 GROWTH AND DECAY

Objectives

After studying this chapter you should

- understand exponential functions;
- be able to construct growth and decay models;
- recognise graphs of exponential functions;
- understand that the inverse of an exponential function is a logarithmic function;
- be able to use logarithms to solve suitable equations;
- be able to differentiate exponential and logarithmic functions.

11.0 Introduction

Amoebae reproduce by dividing after a certain time. Radioactive substances have 'half lives' which are determined by the time it takes the radioactivity to halve. These are examples of systems which are modelled by 'exponential' functions.

The world's human population is growing at about 3% per year. That is after each year the population will be 3% more than it was at the start of the year. In the first activity, you will form a model to describe this population growth, and then use it to find the year when the population will be twice the size it was in 1989.

The population at the end of 1989 was approximately 4.5 billion (4,500,000,000). If the population grew by 3% in 1990, at the end of the year it would be 4.5 billion $\times 1.03 = 4.635$ billion.

The population at the end of 1991 can be found by the calculation

$$4.5 \times 1.03 \times 1.03 = 4.5 \times 1.03^2.$$

By the end of 1992, the population would be $4.5 \times (1.03)^3$.

Activity 1 Modelling population

For the model described above, calculate the population at the end of each year, starting at 1989, and continuing until the population has doubled from its value at 1989. Plot the values on a graph.

The model used in this activity can be represented by the equation

$$P = P_o a^x \qquad (1)$$

when P is the population at the end of the year number x, and P_o is the initial population at year $x = 0$ and a is a constant. So for the world population described above

$$P = 4.5 \times 1.03^x \quad x = 1, 2, 3, \ldots$$

Equations of the form (1) can also be used to describe populations that are declining.

Some species are endangered because they have declining populations, for various reasons like hunting, habitat destruction, new predators or infertility. Many marine species such as whales and some fish give cause for concern. Models are made to help predict future trends in fish stock levels, which take into account many features like fishing techniques and environmental conditions.

In the next activity, you will produce a model of a fish population based on the assumption that it is declining by 15% each year. You then use it to find the number of years before the population becomes so low that it is in danger of being unable to sustain itself.

Activity 2 Endangered species

Assume that a particular fishery has a population of 100,000 fish and that current fishing methods cause this population to decline by 15% in a year.

(a) Copy and complete the table opposite, and use it to help you form a model of the population p in terms of the years elapsed, x, for $x = 1, 2, \ldots, 10$.

(b) Plot and draw the graph of the fish population for the first 10 years.

(c) If the population falls below say 25 000, the fish become quite widely separated. In these conditions it becomes difficult to find good catches, and the fish themselves breed at a much reduced rate. Therefore, using 25 000 as an 'action level' use your model to find the number of years before which the population becomes dangerously low.

Years elapsed	Population
0	100 000
1	100 000 x 0.85 = 85 000
2	...
3	...
4	...
...	...

11.1 Models of growth and decay

The two activities show how mathematics can be used to model growth and decay of populations. Another example is bacteria, which divides in two every minute. The growth in numbers is illustrated in the following table.

Minutes past introduction of bacteria	Number of bacteria
0	$1\ (=2^0)$
1	$2\ (=2^1)$
2	$2\times2=2^2=4$
3	$2\times2\times2=2^3=8$
4	$2\times2\times2\times2=2^4=16$
...	...
t	2^t

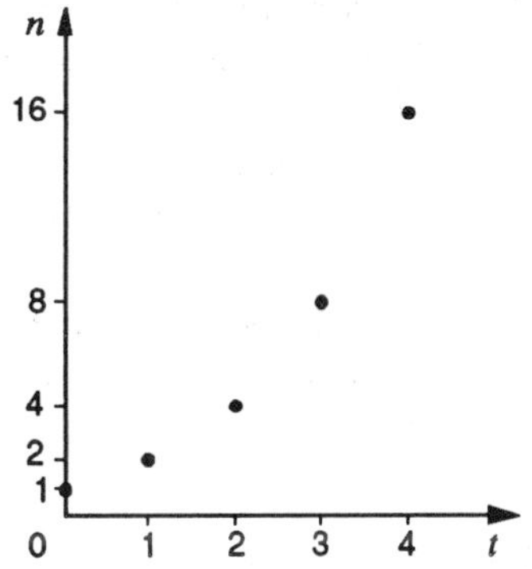

The table shows a 'pattern ' for the number of bacteria at any time after the bacteria was introduced. From this pattern, it is easy to see that after t minutes the number of bacteria will be 2^t.

Therefore, $n=2^t$ is a model for the bacteria growth. The graph for this function is shown here, for values of t between 0 and 4.

Drawing a smooth curve through these discrete points gives a continuous model of growth, although in this example, it only makes sense to use whole numbers for t. However, many situations which have models like this have continuous not discrete domains, so the curve is typical of this type of function.

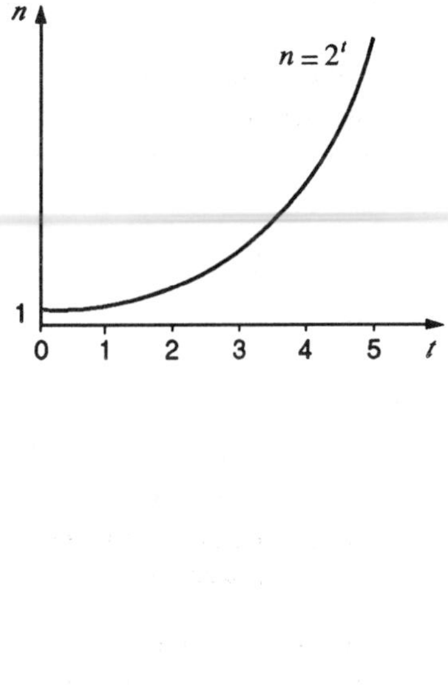

Any function of the form a^x, where a is a positive constant is called an **exponential** function (as x is the 'exponent' or power of a). Although the example above (and the examples developed in Activities 1 and 2) was only defined for positive values of the exponent ($t \geq 0$), exponential functions are defined for any real value.

For instance, if $f(x)=3^x$, then $f(-1)=3^{-1}=\frac{1}{3}$; using the rules for indices, covered in Chapter 9.

Activity 3

(a) Use a graphic calculator or computer to help you make sketches of these functions, using the same pair of axes. Use a range of the values between -3 and $+3$, and -30 to $+30$ on the y-axis.

(i) $y=3^x$ (ii) $y=2^x$ (iii) $y=1.5^x$

(iv) $y=1^x$ (v) $y=(0.5)^x$

Do the curves have a common point? What is the relationship between $y = 2^x$ and $y = (0.5)^x$? What happens as x becomes large and positive or large and negative?

(b) Similarly illustrate the graphs of

(i) $y = 3^{-x}$ (ii) $y = 2^{-x}$ (iii) $y = 1.5^{-x}$

and compare them with $y = 3^x, 2^x, 1.5^x$, and describe their behaviour for large x, positive or negative.

Another example of the use of the exponential function is in the modelling of Radon 219, which is an 'isotope' of the gaseous element Radon. It occurs naturally in some types of rock and its seepage from beneath buildings has been identified as a major concern in some parts of the country. Radon 219 is radioactive, with a half life of about 4 seconds. This means that if there are 1000 atoms of Radon 219 in a sample of the gas, 4 seconds later there will be half this number left, 500. 4 more seconds later, and the number of Radon 219 atoms will halve again, to 250, and so on.

This decaying system can be modelled with an exponential function, with a negative exponent.

Time in seconds after sample is collected (seconds)	Number of atoms left
0	1000
4	$1000 \times (\frac{1}{2})^1$
8	$1000 \times (\frac{1}{2})^2$
12	$1000 \times (\frac{1}{2})^3$

Can you write down a formula for N, the number of atoms left after time t seconds?

Since every 4 seconds increases the **power** of the exponent by 1, you can write the model equation as

$$N(t) = 1000 \times (\tfrac{1}{2})^{\frac{1}{4}t}.$$

Note that this can also be written as

$$N(t) = 1000 \times (2^{-1})^{\frac{1}{4}t}$$

$$= 1000 \times 2^{-\frac{1}{4}t},$$

using the properties of indices.

Activity 4 U.K. population

The government's statistical service made several predictions about the United Kingdom's population in 1989. One of these was that the population would grow by 1% every ten years. If the population in 1990 was 55 millions, form a model for the U.K.'s future population. Use it to draw a graph of the projected population, and from this estimate the year when the population will equal 60 million.

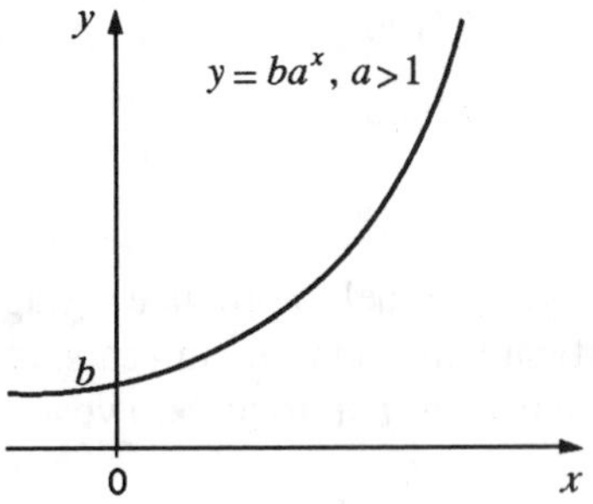

The model used in the activity above is

$$P(t) = P_0 a^{\frac{1}{10}t}$$

when $P_0 = 55$(million) and $a = 1.01$. So far you have used exponential functions to model various populations and radioactive decay. This last application can be used to help date archaeological objects through Carbon dating.

This section is completed with a summary of the general properties of the exponential functions

$$y = ba^x \text{ and } y = ba^{-x}$$

for $a>1$. As is shown opposite, both curves pass through $(0, b)$ and the range of both functions is all real numbers greater than zero. a is the **base** and x the **exponent** of the function.

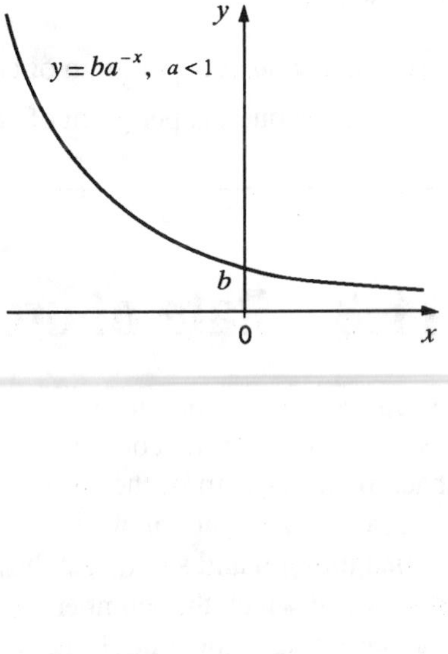

11.2 Carbon dating

Carbon 14 (^{14}C) is an isotope of carbon with a half life of 5730 years. It exists in the carbon dioxide in the atmosphere, and all living things absorb some Carbon 14 as they breathe. This remains in an animal or plant, and is constantly added to until the organism dies. After this time, the Carbon 14 decays, reducing to half the amount stored in the body after 5730 years. The amount halves again after another 5730 years, and so on, with no new Carbon 14 absorbed.

In 1946 an American scientist, *Williard Libby*, developed a way of 'dating' archaeological objects by measuring the Carbon 14 radiation present in them. This radioactivity is compared with that found in things living now.

For instance, if bones of recently dead animals produce 10 becquerels per gram of bone carbon (a becquerel is the unit of radioactivity), and an old bone produces only 5 becquerels, the radioactivity has halved since the animal which had the old bone died. As the half life of Carbon 14 is 5730 years, this would mean the animal died in 3740 BC approximately.

Activity 5 Carbon 14

Complete the table below

Age (in years)	Radiation (becs)
0	10
5730	$10\times\frac{1}{2}=10\times2^{-1}$
11460	$10\times(\frac{1}{2})^2=10\times2^{-2}$
17190	...
22920	...
...	...

Use your model to produce a graph, showing radioactivity on the vertical axis and time, in years, on the horizontal. Draw the graph for values of t up to 50,000 years.

From your graph, estimate the ages of bones with these radioactivities

(a) 8.5 becquerels per gram of carbon;

(b) 1.2 becquerels per gram of carbon.

11.3 Rate of growth

Suppose a colony of bacteria doubles in number every minute as every member of the colony divides in two. So if there are 2 bacteria at the start of the colony, there will be 4 a minute later (an increase of 2 in one minute), 8 two minutes later (an increase of 4 in one minute) and so on. As the number of bacteria increases, so the **rate** at which that number increases goes up. So the rate of increase of an exponential function is closely related to the value of the function at any point. This suggests that exponential functions and their derivatives are closely linked.

The next activity will explore these links.

Activity 6

Plot and draw the curves below for values of x between -2 and $+2$ and on separate axes.

(a) $y=2^x$ (b) $y=3^x$ (c) $y=2.5^x$ (d) $y=2.9^x$

Using a ruler to draw tangents to each of your curves, calculate the gradient of each one at five different points. The figure opposite illustrates the method.

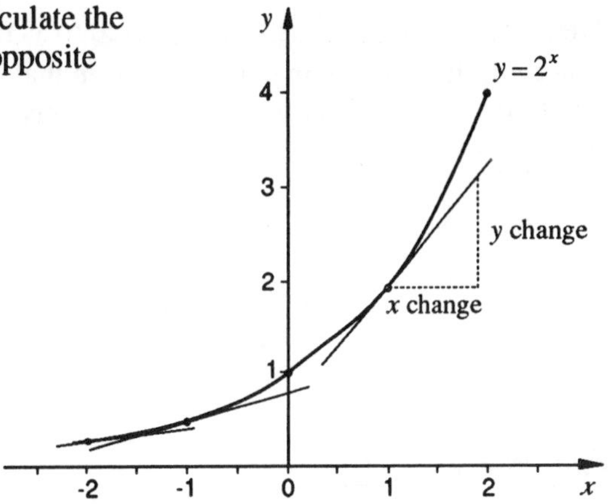

Note that

$$\text{gradient} = \frac{\text{change in } y}{\text{change in } x}.$$

In this case all gradients are positive since a positive change in x results in a positive change in y.

Plot the five values for the gradient of your graph and sketch in the gradient curve. Comment on how the original graph and the gradient curve seem to be related.

If you have access to a computer or calculator that is capable of showing the derivative of a function, then you can find an exponential function whose derivative exactly fits over its own graph by considering $y = a^x$ with a in the range $2.5 < a < 2.9$.

The derivative of 2^x is always less than the value of the function itself. So is the derivative of 2.5^x, although it is a closer fit to the function than that of 2^x.

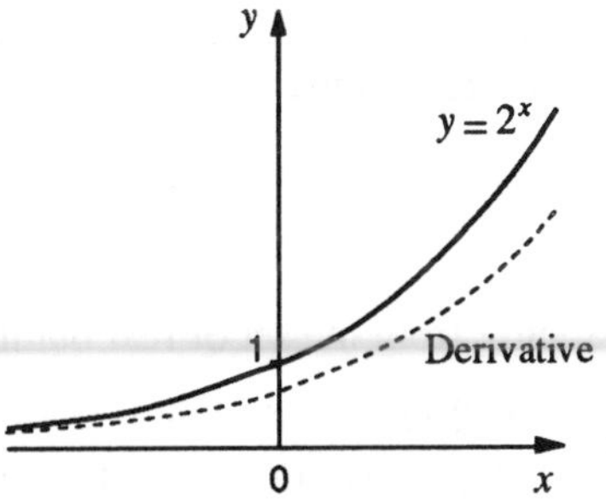

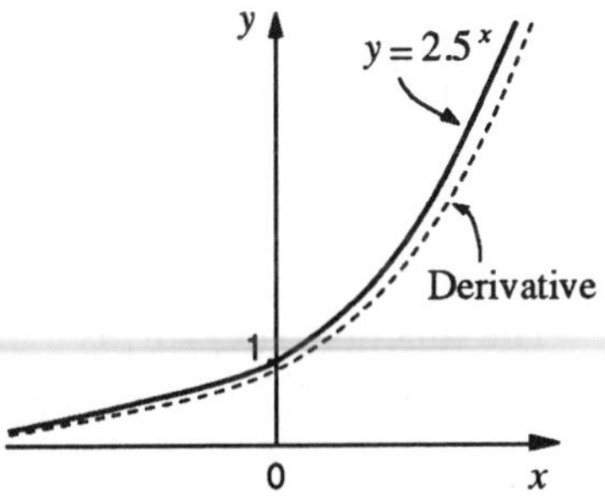

The derivative of 3^x has a greater value than the function. This suggests that there is an exponential function, with a base between 2.5 and 3, which has its derivative the same as itself.

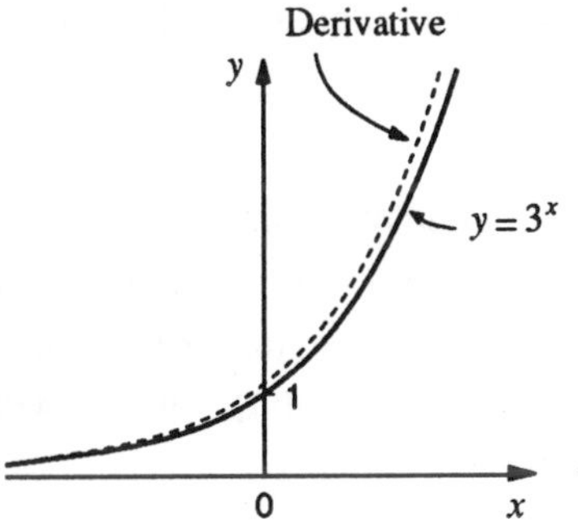

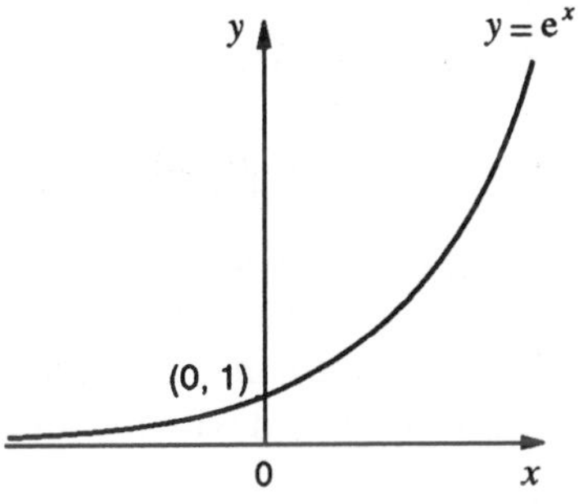

Such a function would therefore be its own derivative. The base required for this to happen is denoted by the letter 'e'.

Unfortunately, its value cannot be given exactly - like π and $\sqrt{2}$ it is irrational, and so it can't be expressed exactly as a fraction or decimal. To five decimal places, it is 2.71828.

The function $f(x)=e^x$ is often referred to as the **exponential function.** It is unique in mathematics, in that it is its own derivative. This property makes it extremely important in many branches of the subject.

To summarise

$$y=e^x \Rightarrow \frac{dy}{dx}=e^x$$

Activity 7

(a) Use a graphic calculator or computer to make sketches of these graphs.

(i) $y=e^x$ (ii) $y=e^{(x+1)}$ (iii) $y=e^{(x-2)}$

(iv) $y=e^x+1$ (v) $y=e^{-x}$.

(Note that your calculator or computer may use the expression $y=\exp(x)$ for $y=e^x$.)

(b) Compare each of your sketches with the graph $y=e^x$, and state the relationship between each graph and that of $y=e^x$.

(c) Use the fact that the derivative of e^x is e^x, to work out the derivatives of each of the other functions.

The function $f(x)=e^x$ is a mapping from the set of real numbers, $\mathbb{R}$, to the positive real numbers. Its graph shows that it is a one to one function. This means that $f(x)=e^x$ has an inverse function. The graph of this inverse function is a reflection in the line $y=x$ of the graph of $y=e^x$.

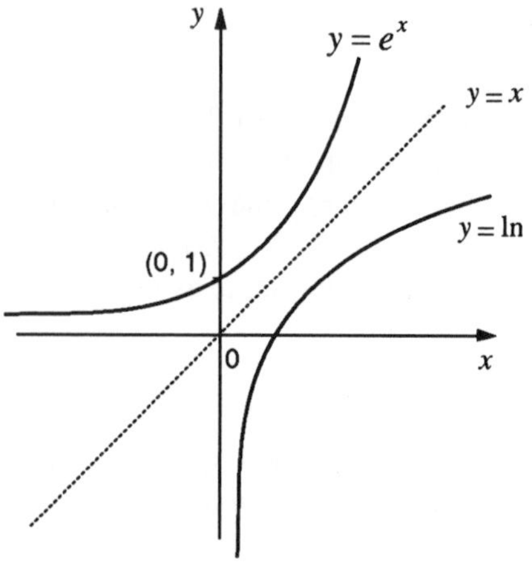

The graph opposite shows e^x and its inverse function, which is usually written as $\ln(x)$. This function is read as 'the natural (or Naperian) logarithm of x' or 'the logarithm to base e of x'. (*Napier* was a Scottish mathematician of the 16th century who pioneered work connected with this function).

Why is the domain of $\ln(x)$ only the set of positive real numbers?

The figure shows that $\ln(x)$ is **not** defined for negative values of x (or zero), as there is no graph to the left of the y axis for $\ln(x)$. So $\ln(-2)$, for instance, does not exist. The range of $\ln(x)$, however, is the full set of real numbers.

Example

Find x if $e^x = 100$. Give your answer to two d.p.

Solution

Since $e^x = 100$, and $y = \ln x$ is the inverse function of e^x,

$$x = \ln 100$$

Using a calculator to find ln (100), gives $x = 4.61$ to 2 d.p.

To summarise, for $a > 0$,

$$\boxed{e^x = a \Rightarrow x = \ln a}$$

Note that the brackets round 'a' in $\ln a$ have been omitted and will be in future except where it might cause confusion.

Example

Solve, to 3 s.f. the equation $3e^{2x-1} = 5$.

Solution

Since $3e^{2x-1} = 5$, then

$$e^{2x-1} = \tfrac{5}{3}$$

Since e^x and $\ln x$ are inverse functions,

$$2x - 1 = \ln\tfrac{5}{3}$$

$$\Rightarrow \quad 2x = 1 + \ln\tfrac{5}{3}$$

$$\Rightarrow \quad x = \tfrac{1}{2}(1 + \ln\tfrac{5}{3}) = 0.755 \text{ to } 3 \text{ s.f.}$$

Exercise 11A

1. Solve $e^x = 5$ to 2 d.p.
2. Solve $e^x = \frac{1}{2}$ to 2 d.p.
3. Solve $4e^x = 3$ to 3 s.f.
4. Solve $e^{2x} = 1$ to 2 d.p.
5. Solve $3e^{\frac{1}{2}x} = 4$ to 3 s.f.
6. Solve $e^{-x} = 1.5$ to 2 d.p.
7. Solve $4e^{3x-2} = 16$ to 1 d.p.
8. Solve $7e^{3-x} = 2$ to 3 s.f.
9. Solve $e^x \times e^x = 3$ to 2 d.p.
10. Solve $e^{2x} = 4e^x$ to 3 s.f.

11.4 Solving exponential equations

Earlier in this chapter, you have produced exponential functions as models, and then used graphs to estimate the solution to a problem. The logarithmic function allows you to calculate rather than estimate these solutions as is shown in the example below.

Example

A bacteria colony doubles in number every minute, from a starting population of one. The population model is $P = 2^m$, where P is the population and m the number of minutes since the colony was started. Find the time when the population first equals 1000.

Solution

The problem requires a solution to the equation

$$P = 1000$$

or $$2^m = 1000$$

Taking log of each side of the equation

$$\ln 2^m = \ln 1000 \qquad (1)$$

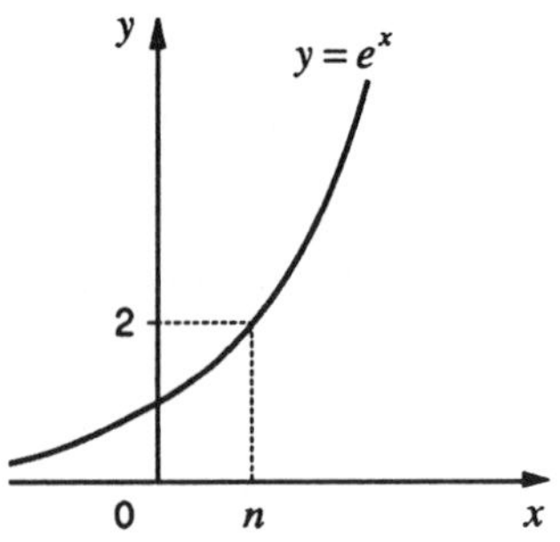

Now, 2 is a positive real number, so there is some number, call it n, such that $e^n = 2$ (see figure opposite). Then $n = \ln(2) \approx 0.693$.

So $2^m = (e^n)^m$ replacing 2 by e^n and since $(e^n)^m = e^{nm}$, using the properties of indices, 2^m in (1) above can be replaced by e^{nm}, where $n = \ln(2)$.

This gives

$$\ln e^{nm} = \ln 1000$$

But $\ln x$ is the inverse of e^x, so $\ln e^{nm} = nm$. Hence

$$mn = \ln 1000$$

Therefore $m = \dfrac{\ln 1000}{n} = \dfrac{\ln 1000}{\ln 2} = 9.97$ minutes.

Hence $m = 9$ minutes, 58 seconds to the nearest second.

The example illustrates how a general method for solving exponential equations works. This process can be made quicker by using the results developed below.

Consider the function a^x, where $a > 0$.

As a is a number greater than zero, there is a real number, n, such that $e^n = a$ (see figure opposite). This means that $n = \ln a$, since $\ln x$ is the inverse function for the exponential function e^x.

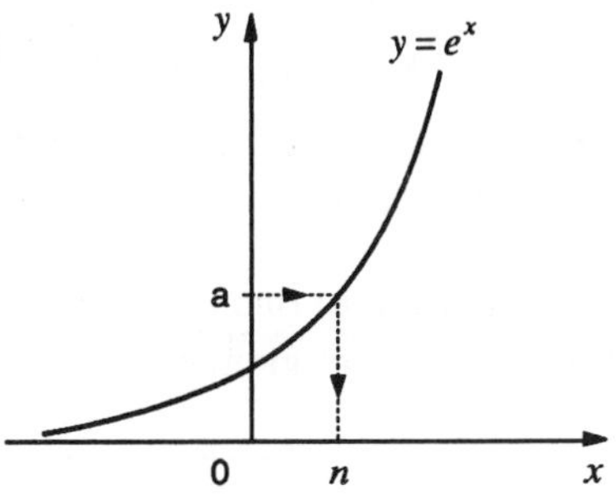

So $a^x = (e^n)^x$ replacing a by e^n

That is, $a^x = e^{xn}$ using laws of indices, and taking logarithms of both sides gives the equation

$$\ln a^x = \ln e^{xn} = xn$$

But $n = \ln a$, so

$$\boxed{\ln a^x = x \ln a}$$

This result is a great help in solving a wide variety of exponential equations.

Example

Solve $3^{2x-1} = 5^x$, giving your answer to 2 d.p.

Solution

Since $\quad 3^{2x-1} = 5^x$

$\Rightarrow \quad \ln(3^{2x-1}) = \ln 5^x$

$\Rightarrow \quad (2x-1)\ln 3 = x \ln 5$

$\Rightarrow \quad 2x \ln 3 - \ln 3 = x \ln 5$

$\Rightarrow \quad 2x \ln 3 - x \ln 5 - \ln 3 = 0$

$\Rightarrow \quad 2x \ln 3 - x \ln 5 = \ln 3$

$\Rightarrow \quad x(2\ln 3 - \ln 5) = \ln 3$

$\Rightarrow \quad x = \dfrac{\ln 3}{2\ln 3 - \ln 5} = 1.87$ to 2 d.p.

Activity 8

A sample of wood has ^{14}C radioactivity of 6 becquerels per gram. New wood has ^{14}C radioactivity of 6.68 becquerels per gram of Carbon 14. The half life of ^{14}C is 5730 years; form a model based on the work in Section 11.2 for the ^{14}C radiation in wood, of the form $R = ba^t$, where R is the radioactivity, b and a are constants, and t is the time in years since the sample was formed.

Use your equation to find to the nearest year when $R = 6$ becquerels per gram of carbon.

Activity 9

In Activity 4, you used a model for the UK population of the form

$$P = 55 \times 1.01^{\frac{1}{10}t}.$$

P is the population in millions, and t the number of years since 1990. You were asked to estimate the year when the population would first equal 60 million. Solve this problem again by substituting $P = 60$ in the equation, and solving for t.

Exercise 11B

1. Solve $2^x = 5$ to 2 d.p.
2. Solve $3^{\frac{1}{2}x} = 1$ to 2 d.p.
3. Solve $4 \times 2^x = 3$ to 3 s.f.
4. Solve $3^x = 5$ to 2 d.p.
5. Solve $2^{-x} = 6$ to 3 s.f.
6. Solve $3^{2x} = 4$ to 2 d.p.
7. Solve $5^{x-1} = 3$ to 3 s.f.
8. Solve $2^{2x+1} = 4$ to 2 d.p.
9. Solve $5^{x-1} = e^{2x}$ to 1 d.p.
10. Solve $6^{2x+1} = 3^{-x}$ to 2 d.p.

11.5 Properties of logarithms

As well as obeying the rule

$$\ln(a^x) = x \ln a,$$

logarithms also obey, for any real numbers a, b,

$$\ln(ab) = \ln a + \ln b \qquad (1)$$

and

$$\ln\left(\frac{a}{b}\right) = \ln a - \ln b \qquad (2)$$

To prove the first result, (1), note that a and b can be written in the form

$$a = e^m, b = e^n$$

for some real numbers m and n. Then

$$\ln(ab) = \ln(e^m e^n)$$
$$= \ln(e^{m+n})$$
$$= m + n$$

Since $\ln x$ is the inverse function of e^x,

$$\ln a = \ln(e^m) = m$$
$$\ln b = \ln(e^n) = n$$

so that

$$\ln(ab) = \ln a + \ln b$$

How can you deduce equation (2) from (1)?

You will see how useful these results are in the following applications.

Before the theory of gravitation was developed by *Sir Isaac Newton*, the best laws available to describe planetary motion were those formulated by *Johann Kepler*, a German astronomer. His laws were based on his own meticulous observations, and were used later as a 'benchmark test' for Newton's own theory. This activity investigates Kepler's third law.

Activity 10 Kepler's third law

This table shows how the average radius of a planet's orbit around the Sun, R, is related to the period of that orbit in years, T. (The orbits are elliptical, not circular, so an average radius is used here). Only the planets known to Kepler are included.

Planet	Radius, R (millions of km)	Period, T (years)
Mercury	57.9	0.24
Venus	108.2	0.62
Earth	149.6	1
Mars	227.9	1.88
Jupiter	778.3	11.86
Saturn	1427.0	29.46

You may assume that T and R are linked by a relationship of the form $T = aR^b$ where a and b are constants to be found.

To fit the model $T = aR^b$ to the data means trying out different values of a and b until you have a good fit with the curve drawn through the data points.

The properties of logarithms will provide us with a better method for finding suitable values of the constants a and b.

Assume a power law of the form

$$T = aR^b.$$

Taking logs of each side gives

$$\ln T = \ln(aR^b)$$

$$= \ln a + \ln\left(R^b\right) \quad \text{(using equation (1))}$$

$$= \ln a + b \ln R$$

This equation resembles a straight line equation $y = mx + c$ with y replaced by $\ln T$ and x by $\ln R$. So a graph of $\ln T$ against $\ln R$ should give a straight line and the constants a and b can be estimated from the graph. The constant b will be the **gradient** of the line, and $\ln a$ will be the **intercept** on the vertical axis.

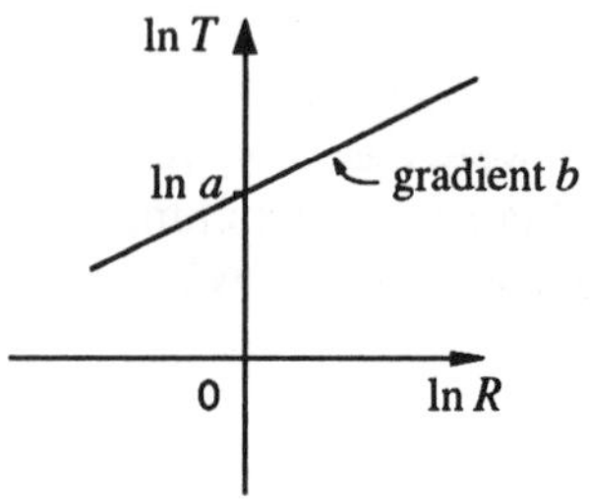

Activity 11

For the data in Activity 10, plot a graph of $\ln T$ against $\ln R$, and use it to estimate the values of the constants a and b.

The note produced by a musical instrument is directly related to its frequency (the number of times the air is caused to vibrate every second). The higher the frequency, the higher the note. In order to set the frets on a guitar in the correct place, the maker must know how the length of a string affects the frequency of the note it produces.

Activity 12 Guitar maker's problem

This relationship between length, l (cm), and frequency, f (hz), can be found experimentally. The table shows some data collected by experiment for a particular type of string.

Length l (cm)	50	60	70	80	90	100
Frequency f (hz)	410	330	275	255	225	195

The relationship is assumed to be of the form $f = al^b$ where a and b are constant.

Use logarithms to 'linearise' the relationship, as described previously. Plot $\ln f$ on a vertical axis and $\ln l$ on the horizontal, and draw a line of best fit. Find the gradient and intercept with the vertical axis of this line, and so determine the values of a and b.

The frequencies produced are also affected by the tension in the string and so, even with frets correctly placed, the guitarist must still 'tune' the instrument by changing the tensions in the strings.

'Middle C' has a frequency of 264 Hz.

What length of string gives this frequency?

The last application in this section is based on the method used by forensic scientists to estimate the time of death of a body.

When a person dies, the body's temperature begins to cool. The temperature of the body at any time after death is governed by Newton's Law of Cooling, which applies to any cooling object:

$$D = ae^{-kt}$$

D is the temperature difference between the cooling object and its surrounding, a and k are constants, and t is the time since the object started to cool. The values of a and k depend on the size, shape and composition of the object and the initial temperature difference.

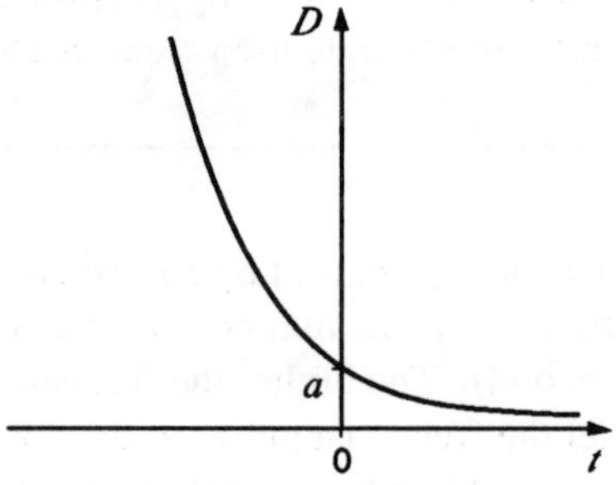

If D is plotted against the time, t, the graph will be similar to the curve shown opposite.

To find out the equation of the curve which applies to a dead body, the values of a and k must be found. This will require two readings of its temperature.

Example

The police arrive at the scene of a murder at 8 a.m.

On arrival, the temperature of the body and its surroundings are measured at 34°C and 17°C respectively. This was taken to be the moment when the time, t, was equal to zero.

At 9 a.m. when $t = 1$, the body temperature was measured as 33°C and the room temperature still as 17°C.

Estimate the time of death.

Solution

The two sets of data are

$$D = 34 - 17 = 17 \text{ at } t = 0$$

$$D = 33 - 17 = 16 \text{ at } t = 1$$

Substituting in the governing equation

$$D = ae^{-kt}$$

gives

$$17 = ae^{-k.0} = ae^{0} = a$$

(since $e^0 = 1$); and

$$16 = ae^{-k.1} = ae^{-k} = 17e^{-k}.$$

Therefore

$$e^{-k} = \frac{16}{17}$$

and taking 'logs',

$$-k = \ln\left(\frac{16}{17}\right) = -0.0606 \Rightarrow k = 0.0606.$$

Hence

$$D = 17e^{-0.0606t}. \qquad (3)$$

Now normal body temperature is given by 36.9°C, so the corresponding value of D is given by

$$D = 36.9 - 17 = 19.9.$$

Substituting this value of D into equation (3) and solving for t will give you the estimated time of death; this gives

$$19.9 = 17e^{-0.0606t}$$

$$\Rightarrow \quad e^{-0.0606t} = \frac{19.9}{17}$$

$$\Rightarrow \quad -0.0606t = \ln\left(\frac{19.9}{17}\right)$$

$$\Rightarrow \quad t = -\frac{1}{0.0606}\ln\left(\frac{19.9}{17}\right)$$

$$= -2.599 \text{ hours}$$

$$\approx -(2 \text{ hours } 36 \text{ minutes}).$$

So the estimated time of death is estimated at 5.24 am, or about 5.30 am.

What important assumptions have been made in this model? Are they reasonable?

Activity 13

A body is found at 11.30 pm. The body temperature at midnight is found to be 33°C and at 2.00 am it is 31.5°C. Assuming the surroundings are at a constant temperature of 30°C, estimate the time of death.

11.6 Other bases

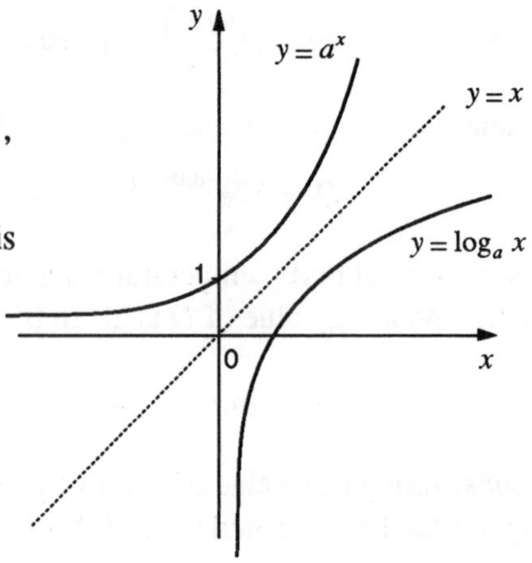

Many applications of exponential functions do not use the base e. Scientists often use a base of 10 for instance. The graph of $y = a^x$, for $a > 1$, shows that the function of a^x is one to one. This means that it has an inverse function, which is denoted $y = \log_a x$. This is read as "logarithm (or log) to base a of x". The figure opposite also shows the graph $y = \log_a x$. The graph also shows that the range of a^x is the positive real numbers, as is the domain of $y = \log_a x$.

Provided logarithms use a suitable base, they obey the same laws developed in earlier sections. That is;

$$\log_a p^n = n \log_a p$$

$$\log_a pq = \log_a p + \log_a q \quad \text{(for any two numbers } p \text{ and } q\text{)}$$

$$\log_a \left(\frac{p}{q}\right) = \log_a p - \log_a q.$$

To summarise;

$$\boxed{\text{if } y = a^x, \text{ then } x = \log_a y}$$

Activity 14

Without using a calculator, answer these questions:

(a) For any base a, $a^0 = 1$. Write down $\log_a 1$.

(b) $a^1 = a$. Write down $\log_a(a)$ for any base a.

Also write down $\log_a\left(a^2\right)$, $\log_a\left(\sqrt{a}\right)$.

(c) $1000 = 10^3$. Write down $\log_{10}(1000)$.

Similarly, find $\log_{10}(100)$, $\log_{10}\left(\frac{1}{10}\right)$ and $\log_{10}(0.01)$.

(d) What is $\log_2(8)$? (Remember $2^3 = 8$.)

Exercise 11C

Without using a calculator, answer these questions

1. $\ln e^2$
2. $\log_{10} 10000$
3. $\log_3 27$
4. $\log_2\left(\frac{1}{16}\right)$
5. $\ln\left(\frac{1}{\sqrt{e}}\right)$
6. $\log_{10}\sqrt{10}$
7. $\log_5 125$
8. $\log_{49} 7$

11.7 Derivative of ln x

You have already seen that if

$$y = e^x \Rightarrow \frac{dy}{dx} = e^x.$$

Now if $y = \ln x$, and $x > 0$

$$x = e^y$$

so that

$$\frac{dx}{dy} = e^y.$$

If δy and δx are corresponding small changes in y and x, then

$$\frac{dy}{dx} = \lim_{\delta x \to 0}\left(\frac{\delta y}{\delta x}\right),$$

but $$\frac{dx}{dy} = \lim_{\delta y \to 0}\left(\frac{\delta x}{\delta y}\right).$$

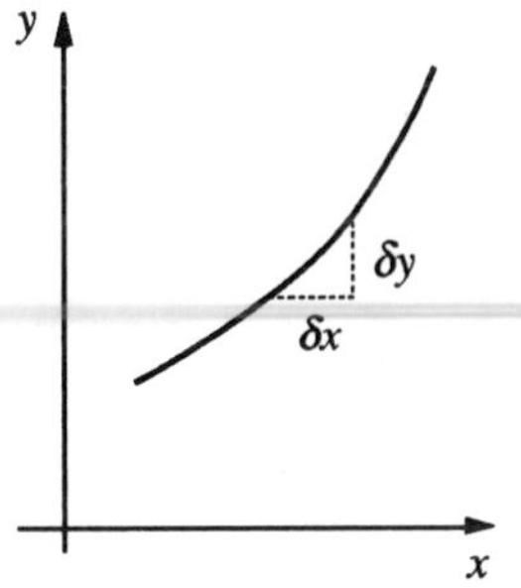

Hence $$\frac{dy}{dx} = 1\bigg/\frac{dx}{dy}$$

so that, when $y = \ln x$,

$$\frac{dy}{dx} = \frac{1}{e^y} = \frac{1}{x}\ (x > 0).$$

So you have the important result that for $x > 0$

$$\boxed{\frac{d}{dx}(\ln x) = \frac{1}{x}}$$

The function $y = \ln x$ and its derivative are illustrated in the figure opposite. Notice that the graph has only been drawn for values of x greater than zero. This is because $\ln x$ is not defined for negative values of x, so it does not have a derivative when x is less than zero.

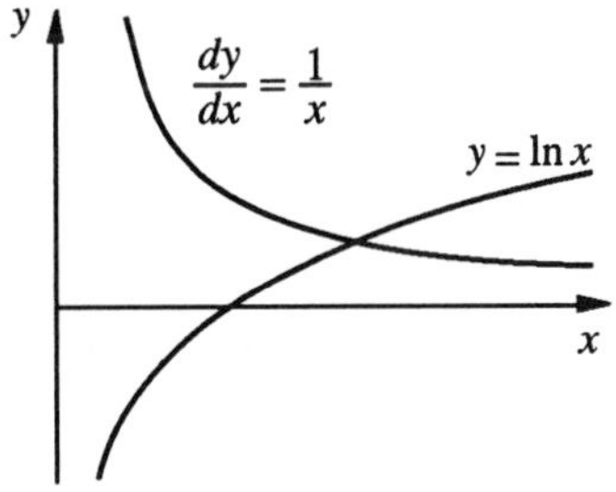

Activity 15

Plot the graphs of the following functions using a calculator or a computer. Now that you know the derivative of $\ln(x)$ is $\frac{1}{x}$, try to write down the derivatives of each of these functions, by comparing the curves of each one to $y = \ln(x)$.

(a) $\ln(x+1)$
(b) $\ln(x+2)$
(c) $\ln(x-3)$
(d) $\ln(x)-1$
(e) $-\ln(x)$

If you have a graph plotting package which is capable of displaying the derivatives of each function, you can check your answers.

11.8 Miscellaneous Exercises

1. Solve these equations to three significant figures where appropriate:

   (a) $e^x = 4$ (b) $e^{3x} = 0.1$

   (c) $e^{2x-1} = 5$ (d) $3^x = 1$

   (e) $10^x = 5$ (f) $4^x = 5^{2x+1}$

   (g) $3x^2 = 1$ (h) $4 \times 7^{2x} = 6$

   (i) $e \times 2^{x-1} = 5^{1-x}$ (j) $10^x = 1000$

   (k) $5^x = 25$ (l) $2^x = \frac{1}{8}$.

2. A physicist conducts an experiment to discover the half life of an element. The radioactivity at one moment from a sample of the element is measured as 30 becquerels. One hour later the radioactivity is just 28 becquerels. Assuming that the radioactivity is governed by a formula of the form

   $$R = a \times 2^{-kt}$$

   where R is the radioactivity in becquerels per gram, t the time in hours, and a and k are constants, find the values of a and k, and hence determine the half life in hours.

12 INTEGRATION

Objectives

After studying this chapter you should

- understand the concept of integration;
- appreciate why finding the area under a graph is often important;
- be able to calculate the area under a variety of graphs given their equation.

12.0 Introduction

Integration is the process of finding the area under a graph. An example of an area that integration can be used to calculate is the shaded one shown in the diagram. There are several ways of **estimating** the area - this chapter includes a brief look at such methods - but the main objective is to discover a way to find the area **exactly**.

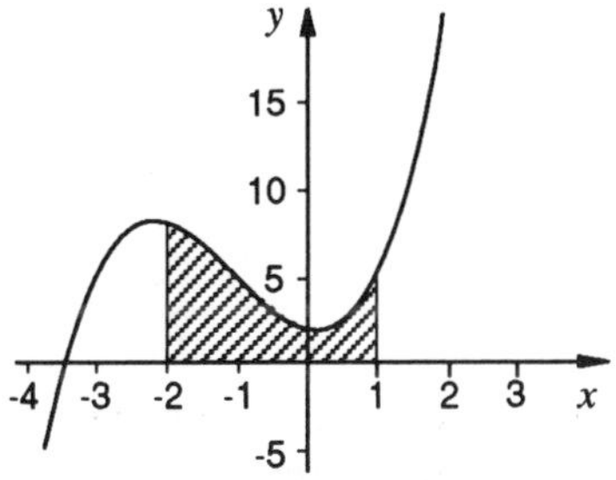

$y = x^3 + 3x^2 - x + 2$

Finding the area under a graph is not just important for its own sake. There are a number of problems in science and elsewhere that need integration for a solution. Section 12.1 starts by looking at an example of such a problem.

12.1 Estimating future populations

Shortly after the Second World War, it was decided to establish several 'new towns'. Two well known examples are Hemel Hempstead, near London, and Newton Aycliffe in the north-east; in these cases the 'new towns' were based on existing small communities. More recently, the city of Milton Keynes was built up where once there was practically nothing.

Clearly such ambitious developments require careful planning and one factor that needs to be considered is population growth. Apart from anything else, the services and infrastructure of a new community need building up in accordance with the projected population: chaos would ensue, for instance, if there were 5000 children but only enough schools for 3000.

Imagine you are planning a new town. You have been advised that planned population growth will conform to the following model:

Initial growth rate 6000 people per year; thereafter the rate of growth will decrease by 30% every five years.

Your task is to estimate what the total population will be 30 years later. One approach to this problem is detailed in the following activity.

Activity 1 Rough estimates

(a) Start by setting up a mathematical model. Let t stand for the time in years; when $t = 0$ the growth rate is 6000 people per year. When $t = 5$ (after 5 years) the growth rate is 6000 less 30%, i.e. $0.7 \times 6000 = 4200$.

Copy and complete this table of growth rates :

Time (years)	Growth Rate
0	6000
5	4200
10	2940
15	...
20	...
25	...
30	706

(b) A very rough estimate can be obtained by following this line of reasoning:

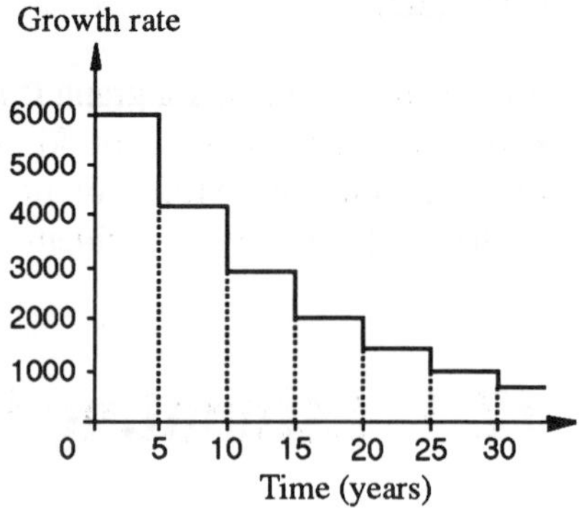

Suppose the growth rate remains fixed at 6000 throughout the first 5 years. Then after 5 years the population will be

$$5 \times 6000 = 30\,000.$$

Now suppose the growth rate over the next five years is a constant 4200 per year. After 10 years the population will be

$$30\,000 + 5 \times 4200 = 51\,000.$$

Continue this process to obtain an estimate for the population after 30 years.

(c) Your figure for (b) will clearly be an over-estimate. A similar process can be applied to give an under-estimate. The process starts as follows:

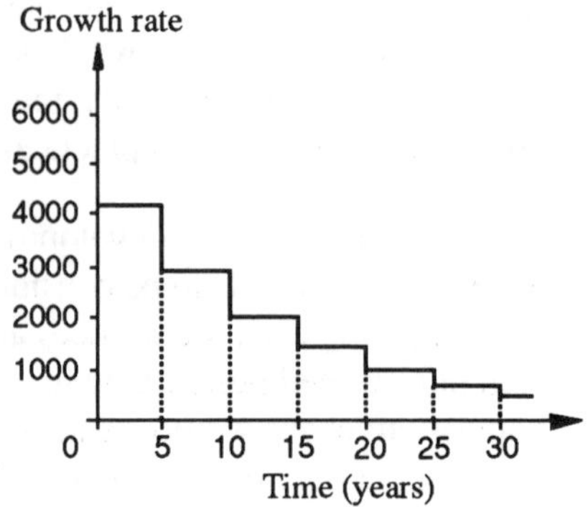

Suppose the growth rate over the first five years is fixed at 4200. Then after five years the population will be

$$5 \times 4200 = 21\,000$$

After 10 years the population will be

$$21\,000 + 5 \times 2940 = 35\,700.$$

Continue this process to obtain a second estimate.

(d) Use your two estimates to make a third, more realistic estimate of the population after 30 years' growth.

The two diagrams alongside the above activity should give a good idea of what the processes you have just completed actually mean. In parts (b) and (c) what you essentially did was to find the area under a bar chart; one estimate was too large, the other too small, with the 'true' answer lying somewhere in the middle.

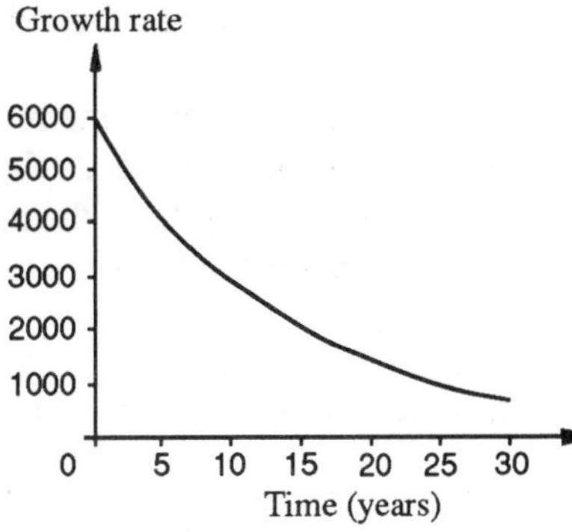

The graph of growth rate against time will not, in truth, be a 'bar chart' at all. More realistically it will resemble the curve shown opposite, which shows the growth rate decreasing continuously. The figure below shows the same curve with the two bar charts superimposed.

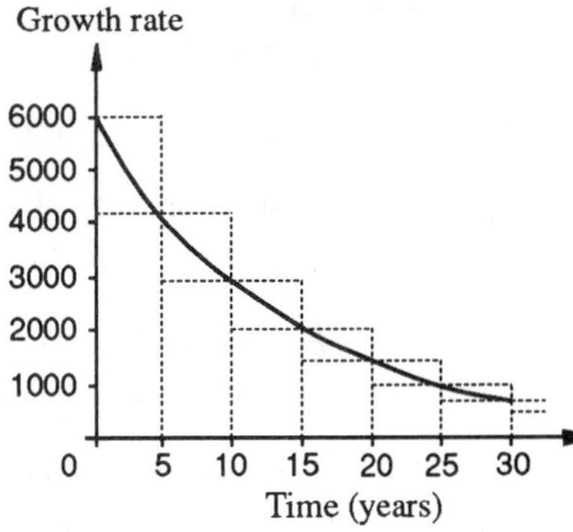

The 'true' population estimate will be the **exact** area under the curve in the figure above.

Activity 2 More accurate estimate

A more refined estimate can be obtained by using growth rates calculated at yearly intervals rather than 5-yearly ones. A decrease of 30% every **five** years is roughly equivalent to a decrease of 6.9% every year.

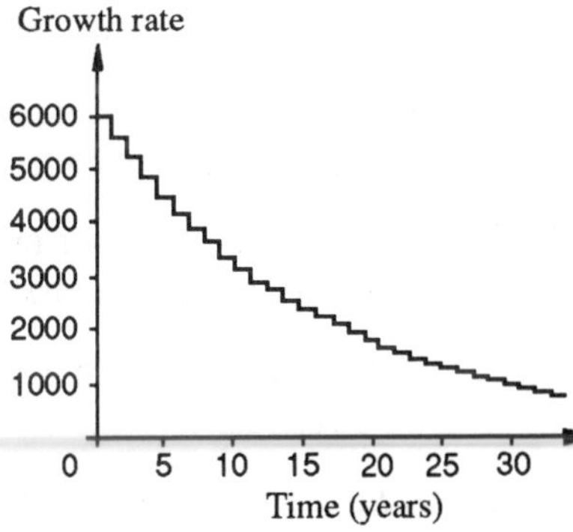

Hence the table of growth rates starts like this:

Time (years)	Growth rate
0	6000
1	5586
2	5201
etc.	etc.

Use these figures to get a closer estimate of the population. Follow the same sort of process as in Activity 1.

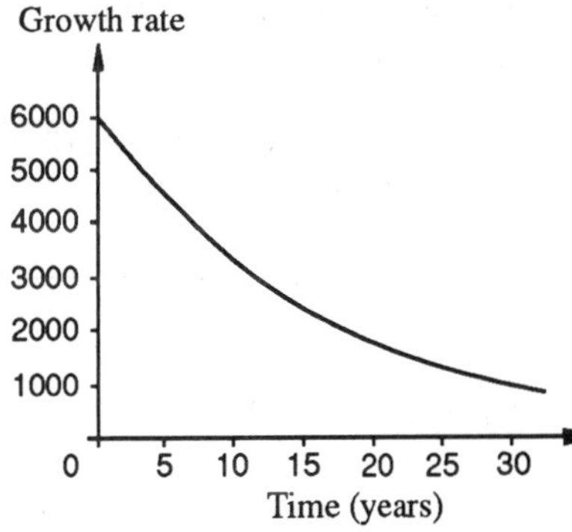

Why was the figure 6.9% used in this activity?

With a little ingenuity you might be able to save tedious calculation by efficient use of a computer. If you do this, try and refine the estimate still further by using smaller intervals.

The graphs alongside Activity 2 illustrate why using smaller intervals leads to increased accuracy. The smaller the intervals, the more the 'bar chart' resembles the continuous curve. Hence the area of the 'bar charts' approaches the exact value of the area under the curve as the interval size is decreased.

The next activity provides a further example of finding estimates for the area under a curve.

Activity 3 Distance travelled

(a) A car is travelling at 36 metres per second when the driver spots an obstruction ahead. The car does an 'emergency stop'; the speed of the car from the moment the obstruction is spotted is shown in the table below.

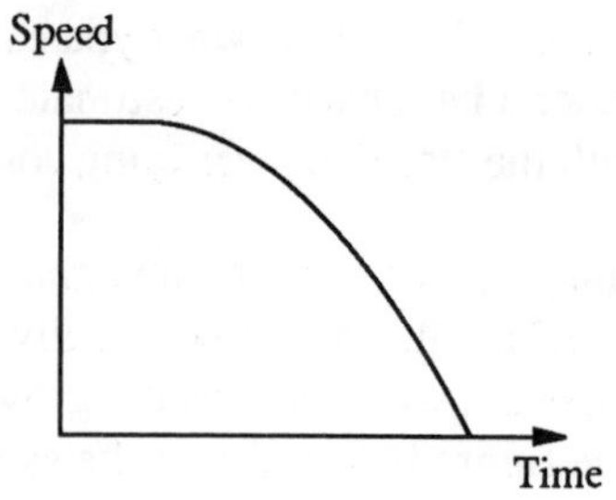

Time (s)	0	1	2	3	4	5	6	7
Speed (ms^{-1})	36	36	34.8	29.9	23.2	15.2	4.8	0

As accurately as you can, draw a speed-time curve describing the car's motion. (The graph opposite is not accurate but shows the general shape).

(b) How far did the car travel in the first second?

(c) If the car travelled at 36 ms^{-1} **throughout** the 2nd second, how far would it have travelled in this second?

(d) If the car travelled at 34.8 ms^{-1} throughout the 3rd second, how far would it have travelled in this second?

(e) Following this procedure up to the 7th second inclusive; work out an estimate of the distance travelled by the car from the moment the obstruction was spotted.

(f) The answer to (e) is an over-estimate. Use the ideas of Activity 1 to produce an under-estimate.

(g) Superimpose two bar charts onto your graph, the areas under which are your answers to (e) and (f).

(h) Use your answers so far to write down a better estimate of the distance travelled.

(i) Increased accuracy can be obtained by halving the interval width. First use your graph to estimate the car's speed after 0.5 seconds, 1.5 seconds, etc. Record your answers clearly.

(j) Now use these figures to produce a more accurate estimate than your answer to (h).

Exercise 12A

1. The sketch opposite shows the graph of the curve with equation

$$y = 4x^3 - 15x^2 + 12x + 5.$$

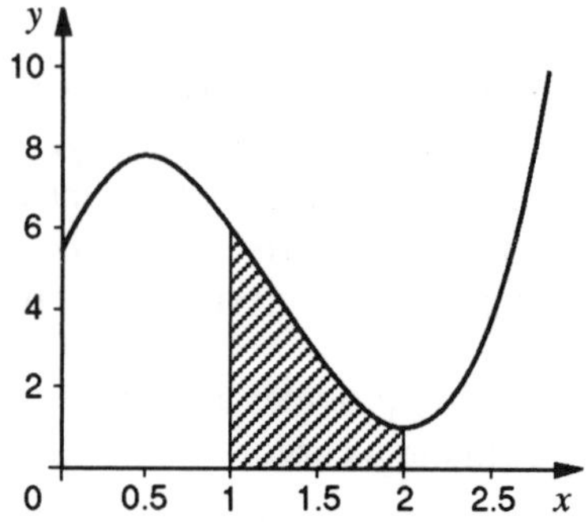

(a) Copy and complete this table of values :

x	1.0	1.1	1.2	1.3	1.4	1.5	1.6	1.7	1.8	1.9	2.0
y	6	5.37	..	..	..	..	2.18	..	..	..	1

(b) Use your table to estimate the shaded area in the diagram. Employ methods like those in the earlier questions and activities.

12.2 Notation for area

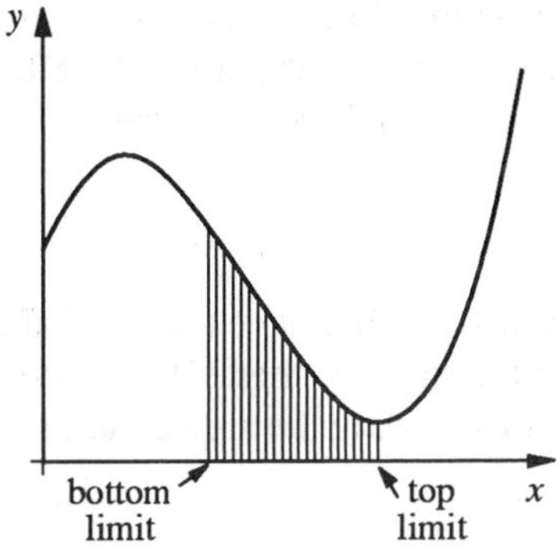

Three examples have now been encountered in which the area under a graph has been of significance. Mathematicians have for many centuries appreciated the importance of areas under curves. The process of working out such areas is called 'integration' and early approaches to the problem were similar to the method investigated so far, namely the splitting of areas into several thin rectangles.

The notation developed by the German mathematician, *Leibnitz*, quickly became widely adopted and is still used today. The area under the curve

$$y = 4x^3 - 15x^2 + 12x + 5$$

between $x = 1$ and $x = 2$ is written as

$$\int_1^2 \left(4x^3 - 15x^2 + 12x + 5\right) dx,$$

and is read as the integral between 1 and 2 of $4x^3 - 15x^2 + 12x + 5$.

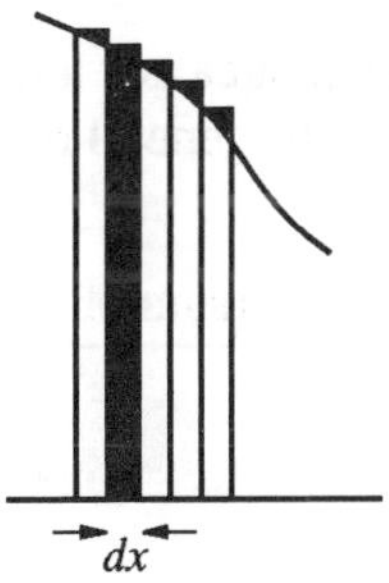

The $\int$ sign, known as the **integral sign**, derives from the ancient form of the letter S, for sum. The '*dx*' represents the width of the small rectangles. The above notation denotes the sum of lots of very thin rectangles between the limits $x = 1$ and $x = 2$.

Hence the area under the curve $y = x^2$ from $x = 0$ to $x = 1$ is written as

$$\int_0^1 x^2 dx$$

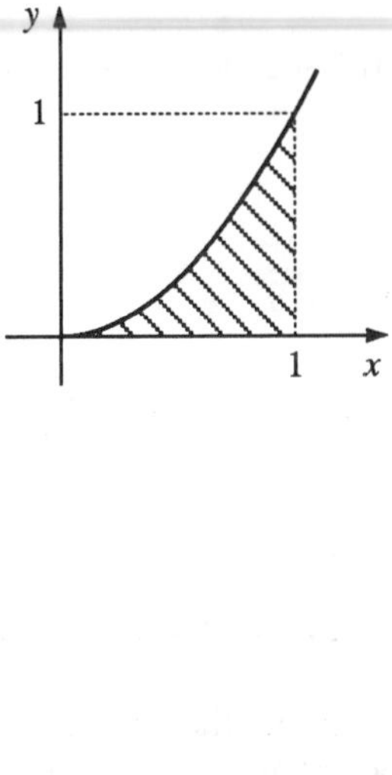

The $\int$ and the '*dx*' enclose the function to be integrated.

Area under straight line

The activities in the previous section highlighted the fact that, at present, the methods used to calculate areas have only been approximate. When the graph is a straight line, however, it is a simple matter to work out the area exactly.

As you have seen, the area under a velocity-time graph gives the distance travelled. In many situations, particularly when a body is moving freely under gravity, the velocity-time graph is a straight line.

Consider the case of a stone thrown vertically downwards from a cliff-top. If its initial velocity is 5 metres per second then its velocity v metres per second after t seconds will be given approximately by the formula

$$v = 5 + 10t.$$

How far will it have travelled after 5 seconds, assuming it hasn't hit anything by then? The answer to this question can be worked out by finding the area under, that is integrating, the velocity-time graph.

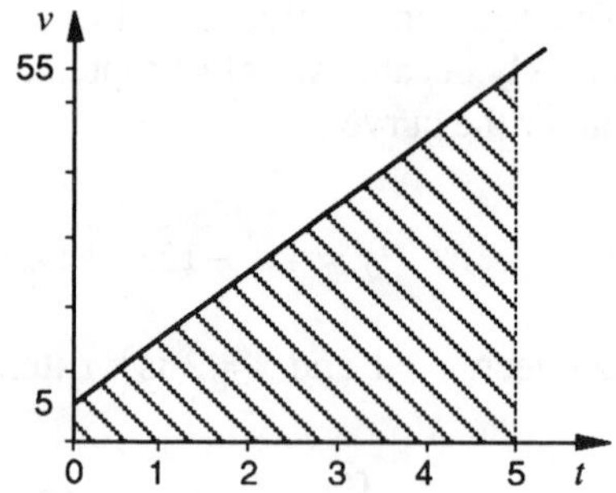

The problem thus boils down to finding the shaded area in the diagram opposite. Using the integral sign, this area can be written

$$\int_0^5 (5 + 10t)\, dt.$$

(Note that dt is used here rather than dx as the variable along the horizontal axis is t).

The shaded area is a trapezium, the area of which can be worked out using the general rule

$$\text{area} = \frac{(\text{sum of parallel sides}) \times (\text{distance between them})}{2}$$

In this case the calculation yields $\dfrac{(55 + 5) \times 5}{2} = 150.$

So in 5 seconds the stone will have fallen 150 metres.

Example

Calculate the integral $\int_4^6 (20 - 3x)\, dx$.

Solution

The area required is shown in this sketch. Again, it is a trapezium.

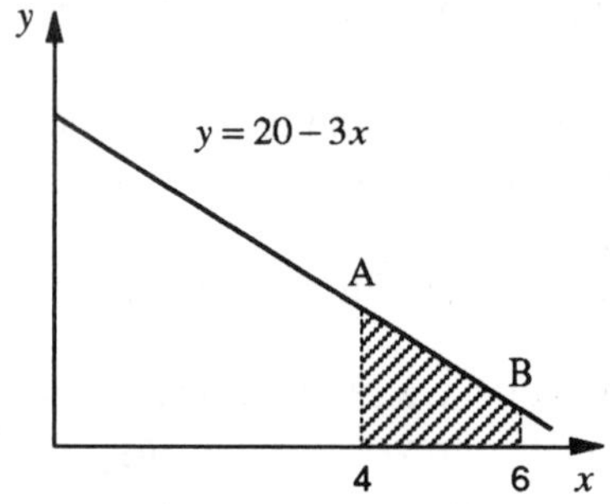

To work out the lengths of the parallel sides you need to know the y-coordinates of A and B. These can be worked out from the equation of the line, $y = 20 - 3x$.

At A: $y = 20 - (3 \times 4) = 8.$

At B: $y = 20 - (3 \times 6) = 2.$

So the area is $\dfrac{(8+2) \times 2}{2} =$ 10 square units.

Exercise 12B

1. Calculate the shaded areas in these diagrams.

(a)

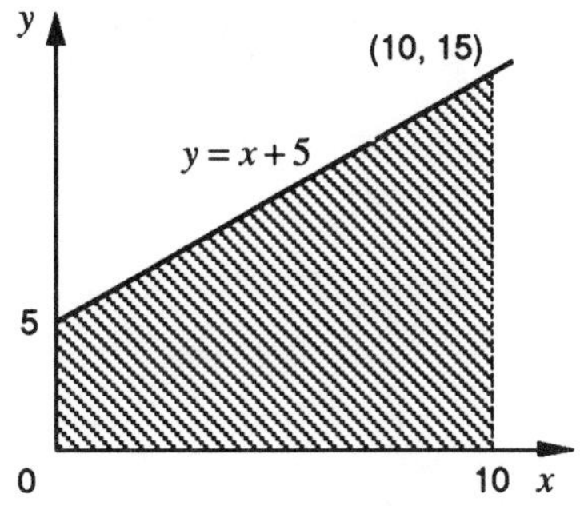

(b)

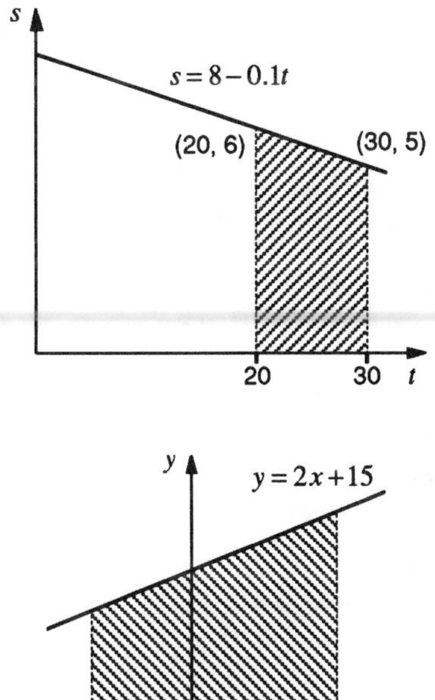

(c)

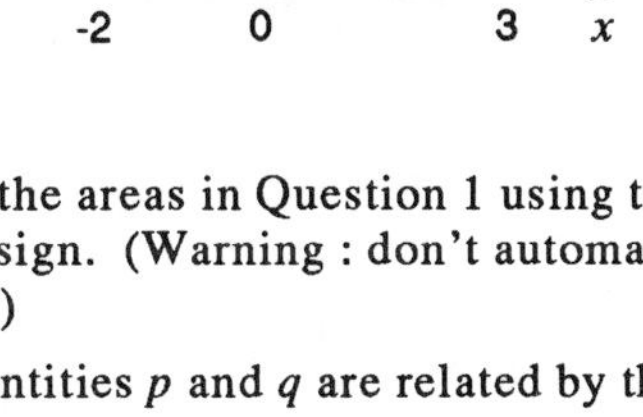

2. Express the areas in Question 1 using the integral sign. (Warning : don't automatically use 'dx'.)

3. Two quantities p and q are related by the equation

$$q = 12p - 45.$$

(a) Sketch the graph of this relationship for values of p between 0 and 10.

(b) Calculate

$$\int_5^8 (12p - 45)\, dp.$$

and shade on your graph the area this represents.

4. Calculate these integrals. Draw a sketch diagram if it helps.

(a) $\int_1^6 (6x+3)\, dx$

(b) $\int_{-1}^1 (25-7t)\, dt$

(c) $\int_{20}^{75} (-p+100)\, dp$

(d) $\int_{2.7}^{6.5} (3.5s+17.1)\, ds$

5. The speed of a car as it rolls up a hill is given by $v = 20 - 3t$ where t is the time in seconds and v is measured in metres per second.

(a) Draw a sketch graph showing speed against time between $t = 0$ and $t = 5$.

(b) Integrate to find how far the car travels in the first 5 seconds.

6. The rate at which a city's population grows is given by the formula

$$R = 1000 + 700t$$

where R is the rate of increase in people per year and t is the number of years since 1st January 1990.

(a) How fast will the population be growing on 1st January 1993, according to this model?

(b) The population starts from zero on 1st January 1990. Calculate, by integration, what the population should be on 1st January 1993. (Draw a sketch graph.)

12.3 General formula

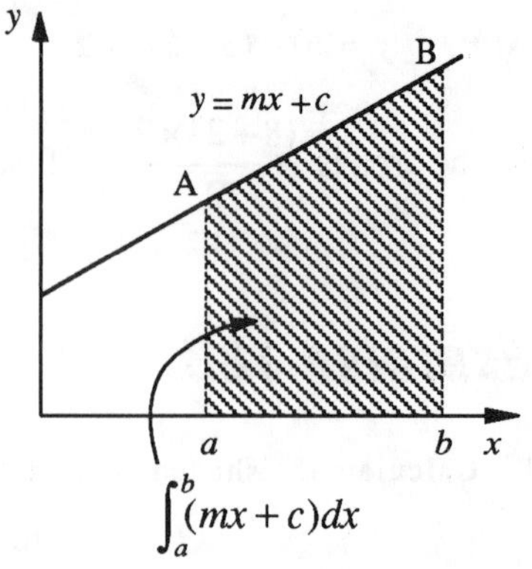

It is straight forward to find the area under any straight line graph, say

$$\boxed{y = mx + c}$$

between $x = a$ and $x = b$, as shown in the figure opposite.

What are the y coordinates of A and B?

The area of the trapezium is given by

$$\tfrac{1}{2}((mb + c) + (ma + c))(b - a)$$

$$= \tfrac{1}{2}(mb + ma + 2c)(b - a)$$

$$= \tfrac{1}{2}(mb^2 + mab + 2cb - mab - ma^2 - 2ca)$$

$$\boxed{\text{area} = \left(\tfrac{1}{2}mb^2 + cb\right) - \left(\tfrac{1}{2}ma^2 + ca\right)}$$

You can use this formula to check your answer to Question 1 in Exercise 12B.

The formula is usually written $\left[\tfrac{1}{2}mx^2 + cx\right]_a^b$

This is short for the 'function $\tfrac{1}{2}mx^2 + cx$ evaluated at the top limit, $x = b$, minus the value of the same function at the lower limit, $x = a$'.

The function $\tfrac{1}{2}mx^2 + cx$ can thus be used to find areas efficiently. It is called an **indefinite integral** of the function $mx + c$, since in this form it has no limits. One way of thinking of it is as the 'area function' for the graph of $y = mx + c$. For the moment the 'area function', or indefinite integral, will be denoted by $A(x)$, whereas the area between $x = a$ and $x = b$ is given by

$$\text{Area} = \int_a^b (mx + c)dx = \left[\tfrac{1}{2}mx^2 + cx\right]_a^b,$$

for the straight line function $y = mx + c$, and this is called a **definite integral**.

Example

Find $A(x)$ for the straight line $y = 3x - 5$. Use it to work out the area under $y = 3x - 5$ between $x = 2$ and $x = 10$.

Solution

Comparing $y = 3x - 5$ with $mx + c$, you see that $m = 3$ and $c = -5$.

Hence

$$A(x) = \frac{3x^2}{2} - 5x$$

$$\text{Area} = \left[\frac{3x^2}{2} - 5x\right]_2^{10}$$

$$= \left(\frac{3\times 10^2}{2} - 5\times 10\right) - \left(\frac{3\times 2^2}{2} - 5\times 2\right)$$

$$= 100 - (-4) = 104 \text{ units}$$

Activity 4

(a) Write down an indefinite integral of the function $12 - 8x$.

(b) Evaluate the area under the graph of $y = 12 - 8x$ between $x = 1$ and $x = 3$.

(c) Draw a sketch graph and interpret your answer.

Activity 5

If $y = 2x - 7$ then the indefinite integral is $A(x) = x^2 - 7x$.

Find $\frac{dA}{dx}$. Investigate further for different straight line formulae.

Exercise 12C

1. Find the area function A for these straight lines :

   (a) $y = 2x + 7$

   (b) $s = 10 - t$

   (c) $z = 2.8 + 11.4w$

   (d) $y = -14 - 11x$

2. Use the area function method to calculate the following areas. Try to set out your working as in the worked example above.

   (a) The area under $y = 6x + 1$ between $x = 0$ and $x = 3$.

   (b) The area under $s = 13 - 5t$ between $t = -2$ and $t = 1$.

   (c) $\int_1^{10} (x + 0.5)\, dx$

12.4 The reverse of differentiation

Activity 5 gives a vital clue in the search for a method of integrating more difficult functions. For straight lines, the formula of the line and its indefinite integral are connected by the following rule.

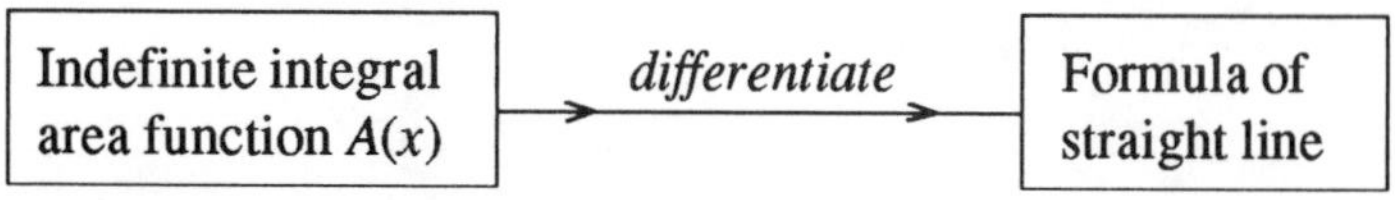

For example, in the worked example just before Activity 5, the equation of the line was $y = 3x - 5$. The corresponding indefinite integral was

$$A(x) = \frac{3x^2}{2} - 5x.$$

It is clear that in this case $\frac{dA}{dx} = y$. If this connection were true for more complex functions than straight lines, the process of finding indefinite integrals and consequently area for functions like $x^2 - 5x + 7$ would automatically be simplified.

In fact, there is one important piece of evidence supporting just such a conclusion. In Section 12.1 the population was estimated by considering the area under the graph of **rate of change** of population. In Activity 3 the distance travelled by a car was calculated by finding the area under the graph of **rate of change** of distance (i.e. velocity).

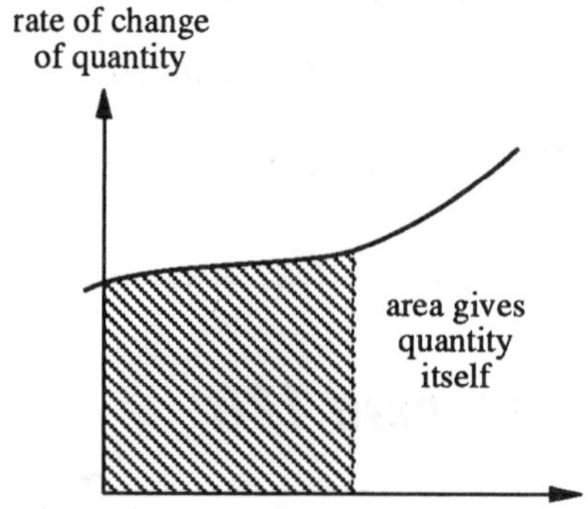

In general you should appreciate that

> the area under a graph showing the **rate of change** of some quantity will give the quantity itself.

But the process of finding rates of change is differentiation, hence integration must be the reverse process.

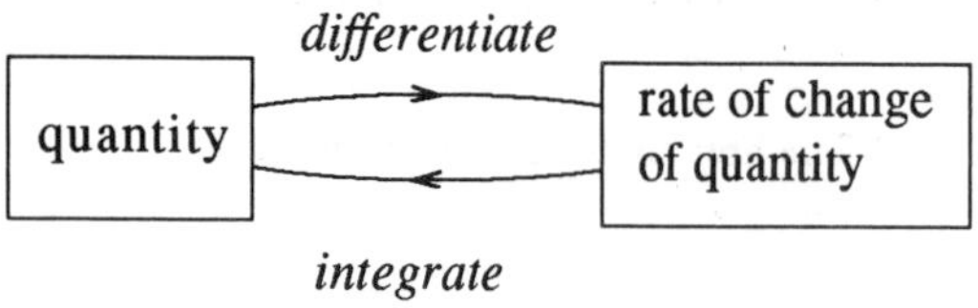

For any function, therefore, it is said that

integration is the reverse of differentiation.

You may feel that the justification for this conclusion is rather vague: too many words and not enough mathematics! This is the way mathematicians often operate, get an instinctive 'feel' for a result and then prove it rigorously. So here is a more mathematical justification for this crucial result.

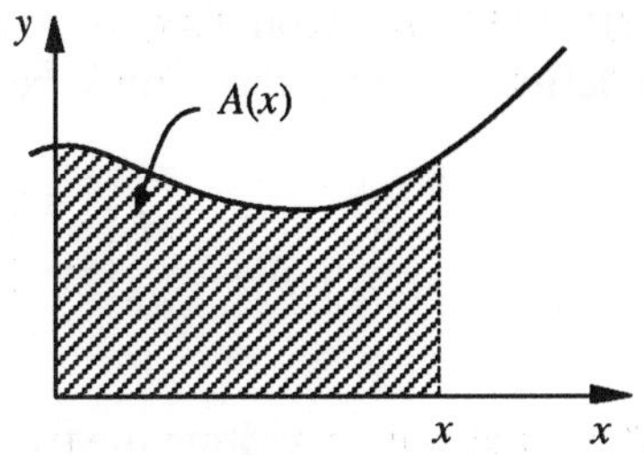

This graph represents y as a function of x. It does not matter at all what sort of function it is. Let $A(x)$ be the area under the graph between $x = 0$ and $x = x$.

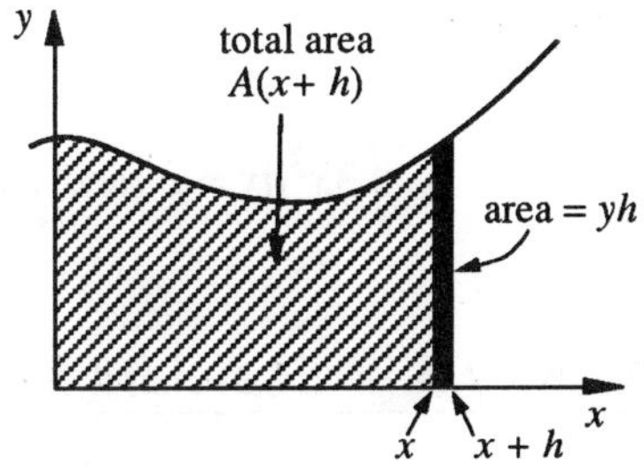

Now suppose an extra strip is added to the area. It has width h and is shaded black in the diagram. The area of both shaded regions together is $A(x + h)$. The area of the black strip is approximately yh, since it is roughly a rectangle with height y.

Hence

$$A(x+h) \approx A(x) + yh$$

$$A(x+h) - A(x) \approx yh$$

$$y \approx \frac{A(x+h) - A(x)}{h}.$$

This is only approximately true (hence the '$\approx$') but the equation becomes more and more exact the smaller h becomes. But as h approaches 0, using the limit definition of differentiation,

$$\frac{A(x+h) - A(x)}{h} \to \frac{dA}{dx}.$$

Hence it can be seen that $y = \dfrac{dA}{dx}$ for any function y.

Example

What is an indefinite integral of the following?

(a) $y = 3x^2$ (b) $y = x^2$

Solution

To answer (a) consider which function, when differentiated, gives the function $3x^2$. The answer is x^3, since

$$\frac{d}{dx}\left(x^3\right) = 3x^2$$

Part (b) follows from this; x^2 is one third of $3x^2$. Hence the indefinite integral for x^2 must be

$$\frac{x^3}{3}, \text{ since } \frac{d}{dx}\left(\frac{x^3}{3}\right) = x^2.$$

The usual way of writing the two answers above, using $\int$ notation, is

$$\int 3x^2 dx = x^3 \text{ and } \int x^2 dx = \tfrac{1}{3}x^3.$$

Activity 6 Standard functions

Following the procedure of the example above, work out these indefinite integrals :

(a) $\int x^3 dx,\ \int x^4 dx,\ \int x^5 dx,$ etc

(b) $\int x^{-2} dx, \int x^{-3} dx, \int x^{-4} dx$ etc

(c) $\int x^{-1} dx$

(d) $\int e^x dx$.

Can you formulate general rules for finding indefinite integrals before turning the page and going on to the next section? Carefully consider the pattern emerging each time.

Is integration unique?

You already know that $\int 3x^2\ dx = x^3$, and that in reverse this is equivalent to saying $\frac{d}{dx}\left(x^3\right) = 3x^2$.

But what about $\frac{d}{dx}\left(x^3 + 1\right)$, $\frac{d}{dx}\left(x^3 + 4\right)$ and $\frac{d}{dx}\left(x^3 - 7\right)$?

They all give the answer $3x^2$. So, in general, you can write

$$\int 3x^2\ dx = x^3 + K$$

where K is any constant.

Activity 7 Integral of a constant

Sketch the graph of $y = 2$. What is $\int 2\,dx$?

Generalise to find $\int k\,dx$, where k is any number.

Standard integrals

Below is a summary of what you should have found out from Activities 6 and 7. These results are most important and, although readily available, should be memorised, so that they can be recalled instantly when needed.

$$\int x^n\,dx = \frac{x^{n+1}}{n+1} + K \text{ for any integer } n, \text{ except } -1.$$

$$\int x^{-1}\,dx = \int \frac{1}{x}\,dx = \log x + K$$

$$\int e^x\,dx = e^x + K$$

Note that each of the results includes the term '+ K '. K is known as the **arbitrary** constant, or constant of integration. You must **always** include the arbitrary constant when working out **indefinite** integrals.

Examples

(1) $\int 5x^3\,dx = 5\int x^3\,dx = 5\frac{x^4}{4} + K = \frac{5x^4}{4} + K.$

(2) $\int \frac{7}{x^3}\,dx = 7\int x^{-3}\,dx$ (because $\frac{7}{x^3} = 7x^{-3}$)

$$= 7\frac{x^{-2}}{(-2)} + K = -\frac{7}{2}x^{-2} + K = -\frac{7}{2}\cdot\frac{1}{x^2} + K$$

$$= -\frac{7}{2x^2} + K.$$

(3) $$\int\left(3x^5 - \frac{2}{x}\right)dx = 3\int x^5\,dx - 2\int \frac{1}{x}\,dx$$

$$= 3\frac{x^6}{6} - 2\ln x + K$$

$$= \frac{x^6}{2} - 2\ln x + K$$

(4) $$\int \frac{x + x^2}{3}\,dx = \frac{1}{3}\int\left(x + x^2\right)dx$$

$$= \frac{1}{3}\left\{\int x\,dx + \int x^2\,dx\right\}$$

$$= \frac{1}{3}\left(\frac{x^2}{2} + \frac{x^3}{3}\right) + K$$

$$= \frac{x^2}{6} + \frac{x^3}{9} + K$$

In the worked examples above, it has been assumed that integration is a **linear** process. For example, in Example (1), the first step was

$$\int 5x^3\,dx = 5\int x^3\,dx.$$

In Example (4) the second step assumed that

$$\int\left(x + x^2\right)dx = \int x\,dx + \int x^2\,dx.$$

Why are these assumptions valid?

If $u(x)$ and $v(x)$ are any functions of x and a and b are any constant numbers, then

$$\boxed{\int\left(au(x) + bv(x)\right)dx = a\int u(x)dx + b\int v(x)dx}$$

Exercise 12D

Evaluate these indefinite integrals.
Numbers 1 to 10 are relatively straightforward.
Numbers 11 to 20 might need more care.
Tidy each answer as much as you can; for example

$-\frac{3}{4x^4}$ is better than $3\frac{x^{-4}}{(-4)}$.

1. $\int x^9 \, dx$
2. $\int x^{-8} \, dx$
3. $\int \frac{1}{x^5} \, dx$
4. $\int \left(x^4 + x^7\right) dx$
5. $\int \left(\frac{1}{x} + \frac{1}{x^2}\right) dx$
6. $\int 6x^7 \, dx$
7. $\int \frac{3}{t^3} \, dt$
8. $\int \frac{2}{w} \, dw$
9. $\int \left(e^p - 3p\right) dp$
10. $\int \left(2 - \frac{1}{q^3}\right) dq$
11. $\int \frac{x^3}{2} \, dx$
12. $\int \frac{4}{3}x^7 \, dx$
13. $\int \frac{3}{2y^3} \, dy$
14. $\int 2\left(x - \frac{1}{3x}\right) dx$
15. $\int \left(\frac{e^k}{4} + k^{-3}\right) dk$
16. $\int \frac{3 - 2x^5}{4} \, dx$
17. $\int \left(e^m - \frac{2}{5m^4}\right) dm$
18. $\int \frac{5x^2 - x + 1}{2} \, dx$
19. $\int \frac{1}{5}\left(z^2 - \frac{1}{z}\right) dz$
20. $\int \frac{2x - 1}{x} \, dx$

12.5 Finding areas

The original aim of this chapter was to calculate exact values for areas under curves. The groundwork for this has now been done. The procedure is best explained through a worked example, but before you read through it you might like to remind yourself how indefinite integrals were used to work out areas under straight lines in Section 12.2.

Example

Calculate the area under the curve $y = x^2 + 2$ between $x = 1$ and $x = 4$.

Solution

The diagram shows the area required.

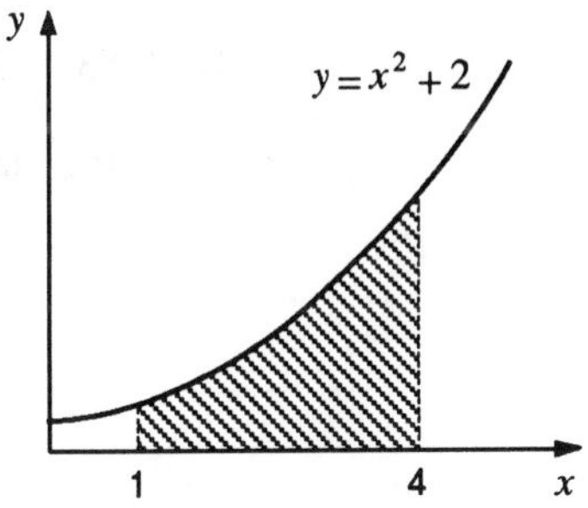

Using integral notation this area would be denoted

$$\int_1^4 \left(x^2 + 2\right) dx.$$

The indefinite integral of $x^2 + 2$ is the function

$$\frac{x^3}{3} + 2x + K$$

Hence

$$\text{Area} = \left[\frac{x^3}{3} + 2x + K\right]_1^4$$

$$= \left(\frac{4^3}{3} + 2\times 4 + K\right) - \left(\frac{1^3}{3} + 2\times 1 + K\right)$$

$$= \left(29\tfrac{1}{3} + K\right) - \left(2\tfrac{1}{3} + K\right)$$

$$= 27 \text{ units.}$$

An important point to note in this calculation is that the arbitrary constant **cancels** out. Integrals with limits, such as

$$\int_1^4 \left(x^2 + 2\right) dx$$

are called **definite** integrals, and it is customary when evaluating these to omit the arbitrary constant altogether.

Example

Work out the area under the graph of $y = 10e^x + 3x$ between $x = -1$ and $x = 3$, to one decimal place.

Solution

$$\text{Area} = \int_{-1}^{3} \left(10e^x + 3x\right) dx$$

$$= \left[10e^x + \frac{3x^2}{2}\right]_{-1}^{3}$$

$$= \left(10e^3 + \frac{3\times 3^2}{2}\right) - \left(10e^{-1} + \frac{3\times(-1)^2}{2}\right)$$

$$= 214.35537 - 5.1787944$$

$$= 209.2 \text{ to 1 d.p.}$$

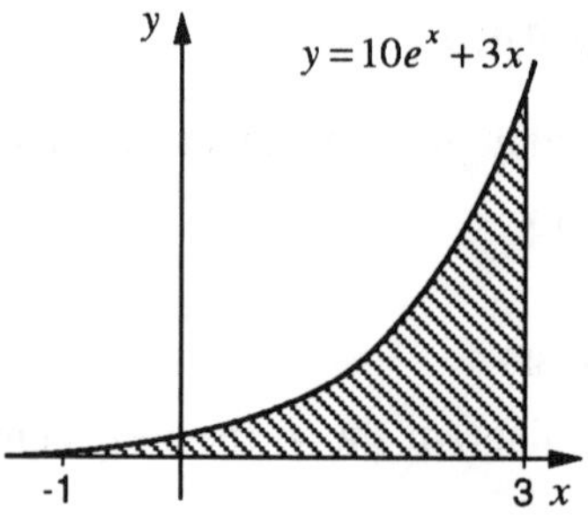

Activity 8 Negative areas

(a) Evaluate $\int_0^6 \left(x^2 - 2x - 8\right) dx$.

(b) Sketch the curve $y = x^2 - 2x - 8$ and interpret the value of the integral.

(c) Calculate the total shaded area in this diagram.

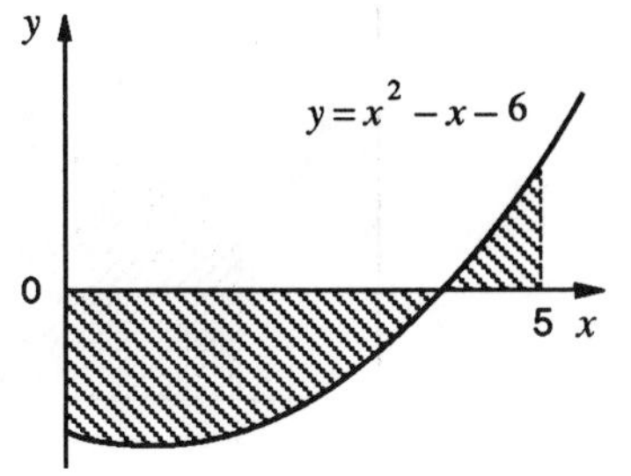

Activity 9 Simple products

Is it true that

$$\int (x+3)(x+5)\,dx = \left(\int (x+3)\,dx\right) \times \left(\int (x+5)\,dx\right)?$$

What is the best way to evaluate $\int (x+3)(x+5)\,dx$?

Exercise 12E

1. Work out the shaded areas below. Use integral notation when setting out your solutions.

(a)

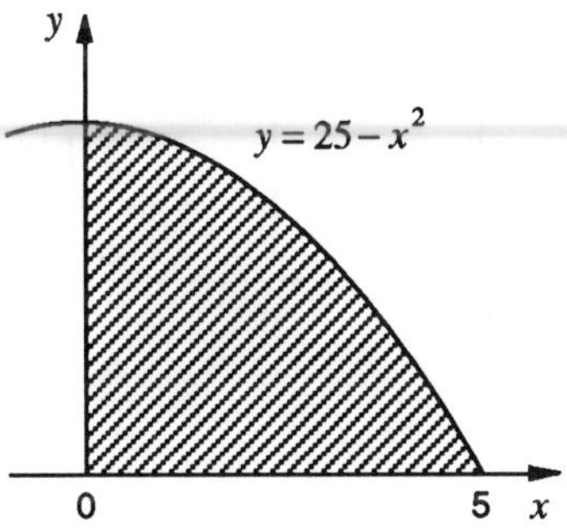

(c)

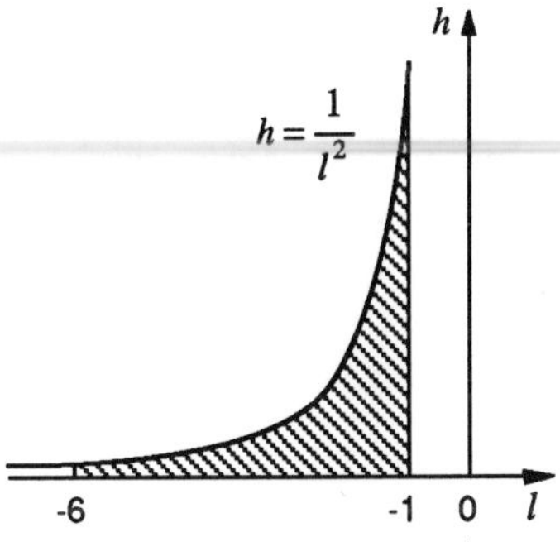

(b)

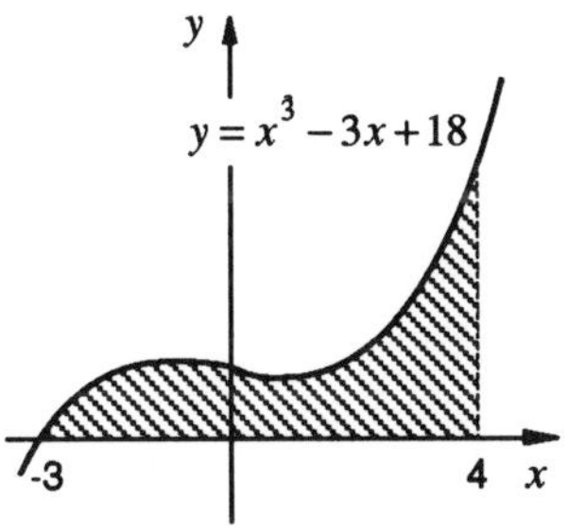

(d)

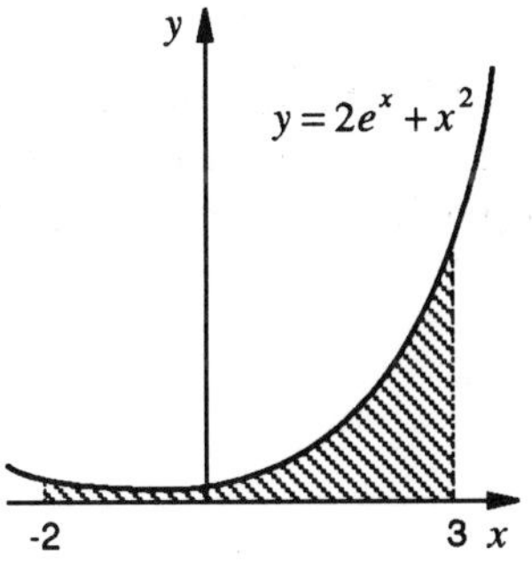

(e)

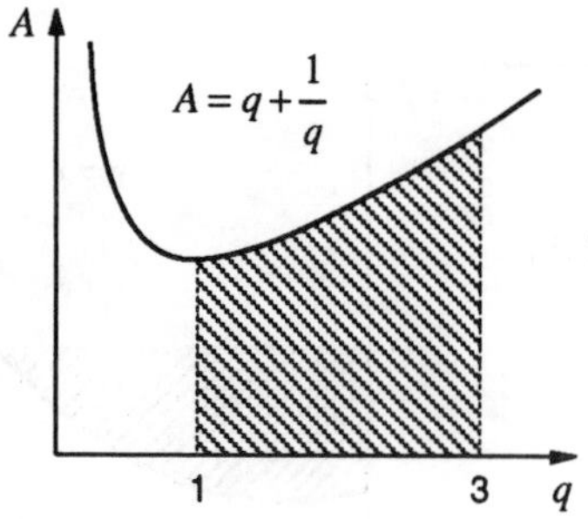

(f)

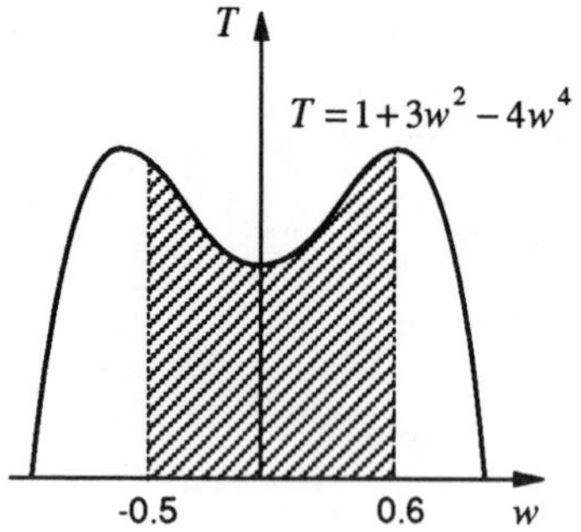

2. Evaluate these to 3 significant figures.

(a) $\int_1^5 \left(x^2 - \frac{1}{x^2}\right) dx$ (b) $\int_{-2}^{-1} \left(6z^2 - 1\right) dz$

(c) $\int_0^1 \frac{1 + 5m^3}{6} \, dm$ (d) $\int_{2.5}^{3} \left(4 + \frac{2}{3x}\right) dx$

3. The diagram below shows a sketch of $y = x - x^2$. Find the shaded area to 3 significant figures.

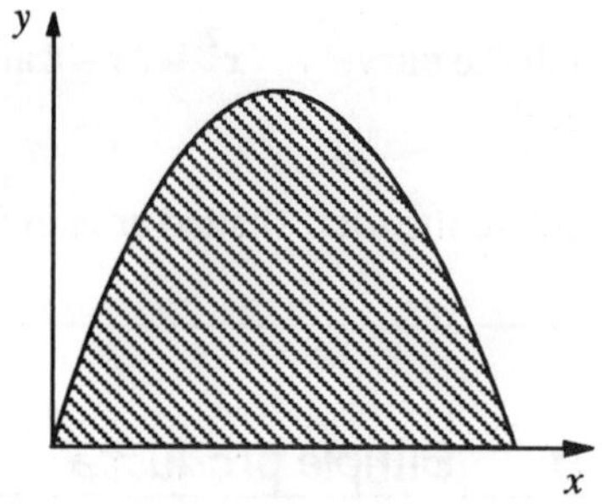

4. A pig-trough has a cross-section in the shape of the curve

$$y = x^{10},$$

for x between -1 and $+1$.

(a) Calculate $\int_{-1}^{1} x^{10} \, dx$.

(b) Work out the cross-sectional area of the trough, given that one unit on the graph represents one metre.

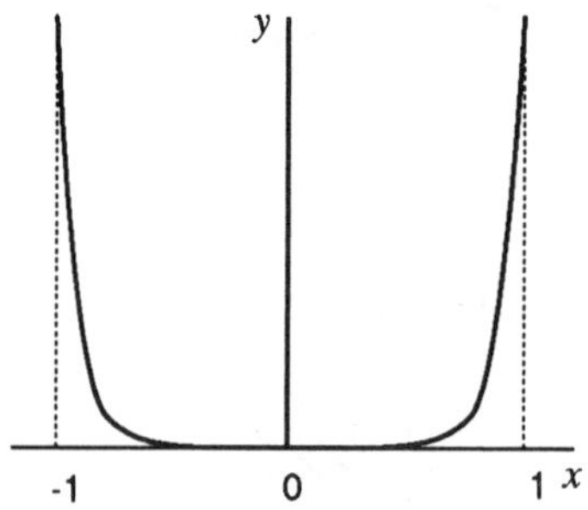

12.6 Using integration

This chapter began with illustrations of particular situations where the area under a graph had significance. Activity 10 should remind you of some of them and introduce you to some more.

Activity 10 What does the area mean?

For each of these graphs, describe in words what quantity is represented by the shaded area.

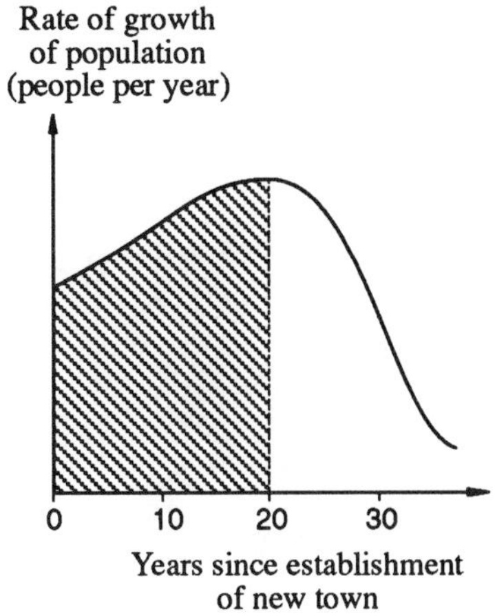

A

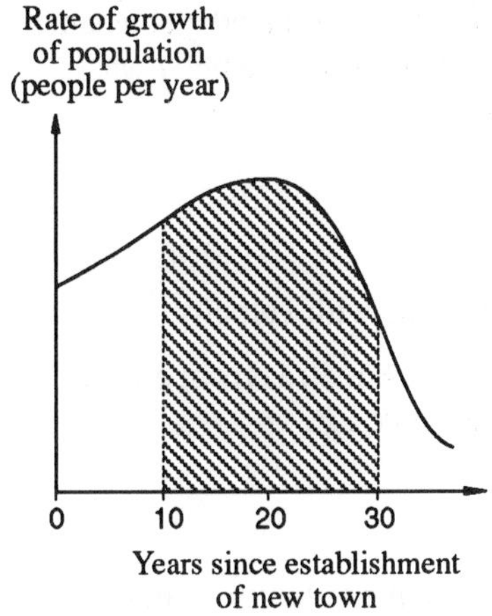

B

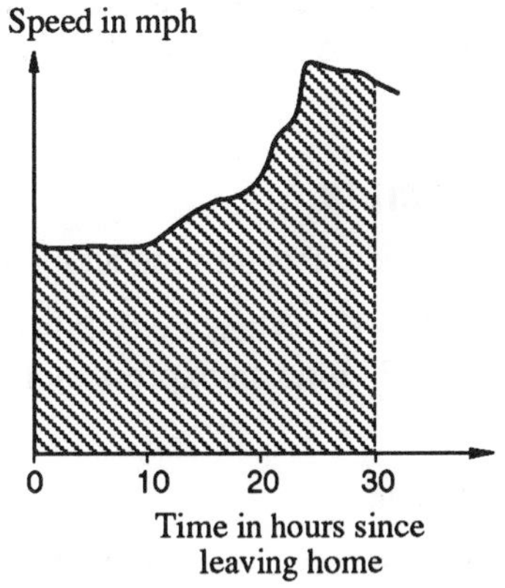

C

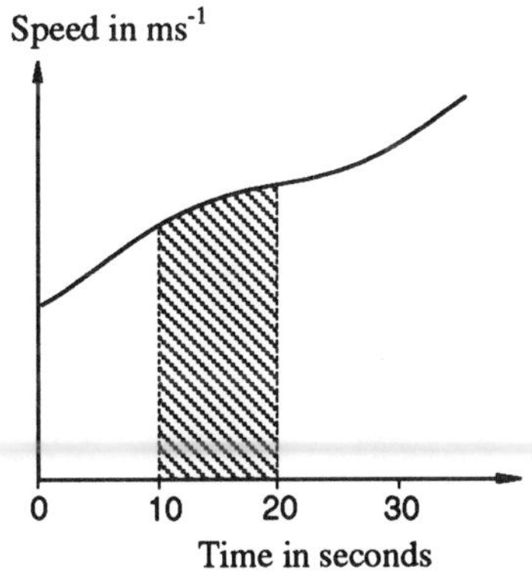

D

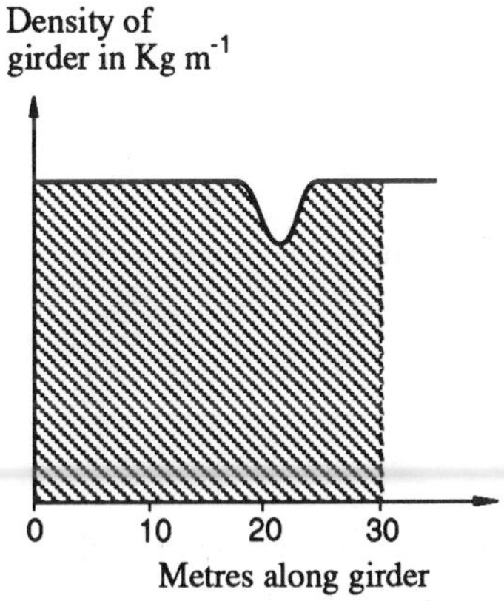

E

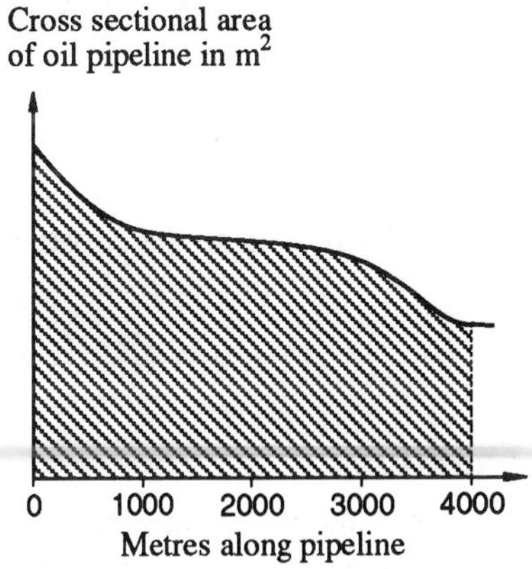

F

Activity 11 The rogue car

A motorist parks his car next to a telephone box. He makes a call from the box but, during the conversation, suddenly sees the car rolling down the hill; he clearly forgot to apply the handbrake. When he first noticed the car it was 20 metres away moving with speed $0.7+0.2t$, where t is the time in seconds after the first time he noticed the car rolling away.

(a) How far does the car travel between $t=0$ and $t=5$?

(b) Find a formula for the car's distance from the phone box, in terms of t.

12.7 Initial conditions

Activity 11 gave an example of how integration can be used to find a formula, not just a numerical value. To find the answer to part (b) properly, you needed to apply what are called initial conditions. Integrating the velocity formula produced a constant, which could be evaluated by knowing the distance when t was zero. Here are two further examples.

Example

A particle P is moving along a straight line with velocity $4+6t+t^2$. When $t=0$, P is a distance of 8 metres from a fixed point F. Find an expression for the distance FP.

Solution

The distance can be found by integrating the velocity formula.

$$\text{FP} = \int (4+6t+t^2)\,dt$$

$$= 4t + 3t^2 + \frac{t^3}{3} + \text{constant}$$

FP = 8 when $t=0$, so the constant = 8. Hence

$$\text{FP} = 4t + 3t^2 + \frac{t^3}{3} + 8.$$

Example

A town planning committee notes that the rate of growth of the town's population since 1985 has followed the formula

$$(1500 + 200t) \text{ people per year}$$

where t is the number of years since 1st January 1985. On 1st January 1992 the population was 25 000. Find a formula for the city's population valid from 1985 onwards.

Solution

$$\text{Population} = \int (1500+200t)\,dt$$

$$= 1500t + 100t^2 + K.$$

When $t=7$, $P = 25\ 000$. Putting this information into the formula gives

$$25\ 000 = 10\ 500 + 4900 + K$$

$$\Rightarrow \quad K = 9600$$

$$\text{Population} = 100t^2 + 1500t + 9600.$$

Exercise 12F

1. The speed of a falling object in ms^{-1} is given by the formula $2-10t$, where t is the time in seconds. When $t=0$ its height h above the ground is 1000 m.
   (a) Find a formula for h in terms of t.
   (b) When does the object hit the ground?

2. The speed of a particle P moving along a straight line is given by the formula
$$5+t-\frac{t^2}{4}.$$
When $t=6$, the particle is at the point A.
   (a) Find a formula for the distance AP.
   (b) Verify that the particle is again at A when t is between 7.7 and 7.8 seconds.

3. You have encountered the total cost function $C(Q)$ in previous questions in this book. A related economic concept is that of the marginal cost function $M(Q)$. This gives the change in total cost if the level of output (Q) is increased by 1 unit. $M(Q)$ and $C(Q)$ are thus related as follows
$$M(Q)=\frac{dC}{dQ}$$
   (a) The marginal cost function for a particular firm is Q^2-3Q+5. Find the total cost function $C(Q)$, given that $C(0)=5$. [$C(0)$ is the total cost when the level of output is zero, and hence gives the firm's fixed costs.]
   (b) For a different firm, $M(Q)=2Q^2-10Q+17$. Find the increase from 5 to 8 units.

12.8 Miscellaneous Exercises

1. Work out these indefinite integrals:
   (a) $\int (5x+2)\,dx$
   (b) $\int \left(\frac{t^3}{2}+\frac{2t^2}{3}\right) dt$
   (c) $\int \left(\frac{7}{p}-p\right) dp$
   (d) $\int \frac{5}{4s^6}\,ds$
   (e) $\int \left(x-\frac{2}{x}\right)^2 dx$

2. Evaluate these definite integrals:
   (a) $\int_0^{15} (e^x+2x^2)\,dx$
   (b) $\int_{-3}^{3} (e^x+2x^2)\,dx$
   (c) $\int_1^2 \left(\frac{2}{x}+\frac{3}{5x^2}\right) dx$
   (d) $\int_2^3 (x+5)(x-2)\,dx$
   (e) $\int_{-2}^{-1} (x^2-2)(x+1)\,dx$

3. The graph shows the function
$$f(x)=x(x+1)(x-2).$$
Find the areas labelled A and B.

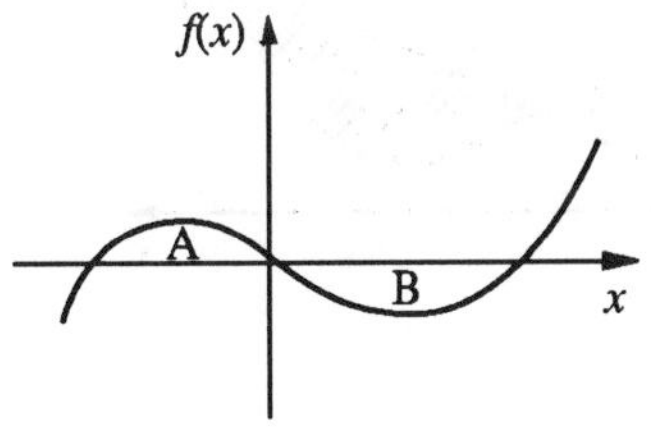

4. This graph shows a function $p(x)$.

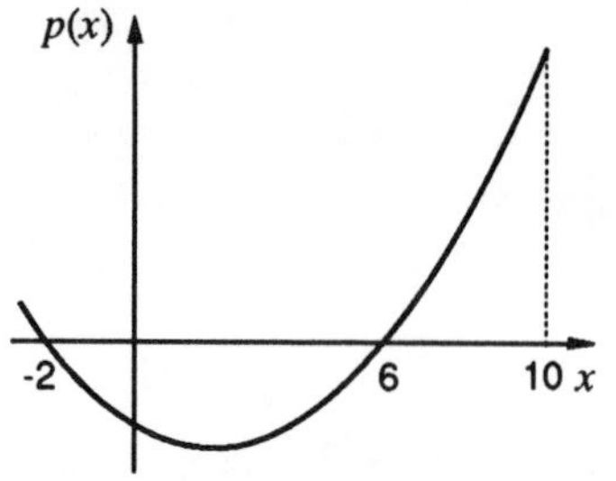

If $\int_{-2}^{6} p(x)\,dx = -10$ and $\int_{-2}^{10} p(x)\,dx = 1$, write down the value of $\int_{6}^{10} p(x)\,dx$.

5.

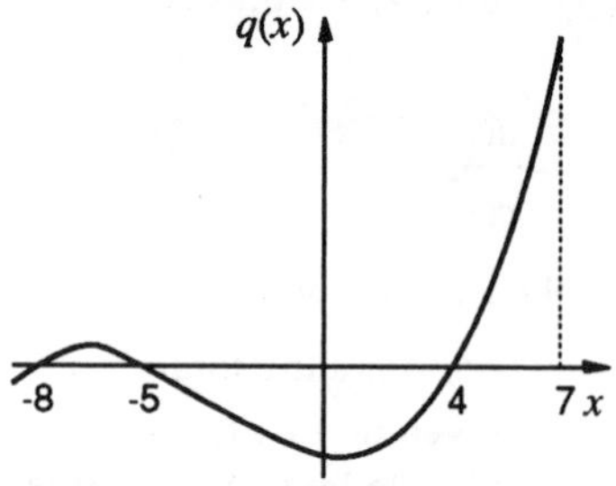

Given that

$\int_{-8}^{7} q(x)\,dx = -4, \int_{4}^{7} q(x)\,dx = 4$ and $\int_{-5}^{4} q(x)\,dx = -11,$

find the value of $\int_{-8}^{-5} q(x)\,dx$.

6. Find the shaded area in these diagrams.

(a)

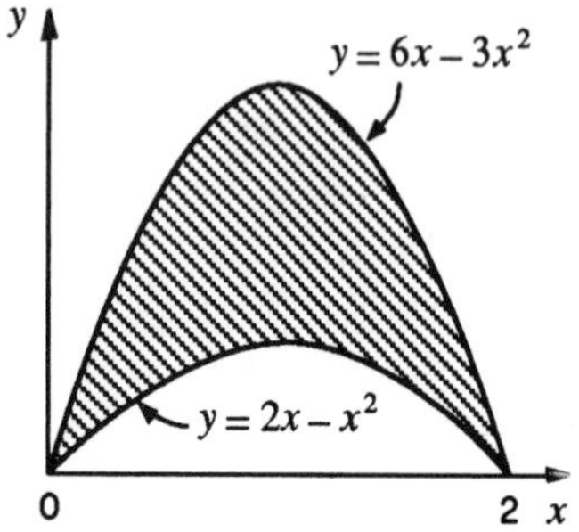

(b)

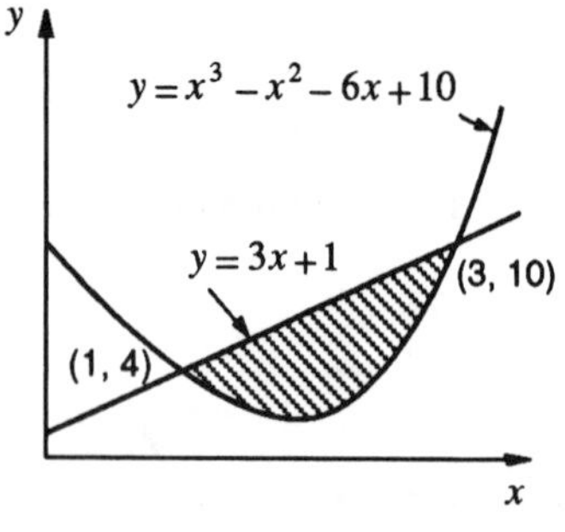

(c)

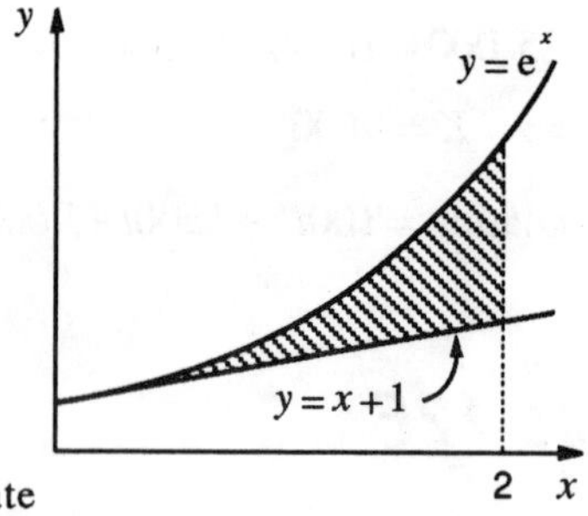

7. Evaluate

(a) $\int_{1}^{3} \frac{x-1}{x}\,dx$ (b) $\int_{-4}^{-1} \frac{xe^{x}-3}{2x}\,dx$

8. A petrol tank, when full, contains 36 litres of petrol. It develops a small hole which widens as time goes by. The rate at which fuel leaks out (in litres per day) is given by the formula

$$0.009t^2 + 0.08t + 0.01$$

where t is the time in days. When $t = 0$ the tank is full.

(a) Find the formulas for

(i) the amount of fuel lost
(ii) the amount of fuel left in the tank after t days.

(b) How many cm^3 does the tank lose on

(i) the first day;
(ii) the tenth day?

(c) How much fuel is left in the tank after

(i) 5 days;
(ii) 15 days?

9. A gas is being kept in a large cylindrical container, the height of which can be altered by means of a piston. The pressure of the gas (p), volume in which it is kept (V) and temperature (T) are related by the equation

$$pV = 5430T.$$

(a) If $T = 293$ (degrees Kelvin) and the radius of the base of the cylinder is 1 metre, show that

$$p \approx \frac{5.06 \times 10^5}{h}$$

where h is the height of the piston above the base of the cylinder.

(b) The energy (in joules) required to compress the gas from a height h_1, to a height h_2 is given by

$$\int_{h_2}^{h_1} p\,dh$$

Initially the piston is at a height of 5 metres. How much energy is required to push the piston down to a height of

(i) 4 m (ii) 1 m?

10. $u(x)$ and $v(x)$ are two functions of x.

$$\int_0^3 u(x)\,dx = 5 \text{ and } \int_0^3 v(x)\,dx = 8.$$

Use this information to calculate these, where possible.

(a) $\int_0^3 (u(x)+v(x))dx$

(b) $\int_0^3 u(x)v(x)dx$

(c) $\int_0^3 xu(x)dx$

(d) $\int_0^3 (2u(x)-3v(x))\,dx$

(e) $\int_0^3 \left[(u(x))^2+(v(x))^2\right]dx$

(f) $\int_0^6 u(x)dx$

(g) $\int_0^3 \frac{u(x)}{v(x)}\,dx.$

11. The graph of a function $f(x)$ looks like this:

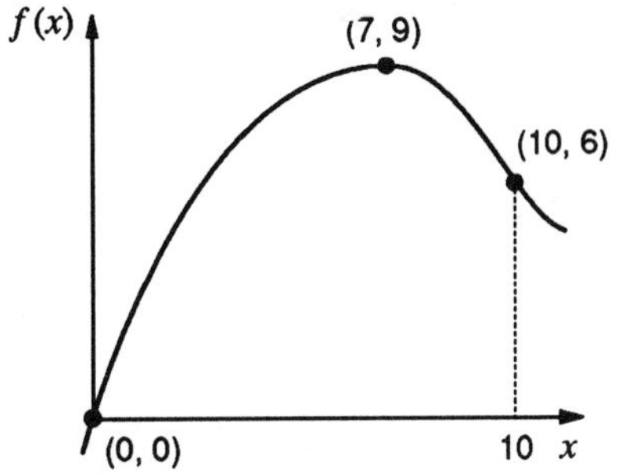

(a) Sketch the graphs of the following. Each sketch should have three points clearly labelled with their coordinates.

(i) $f(x)+1$ (ii) $f(x-4)$

(iii) $2f(x)$ (iv) $f(2x)$

(b) You are given

$$\int_0^{10} f(x)dx = 56.$$

Use this to calculate

(i) $\int_0^{10} [f(x)+1]dx$

(ii) $\int_0^{10} 2f(x)dx$

13 SEQUENCES AND SERIES

Objectives

After studying this chapter you should

- be able to recognise geometric and arithmetic sequences;
- understand Σ notation for sums of series;
- be familiar with the standard formulas for Σr, Σr^2 and Σr^3;

13.0 Introduction

Suppose you go on a sponsored walk. In the first hour you walk 3 miles, in the second hour 2 miles and in each succeeding hour $\frac{2}{3}$ of the distance the hour before. How far would you walk in 10 hours? How far would you go if you kept on like this for ever?

This gives a sequence of numbers: 3, 2, $1\frac{1}{3}$, .. etc. This chapter is about how to tackle problems that involve sequences like this and gives further examples of where they might arise. It also examines sequences and series in general, quick methods of writing them down, and techniques for investigating their behaviour.

Legend has it that the inventor of the game called **chess** was told to name his own reward. His reply was along these lines.

> 'Imagine a chessboard.
>
> Suppose 1 grain of corn is placed on the first square,
>
> 2 grains on the second,
> 4 grains on the third,
> 8 grains on the fourth,
>
> and so on, doubling each time up to and including the 64th square. I would like as many grains of corn as the chessboard now carries.'

Number of grains of corn shown

It took his patron a little time to appreciate the enormity of this request, but not as long as the inventor would have taken to use all the corn up.

Activity 1

(a) How many grains would there be on the 64th square?

(b) How many would there be on the nth square?

(c) Work out the numerical values of the first 10 terms of the sequence.

$$2^0,\ 2^0+2^1,\ 2^0+2^1+2^2 \text{ etc.}$$

(d) How many grains are there on the chessboard?

13.1 Geometric sequences

The series of numbers 1, 2, 4, 8, 16 ... is an example of a **geometric sequence** (sometimes called a geometric progression). Each term in the progression is found by **multiplying** the previous number by 2.

Number of years	Money in account (£)
0	2000
1	2160
2	2332.80
3	2159.42
4	2720.98

Such sequences occur in many situations; the multiplying factor does not have to be 2. For example, if you invested £2000 in an account with a fixed interest rate of 8% p.a. then the amounts of money in the account after 1 year, 2 years, 3 years etc. would be as shown in the table. The first number in the sequence is 2000 and each successive number is found by multiplying by 1.08 each time.

Year	Value (£)
0	35 000
1	31 500
2	28 350
3	25 515
4	22 963.50

Accountants often work out the residual value of a piece of equipment by assuming a fixed depreciation rate. Suppose a piece of equipment was originally worth £35 000 and depreciates in value by 10% each year. Then the values at the beginning of each succeeding year are as shown in the table opposite. Notice that they too form a geometric progression.

The chessboard problem in Activity 1 involved adding up

$$2^0+2^1+2^2+\ldots+2^{63}.$$

The sum of several terms of a sequence is called a **series**. Hence the sum $2^0+2^1+2^2+\ldots+2^{63}$ is called a **geometric series** (sometimes geometric progression, GP for short)

Activity 2 Summing a GP

In Activity 1 you might have found a formula for

$$1+2+2^2+\ldots+2^{n-1}.$$

(a) Work out the values of

$$3^0,\ 3^0+3^1,\ 3^0+3^1+3^2$$

(b) Find a formula for

$$1+3+3^2+\ ...\ +3^{n-1}$$

(c) Find a formula for $1+4+4^2\ ...\ +\ 4^{n-1}$

(d) Now find a formula for

$$1+r+r^2+\ ...\ +r^{n-1}$$

where r is any number. Test your theory.

(e) In practice, geometric series do not always start with 1. Suppose the first term is a. How is the series in part (d) altered? How can you adapt your formula for the total of all terms?

The general form of a geometric sequence with n terms is

$$a,\ ar,\ ar^2,\ ...,\ ar^{n-1}$$

The ratio r of consecutive terms, is known as the **common ratio.** Notice that the nth term of the sequence is ar^{n-1}.

In the chessboard problem the solution involved adding up the first 64 terms. The sum of the first n terms of a series is often denoted by S_n, and there is a formula for S_n which you may have found in Activity 2. Here is a way of proving the formula, when $r \neq 1$.

$$S_n = a+ar+ar^2+\ ...\ +ar^{n-1} \qquad (1)$$

Multiply both sides by r :

$$rS_n = ar+ar^2+\ ...\ +ar^{n-1}+ar^n \qquad (2)$$

Notice that the expressions for S_n and rS_n are identical, with the exception of the terms a and ar^n. Subtracting equation (1) from equation (2) gives

$$rS_n - S_n = ar^n - a$$

$$\Rightarrow \quad S_n(r-1) = a(r^n-1)$$

$$\Rightarrow \quad S_n = \frac{a(r^n-1)}{r-1}$$

Activity 3 Understanding and using the formula

(a) Sometimes it is useful to write

$$S_n = \frac{a\left(1-r^n\right)}{1-r} \text{ instead of } S_n = \frac{a\left(r^n-1\right)}{r-1}$$

Why are these formulae identical? When might it be more convenient to use the alternative form?

(b) For what value of r do these formulas not hold? What is S_n in this case?

Example:

Find

(a) $4+6+9+ \ldots + 4\times(1.5)^{10}$

(b) $8+6+4.5+ \ldots + 8\times(0.75)^{25}$

Solution

(a) First term $a=4$, common ratio $r=1.5$, number of terms $n=11$;

$$S_{11} = \frac{4\left(1.5^{11}-1\right)}{1.5-1} = 684.0 \text{ to 4 s.f.}$$

(b) First term $a=8$, common ratio $r=0.75$, number of terms $n=26$;

$$S_{26} = \frac{8\left(1-0.75^{26}\right)}{1-0.75} = 31.98 \text{ to 4 s.f.}$$

Example:

A plant grows 1.67 cm in its first week. Each week it grows by 4% more than it did the week before. By how much does it grow in nine weeks, including the first week?

Solution

The growths in the first 9 weeks are as follows :

$$1.67,\ 1.67\times1.04,\ 1.67\times1.04^2, \ldots$$

Total growth in first nine weeks is

$$S_9 = \frac{1.67\left(1.04^9 - 1\right)}{1.04 - 1} = 17.67 \text{ cm to 4 s.f.}$$

Example:

After how many complete years will a starting capital of £5000 first exceed £10 000 if it grows at 6% per annum?

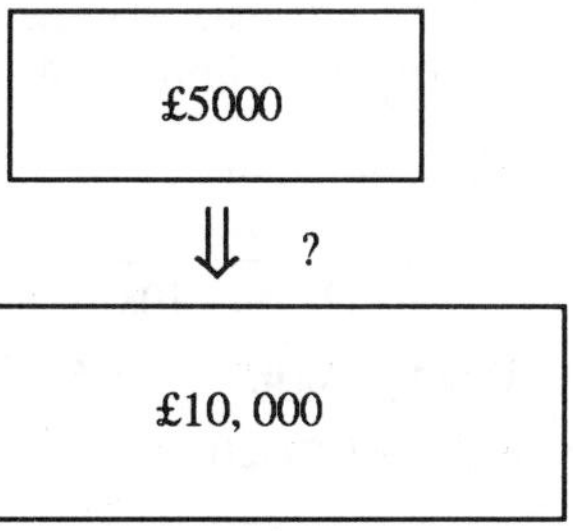

How many years later?

Solution

After n years, the capital sum has grown to

$$5000 \times (1.06)^n$$

When is this first greater than 10 000, n being a natural number? In other words, the smallest value of n is required so that

$$5000 \times (1.06)^n > 10\,000, \; n \in \mathbb{N}$$

$$\Rightarrow \quad (1.06)^n > 2$$

Now take logs of both sides:

$$n \ln 1.06 > \ln 2$$

$$\Rightarrow \quad n > \frac{\ln 2}{\ln 1.06}$$

$$\Rightarrow \quad n > 11.9$$

After 12 years, the investment has doubled in value.

Activity 4 GP in disguise

(a) Why is this a geometric sequence?

$1, -2, 4, -8, 16, \ldots$?

What is its common ratio? What is its nth term? What is S_n?

(b) Investigate in the same way, the sequence

$1, -1, 1, -1, \ldots$

Exercise 13A

1. Write down formulae for the nth term of these sequences:
   (a) 3, 6, 12, 24, ...
   (b) 36, 18, 9, 4.5, ...
   (c) 2, –6, 18, –54, ...
   (d) 90, –30, 10, $-3\frac{1}{3}$, ...
   (e) 10, 100, 1000, ...
   (f) 6, –6, 6, –6, ...
   (g) $\frac{1}{4}, \frac{1}{12}, \frac{1}{36}, \frac{1}{108}, \ldots$
2. Use the formula for S_n to calculate to 4 s.f.
   (a) 5 + 10 + 20 + ... to 6 terms
   (b) 4 + 12 + 36 + ... to 10 terms
   (c) $\frac{1}{3}+\frac{1}{6}+\frac{1}{12}+\ldots$ to 8 terms
   (d) 100 – 20 + 4 – ... to 20 terms
   (e) 16 +17.6 + 19.36 + ... to 50 terms
   (f) 26 – 16.25 + 10.15625 ... to 15 terms
3. Give the number (e.g. 12th term) of the earliest term for which
   (a) the sequence 1, 1.5, 2.25, ... exceeds 50;
   (b) the sequence 6, 8, $10\frac{2}{3}$, ... exceeds 250;
   (c) the sequence $\frac{2}{5}, \frac{1}{5}, \frac{1}{10}, \ldots$ goes below $\frac{1}{1000}$
4. (a) For what value of n does the sum 50 + 60 + 72 + ... + $50\times(1.2)^{n-1}$ first exceed 1000?
   (b) To how many terms can the following series be summed before it exceeds 2 000 000?
   $$2 + 2.01 + 2.02005 + \ldots$$
5. Dave invests £500 in a building society account at the start of each year. The interest rate in the account is 7.2% p.a. Immediately after he invests his 12th instalment he calculates how much money the account should contain. Show this calculation as the sum of a GP and use the formula for S_n to evaluate it.

13.2 Never ending sums

Many of the ideas used so far to illustrate geometric series have been to do with money. Here is one example that is not. If you drop a tennis ball, or any elastic object, onto a horizontal floor it will bounce back up part of the way. If left to its own devices it will continue to bounce, the height of the bounces decreasing each time.

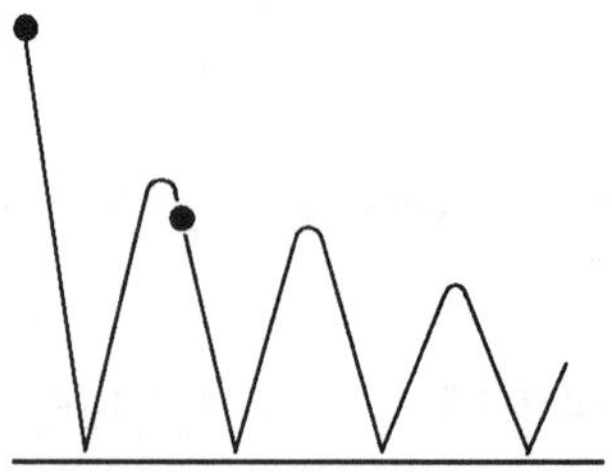

The ratio between the heights of consecutive bounces is constant, hence these heights follow a GP. The same thing is true of the times between bounces.

Activity 5 Bouncing ball

(a) A tennis ball is dropped from a height of 1 metre onto a concrete floor. After its first bounce, it rises to a height of 49cm. Call the height after the nth bounce h_n. Find a formula for h_n and say what happens to h_n as n gets larger.

(b) Under these circumstances the time between the first and second bounces is 0.6321 seconds. Call this t_1. The next time, t_2, is $0.7t_1$, and each successive time is 0.7 times the previous one. Find a formula for t_n.

(c) If $S_2 = t_1 + t_2$, what does S_2 represent? What does S_n mean? Calculate S_{10}, S_{20} and S_{50}. How long after the first bounce does the ball stop bouncing altogether, to the nearest tenth of a second?

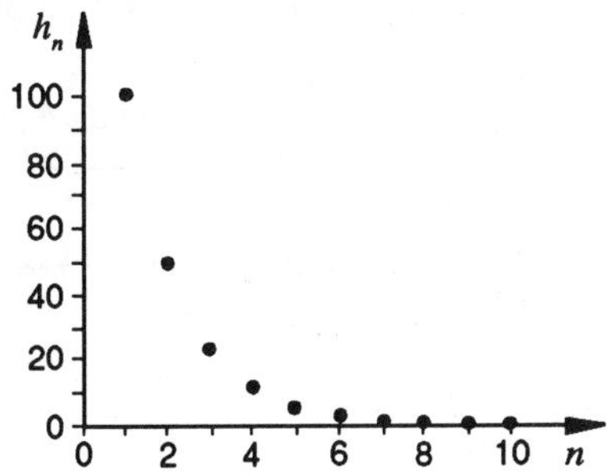

Activity 5 gave an example of a **convergent** sequence. Convergence, in this context, means that the further along the sequence you go, the closer you get to a specific value. For example, in part (a) the sequence to the nearest 0.1 cm is

100, 49.0, 24.0, 11.8, 5.8, 2.8, 1.4, ...

and the numbers get closer and closer to zero. Zero is said to be the **limit** of the sequence.

Part (b) also gave a sequence that converged to zero. In part (c), the sequence of numbers $S_1, S_2, S_3, \ldots$ start as follows :

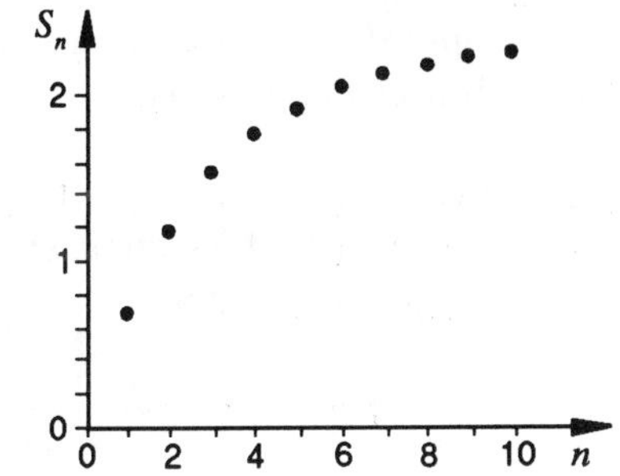

0.6321, 1.0746, 1.3844, 1.6012, 1.7530, ...

You should have found that this sequence did approach a limit, but that this was not zero. Hence the series has a convergent **sum**, that is, the sum S_n of the series also converges.

The series 1, 2, 4, 8 ...... is a **divergent** sequence. It grows without limit as the number of terms increases. The same is true, in a slightly different sense, of the sequence 1, –2, 4, –8 ...... Any sequence that does **not** converge is said to be **divergent**.

Activity 6 Convergent or divergent?

For each of these sequences

(i) write a formula for the nth term;

(ii) find whether the sequence converges;

(iii) find whether the sum S_n converges.

(a) $6, 2, \frac{2}{3}, \frac{2}{9}, \ldots$

(b) 1, 1.5, 2.25, 3.375, ...

(c) $4, -3, \frac{9}{4}, -\frac{27}{16} \ldots$

(d) 1, 1.01, 1.012, 1.0123, ...

(e) 8, –9.6, 11.52, –13.824 ...

Activity 7 Behaviour of r^n

(a) What happens to r^n as n gets larger (i.e. as $n \to \infty$)? (You might need to see what happens for a variety of different values of r, positive and negative, large and small.)

(b) The sum of the first n terms of a geometric sequence is given by

$$S_n = \frac{a(1-r^n)}{1-r}$$

If r^n converges to 0 as $n \to \infty$, what can you say about the limit of S_n as $n \to \infty$?

Activity 8 Experimental verification

Conduct an experiment with a bouncing ball. Calculate the theoretical time from the first bounce until it stops bouncing. Then use a stop-watch to see how close the answer is to your calculation. You will need to know that:

If a ball is dropped from a height of 1 metre and rises after the first bounce to a height of h metres, then the time between the first and second bounce is given by

$$t_1 = 0.90305\sqrt{h},$$

and the common ratio in the sequence $t_1, t_2, t_3 \ldots$ is $\sqrt{h}$.

A geometric series, $a + ar + ar^2 + \ldots + ar^{n-1}$ converges when $|r| < 1$; i.e. for $-1 < r < 1$. Since if $|r| < 1$, $r^n \to 0$ as $n \to \infty$ and

$$\boxed{S_n \to \frac{a}{1-r} \text{ as } n \to \infty}$$

The limit $\dfrac{a}{1-r}$ is known as the 'sum to infinity' and is denoted S_∞.

Example

Find

(a) $8 + 4 + 2 + 1 + \ldots$

(b) $20 - 16 + 12.8 - 10.24 + \ldots$

Solution

(a) This is a geometric series with first term 8 and common ratio $\frac{1}{2}$, so

$$S_\infty = \frac{8}{1-\frac{1}{2}} = 16.$$

(b) This is a geometric series with first term 20 and common ratio – 0.8, so

$$S_\infty = \frac{20}{1-(-0.8)} = \frac{20}{1.8} = \frac{100}{9} = 11.1 \text{ (to 3 s.f.)}.$$

Exercise 13B

1. Find these sums to infinity, where they exist.
   (a) 80 + 20 + 5 + 1.25 + ...
   (b) 180 – 60 + 20 – 20/3 + ...
   (c) 2 + 1.98 + 1.9602 + ...
   (d) –100 + 110 – 121 + ...
   (e) 1/10 + 1/100 + 1/1000 + ...
2. (a) What is 1/10 + 1/100 + 1/1000 + ... as a recurring decimal?
   (b) Express 0.37373737 ... as an infinite geometric series and find the fraction it represents.
3. What fractions do these decimals represent?
   (a) 0.52525252 ...
   (b) 0.358358358...
   (c) 0.194949494 ...
4. (a) A GP has a common ratio of 0.65. Its sum to infinity is 120. What is the first term?
   (b) Another GP has 2.8 as its first term and its sum to infinity is 3.2 Find its common ratio.
5. Rosita is using a device to extract air from a bottle of wine. This helps to preserve the wine left in the bottle.

   The pump she uses can extract a maximum of 46 cm^3. In practice what happens is that the first attempt extracts 46 cm^3 and subsequent extractions follow a geometric sequence.

   Rosita's second attempt extracts 36 cm^3. What is the maximum amount of air she can remove in total?

6. A rubber ball is dropped from a height of 6 metres and after the first bounce rises to a height of 4.7 m. It is left to continue bouncing until it stops.
   (a) A computerized timer is started when it first hits the ground. The second contact with the ground occurs after 1.958 seconds and the third after 3.690 seconds. Given that the times between consecutive contacts with the ground follow a geometric sequence, how long does the ball take to stop bouncing?
   (b) The heights to which the ball rises after each impact also follow a geometric sequence. Between the release of the ball and the second bounce the ball travels 6 + 2 x 4.7 = 15.4 m. How far does the ball travel altogether?

13.3 Arithmetic sequences

Geometric sequences involve a constant ratio between consecutive terms. Another important type of sequence involves a constant **difference** between consecutive terms; such a sequence is called an **arithmetic** sequence.

In an experiment to measure the descent of a trolley rolling down a slope a 'tickertape timer' is used to measure the distance travelled in each second. The results are shown in the table.

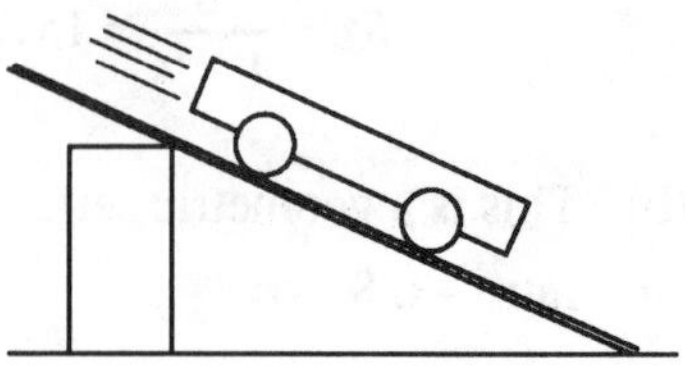

Second	cm travelled in second
1	3
2	5
3	7
4	9
5	11
6	13

The sequence 3, 5, 7, 9, 11, 13 is an example of an arithmetic sequence. The sequence starts with 3 and thereafter each term is 2 more than the previous one. The difference of 2 is known as the **common difference**.

It would be useful to find the total distance travelled in the first 6 seconds by adding the numbers together. A quick numerical trick for doing this is to imagine writing the numbers out twice, once forwards once backwards, as shown below

$$\begin{array}{cccccc} 3 & 5 & 7 & 9 & 11 & 13 \\ 13 & 11 & 9 & 7 & 5 & 3 \end{array}$$

Each pair of vertical numbers adds up to 16. So adding the two sequences, you have 6×16 between them. Hence the sum of the original series is

$$\frac{1}{2} \times (6 \times 16) = 48.$$

The sum of terms of an arithmetic sequence is called an **arithmetic series** or **progression**, often called AP for short.

Activity 9 Distance travelled

Use the example above of a trolley rolling down a slope to answer these questions.

(a) Work out the distance travelled in the 20th second.

(b) Calculate S_{20}, the distance travelled in the first 20 seconds, using the above method.

(c) What is the distance travelled in the nth second?

(d) Show that the trolley travels a distance of $n(n+2)$ cm in the first n seconds.

Example

Consider the arithmetic sequence 8, 12, 16, 20 ...

Find expressions

(a) for u_n, (the nth term) (b) for S_n.

Solution

In this AP the first term is 8 and the common difference 4.

(a) $u_1 = 8$

$u_2 = 8 + 4$

$u_3 = 8 + 2 \times 4$

$u_4 = 8 + 3 \times 4$ etc.

u_n is obtained by adding on the common difference $(n-1)$ times.

$$\Rightarrow \quad u_n = 8 + 4(n-1)$$

$$= 4n + 4$$

(b) To find S_n, follow the procedure explained previously:

8	12	....	$4n$	$4n+4$
$4n+4$	$4n$	....	12	8

Each pair adds up to $4n+12$. There are n pairs.

So $$2S_n = n(4n+12)$$

$$= 4n(n+3)$$

giving $$S_n = 2n(n+3).$$

Exercise 13C

1. Use the 'numerical trick' to calculate
   (a) $3 + 7 + 11 + ... + 27$
   (b) $52 + 46 + 40 + ... + 4$
   (c) the sum of all the numbers on a traditional clock face;
   (d) the sum of all the odd numbers between 1 and 99.

2. Find formulae for u_n and S_n in these sequences :
   (a) 1, 4, 7, 10, ...
   (b) 12, 21, 30, 39, ...
   (c) 60, 55, 50, 45, ...
   (d) 1, $2\frac{1}{2}$, 4, $5\frac{1}{2}$, ...

3. A model railway manufacturer makes pieces of track of lengths 8 cm, 10 cm, 12 cm, etc. up to and including 38 cm. An enthusiast buys 5 pieces of each length. What total length of track can be made?

The general arithmetic sequence is often denoted by

$a,\ a+d,\ a+2d,\ a+3d,$ etc. ...

To sum the series of the first n terms of the sequence,

$$S_n = a + (a+d) + (a+2d) + \ \dots\ + (a+(n-1)d)$$

Note that the order can be reversed to give

$$S_n = (a+(n-1)d) + (a+(n-2)d) + \ \dots\ + a$$

Adding the two expressions for S_n gives

$$2S_n = (2a+(n-1)d) + (2a+(n-1)d) + \ \dots\ + (2a+(n-1)d)$$
$$= n[2a+(n-1)d]$$

So

$$\boxed{S_n = \tfrac{n}{2}(2a+(n-1)d)}$$

An alternative form for S_n is given in terms of its first and last term, a and l, where

$$l = a+(n-1)d$$

since the nth term of the sequence is given by

$$u_n = a+(n-1)d.$$

Thus

$$S_n = \tfrac{n}{2}(a+l)$$

Example

Sum the series 5 + 9 + 13 + ... to 20 terms.

Solution

This is an arithmetic sequence with first term 5 and common difference 4; so

$$S_{20} = \frac{20}{2}(2\times 5 + 19\times 4) = 860$$

Example

The sum of the series 1 + 8 + 15 + ... is 396. How many terms does the series contain?

Solution

This is an arithmetic sequence with first term 1 and common difference 7. Let the number of terms in the sequence be n.

$$S_n = 396$$

$$\Rightarrow \quad \frac{n}{2}\left(2+7(n-1)\right) = 396$$

$$\Rightarrow \quad n(7n-5) = 792$$

$$\Rightarrow \quad 7n^2 - 5n - 792 = 0$$

$$\Rightarrow \quad (7n+72)(n-11) = 0$$

$$\Rightarrow \quad n = 11 \text{ since } -\frac{72}{7} \text{ is not an integer.}$$

The number of terms is 11.

Activity 10 Ancient Babylonian problem

Ten brothers receive 100 shekels between them. Each brother receives a constant amount more than the next oldest. The seventh oldest brother receives 7 shekels. How much does each brother receive?

Exercise 13D

1. Find the sum of

   (a) 11 + 14 + 17 + ... to 16 terms

   (b) 27 + 22 + 17 + ... to 10 terms

   (c) 5 + 17 + 29 + ... + 161

   (d) 7.2 + 7.8 + 8.4 + ... to 21 terms

   (e) 90 + 79 + 68 + ... −20

   (f) 0.12 + 0.155 + 0.19 + ... to 150 terms

2. The last three terms of an arithmetical sequence with 18 terms is as follows : ...67, 72, 77. Find the first term and the sum of the series.

3. How many terms are there if

   (a) 52 + 49 + 46 + ... = 385?

   (b) 0.35 + 0.52 + 0.69 + ... = 35.72?

4. The first term of an arithmetic series is 16 and the last is 60. The sum of the arithmetic series is 342. Find the common difference.

5. New employees joining a firm in the clerical grade receive an annual salary of £8500. Every year they stay with the firm they have a salary increase of £800, up to a maximum of £13300 p.a. How much does a new employee earn in total, up to and including the year on maximum salary?

13.4 Sigma notation

Repeatedly having to write out terms in a series is time consuming. Mathematicians have developed a form of notation which both shortens the process and is easy to use. It involves the use of the Greek capital letter Σ (sigma), the equivalent of the letter S, for sum.

The series $2 + 4 + 8 + \ldots + 2^{12}$ can be shortened to $\sum_{r=1}^{12} 2^r$.

This is because every term in the series is of the form 2^r, and all the values of 2^r, from $r = 1$ to $r = 12$ are added up. In this example the '2^r' is called the **general term**; 12 and 1 are the top and bottom **limits** of the sum.

Similarly, the series

$$60 + 60 \times (0.95) + \ldots + 60 \times (0.95)^{30}$$

can be abbreviated to

$$\sum_{r=0}^{30} 60 \times (0.95)^r.$$

Often there is more than one way to use the notation. The series

$$\frac{1}{2} + \frac{2}{3} + \frac{3}{4} + \ \ldots \ + \frac{99}{100}$$

has a general term that could be thought of as either

$\frac{r}{r+1}$ or as $\frac{r-1}{r}$. Hence the series can be written as either

$$\sum_{r=1}^{99} \frac{r}{r+1} \text{ or } \sum_{r=2}^{100} \frac{r-1}{r}.$$

Example

Write out what $\sum_{r=1}^{9} (10-r)^2$ means and write down another way of expressing the same series, using Σ notation.

Solution

$$\sum_{r=1}^{9}(10-r)^2 = (10-1)^2+(10-2)^2+\ \dots\ +(10-9)^2$$

$$= 9^2+8^2+\ \dots\ +1^2$$

An alternative way of writing the same series is to think of it in reverse:

$$1^2+2^2+\ \dots\ +8^2+9^2 = \sum_{r=1}^{9} r^2$$

Example

Express in Σ notation 'the sum of all multiples of 5 between 1 and 100 inclusive'.

Solution

All multiples of 5 are of the form $5r, r \in \mathbb{N}$.

$100 = 5 \times 20$, so the top limit is 20. The lowest multiple of 5 to be included is 5×1. The sum is therefore

$$5+10+15+\ \dots\ +100 = \sum_{r=1}^{20} 5r$$

Example

Express in Σ notation 'the sum of the first n positive integers ending in 3'.

Solution

Numbers ending in 3 have the form $10r+3$, $r \in \mathbb{N}$. The first number required is 3 itself, so the bottom limit must be $r = 0$. This means that the top limit must be $n-1$. Hence the answer is

$$\sum_{r=0}^{n-1}(10r+3) \qquad (= 3+13+\ \dots\ +(10n-7))$$

[An alternative answer is $\sum_{r=1}^{n}(10r-7)$]

Exercise 13E

1. Write out the first three and last terms of:

   (a) $\sum_{r=5}^{15} r^2$ (b) $\sum_{r=1}^{10} (2r-1)$

   (c) $\sum_{r=1}^{n} r$ (d) $\sum_{r=3}^{10} \frac{r-2}{r}$

   (e) $\sum_{r=6}^{100} (r-2)^2$

2. Shorten these expressions using Σ notation.

   (a) $1+\frac{1}{2}+\frac{1}{3}+...+\frac{1}{25}$

   (b) $10+11+12+...+50$

   (c) $1+8+27+...+n^3$

   (d) $1+3+9+27+...+3^{12}$

   (e) $6+11+16+...+(5n+1)$

   (f) $14+17+20+...+62$

   (g) $5+50+500+...+5\times10^n$.

   (h) $\frac{1}{6}+\frac{2}{12}+\frac{3}{20}+...+\frac{20}{21\times22}$

3. Use Σ notation to write:

   (a) the sum of all natural numbers with two digits;

   (b) the sum of the first 60 odd numbers;

   (c) the sum of all the square numbers from 100 to 400 inclusive;

   (d) the sum of all numbers between 1 and 100 inclusive that leave remainder 1 when divided by 7.

4. Find alternative ways, using Σ notation, of writing these:

   (a) $\sum_{r=1}^{19} (20-r)$ (b) $\sum_{r=2}^{41} \frac{1}{r-1}$ (c) $\sum_{r=-3}^{3} r^2$

13.5 More series

Activity 11

(a) Write down the values of $(-1)^0$, $(-1)^1$, $(-1)^2$, $(-1)^3$ etc. Generalise your answers.

(b) Write down the first three terms and the last term of

(i) $\sum_{r=0}^{10} (-1)^r \frac{1}{2^r}$ (ii) $\sum_{r=0}^{10} (-1)^{r+1}\left(\frac{r^2}{r^2+1}\right)$

(c) How can you write the series

$$100-100\times(0.8)+100\times(0.8)^2 \text{ ... to } n \text{ terms}$$

using Σ notation?

Activity 12 Properties of Σ

(a) Calculate the numerical values of

$$\sum_{r=1}^{5} r \quad \sum_{r=1}^{5} r^2 \quad \sum_{r=1}^{5} r^3 \quad \sum_{r=1}^{5} \left(r+r^2\right) \quad \sum_{r=1}^{5} 3r$$

(b) If $u_1, u_2, \ldots u_n$ and $v_1, v_2, \ldots, v_n$ are two sequences of numbers, is it true that

$$\sum_{r=1}^{n}(u_r+v_r)=\sum_{r=1}^{n}u_r+\sum_{r=1}^{n}v_r?$$

Justify your answer.

(c) Investigate the truth or falsehood of these statements:

(i) $\sum_{r=1}^{n}u_r v_r=\left(\sum_{r=1}^{n}u_r\right)\left(\sum_{r=1}^{n}v_r\right)$

(ii) $\sum_{r=1}^{n}u_r^2=\left(\sum_{r=1}^{n}u_r\right)^2$

(iii) $\sum_{r=1}^{n}\alpha u_r=\alpha\left(\sum_{r=1}^{n}u_r\right)$ [α is any number.]

Again, justify your answers fully.

(d) What is the value of $\sum_{r=1}^{5}(r+1)$?

What is $\sum_{r=1}^{n}1$? and $\sum_{r=1}^{n}r$?

Exercise 13F

1. Work out the numerical value of

(a) $\sum_{r=1}^{10}1$ (b) $\sum_{r=1}^{25}4$

(c) $\sum_{r=0}^{16}(3+5r)$ (d) $\sum_{r=0}^{30}3\times(3.5)^r$

(e) $\sum_{r=1}^{\infty}(0.7)^r$ (f) $\sum_{r=0}^{\infty}5\times(-\frac{2}{3})^r$

2. Use $\sum$ notation to write these:

(a) $1-\frac{1}{2}+\frac{1}{3}-\frac{1}{4}+\ldots-\frac{1}{6}$

(b) $-1+4-9+16-\ldots+144$

(c) $12-12\times0.2+12\times0.04-\ldots+12\times(0.2)^{50}$

3. If you know that

$$\sum_{r=1}^{n}u_r=20 \text{ and } \sum_{r=1}^{n}v_r=64$$

calculate where possible:

(a) $\sum_{r=1}^{n}(u_r+v_r)$ (b) $\sum_{r=1}^{n}u_r v_r$

(c) $\sum_{r=1}^{n}u_r^2$ (d) $\sum_{r=1}^{n}\frac{1}{2}v_r$

(e) $\sum_{r=1}^{n}(v_r-u_r)$ (f) $\sum_{r=1}^{n}(5u_r-v_r)$

(g) $\sum_{r=1}^{2n}u_r$ (h) $\sum_{r=1}^{n}(-1)^r v_r$

*13.6 Useful formulae

You will find it useful to know three important results

- a formula for $\sum_{r=1}^{n} r \quad (1+2+3+ \ldots +n)$
- a formula for $\sum_{r=1}^{n} r^2 \quad \left(1^2+2^2+3^2+ \ldots +n^2\right)$
- a formula for $\sum_{r=1}^{n} r^3 \quad \left(1^3+2^3+3^3+ \ldots +n^3\right)$

The following few activities are designed to illustrate cases where these series arise, and to work out what these formulae are.

Activity 13 Sum of first n natural numbers

Find a formula for $\sum_{r=1}^{n} r$ by

(a) treating the sum as an arithmetic series:

(b) using a geometrical argument based on the diagram on the right;

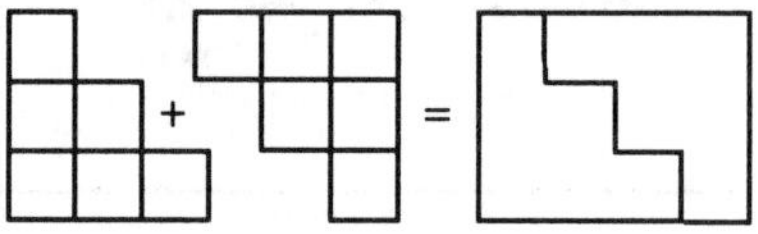

(c) starting from the statement

$$\sum_{r=1}^{n} r = \sum_{r=1}^{n}((n+1)-r).$$

Activity 14 Another chess board problem

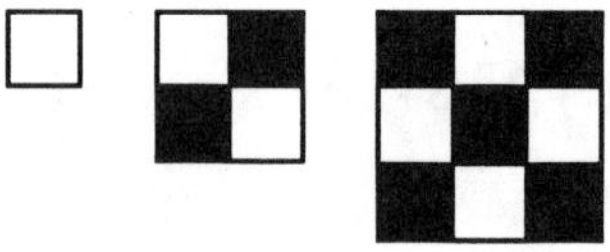

(a) How many squares are there in each of the 'mini chessboards' on the right?

(b) How many squares are there on a chessboard? Express your answer using $\sum$ notation.

(c) What is a corresponding three dimensional problem?

Activity 15 Sum of squares

(a) Work out $\sum_{r=1}^{n} r(r+1)$ for $n = 1, 2, 3, \ldots 8$.

Copy and complete the table of results opposite.

(b) Prepare formula for $\sum_{r=1}^{n} r(r+1)$.

(c) Use your formulae for $\sum_{r=1}^{n} r(r+1)$ and $\sum_{r=1}^{n} r$ to obtain a formula for $\sum_{r=1}^{n} r^2$.

n	$\sum_{r=1}^{n} r(r+1)$
1	2
2	8
3	20
4	...
5	...
6	...
7	168
8	...

Activity 16 Sum of cubes

(a) For $n = 1, 2, 3$ and 4, work out $\sum_{r=1}^{n} r$ and $\sum_{r=1}^{n} r^3$.

Conjecture a formula for $\sum_{r=1}^{n} r^3$.

(b) Prove this formula by starting from the statement

$$\sum_{r=1}^{n} r^3 = \sum_{r=1}^{n} \left((n+1) - r\right)^3 .$$

Why could a similar approach not be used to prove the formula for $\sum r^2$?

The results of the last few activities can be summarised as follows.

$$\sum_{r=1}^{n} r = \frac{1}{2} n(n+1)$$

$$\sum_{r=1}^{n} r^2 = \frac{1}{6} n(n+1)(2n+1)$$

$$\sum_{r=1}^{n} r^3 = \frac{1}{4} n^2 (n+1)^2$$

The useful fact that $\sum r^3 = \left(\sum r\right)^2$ is a coincidence (if there is such a thing in maths). It is not possible to extend this to find $\sum r^4, \sum r^5$ etc. Formulae do exist for sums of higher powers, but they are somewhat cumbersome and seldom useful.

Exercise 13G

1. Write down the general term, and hence evaluate:
   (a) $1+2+3+ ... +20$
   (b) $1^2+2^2+3^2+ ... +10^2$
   (c) $2+8+18+ ... +(2\times15^2)$
   (d) $2+4+6+ ... +100$
   (e) $1+3+5+ ... +25$
   (f) $1+8+27+ ... +1000$

2. Work out $\sum_{r=10}^{20} r$. Use the fact that

$$\sum_{r=10}^{20} r = \sum_{r=0}^{20} r - \sum_{r=0}^{9} r.$$

3. Use techniques similar to that in Question 2 to calculate
   (a) $11^2+12^2+ ... +24^2$
   (b) $7^3+8^3+ ... +15^3$
   (c) $21+23+ ... +61$

4. Calculate $21+23+25 ... +161$

5. Prove that $\sum_{r=0}^{2n} r = n(2n+1)$

   and hence that $\sum_{r=n+1}^{2n} r = \frac{1}{2}n(3n+1)$

13.7 Miscellaneous Exercises

1. A piece of paper is 0.1 mm thick. Imagine it can be folded as many times as desired. After one fold, for example, the paper is 0.2 mm thick, and so on.
   (a) How thick is the folded paper after 10 folds?
   (b) How many times should the paper be folded for its thickness to be 3 metres or more? (About the height of a room.)
   (c) How many more times would it need to be folded for the thickness to reach the moon? (400 000 km away)

2. Find formulae for the nth terms of each of these sequences:
   (a) 4, 6, 9, 13.5, ...
   (b) 250, 244, 238, 232, ...
   (c) 10, 2, 0.4, 0.08, ...
   (d) 0.17, 0.49, 0.81, 1.13, ...

3. Evaluate these sums:
   (a) 12+15+18+21+ ... to 20 terms;
   (b) 4+12+36+108+ ... to 12 terms;
   (c) 5–2–9–16– ... –65;
   (d) 240+180+135+ ... to infinity.

4. The first term of a geometric sequence is 7 and the third term is 63. Find the second term.

5. Consider the arithmetic series 5+9+13+17+...
   (a) How many terms of this series are less than 1000?
   (b) What is the least value of n for which $S_n > 1000$?

6. The ninth term of an arithmetic progression is 52 and the sum of the first twelve terms is 414. Find the first term and the common difference.
   (AEB)

7. In an arithmetic progression, the eighth term is twice the 3rd term and the 20th term is 110.
   (a) Find the common difference.
   (b) Determine the sum of the first 100 terms.
   (AEB)

8. The first term of a geometric progression is 8 and the sum to infinity is 400.
   (a) Find the common ratio.
   (b) Determine the least number of terms with a sum greater than 399. (AEB)

9. The sum of the first and second terms of a geometric progression is 108 and the sum of the third and fourth term is 12. Find the two posible values of the common ratio and the corresponding values of the first term.
   (AEB)

14 FURTHER CALCULUS

Objectives

After studying this chapter you should

- be able to find the second derivatives of functions;
- be able to use calculus to find maximum or minimum of functions;
- be able to differentiate composite functions or 'function of a function';
- be able to differentiate the product or quotient of two functions;
- be able to use calculus in curve sketching.

14.0 Introduction

You should have already covered the material in Chapters 8, 11 and 12 before starting this chapter. By now, you will already have met the ideas of calculus, both differentiation and integration, and you will have used the techniques developed in the earlier chapters to solve problems. This section extends the range of problems you can solve, including finding the greatest or least value of a function and differentiating complicated functions.

14.1 Rate of change of the gradient

The sketch opposite shows the graph of

$$y = x^3 + 3x^2 - 9x - 4.$$

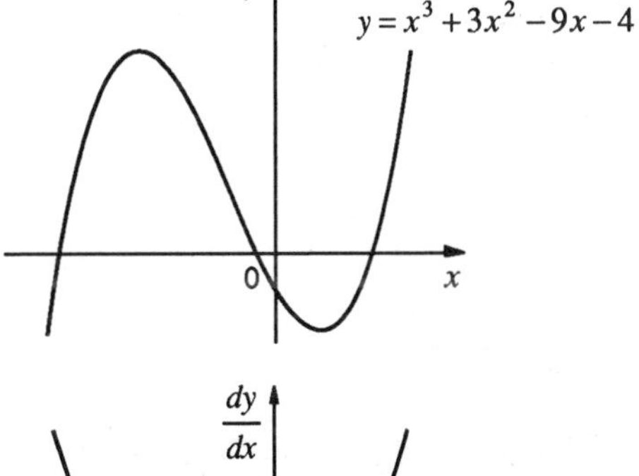

You have already seen that the derivative of this function is given by

$$\frac{dy}{dx} = 3x^2 + 6x - 9.$$

This is also illustrated opposite.

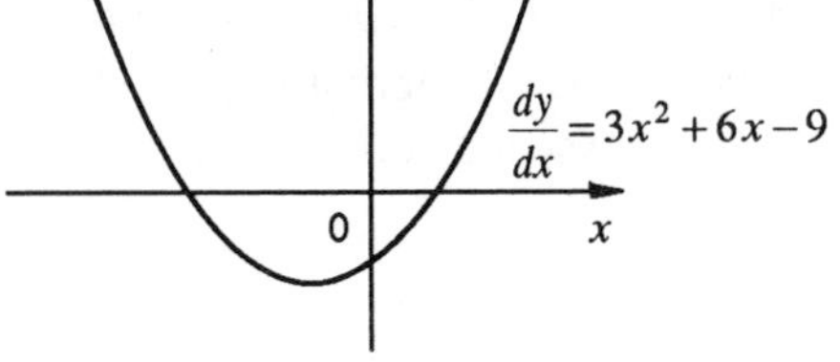

The gradient function, $\frac{dy}{dx}$, is also a function of x, and can be differentiated again to give the **second** differential

$$\frac{d^2y}{dx^2} = 6x + 6.$$

Again this is illustrated opposite.

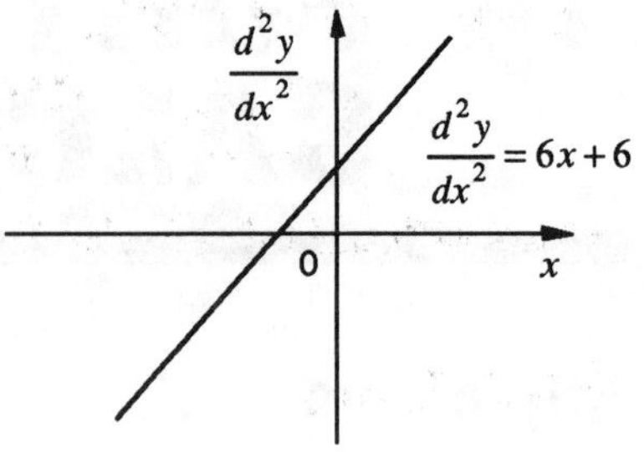

Exercise 14A

1. Find the second derivative of these functions :

   (a) $y = x^3$ (b) $y = x^4$ (c) $y = x^2$

   (d) $y = x$ (e) $y = \frac{1}{x}$ (f) $y = 4x^3 - 12x^2 + 5$

   (g) $y = 3x + 1$ (h) $y = e^x$ (i) $y = \ln x$

2. Find $\frac{d^3y}{dx^3}$ if y is

   (a) x^4 (b) $5x^2 + \frac{3}{x^2}$ (c) e^x

   (d) $\ln x$ (e) $2x$

14.2 Stationary points

In this section you will consider the curve with equation

$$y = 2x^3 + 3x^2 - 12x.$$

This is cubic, and a rough sketch of its graph is shown opposite. It has two **stationary points** (sometimes called **turning points**) at which the gradient is zero.

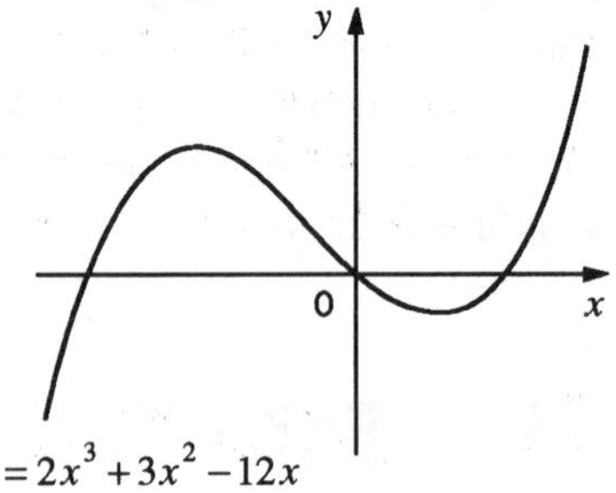

$y = 2x^3 + 3x^2 - 12x$

How can you find the coordinates of the stationary points?

Activity 1

Find the coordinates of the stationary points for the curve with equation

$$y = 2x^3 + 3x^2 - 12x.$$

In Chapter 8 you saw that the nature of the stationary points can be determined by looking at the gradient on each side of the stationary point. Here an alternative more formal method is developed, based on using second derivatives.

Activity 2

Draw an accurate sketch of the curve with equation

$$y = 2x^3 + 3x^2 - 12x$$

between $x = -3$ and $+2$. Choose the y axis to show values between -10 and $+20$.

For every x value –3, –2.8, –2.6, –2.4, ..., 2, note the gradient on the diagram.

Plot a graph of the gradient function and note how it behaves near the stationary point of the function.

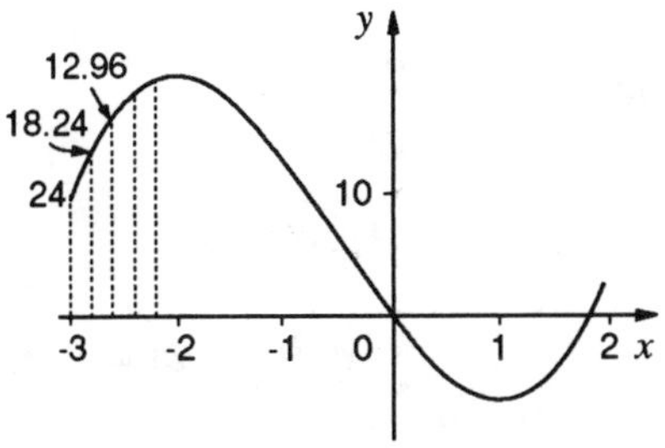

For a **maximum** value of a function, note that the gradient is decreasing in value as it passes through the value zero at the stationary point, whereas for a **minimum** value this gradient is increasing.

The result can be summarised as

> For **stationary points** of a function $y(x)$
>
> $$\frac{dy}{dx} = 0.$$
>
> If $\frac{d^2y}{dx^2} < 0$ at a stationary point, it corresponds to a **maximum** value of y.
>
> If $\frac{d^2y}{dx^2} > 0$ at a stationary point, it corresponds to a **minimum** value of y.

Example

Find maxima and minima of the curve with equation

$$y = \frac{1}{4}x^4 + \frac{1}{3}x^3 - 6x^2 + 3.$$

Hence sketch the curve.

Solution

For stationary points, $\frac{dy}{dx}=0$, which gives

$$\frac{dy}{dx}= x^3+x^2-12x.$$

So
$$\frac{dy}{dx}=0$$

$$\Rightarrow \quad x^3+x^2-12x = 0$$

$$x(x^2+x-12) = 0$$

$$x(x+4)(x-3) = 0.$$

Hence there are stationary points at $x=0,-4$ and 3. To find out their nature, the second derivative is used. Now

$$\frac{d^2y}{dx^2}=3x^2+2x-12.$$

At $x=0$, $\frac{d^2y}{dx^2}=-12<0$

$\Rightarrow$ a maximum at $x=0$ of value $y=3$.

At $x=-4$, $\frac{d^2y}{dx^2} = 3(-4)^2+2(-4)-12 = 28>0$

$\Rightarrow$ minimum at $x=-4$ of value

$$y = \frac{1}{4}(-4)^4+\frac{1}{3}(-4)^3-6(-4)^2+3 = -\frac{151}{3}.$$

At $x=3$, $\frac{d^2y}{dx^2} = 3(3)^2+2(3)-12 = 21>0$

$\Rightarrow$ minimum at $x=3$ of value

$$y = \frac{1}{4}(3)^4+\frac{1}{3}(3)^3-6(3)^2+3 = -\frac{87}{4}.$$

The information so far found can be sketched on a graph (not to scale). You also know that as $x\to\pm\infty$, $y\to+\infty$. It is now clear how to sketch the shape - shown dashed on the diagram.

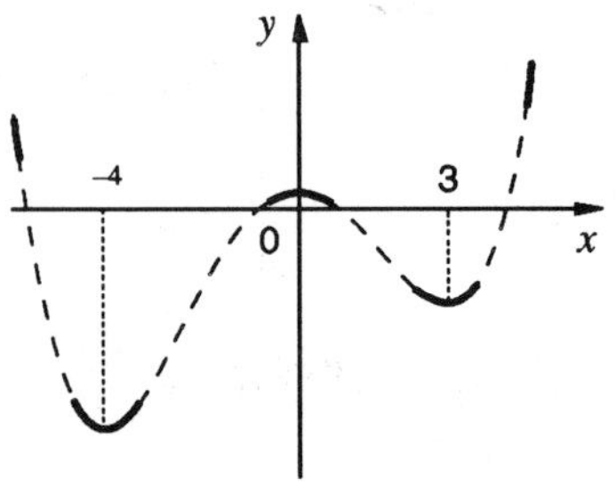

There is one further type of stationary point to be considered and that is a **point of inflection**. An example is given in the next activity.

Activity 3

Find the stationary point of $y = x^3$.

What is the value of $\frac{d^2y}{dx^2}$ at the stationary point?

Sketch the graph of $y = x^3$.

For a **horizontal** point of inflection, not only does $\frac{dy}{dx} = 0$, but also $\frac{d^2y}{dx^2} = 0$, and $\frac{d^3y}{dx^3} \neq 0$, at the point. These are **sufficient** but not **necessary** conditions, as can be seen by considering $y = x^5$.

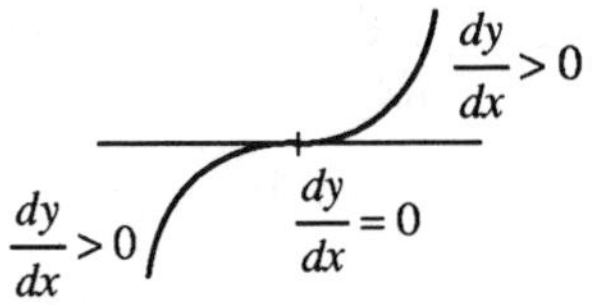

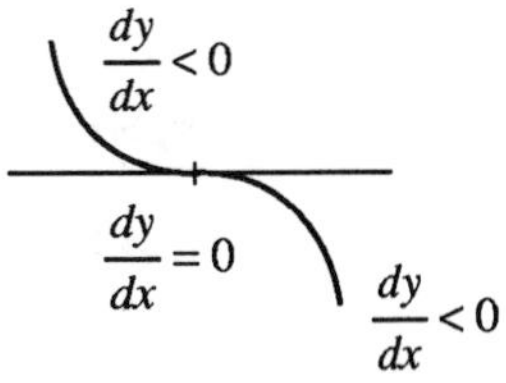

Activity 4

Find the stationary point of $y = x^5$.

What is the value of $\frac{d^2y}{dx^2}$ and $\frac{d^3y}{dx^3}$ at its stationary point?

Sketch the graph of $y = x^5$.

Example

Find the nature of the stationary points of the curve with equation

$$y = x^4 + 4x^3 - 6$$

Sketch a graph of the curve.

Solution

Now

$$\frac{dy}{dx} = 4x^3 + 12x^2$$

$$= 0 \text{ when } 4x^3 + 12x^2 = 0$$

$$\Rightarrow \quad 4x^2(x+3) = 0$$

$$\Rightarrow \quad x = 0, -3 \text{ for stationary points}$$

But $$\frac{d^2y}{dx^2} = 12x^2 + 24x$$

At $x = 0, \dfrac{d^2y}{dx^2} = 0$, but $\dfrac{d^3y}{dx^3} = 24x + 24 = 24 > 0$ at $x = 0$.

So there is a point of inflection at (0, – 6).

$$\text{At } x = -3, \frac{d^2y}{dx^2} = 12(-3)^2 + 24(-3)$$
$$= 108 - 72 = 36 > 0$$

So there is a minimum at $x = -3$ of value

$$y(-3) = (-3)^4 + 4(-3)^3 - 6$$
$$= 81 - 4 \times 27 - 6$$
$$= -33$$

To sketch the curve, also note that

$$y \to \infty \text{ as } x \to \pm\infty.$$

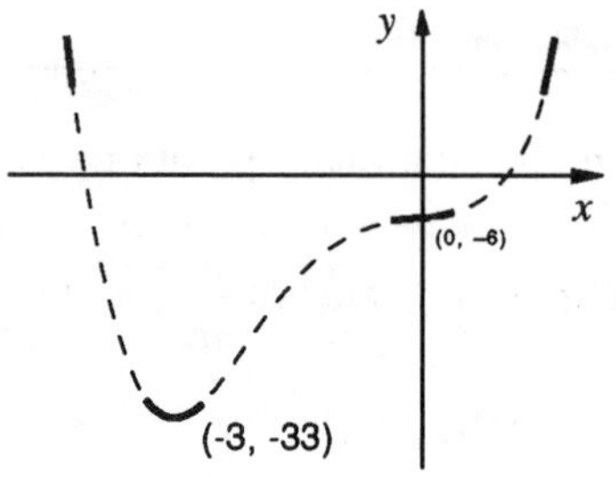

You can then deduce the form of curve, shown dashed opposite.

Finally, in this section, it should be noted that the conditions given earlier are **sufficient** conditions to guarantee max/min values, but not **necessary**.

Activity 5

Draw the graph of $y = x^4$.

Does it have any maximum or minimum values?

Do the conditions hold?

By now you are probably getting confused since there is a rule to determine the nature of stationary points, yet not all functions satisfy it. So let it be stressed that

(a) Stationary points are always given by $\dfrac{dy}{dx} = 0$.

(b) If, at the stationary point, $\dfrac{d^2y}{dx^2} > 0$, there is a minimum,

whereas if $\dfrac{d^2y}{dx^2} < 0$, there is a maximum.

(c) If, at the stationary point, $\frac{d^2y}{dx^2} = 0$, then there is a point of inflection provided $\frac{d^3y}{dx^3} \neq 0$.

Conditions (b) and (c) are sufficient to guarantee the nature of the stationary point, but, as you have already seen **not** necessary.

When this analysis does not hold, that is when $\frac{d^2y}{dx^2} = \frac{d^3y}{dx^3} = 0$ at a stationary point, it is easier to consider the **sign** of the gradient each side of the stationary point.

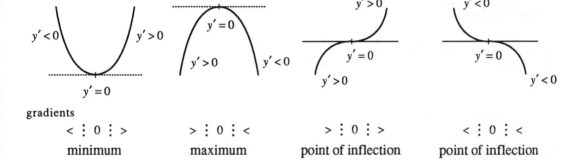

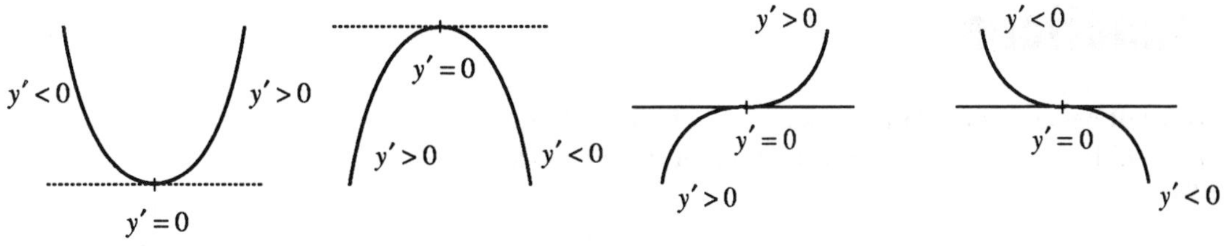

gradients

< ⋮ 0 ⋮ >	> ⋮ 0 ⋮ <	> ⋮ 0 ⋮ >	< ⋮ 0 ⋮ <
minimum	maximum	point of inflection	point of inflection

Example

Show that $y = x^4$ has a minimum at $x = 0$.

Solution

For stationary points $\quad \frac{dy}{dx} = 4x^3$

$$= 0 \Rightarrow x = 0$$

But, if $x = 0$, $\quad \frac{d^2y}{dx^2} = 12x^2 = 0$

and $\quad \frac{d^3y}{dx^3} = 24x = 0$

So you cannot use the usual results, but at, for example,

$$x = -0.1 \Rightarrow \frac{dy}{dx} = 4(-0.1)^3 = -0.004 < 0$$

$$x = 0.1 \Rightarrow \frac{dy}{dx} = 4(0.1)^3 = 0.004 > 0$$

So there is a **minimum** at $x = 0$.

Exercise 14B

1. Find the turning points of these curves using differentiation. In each case, find out whether the points found are maxima, minima or points of inflection.

   (a) $y = 2x^2 + 3x - 1$ (b) $y = x^3 - 12x + 6$

   (c) $y = x^3 + 2x^2 - 5x - 6$ (d) $y = x^2 - 4x + 2\ln(x)$

   (e) $y = e^x - 4x$ (f) $y = e^x + 5$

2. Investigate the nature of the stationary points of the curve

   $$y = (x-1)(x-a)^2$$

   when (a) $a > 1$ (b) $0 < a < 1$. In each case give a sketch of the curve.

14.3 Differentiating composite functions

The crucial result needed here is the 'function of a function' rule. It can be justified by noting that if y is a function of u, and u is a function of x

i.e. $y = f(u)$ and $u = g(x)$

then a small change, δx say, in x will result in a small change, say δu in u, which in turn results in a small change, δy in y. Now

$$\frac{\delta y}{\delta x} = \frac{\delta y}{\delta u} \times \frac{\delta u}{\delta x}$$

and if you let $\delta x \to 0$, then $\delta u \to 0$ and $\delta y \to 0$, and the equation becomes

$$\frac{dy}{dx} = \frac{dy}{du} \times \frac{du}{dx}$$

For example, suppose

$$y = (3x+2)^2$$

then one way to differentiate this function is to multiply out the brackets and differentiate term by term;

$$y = (3x+2)(3x+2)$$

$$= 9x^2 + 12x + 4$$

and $\dfrac{dy}{dx} = 18x + 12.$

Another method, which will be even more useful as the functions get more complicated, is to introduce a new variable u defined by

$$u = 3x + 2$$

so that $\quad y = u^2.$

Now $\dfrac{dy}{du} = 2u$ and $\dfrac{du}{dx} = 3$, so using the result above

$$\frac{dy}{dx} = (2u) \times 3 = 6(3x + 2), \text{ as before.}$$

Activity 6

Use both methods described above to differentiate the functions:

(a) $y = (5x - 1)^2$ (b) $y = (3 - 2x)^3$.

Example

If $y = e^{x^2}$, find $\dfrac{dy}{dx}$.

Solution

As before, introduce a new variable u defined by

$$u = x^2$$

so that

$$y = e^u.$$

Now $\quad \dfrac{dy}{du} = e^u$ and $\dfrac{du}{dx} = 2x$

giving $\quad \dfrac{dy}{dx} = \dfrac{dy}{du} \times \dfrac{du}{dx} = (e^u)2x = 2xe^{x^2}.$

What is the value of $\int xe^{x^2} dx$?

Another important result needed is given by

$$\boxed{\frac{dy}{dx} = 1 / \frac{dx}{dy}}$$

but note that this is only true for **first** derivatives.

For example, if $y = x^2$

then $$\frac{dy}{dx} = 2x$$

But, expressing x as a function of y,

$$x = y^{\frac{1}{2}}$$

and $$\frac{dx}{dy} = \frac{1}{2} y^{-\frac{1}{2}} = \frac{1}{2y^{\frac{1}{2}}} = \frac{1}{2x}$$

So, as expected $\frac{dy}{dx} = 1 / \frac{dx}{dy}$

Activity 7

Verify the result $\frac{dy}{dx} = 1 / \frac{dx}{dy}$ when

(a) $y = x^3$ (b) $y = \frac{1}{2}(x + 3)$

The proof of the result is based on using small increments (increase) δx and δy, noting that

$$\frac{\delta y}{\delta x} = 1 / \frac{\delta x}{\delta y}$$

and taking the limit as $\delta x \to 0$ (and $\delta y \to 0$).

This section is concluded by using this result in finding the derivative of the function

$$y = a^x$$

To achieve this, you must first take 'logs' of both sides to give

$$\ln y = \ln(a^x) = x \ln a \text{ (properties of logs)}$$

Defining $u = (\ln a)x \Rightarrow \frac{du}{dx} = \ln a$

and $u = \ln y$

Hence $\dfrac{du}{dy}=\dfrac{1}{y}$

giving $\dfrac{dy}{dx}=\dfrac{dy}{du}\dfrac{du}{dx}$

$=\left(1/\dfrac{du}{dy}\right)\ln a$

$=y\ln a$

$\dfrac{d}{dx}(a^x)=(\ln a)a^x$

so, for example

$\dfrac{d}{dx}(2^x)=(\ln 2)2^x$

What happens if $a=e$ in the formula above?

Exercise 14C

1. Differentiate these functions :

   (a) $y=(2x-5)^8$ $(u=2x-5)$

   (b) $y=(x^2+x^3)^{10}$ $(u=x^2+x^3)$

   (c) $y=\dfrac{1}{x-2}(u=x-2,\ y=u^{-1})$

   (d) $y=\dfrac{1}{(3x+1)^2}$ $(u=3x+1,\ y=u^{-2})$

   (e) $y=\sqrt{x+1}$ $(u=x+1,\ y=u^{\frac{1}{2}})$

   (f) $y=(e^x-x)^6$ $(u=e^x-x)$

   (g) $y=\ln(3x+4)$ $(u=3x+4)$

   (h) $y=e^{\sqrt{x}}$ $(u=-\sqrt{x})$

2. Find any turning points on these curves :

   (a) $y=e^{x^2}$

   (b) $y=e^{-(x+4)^2}$ $\left(u=-(x+4)^2\right)$

   (c) $y=(\ln(x))^2$ $(u=\ln(x))$

   (d) $y=\left(x+\dfrac{1}{x}\right)^4$ $\left(u=x+\dfrac{1}{x}\right)$

3. A kettle contains water which is cooling according to the equation $W=80e^{-0.04t}+20$ where W is the temperature of the water in °C at time t (in minutes) after the kettle was switched off. Find the rate at which the water is cooling in °C/min when $t=30$ and when $t=60$.

4. The population of a country is modelled by the function

   $P=12\times(1.03)^t$

   where P is the population in millions and t is the time in years after the start of 1990. Find the rate at which the population is increasing in millions per year at the start of the year 2000.

5. (a) Differentiate e^{2x}. Hence write down $\int e^{2x}dx$.

   (b) Differentiate e^{-x}, and so write down $\int e^{-x}dx$.

6. Differentiate e^{x^2}, and use your result to find $\int xe^{x^2}dx$.

7. The derivative of $\ln x$ is $\dfrac{1}{x}$.

   By differentiating a suitable logarithmic function, find $\int\dfrac{1}{x+2}dx$.

14.4 Integration again

The results that have been developed in the last section are, as you will see, very useful in integration. For example, if

$$y = (x+5)^4$$

then $$\frac{dy}{dx} = 4(x+5)^3 \text{ (using the methods in the last section).}$$

Hence $$\int 4(x+5)^3 dx = (x+5)^4 + C \quad (C \text{ is arbitrary constant})$$

or $$\int (x+5)^3 dx = \frac{1}{4}(x+5)^4 + C' \quad (C' = \frac{1}{4}C).$$

Activity 8

Differentiate $y = (ax+b)^{n+1}$ and hence deduce the value of

$$\int (ax+b)^n dx.$$

Use your results to find:

(a) $\int (3x-1)^9 dx$ (b) $\int \frac{1}{(2x+4)^2} dx$ (c) $\int \sqrt{x-1}\, dx.$

Similarly, it can be seen that if

$$y = \ln(ax+b)$$

then $$\frac{dy}{dx} = \frac{a}{(ax+b)}.$$

Hence $$\int \frac{a dx}{(ax+b)} = \ln(ax+b) + C$$

or $$\boxed{\int \frac{dx}{(ax+b)} = \frac{1}{a}\ln(ax+b) + C'} \qquad C' = \frac{1}{a}C$$

Activity 9

Use the result above to evaluate:

(a) $\int \frac{dx}{(x+1)}$ (b) $\int \frac{dx}{4-x}$ (c) $\int \frac{dx}{1-2x}.$

Another important method of integration is based on the result that if

$$y = \ln f(x)$$

then defining $u = f(x)$, $y = \ln u$ and

$$\begin{aligned}\frac{dy}{dx} &= \frac{dy}{du} \times \frac{du}{dx} \\ &= \frac{1}{u} \times f'(x) \\ &= \frac{f'(x)}{f(x)}\end{aligned}$$

Hence $$\boxed{\int \frac{f'(x)}{f(x)}\, dx = \ln f(x) + C}$$

Example

Find $$\int \frac{(3x^2 + x)}{(2x^3 + x^2)}\, dx$$

Solution

If $f(x) = 2x^3 + x^2$, then $f'(x) = 6x^2 + 2x$, so the integral can be written as

$$\begin{aligned}I &= \int \frac{(3x^2 + x)}{(2x^3 + x^2)}\, dx \\ &= \frac{1}{2}\int \frac{2(3x^2 + x)}{(2x^3 + x^2)}\, dx \\ &= \frac{1}{2}\int \frac{f'(x)}{f(x)}\, dx \qquad (\text{when } f(x) = 2x^3 + x^2) \\ &= \frac{1}{2}\int \ln f(x) + C \\ &= \frac{1}{2}\ln(6x^2 + 2x) + C\end{aligned}$$

Exercise 14D

1. Find

(a) $\int (2x+1)^4\,dx$ (b) $\int \frac{1}{(x-5)^2}\,dx$

(c) $\int \frac{1}{\sqrt{x+1}}\,dx$ (d) $\int \sqrt{4x-1}\,dx$

2. Evaluate

(a) $\int_0^1 \frac{dx}{(x+1)}$ (b) $\int_1^2 \frac{dx}{(2x-1)}$

3. Find

(a) $\int \frac{dx}{(3x+2)}$ (b) $\int \frac{x}{x^2+1}\,dx$

(c) $\int \frac{e^x}{1+e^x}\,dx$

4. Evaluate $\int_0^1 xe^{-x^2}\,dx$

14.5 Differentiating products and quotients

These are very useful formulae for differentiating both products and quotients. For example, if y is defined as the product of the functions, u and v of x, then

$$y(x)=u(x)\,v(x)$$

Using the basic definition of a derivative, let δx be a small change in x, then consider

$$\begin{aligned} y(x+\delta x)-y(x) &= u(x+\delta x)\,v(x+\delta x)-u(x)\,v(x) \\ &= \left[u(x+\delta x)-u(x)\right]v(x+\delta x) \\ &\quad +u(x)\left[v(x+\delta x)-v(x)\right] \end{aligned}$$

(the middle two terms cancel)

Diving both sides by δx gives

$$\frac{y(x+\delta x)-y(x)}{\delta x}=\frac{(u(x+\delta x)-u(x))}{\delta x}v(x+\delta x)+u(x)\frac{(v(x+\delta x)-v(x))}{\delta x}$$

and taking the limit as $\delta x \to 0$, gives

$$\boxed{\frac{d}{dx}(uv)=\frac{du}{dx}v+u\frac{dv}{dx}}$$

(since $v(x+\delta x)\to v(x)$ as $\delta x \to 0$)

Example

If $y = x^2(x-1)^2$, find $\frac{dy}{dx}$ by

(a) using the formula above;

(b) multiplying out and differentiating term by term.

Solution

(a) Here $u = x^2, v = (x-1)^2$,

$$\text{so} \quad \frac{dy}{dx} = 2x(x-1)^2 + x^2\,2(x-1)$$

$$= 2x(x-1)(x-1+x)$$

$$= 2x(x-1)(2x-1).$$

(b) $y = x^2(x^2 - 2x + 1) = x^4 - 2x^3 + x^2$.

$$\frac{dy}{dx} = 4x^3 - 6x^2 + 2x$$

$$= 2x(2x^2 - 3x + 1)$$

$$= 2x(x-1)(2x-1) \quad \text{(as before).}$$

Example

If $y = (x+1)e^{-x}$, find $\frac{dy}{dx}$.

Solution

This time, you must use the formula, with $u = x+1, v = e^{-x}$.

$$\text{So} \quad \frac{dy}{dx} = 1 \times \left(e^{-x}\right) + (x+1)\left(-e^{-x}\right)$$

$$= -xe^{-x}.$$

Turning to the equivalent formula for a quotient, with

$$y = \frac{u}{v} = u\left(\frac{1}{v}\right)$$

which is the product of u and $\frac{1}{v}$.

Now
$$\frac{d}{dx}\left(\frac{1}{v}\right)=\frac{d}{dv}\left(\frac{1}{v}\right)\frac{dv}{dx} \quad \text{('function of a function')}$$
$$=-\frac{1}{v^2}\frac{dv}{dx}$$

and
$$\frac{dy}{dx}=\frac{du}{dx}\times\frac{1}{v}+u\frac{d}{dx}\left(\frac{1}{v}\right)$$
$$=\frac{du}{dx}\times\frac{1}{v}+u\left(-\frac{1}{v^2}\frac{dv}{dx}\right).$$

i.e.
$$\boxed{\frac{d}{dx}\left(\frac{u}{v}\right)=\frac{\left(v\frac{du}{dx}-u\frac{dv}{dx}\right)}{v^2}}$$

Example

Use the quotient formula to find $\frac{d}{dx}((1+x)e^{-x})$.

Solution

Here $u=(1+x), v=e^x$, so that

$$y=\frac{u}{v}=\frac{(1+x)}{(e^x)}=(1+x)e^{-x}\ .$$

Thus $\frac{dy}{dx}=\frac{e^x\times1-(1+x)e^x}{(e^x)^2}$, since $\frac{d}{dx}(e^x)=e^x$

$$=-\frac{xe^x}{(e^x)^2}$$
$$=-\frac{x}{e^x}$$
$$=-xe^{-x} \qquad \text{(as in the previous example).}$$

So you can see that the quotient formula is just another form of the product formula. It is though sometimes very convenient to use.

Example

Differentiate $y = \dfrac{x-1}{2x-3}$ with respect to x.

Solution

Here $u = x-1$, $v = 2x-3$ and using the quotient formula

$$\frac{dy}{dx} = \frac{1\times(2x-3) - 2(x-1)}{(2x-3)^2}$$

$$= \frac{2x-3-2x+2}{(2x-3)^2}$$

$$= \frac{-1}{(2x-3)^2}.$$

***Activity 10**

Develop a formula for differentiating the product of **three** functions .

i.e. $y(x) = u(x)\,v(x)\,w(x)$.

Example

Find any stationary points for the curve with equation

$$y = \frac{x^3}{(1+x)}.$$

Sketch the curve.

Solution

Here $u = x^3$, $v = 1+x$, so $y = \dfrac{u}{v}$ and using the quotient formula

$$\frac{dy}{dx} = \frac{3x^2(1+x) - x^3\times 1}{(1+x)^2}$$

$$= \frac{3x^2+2x^3}{(1+x)^2}.$$

For stationary points,

$$3x^2 + 2x^3 = 0$$

$$x^2(3+2x) = 0$$

$$\Rightarrow \quad x = 0, -\tfrac{3}{2}$$

To determine the nature of these stationary points, you can check the sign of $\frac{dy}{dx}$ each side of the points.

So, for $x = 0$

$$\frac{dy}{dx}(-0.1) = \frac{3(-0.1)^2 + 2(-0.1)^3}{(1-0.1)^2} = \frac{0.03 - 0.002}{(0.9)^2}$$

$$= \frac{0.028}{0.81} > 0$$

and $$\frac{dy}{dx}(0.1) = \frac{3(0.1)^2 + 2(0.1)^3}{(1+0.1)^2} = \frac{0.03 + 0.002}{(1.1)^2}$$

$$= \frac{0.032}{1.21} > 0$$

So there is a point of inflection at $x = 0$ and value of function here is $y = 0$.

For $x = -1.5$,

$$\frac{dy}{dx}(-1.6) = \frac{3(-1.6)^2 + 2(-1.6)^3}{(1-1.6)^2} = \frac{-0.512}{0.36} < 0$$

$$\frac{dy}{dx}(-1.4) = \frac{3(-1.4)^2 + 2(-1.4)^3}{(1-1.4)^2} = \frac{0.392}{0.16} > 0$$

Hence there is a minimum at $x = -1.5$ of value $y = \frac{27}{4}$.

Also note that the function has an **asymptote** at $x = -1$, that is

$$y \to \pm\infty \text{ as } x \to -1.$$

As $x \to \pm\infty$, $y = \frac{x^3}{1+x} \approx \frac{x^3}{x} = x^2$

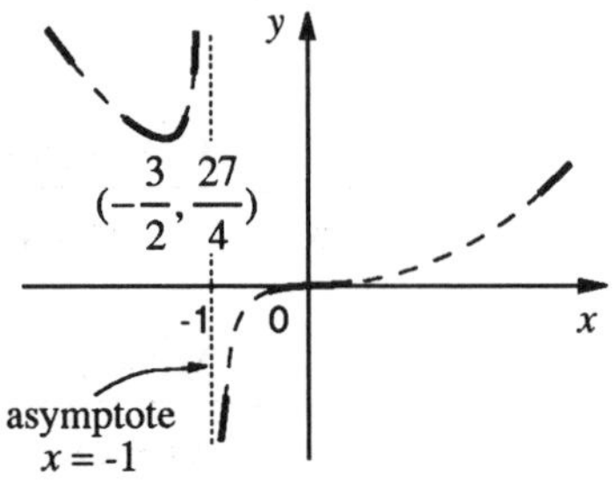

All this information is marked on the diagram opposite, and the curve is sketched in dotted.

Exercise 14E

1. Differentiate the following functions with respect to x :

   (a) $y = x e^x$ (b) $y = x^2 \ln(x)$

   (c) $y = \dfrac{2x+1}{x^2-3}$ (d) $y = \dfrac{e^x}{1+x}$

2. Find any stationary points on the curves in Question 1.

3. Find any stationary points on the curve

$$y = \frac{\ln(\sqrt{x+1})}{e^x}$$

4. Differentiate $\sqrt{\dfrac{x+1}{2x-1}}$

5. Differentiate $\sqrt{e^x(1+x)}$

6. Differentiate $\dfrac{\ln(x-2)}{\sqrt{x}}$

7. Sketch the curve with equation

$$y = x^3 + \frac{3}{2}x^2 - 6x$$

   by first finding all stationary points and their nature.

8. Sketch the curve with equation

$$y = \frac{1}{x^2} e^{-\frac{1}{x^2}}$$

9. Find any stationary points of the curve with equation

$$y = \frac{x^2}{1-x}$$

   Hence sketch the curve, indicating any asymptotes.

14.6 Miscellaneous Exercises

1. Find the maxima and/or minima of these functions :

   (a) $y = x^2 - 5x + 6$ (b) $y = 3x - 2x^2 + 8$

   (c) $y = x^3 + 2x^2 + x - 4$ (d) $y = 6x^2 - 2x^3 + 48x$

   (e) $y = \dfrac{e^x}{x}$

2. Differentiate these functions with respect to x

   (a) $(5-3x)^8$ (b) $\dfrac{1}{\left(\sqrt{x}+1\right)}$ (c) 3^x

   (d) $\sqrt{\dfrac{1+x}{1-x}}$ (e) $\ln(2^x)$ (f) $e^{-x^{-2}}$

3. Differentiate e^{3x-1}. Hence write down $\int e^{3x-1} dx$

4. Find $\int (2x-4)^5 dx$.

5. Calculate $\int_3^6 \dfrac{1}{3x-1} dx$.

6. Differentiate $\ln(x^2+1)$. Hence find $\int_0^1 \dfrac{x}{x^2+1} dx$.

15 FURTHER TRIGONOMETRY

Objectives

After studying this chapter you should

- know all six trigonometric functions and their relationships to each other;
- be able to use trigonometric identities;
- be able to solve simple trigonometric equations;
- be able to use the sine and cosine rules.

15.0 Introduction

You will need to work both in degrees and radians, and to have a working familiarity with the sine, cosine and tangent functions, their symmetries and periodic properties. In addition, you will need freely available access to graph plotting facilities.

Three further trigonometric functions are defined as follows :

cosecant of an angle, where $\operatorname{cosec} x = \dfrac{1}{\sin x}$,

secant of an angle, where $\sec x = \dfrac{1}{\cos x}$, and

cotangent of an angle, where $\cot x = \dfrac{1}{\tan x}$.

Hence , in terms of the ratios in a right-angled triangle,

$$\operatorname{cosec}\theta = \frac{\text{hyp}}{\text{opp}}, \quad \sec\theta = \frac{\text{hyp}}{\text{adj}}, \quad \cot\theta = \frac{\text{adj}}{\text{opp}}$$

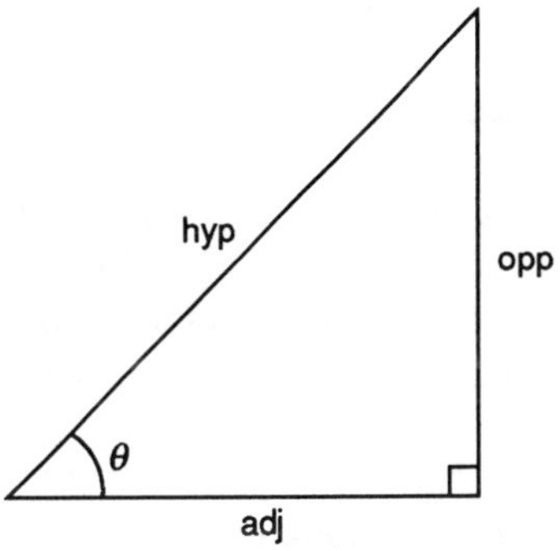

and, for example,

$$\frac{1}{\sin^2 x} = \left(\frac{1}{\sin x}\right)^2 = \operatorname{cosec}^2 x, \text{ etc.}$$

Note that by Pythagoras' Theorem, $(\text{opp})^2 + (\text{adj})^2 = (\text{hyp})^2$, so dividing by $(\text{hyp})^2$ gives

$$\left(\frac{\text{opp}}{\text{hyp}}\right)^2 + \left(\frac{\text{adj}}{\text{hyp}}\right)^2 = 1^2$$

as the familiar result

$$\boxed{\sin^2\theta + \cos^2\theta = 1}$$

But dividing by $(\text{adj})^2$ gives

$$\left(\frac{\text{opp}}{\text{adj}}\right)^2 + 1^2 = \left(\frac{\text{hyp}}{\text{adj}}\right)^2$$

so that $\boxed{\tan^2\theta + 1 = \sec^2\theta}$

and dividing by opp^2 gives

$$1^2 + \left(\frac{\text{adj}}{\text{opp}}\right)^2 = \left(\frac{\text{hyp}}{\text{opp}}\right)^2$$

giving $\boxed{1 + \cot^2\theta = \text{cosec}^2\theta}$

These three results are sometimes refered to as the **Pythagorean identities**, and are true for **all** angles θ.

Activity 1

Use a graph-plotter to draw the graphs of cosec x, sec x and cot x for values of x in the range $-2\pi \le x \le 2\pi$ (remember the graph plotter will work in radians). Write down in each case the period of the functions and any symmetries of the graphs.

From the definitions of cosec, sec and cot, how could you have obtained these graphs for yourself?

15.1 Identities

An identity is an equation which is true for all values of the variable. It is sometimes disinguished by the symbol $\equiv$, rather than $=$.

Example

Establish the identity $\sin A \tan A \equiv \sec A - \cos A$.

Solution

In proving results such as this sometimes it is helpful to follow this procedure: start with the left hand side (LHS), perform whatever manipulations are necessary, and work through a step at a time until the form of the right hand side (RHS) is obtained. In this case,

$$\begin{aligned}
\text{LHS} &= \sin A \ \tan A \\
&= \sin A \ \frac{\sin A}{\cos A} \\
&= \frac{\sin^2 A}{\cos A} \\
&= \frac{1-\cos^2 A}{\cos A} \qquad \text{using } \sin^2 A + \cos^2 A = 1 \\
&= \frac{1}{\cos A} - \frac{\cos^2 A}{\cos A} \\
&= \sec A - \cos A \\
&= \text{RHS}
\end{aligned}$$

Exercise 15A

Using the basic definitions and relationships between the six trigonometric functions, prove the following identities:

1. $\sec A + \tan A = \dfrac{1+\sin A}{\cos A}$
2. $\tan A + \cot A = \sec A \ \operatorname{cosec} A$
3. $\sec^2 \theta + \operatorname{cosec}^2 \theta = \sec^2 \theta \operatorname{cosec}^2 \theta$
4. $\dfrac{\operatorname{cosec}\theta - \cot\theta}{1-\cos\theta} = \operatorname{cosec}\theta$
5. $\operatorname{cosec} x - \sin x = \cos x \cot x$
6. $1 + \cos^4 x - \sin^4 x = 2\cos^2 x$
7. $\sec\theta + \tan\theta = \dfrac{\cos\theta}{1-\sin\theta}$
8. $\dfrac{\sin A \tan A}{1-\cos A} = 1 + \sec A$

15.2 The addition formulae

A proof of the formula for sin $(A+B)$ will be given here.

Consider the diagram opposite which illustrates the geometry of the situation.

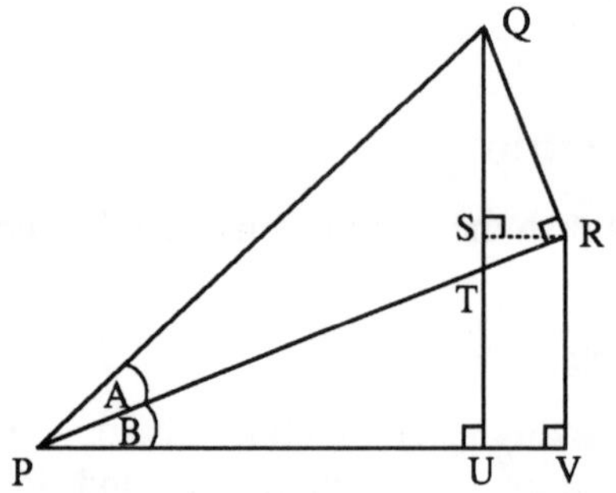

In triangle PQU,

$$\sin(A+B)=\frac{\mathrm{QU}}{\mathrm{PQ}}$$

$$=\frac{\mathrm{QS}+\mathrm{SU}}{\mathrm{PQ}}$$

$$=\frac{\mathrm{QS}}{\mathrm{PQ}}+\frac{\mathrm{RV}}{\mathrm{PQ}}\quad(\text{since SU}=\text{RV})$$

Now notice that, since $\mathrm{P\hat{T}U}=90-B$, $\mathrm{S\hat{T}R}=90-B$ also,

and so $\mathrm{S\hat{Q}R}=B$ (since $\mathrm{T\hat{R}Q}=90°$).

Then in triangle QRS

$$\mathrm{QS}=\mathrm{QR}\cos B.$$

Also, in triangle PVR,

$$\mathrm{RV}=\mathrm{PR}\sin B.$$

You now have

$$\sin(A+B)=\frac{\mathrm{QR}}{\mathrm{PQ}}\cos B+\frac{\mathrm{PR}}{\mathrm{PQ}}\sin B.$$

But in triangle PQR, $\frac{\mathrm{QR}}{\mathrm{PQ}}=\sin A$ and $\frac{\mathrm{PR}}{\mathrm{PQ}}=\cos A$ so,

$$\boxed{\sin(A+B)=\sin A\cos B+\cos A\sin B}$$

Rather than reproducing similar proofs for three more formulae, the following approach assumes this formula for $\sin(A+B)$ and uses prior knowledge of the sine and cosine functions.

Given $\sin(A+B)=\sin A\cos B+\cos A\sin B$, replacing B by $-B$ throughout gives

$$\sin(A-B)=\sin A\cos(-B)+\cos A\sin(-B)\ .$$

Now $\cos(-B)=+\cos B$ and $\sin(-B)=-\sin B$, so

$$\boxed{\sin(A-B)=\sin A\cos B-\cos A\sin B}$$

Next use the fact that $\cos\theta = \sin(90-\theta)$, so that

$$\begin{aligned}\cos(A+B) &= \sin(90-(A+B))\\ &= \sin((90-A)-B)\\ &= \sin(90-A)\cos B - \cos(90-A)\sin B\end{aligned}$$

from the second result just obtained. And since

$$\cos A = \sin(90-A), \quad \sin A = \cos(90-A),$$

it follows that

$$\boxed{\cos(A+B) = \cos A \cos B - \sin A \sin B}$$

Replacing B by $-B$, as before, this gives the fourth result

$$\boxed{\cos(A-B) = \cos A \cos B + \sin A \sin B}$$

Example

Show that $\sin 15° = \frac{\sqrt{2}}{4}\left(\sqrt{3}-1\right)$.

Solution

$$\begin{aligned}\sin 15° &= \sin(60°-45°)\\ &= \sin 60° \cos 45° - \cos 60° \sin 45°\end{aligned}$$

Now $\sin 60° = \frac{\sqrt{3}}{2}$, $\cos 60° = \frac{1}{2}$ and $\cos 45° = \frac{\sqrt{2}}{2}$ or $\frac{1}{\sqrt{2}}$

giving

$$\sin 15° = \frac{\sqrt{3}}{2} \times \frac{\sqrt{2}}{2} - \frac{1}{2} \times \frac{\sqrt{2}}{2} = \frac{\sqrt{2}}{4}\left(\sqrt{3}-1\right)$$

Exercise 15B

1. Using the values $\cos 0° = 1$, $\cos 30° = \frac{\sqrt{3}}{2}$, $\cos 45° = \frac{1}{\sqrt{2}}$, $\cos 60° = \frac{1}{2}$ and $\cos 90° = 0$ and related values of sine and tangent,determine, in similar form,

   (a) $\sin 75°$ (b) $\cos 15°$ (c) $\cos 105°$

   (d) $\cos 75°$ (e) $\tan 75°$ (f) $\tan 105°$

   (g) $\sin 255°$ (h) $\cos 285°$ (i) $\cot 75°$

2. Show that

   $$\cos(45°-A) - \cos(45°+A) = \sqrt{2}\sin A$$

3. Show that

   $$\sin x + \sin\left(x + \frac{2}{3}\pi\right) + \sin\left(x + \tfrac{4}{3}\pi\right) = 0$$

4. Given that $\sin(A+B) = 3\sin(A-B)$, show that $\tan A = 2\tan B$

5. Show that

   $$\sin(x+y)\sin(x-y) = \sin^2 x - \sin^2 y.$$

15.3 Further identities

Now

$$\begin{aligned}\tan(A+B) &= \frac{\sin(A+B)}{\cos(A+B)} \\ &= \frac{\sin A\cos B+\cos A\sin B}{\cos A\cos B-\sin A\sin B} \\ &= \frac{\left(\dfrac{\sin A\cos B}{\cos A\cos B}+\dfrac{\cos A\sin B}{\cos A\cos B}\right)}{\left(\dfrac{\cos A\cos B}{\cos A\cos B}-\dfrac{\sin A\sin B}{\cos A\cos B}\right)}\end{aligned}$$

Here, you can divide every term of the fraction by cos *A* cos *B*, giving

$$\boxed{\tan(A+B)=\frac{\tan A+\tan B}{1-\tan A\ \tan B}}$$

Replacing *B* by –*B* gives

$$\boxed{\tan(A-B)=\frac{\tan A-\tan B}{1+\tan A\ \tan B}}$$

Multiple angles

If, in the formula for sin (*A*+*B*), you put *B* = *A*, then you get

$$\sin(A+A)=\sin A\cos A+\cos A\sin A$$

or

$$\boxed{\sin 2A = 2\sin A\cos A}$$

Activity 2

Use the addition formulae to find expressions for

(a) cos 2*A* in terms of cos *A* and sin *A*;

(b) cos 2*A* in terms of cos *A* only;

(c) cos 2*A* in terms of sin *A* only;

(d) tan 2*A* in terms of tan *A* only;

(e) sin 3*A* in terms of powers of sin *A* only;

(f) cos 3*A* in terms of powers of cos *A* only.

Example

Establish the identity $\dfrac{\cos 2A+\sin 2A-1}{\cos 2A-\sin 2A+1}=\tan A$.

Solution

Here, you should first look to simplify the numerator and denominator by using the identities for cos 2*A* and sin 2*A*.

In the numerator, re-writing $\cos 2A$ as $1-2\sin^2 A$ will help cancel the –1 on the end; while $\cos 2A = 2\cos^2 A - 1$ will be useful in the denominator.

$$\begin{aligned}\text{LHS} &= \frac{1-2\sin^2 A+2\sin A\cos A-1}{2\cos^2 A-1-2\sin A\cos A+1}\\ &= \frac{2\sin A\cos A-2\sin^2 A}{2\cos^2 A-2\sin A\cos A}\\ &= \frac{2\sin A(\cos A-\sin A)}{2\cos A(\cos A-\sin A)}\\ &= \frac{\sin A}{\cos A}\\ &= \tan A\\ &= \text{RHS}\end{aligned}$$

Example

Show that $\sec^2\theta+\operatorname{cosec}^2\theta = 4\operatorname{cosec}^2 2\theta$.

Solution

To begin with, for shorthand write $s=\sin\theta$ and $c=\cos\theta$.

Then

$$\begin{aligned}\text{LHS} &= \frac{1}{c^2}+\frac{1}{s^2}\\ &= \frac{s^2+c^2}{s^2c^2}\\ &= \frac{1}{s^2c^2}\end{aligned}$$

Now notice that $2sc=\sin 2\theta$,

so $4s^2c^2=\sin^2 2\theta$ and $s^2c^2=\frac{1}{4}\sin^2 2\theta$, giving

$$\text{LHS} = \frac{1}{\frac{1}{4}\sin^2 2\theta} = 4\operatorname{cosec}^2 2\theta = \text{RHS}.$$

Example

Prove the identity $\dfrac{\cos A+\sin A}{\cos A-\sin A}=\sec 2A+\tan 2A$

Solution

This problem is less straightforward and requires some ingenuity. It helps to note that the

$$\text{RHS}=\frac{1}{\cos 2\text{A}}+\frac{\sin 2A}{\cos 2A}$$

with a common denominator of $\cos 2A$. One formula for cos 2*A* is

$$\begin{aligned}\cos 2A &= \cos^2 A-\sin^2 A\\ &= (\cos A-\sin A)(\cos A+\sin A)\end{aligned}$$

by the difference of two squares.

Hence

$$\begin{aligned}\text{LHS} &= \frac{\cos A+\sin A}{\cos A-\sin A}\\ &= \frac{(\cos A+\sin A)}{(\cos A-\sin A)}\times\frac{(\cos A+\sin A)}{(\cos A+\sin A)}\end{aligned}$$

This is done to get the required form in the denominator.

$$\begin{aligned}\text{LHS} &= \frac{\cos^2 A+2\sin A\cos A+\sin^2 A}{\cos^2 A-\sin^2 A.}\\ &= \frac{\left(\cos^2 A+\sin^2 A\right)+2\sin A\cos A}{\cos 2A}\\ &= \frac{1+\sin 2A}{\cos 2A}\\ &= \frac{1}{\cos 2A}+\frac{\sin 2A}{\cos 2A}\\ &= \sec 2A+\tan 2A\\ &= \text{RHS.}\end{aligned}$$

Exercise 15C

Prove the following identities in Questions 1 to 6.

1. $\dfrac{\sin 2A}{1+\cos 2A} = \tan A$

2. $\tan\theta + \cot\theta = 2\operatorname{cosec} 2\theta$

3. $\dfrac{\sin 2A + \cos 2A + 1}{\sin 2A - \cos 2A + 1} = \cot A$

4. $\cot x - \operatorname{cosec} 2x = \cot 2x$

5. $\dfrac{\sin 3A + \sin A}{2\sin 2A} = \cos A$

6. $\dfrac{\cos 3\theta - \sin 3\theta}{1 - 2\sin 2\theta} = \cos\theta + \sin\theta$

   [You may find it useful to refer back to the results of Activity 2 for Questions 5 and 6.]

7. Use the fact that $4A = 2\times 2A$ to show that

   $$\frac{\sin 4A}{\sin A} = 8\cos^3 A - 4\cos A.$$

8. By writing $t = \tan\theta$ show that

   $$\tan(\theta + 45°) + \tan(\theta - 45°) = \frac{1+t}{1-t} - \frac{1-t}{1+t}.$$

   Hence show that

   $$\tan(\theta + 45°) + \tan(\theta - 45°) = 2\tan 2\theta.$$

9. Using $t = \tan\theta$, write down $\tan 2\theta$ in terms of t. Hence prove the identities

   (a) $\cot\theta - \tan\theta = 2\cot 2\theta$

   (b) $\cot 2\theta + \tan\theta = \operatorname{cosec} 2\theta$

10. Write down $\cos 4x$ in terms of $\cos 2x$, and hence in terms of $\cos x$ show that

    $$\cos 4x + 4\cos 2x = 8\cos^4 x - 3$$

11. Prove the identity

    $$\frac{\sin 4A + \cos A}{\cos 4A + \sin A} = \sec 3A + \tan 3A$$

*15.4 Sum and product formulae

You may recall that

$$\sin(A+B) = \sin A\cos B + \cos A\sin B$$

$$\sin(A-B) = \sin A\cos B - \cos A\sin B$$

Adding these two equations gives

$$\sin(A+B) + \sin(A-B) = 2\sin A\cos B \qquad (1)$$

Call $C = A+B$ and $D = A-B$,

then $C+D = 2A$ and $C-D = 2B$. Hence

$$A = \frac{C+D}{2},\ B = \frac{C-D}{2}$$

and (1) can be written as

$$\sin C + \sin D = 2\sin\left(\frac{C+D}{2}\right)\cos\left(\frac{C-D}{2}\right)$$

This is more easily remembered as

'sine plus sine = twice sine(half the sum) cos(half the difference)'

Activity 3

In a similar way to above, derive the formulae for

(a) $\sin C - \sin D$ (b) $\cos C + \cos D$ (c) $\cos C - \cos D$

By reversing these formulae, write down further formulae for

(a) $2\sin E \cos F$ (b) $2\cos E \cos F$ (c) $2\sin E \sin F$

Example

Show that $\cos 59° + \sin 59° = \sqrt{2}\cos 14°$.

Solution

Firstly, $\sin 59° = \cos 31°$, since $\sin\theta = \cos(90-\theta)$

So

$$\begin{aligned}\text{LHS} &= \cos 59° + \cos 31° \\ &= 2\cos\left(\frac{59+31}{2}\right)\cos\left(\frac{59-31}{2}\right) \\ &= 2\cos 45° \times \cos 14° \\ &= 2\times\frac{\sqrt{2}}{2}\cos 14° \\ &= \sqrt{2}\cos 14° \\ &= \text{RHS}\end{aligned}$$

Example

Prove that $\sin x + \sin 2x + \sin 3x = \sin 2x(1 + 2\cos x)$.

Solution

$$\begin{aligned}\text{LHS} &= \sin 2x + (\sin x + \sin 3x) \\ &= \sin 2x + 2\sin\left(\frac{x+3x}{2}\right)\cos\left(\frac{x-3x}{2}\right) \\ &= \sin 2x + 2\sin 2x\cos(-x) \\ &= \sin 2x(1+2\cos x) \quad \text{since } \cos(-x) = \cos x.\end{aligned}$$

Example

Write $\cos 4x \cos x - \sin 6x \sin 3x$ as a product of terms.

Solution

Now $\cos 4x \cos x = \frac{1}{2}\{\cos(4x+x)+\cos(4x-x)\}$

$$= \frac{1}{2}\cos 5x + \frac{1}{2}\cos 3x$$

and $\sin 6x \sin 3x = \frac{1}{2}\{\cos(6x-3x)-\cos(6x+3x)\}$

$$= \frac{1}{2}\cos 3x - \frac{1}{2}\cos 9x.$$

Thus, LHS $= \frac{1}{2}\cos 5x + \frac{1}{2}\cos 3x - \frac{1}{2}\cos 3x + \frac{1}{2}\cos 9x$

$$= \frac{1}{2}(\cos 5x + \cos 9x)$$

$$= \frac{1}{2} \times 2\cos\left(\frac{5x+9x}{2}\right)\cos\left(\frac{5x-9x}{2}\right)$$

$$= \cos 7x \cos 2x.$$

The sum formulae are given by

$$\sin A + \sin B = 2\sin\left(\frac{A+B}{2}\right)\cos\left(\frac{A-B}{2}\right)$$

$$\sin A - \sin B = 2\cos\left(\frac{A+B}{2}\right)\sin\left(\frac{A-B}{2}\right)$$

$$\cos A + \cos B = 2\cos\left(\frac{A+B}{2}\right)\cos\left(\frac{A-B}{2}\right)$$

$$\cos A - \cos B = -2\sin\left(\frac{A+B}{2}\right)\sin\left(\frac{A-B}{2}\right)$$

and the product formulae by

$$\sin A \cos B = \tfrac{1}{2}(\sin(A+B)+\sin(A-B))$$

$$\cos A \cos B = \tfrac{1}{2}(\cos(A+B)+\cos(A-B))$$

$$\sin A \sin B = \tfrac{1}{2}(\cos(A-B)-\cos(A+B))$$

*Exercise 15D

1. Write the following expressions as products:

   (a) $\cos 5x - \cos 3x$ (b) $\sin 11x - \sin 7x$

   (c) $\cos 2x + \cos 9x$ (d) $\sin 3x + \sin 13x$

   (e) $\cos\frac{2\pi}{15} + \cos\frac{14\pi}{15} + \cos\frac{4\pi}{15} + \cos\frac{8\pi}{15}$

   (f) $\sin 40° + \sin 50° + \sin 60°$

   (g) $\cos 114° + \sin 24°$

2. Evaluate in rational/surd form

   $\sin 75° + \sin 15°$

3. Write the following expressions as sums or differences:

   (a) $2\cos 7x \cos 5x$

   (b) $2\cos\left(\frac{1}{2}x\right)\cos\left(\frac{5x}{2}\right)$

   (c) $2\sin\left(\frac{\pi}{4} - 3\theta\right)\cos\left(\frac{\pi}{4} + \theta\right)$

   (d) $2\sin 165° \cos 105°$

4. Establish the following identities:

   (a) $\cos\theta - \cos 3\theta = 4\sin^2\theta\cos\theta$

   (b) $\sin 6x + \sin 4x - \sin 2x = 4\cos 3x \sin 2x \cos x$

   (c) $\dfrac{2\sin 4A + \sin 6A + \sin 2A}{2\sin 4A - \sin 6A - \sin 2A} = \cot^2 A$

   (d) $\dfrac{\sin(A+B) + \sin(A-B)}{\cos(A+B) - \cos(A-B)} = -\cot B$

   (e) $\dfrac{\cos(\theta + 30°) + \cos(\theta + 60°)}{\sin(\theta + 30°) + \sin(\theta + 60°)} = \dfrac{1 - \tan\theta}{1 + \tan\theta}$

5. Write $\cos 12x + \cos 6x + \cos 4x + \cos 2x$ as a product of terms.

6. Express $\cos 3x \cos x - \cos 7x \cos 5x$ as a product of terms.

15.5 General formula

For this next activity you will find it very useful to have a graph plotting facility. Remember, you will be working in radians.

Activity 4

Sketch the graph of a function of the form

$$y = a\sin x + b\cos x$$

(where a and b are constants) in the range $-\pi \le x \le \pi$.
From the graph, you must identify the amplitude of the function and the x-coordinates of

(i) the crossing-point on the x-axis nearest to the origin, and

(ii) the first maximum of the function

as accurately as you can.

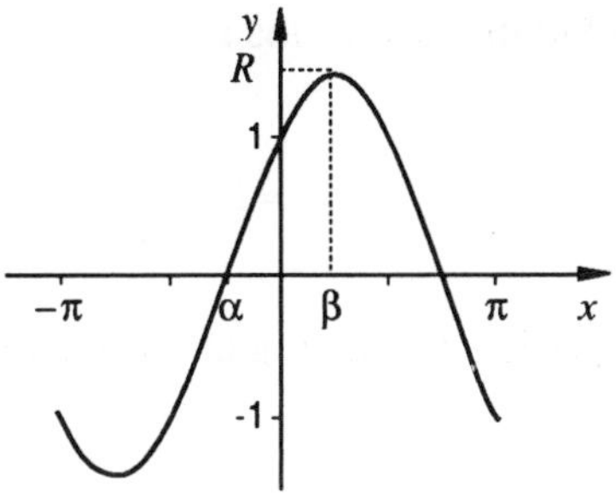

An example has been done for you; for $y = \sin x + \cos x$, you can see that amplitude ≈ 1.4

crossing-point nearest to O at $x = \alpha = -\frac{\pi}{4}$

maximum occurs at $x = \beta = \frac{\pi}{4}$

Try these for yourself :

(a) $y = 3\sin x + 4\cos x$ (b) $y = 12\cos x - 5\sin x$

(c) $y = 9\cos x + 12\sin x$ (d) $y = 15\sin x - 8\cos x$

(e) $y = 2\sin x + 5\cos x$ (f) $y = 3\cos x - 2\sin x$

In each case, make a note of

R, the amplitude;

α, the crossing - point nearest to O;

β, the x - coordinate of the maximum.

In each example above, you should have noticed that the curve is itself a sine/cosine 'wave', each of which can be obtained from the curves of either $y = \sin x$ or $y = \cos x$ by means of two simple transformations (taken in any order):

1. a **stretch** parallel to the y-axis by a factor of R, the amplitude, and

2. a **translation** parallel to the x-axis by either α or β (depending on whether you wish to start with $\sin x$ or $\cos x$ as the original function).

Consider, for example $y = \sin x + \cos x$. This can be written in the form $y = R\sin(x + \alpha)$, since

$$R\sin(x+\alpha) = R\{\sin x \cos\alpha + \cos x \sin\alpha\}$$

$$= R\cos\alpha \sin x + R\sin\alpha \cos x$$

This expression should be the same as $\sin x + \cos x$.

Thus

$R\cos\alpha = 1$ and $R\sin\alpha = 1$

Dividing these terms gives

$$\tan\alpha = 1 \Rightarrow \alpha = \frac{\pi}{4}$$

Squaring and adding the two terms gives

$$R^2\cos^2\alpha + R^2\sin^2\alpha = 1^2 + 1^2$$

$$R^2\left(\cos^2\alpha + \sin^2\alpha\right) = 2$$

Since $\cos^2\alpha + \sin^2\alpha = 1$,

$$R^2 = 2 \Rightarrow R = \sqrt{2} \text{ (negative root does not make sense)}$$

Thus

$$\sin x + \cos x = \sqrt{2}\sin\left(x + \tfrac{\pi}{4}\right).$$

Activity 5

Express the function $\sin x + \cos x$ in the form

$$\sin x + \cos x = R\cos(x - \alpha).$$

Find suitable values for R and α using the method shown above.

Another way of obtaining the result in Activity 5 is to note that

$$\sin\theta = \cos(\tfrac{\pi}{2} - \theta)$$

so that

$$\begin{aligned}\sin x + \cos x &= \sqrt{2}\sin(x + \tfrac{\pi}{4}) \\ &= \sqrt{2}\cos(\tfrac{\pi}{2} - (x + \tfrac{\pi}{4})) \\ &= \sqrt{2}\cos(\tfrac{\pi}{4} - x) \\ &= \sqrt{2}\cos(x - \tfrac{\pi}{4})\end{aligned}$$

since $\cos(-\theta) = \cos\theta$.

Example

Write $7\sin x - 4\cos x$ in the form $R\sin(x-\alpha)$

where $R>0$ and $0<\alpha<\frac{\pi}{2}$.

Solution

Assuming the result,

$$7\sin x - 4\cos x = R\sin(x-\alpha)$$
$$= R\sin x\cos\alpha - R\cos x\sin\alpha$$

To satisfy the equation, you need

$$R\cos\alpha = 7$$

$$R\sin\alpha = 4$$

Squaring and adding, as before, gives

$$R=\sqrt{7^2+4^2}=\sqrt{65}.$$

Thus

$$\cos\alpha=\frac{7}{\sqrt{65}},\quad \sin\alpha=\frac{4}{\sqrt{65}}\quad\left(\text{or }\tan\alpha=\frac{4}{7}\right)$$

$$\Rightarrow \alpha = 0.519 \text{ radians,}$$

so $$7\sin x - 4\cos x = \sqrt{65}\sin(x-0.519)$$

Exercise 15E

Write (in each case, $R>0$ and $0<\alpha<\frac{\pi}{2}$)

1. $3\sin x + 4\cos x$ in the form $R\sin(x+\alpha)$
2. $4\cos x + 3\sin x$ in the form $R\cos(x-\alpha)$
3. $15\sin x - 8\cos x$ in the form $R\sin(x-\alpha)$
4. $6\cos x - 2\sin x$ in the form $R\cos(x+\alpha)$
5. $20\sin x - 21\cos x$ in the form $R\sin(x-\alpha)$
6. $14\cos x + \sin x$ in the form $R\cos(x-\alpha)$
7. $2\cos 2x - \sin 2x$ in the form $R\cos(2x+\alpha)$
8. $3\cos\frac{1}{2}x + 5\sin\frac{1}{2}x$ in the form $R\sin\left(\frac{1}{2}x+\alpha\right)$

15.6 Equations in one function

In Chapter 10 you looked at equations of the form

$$a\sin(bx+c)=d$$

for constants a, b, c, d, or similar equations involving cos or tan.

In this and the following sections you will be introduced to a variety of different types of trigonometric equation and the appropriate ways of solving them within a given range.

Here, you will be asked only to solve polynomials in one function. It is important, therefore, that you are able to determine factors of polynomials and use the quadratic formula when necessary.

Example

Solve $2\sin^2\theta+3\sin\theta=2$ for values of θ between $0°$ and $360°$.

Solution

Rearrange the equation as $2\sin^2\theta+3\sin\theta-2=0$, which is a quadratic in $\sin\theta$. This factorises as

$$(2\sin\theta-1)(\sin\theta+2)-0$$

giving

(a) $2\sin\theta-1=0\Rightarrow\sin\theta=\frac{1}{2}\Rightarrow\theta=30°, 150°$

or

(b) $\sin\theta+2=0\Rightarrow\sin\theta=-2$ which has no solutions.

Exercise 15F

Solve the following equations for values of x in the range given:

1. $4\sin^2x-\sin x-3=0, 0\le x\le 2\pi$

2. $6\cos^2x+\cos x=1, -180°\le x\le 180°$

3. $\tan^2x+3\tan x-10=0, 0°\le x\le 360°$

4. $\cos^2x=2\cos x+1, 0°\le x\le 180°$

5. $\tan^4x-4\tan^2x+3=0, 0\le x\le\pi$

6. $\frac{1}{2}\sec^2x=\sec x+2, 0\le x\le\pi$

7. Use the factor theorem to factorise

$$6c^3-19c^2+c+6=0$$

and hence solve

$$6\cos^3x-19\cos^2x+\cos x+6=0$$

for $0\le x\le\pi$

15.7 Equations in two functions reducible to one

Equations involving two (or more) trigonometric functions cannot, in general, be solved by the simple methods you have encountered up to now. However, many such equations can be tackled using some of the basic identities introduced in the first part of this chapter.

Example

Solve $5\sin\theta = 2\cos\theta$ for $0 \le \theta \le 2\pi$.

Solution

Dividing both sides by $\cos\theta$ assuming $\cos\theta \ne 0$ gives

$$5\tan\theta = 2$$

$$\Rightarrow \quad \tan\theta = 0.4$$

$$\Rightarrow \quad \theta = 0.381,\ 3.52$$

Example

Solve $2\sec^2 x + 3\tan x - 4 = 0$ for $0° \le x \le 180°$.

Solution

From earlier work, $\sec^2 x = 1 + \tan^2 x$, leading to

$$2 + 2\tan^2 x + 3\tan x - 4 = 0$$

$$\Rightarrow \quad 2\tan^2 x + 3\tan x - 2 = 0$$

$$\Rightarrow \quad (2\tan x - 1)(\tan x + 2) = 0$$

giving

(a) $2\tan x - 1 = 0 \Rightarrow \tan x = \frac{1}{2} \Rightarrow x = 26.6°$

or

(b) $\tan x + 2 = 0 \Rightarrow \tan x = -2 \Rightarrow x = 116.6°$

Example

Solve $3\sin 2\theta = 5\cos\theta$ for $0° \le \theta \le 180°$

Solution

Since $\sin 2\theta = 2\sin\theta\cos\theta$, the equation reduces to

$$6\sin\theta\cos\theta = 5\cos\theta.$$

Method 1 – divide by cos θ to get

$$\sin\theta = \frac{5}{6}$$

$$\Rightarrow \theta = 56.4°,\ 123.6°$$

Method 2 – factorise to give

$$6\sin\theta\cos\theta - 5\cos\theta = 0$$

$$\cos\theta(6\sin\theta - 5) = 0$$

giving

(a) $\cos\theta = 0 \Rightarrow \theta = 90°$

or

(b) $\sin\theta = \frac{5}{6} \Rightarrow \theta = 56.4°, 123.6°$

You should see the error in **Method 1**, which throws away the solution for $\cos\theta = 0$. Division can only be done provided that the quantity concerned is **not** zero. [You might like to check back in the first example to see that exactly the same division was quite legitimate in that situation].

Exercise 15G

Solve the following equations in the required domain :

1. $2\sin^2\theta + 5\cos\theta + 1 = 0$ $\quad -\pi \le \theta \le \pi$
2. $2\sin 2\theta = \tan\theta$ $\quad 0° \le \theta \le 180°$
3. $2\operatorname{cosec} x = 5\cot x$ $\quad 0° \le x \le 180°$
4. $3\cos\theta = 2\cos 2\theta$ $\quad 0° \le \theta \le 360°$
5. $\sin x + \frac{1}{2}\sin 2x = 0$ $\quad 0 \le x \le 2\pi$
6. $6\cos\theta - 1 = \sec\theta$ $\quad 0° \le \theta \le 180°$
7. $\tan^2 x + 3\sec x = 0$ $\quad 0 \le x \le 2\pi$
8. $6\tan^2 A = 4\sin^2 A + 1$ $\quad 0° \le A \le 360°$
9. $3\cot^2\theta + 5\operatorname{cosec}\theta + 1 = 0$ $\quad 0 \le \theta \le 2\pi$
10. $\operatorname{cosec} x = \sqrt{3}\sec^2 x$ $\quad 0 \le x \le \pi$
11. $\sec^4\theta + 2 = 6\tan^2\theta$ $\quad 0° \le \theta \le 180°$
12. $\cos 2\theta\cos\theta = \sin 2\theta\sin\theta$ $\quad -180° \le \theta \le 180°$

*15.8 The sine rule

In this section and the next you will be introduced to the sine and cosine rules for use in any triangle. Before you start, you should be aware of the convention for referring to the sides and angles of a triangle.

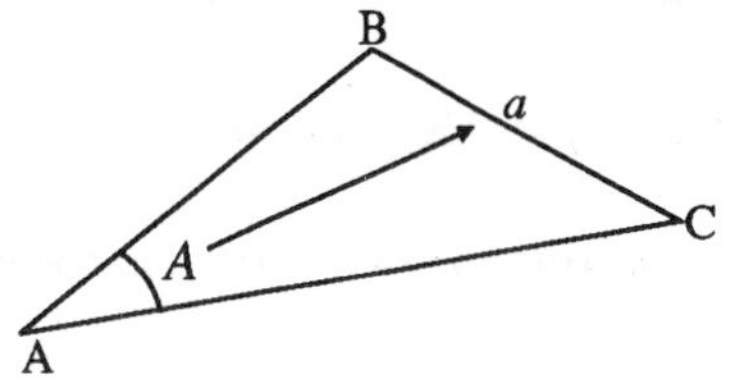

In triangle ABC shown opposite, the angles are labelled as the vertices at which they occur, and are denoted by capital letters, so that

$$\text{angle ABC} = B.$$

Lower case letters refer to the sides of the triangle, so that

$$\text{side BC} = a,$$

with the convention that a is opposite angle A (as shown), b opposite angle B, and so on.

Activity 6 Finding a rule for sides and angles

For this activity you will need a ruler measuring in mm, an angle measurer or protractor, and a calculator.

Draw four different shaped triangles. (You should include some obtuse-angled triangles).

Label the vertices A, B and C and the opposite sides a, b and c corresponding to the angles.

Measure the size of angles A, B and C (an accuracy to the nearest half-degree should be possible) and the lengths of the sides a, b and c to the nearest mm. Then for each triangle, evaluate

$$\frac{a}{\sin A}, \frac{b}{\sin B} \text{ and } \frac{c}{\sin C}.$$

What do you notice?

A proof of the sine rule

Oddly enough, in order to work with the sine and cosine functions in a non right-angled triangle it is necessary to create a right-angle.

In the triangle ABC, a perpendicular has been drawn from A to BC, meeting BC at the point X at 90°.

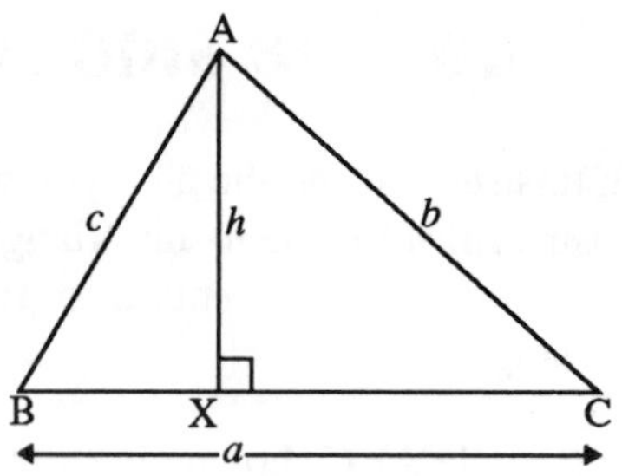

Here, then, AX is the height of ABC and BC is the base.

In triangle ABX, $h = c\sin B$.

In triangle AXC, $h = b\sin C$.

By putting the two formulas for h together

$$c\sin B = b\sin C \text{ or } \frac{c}{\sin C} = \frac{b}{\sin B}$$

If side AC had been taken as the base, the relationship

$\frac{c}{\sin C} = \frac{a}{\sin A}$ would have been obtained, and taking AB as base

would have given $\frac{a}{\sin A} = \frac{b}{\sin B}$.

Together, the set of equations obtained is

$$\boxed{\frac{a}{\sin A} = \frac{b}{\sin B} = \frac{c}{\sin C}}$$

This is called the **sine rule**, relating the sides of any triangle to the sines of its angles.

(Remember: this rule applies to **any** triangle, with or without a right angle).

Example

In triangle ABC, $A = 40°$ and $a = 17$ mm; $c = 11$ mm. Find b, B and C.

Solution

In attempting to solve a problem of this sort a sketch is necessary.

In the equation $\frac{a}{\sin A} = \frac{c}{\sin C}$, three of the four quantities are known, or can be found. The fourth, $\sin C$, can be calculated, and hence C.

Substituting,

$$\frac{17}{\sin 40^\circ} = \frac{11}{\sin C}.$$

Rearranging,

$$\sin C = \frac{11\sin 40^\circ}{17} = 0.415921\ldots$$

$$\Rightarrow \quad C = 24.6^\circ.$$

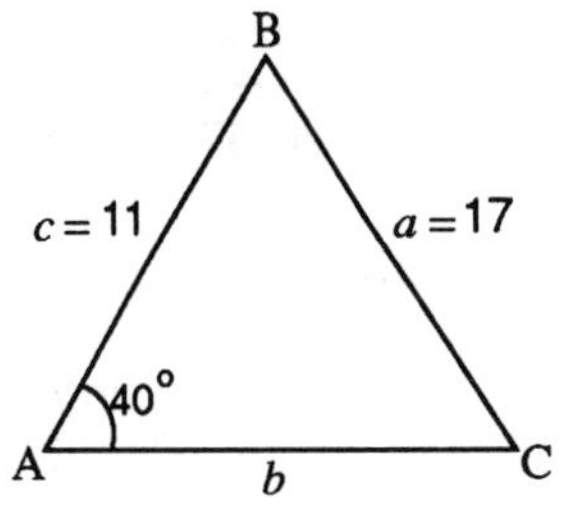

Knowing A and C,

$$B = 180^\circ - A - C$$

$$= 115.4^\circ.$$

b can now be found using

$$\frac{b}{\sin B} = \frac{a}{\sin A} \qquad \left(\text{or } \frac{c}{\sin C}\right).$$

Substituting,

$$\frac{b}{\sin 115.4^\circ} = \frac{17}{\sin 40^\circ}.$$

Rearranging,

$$b = \frac{17\sin 115.4^\circ}{\sin 40^\circ}$$

$$= 23.9 \text{ mm} \quad \text{(to 3 significant figures)}.$$

Example

In triangle PQR, $P = 52°$, $R = 71°$ and $q = 9.3$ m.

Find Q, p and r.

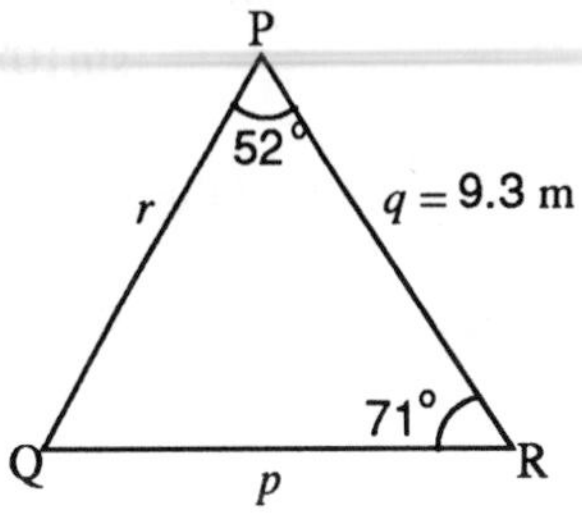

Solution

Firstly, $Q = 180° - 52° - 71° = 57°$.

Next, using $\dfrac{q}{\sin Q} = \dfrac{p}{\sin P}$,

$$\frac{9.3}{\sin 57^\circ} = \frac{p}{\sin 52^\circ}.$$

Rearranging,

$$p = \frac{9.3\sin 52^\circ}{\sin 57^\circ} = 8.74 \text{ m}.$$

Also, $\dfrac{q}{\sin Q} = \dfrac{r}{\sin R}$,

giving $\dfrac{9.3}{\sin 57^\circ} = \dfrac{r}{\sin 71^\circ}$.

Rearranging,

$$r = \frac{9.3 \sin 71^\circ}{\sin 57^\circ} = 10.5 \text{ m} \quad \text{(to 3 significant figures).}$$

Example

From a point P on the same level as the base of a tower, the angle of elevation of the top of the tower is 30°. From a point Q, 20 m further away than P from the tower the angle is 20°. What is the height of the tower?

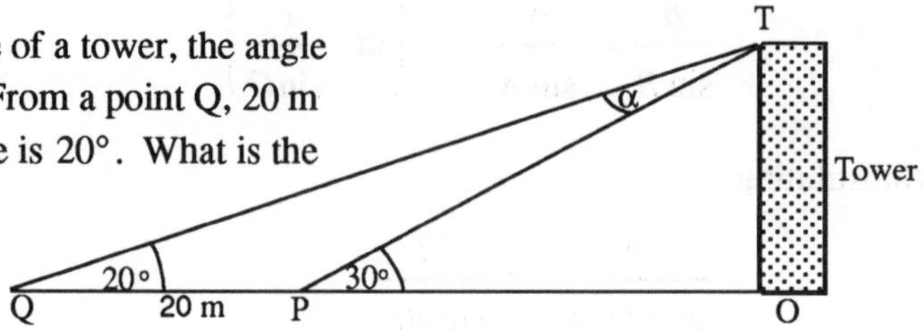

Solution

TP is first found by using the sine rule in triangle QPT;

$$\frac{\text{TP}}{\sin 20^\circ} = \frac{\text{QP}}{\sin \alpha}$$

But $20^\circ + \alpha = 30^\circ \Rightarrow \alpha = 10^\circ$

$$\text{TP} = \frac{20 \sin 20^\circ}{\sin 10^\circ} = 39.39 \text{ m}.$$

Finally, from triangle TOP,

height, $\text{TO} = \text{TP} \sin 30^\circ = 39.39 \times \sin 30^\circ = 19.7$ m (to 3 significant figures).

A possible difficulty

Example

Solve the triangle ABC, given $A = 33^\circ$, $a = 20$ cm and $b = 28$ cm.

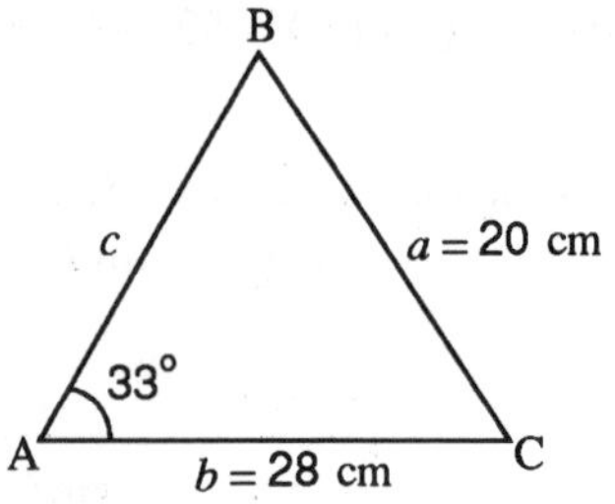

In this context 'solve' means 'find all the other sides and angles not already given'.

Solution

Now $\dfrac{a}{\sin A} = \dfrac{b}{\sin B}$ gives $\dfrac{20}{\sin 33^\circ} = \dfrac{28}{\sin B}$.

Hence $\sin B = \dfrac{28\sin 33°}{20} = 0.762\,495,$

which gives $B = 49.7°$. But B could be obtuse, and another possible solution is given by

$$B = 180° - 49.7° = 130.3°.$$

Now if $B = 49.7°,$

$$C = 180° - 33° - 49.7° = 97.3°,$$

and $\dfrac{20}{\sin 33°} = \dfrac{c}{\sin 97.3°}$

gives $c = \dfrac{20\sin 97.3°}{\sin 33°} = 36.4 \text{ cm (3 s.f.)}.$

But if $B = 130.3°,$

$$C = 180° - 33° - 130.3° = 16.7°$$

and $c = \dfrac{20\sin 16.7°}{\sin 33°} = 10.6 \text{ cm (3s.f.)}.$

So there appear to be two possible solutions.

Does this make sense?

In order to visualise the reason for this ambiguity, imagine trying to draw the triangle as described:

$$A = 33°,\ a = 20,\ b = 28.$$

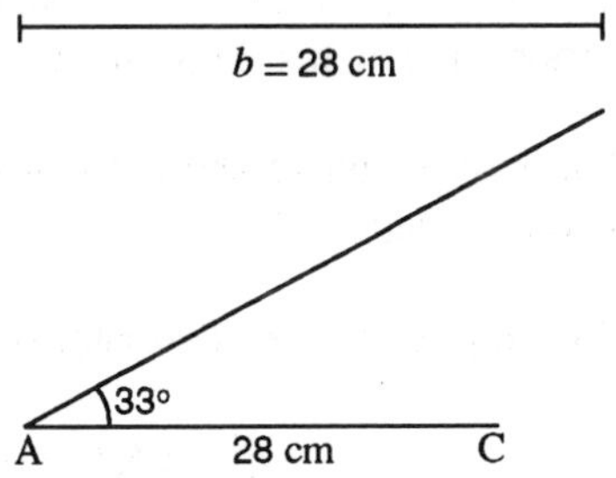

1. Draw the longest side first : $b = 28$.
2. Measure an angle of 33° at A - the position of B on this line is not yet known.
3. CB = 20, so B is 20 cm from C and somewhere on the line from A. Now all possible positions of a point B such that BC = 20 lie on a circle, centre at C, and radius 20. Part of this circle is drawn on the diagram.

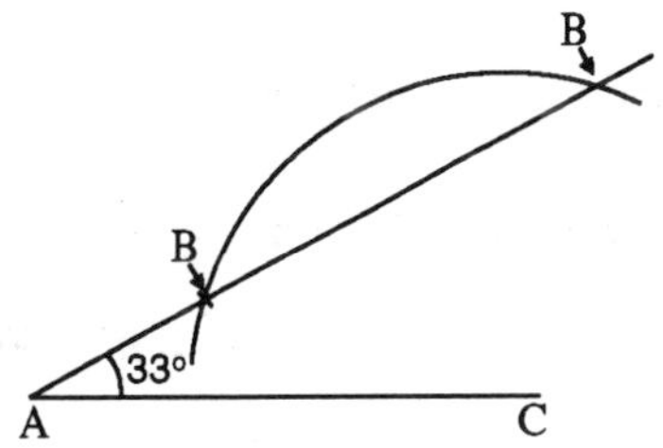

You will see that the circle and line intersect in two points corresponding to the **two** possible positions of B.

This situation arises when you are given two sides and a non-included angle (i.e. not the angle between them) because the triangle is not necessarily uniquely defined by the information given. It is called the **ambiguous case** , and you must watch out for it when using the sine rule to find angles.

Turn back to the first example in this chapter and see if you can decide why the problem did not arise there.

*Exercise 15H

In the following triangles, find the sides and angles not given. Give your answers to 1 d.p. for angles and 3 s.f. for sides where appropriate.

1. In triangle LMN, $m = 32$m, $M = 16°$ and $N = 56.7°$.
2. In triangle XYZ, $X = 120°$, $x = 11$ cm and $z = 5$ cm.
3. In triangle ABC, $A = 49°$, $a = 127$ m, and $c = 100$ m.
4. In triangle PQR, $R = 27°$, $p = 9.2$ cm and $r = 8.3$ cm.
5. In triangle DEF, $E = 81°$, $F = 62°$ and $d = 4$ m.
6. In triangle UVW, $u = 4.2$ m, $w = 4$ m and $W = 43.6°$.

*15.9 The cosine rule

Activity 7

Why is it that the sine rule does not enable you to solve triangles ABC and XYZ when

(a) in triangle ABC you are given :

$A = 35°$, $b = 84$ cm and $c = 67$ cm;

(b) in triangle XYZ you are given :

$x = 43$ m, $y = 60$ m and $z = 81$ m?

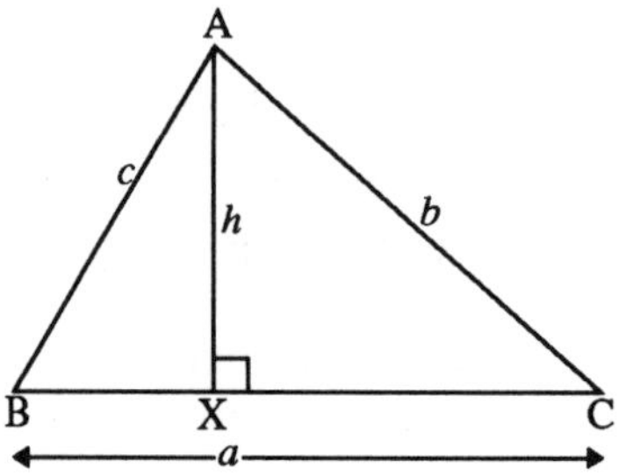

As with the introduction of the sine rule, it is necessary to create a right-angle in order to establish the cosine rule. Again, it is not important which side is taken as base.

The activity above shows the need for another rule in order to 'solve' triangles.

Two applications of Pythagoras' Theorem give

$$c^2 = h^2 + \text{BX}^2 \text{ in triangle ABX,}$$

and $$b^2 = h^2 + \text{XC}^2 \text{ in triangle ABC.}$$

Rearranging in terms of h^2,

$$c^2 - \text{BX}^2 = b^2 - \text{XC}^2$$

i.e. $$c^2 = b^2 + \text{BX}^2 - \text{XC}^2.$$

Now $BX^2 - XC^2$ is the difference of two squares and can be factorised as $(BX+XC)(BX-XC)$.

Notice that $BX + XC = a$, and

$$BX - XC = BX + XC - 2XC$$
$$= a - 2XC.$$

Whereas, in triangle AXC, $XC = b\cos C$.

Putting all these together gives

$$c^2 = b^2 + (BX+XC)(BX-XC)$$

$$\Rightarrow \quad c^2 = b^2 + a(a - 2b\cos C)$$

$$\Rightarrow \quad \boxed{c^2 = a^2 + b^2 - 2ab\cos C.}$$

Thus, given two sides of a triangle and the included angle, the **cosine rule** enables you to find the remaining side. Similarly

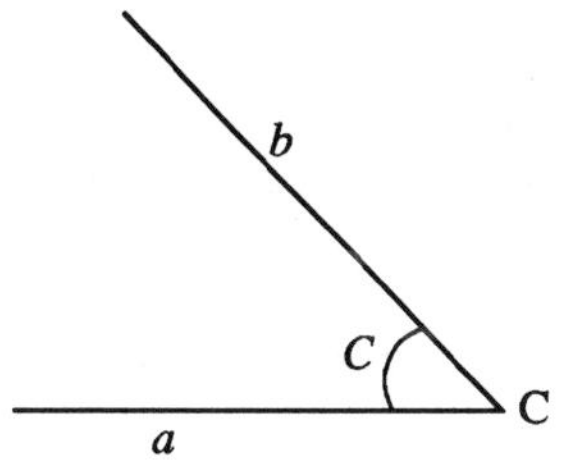

$$a^2 = b^2 + c^2 - 2bc\cos A$$

and $$b^2 = c^2 + a^2 - 2ca\cos B$$

are equivalent forms of the **cosine rule**, which you could have found by choosing one of the other sides as base in the diagram.

Formula for the cosine of an angle

$$c^2 = a^2 + b^2 - 2ab\cos C$$

$$\Rightarrow \quad c^2 + 2ab\cos C = a^2 + b^2$$

$$\Rightarrow \quad 2ab\cos C = a^2 + b^2 - c^2$$

$$\Rightarrow \quad \boxed{\cos C = \frac{a^2 + b^2 - c^2}{2ab}}$$

This arrangement (and the corresponding formulae for cos A or cos B) will enable you to find any angle of a triangle given all three sides.

What will the formulas be for cos *A* or cos *B*?

Unlike the sine rule, there is no possible ambiguity since, if C is obtuse, cos C will turn out to be negative rather than positive. (So with the cosine rule you can trust the inverse cosine function on your calculator!)

Example

Find all three angles of triangle LMN given $l = 72$, $m = 38$ m and $n = 49$ m.

Solution

To find L, use

$$\cos L = \frac{m^2 + n^2 - l^2}{2mn}$$

$$= \frac{38^2 + 49^2 - 72^2}{2 \times 38 \times 49}$$

$$= \frac{-1339}{3724} = -0.359560.$$

$$\Rightarrow \quad L = 111.1°.$$

Having found one angle, the next step could be to use either the cosine rule again or the sine rule.

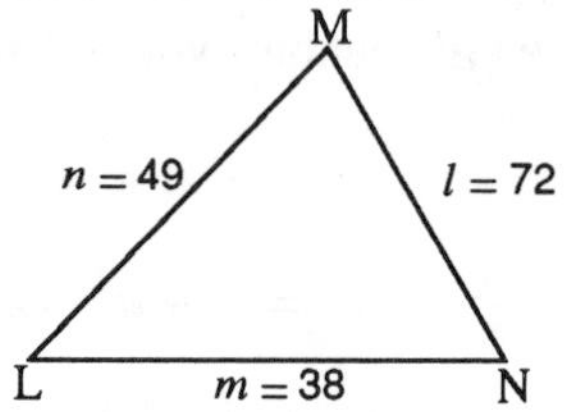

$$\cos M = \frac{l^2 + n^2 - m^2}{2ln}$$

$$= \frac{72^2 + 49^2 - 38^2}{2 \times 72 \times 49} = 0.859410$$

$$\Rightarrow \quad M = 30.7°$$

$$\Rightarrow \quad N = 180° - 111.1° - 30.7°$$

$$= 38.2°.$$

Example

In triangle ABC, $b = 19$ m, $c = 8$ m and $A = 127°$.

Find a and angles B and C.

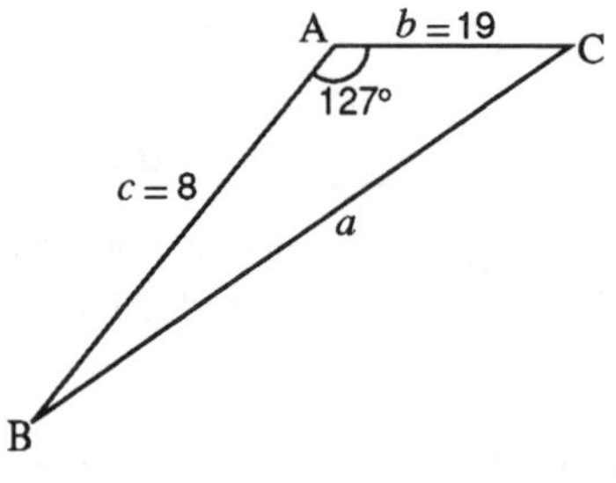

Solution

Using the cosine rule,

$$\begin{aligned} a^2 &= b^2 + c^2 - 2bc\cos A \\ &= 19^2 + 8^2 - 2\times 19\times 8\cos 127° \\ &= 425 - 304\times(-0.601\,815) \\ &= 425 + 182.95176 \\ &= 607.95176 \end{aligned}$$

$$\Rightarrow \quad a = 24.7 \text{ m}$$

Next, the sine rule can be used to find B and C.

Now $$\frac{a}{\sin A} = \frac{b}{\sin B}$$

$$\Rightarrow \quad \frac{24.7}{\sin 127°} = \frac{19}{\sin B}$$

$$\Rightarrow \quad \sin B = \frac{19\sin 127°}{24.7} = 0.614335$$

$$\Rightarrow \quad B = 37.9°$$

and $C = 180° - 127° - 38° = 15°$ to the nearest degree.

*Exercise 15I

Solve the following triangles given the relevant information :

1. In triangle ABC: $a = 18$ cm, $b = 13$ cm, $c = 8$ cm.
2. In triangle DEF: $D = 13.8°$, $e = 9.2$ m, $f = 13.4$ m.
3. In triangle LMN: $l = 33$ mm, $m = 20$ mm, $N = 71°$.
4. In triangle XYZ: $x = 4$ m, $y = 7$ m, $z = 9.5$ m.
5. In triangle PQR: $p = 9$ cm, $q = 40$ cm, $r = 41$ cm.
6. In triangle UVW: $U = 37°$, $u = 88.3$ m, $w = 97$ m.

*15.10 Area of a triangle

The approach adopted in obtaining the sine rule gives an easy way of finding a formula for the area of any triangle.

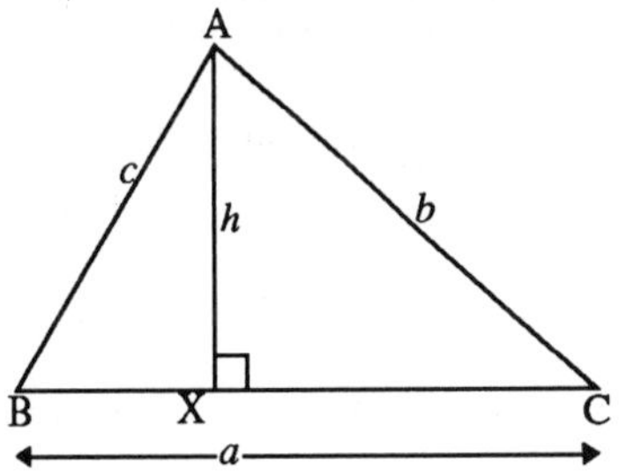

With base a, the height $h = b\sin C$ [or $c\sin B$] and the area of a triangle is given by

$$\text{area} = \frac{1}{2}\text{ base} \times \text{height}$$

$$= \frac{1}{2} \times a \times b \sin C$$

$$\Rightarrow \quad \boxed{\text{area} = \frac{1}{2} ab \sin C}$$

$$= \frac{1}{2} ac \sin B$$

$$= \frac{1}{2} bc \sin A$$

depending upon the choice of base.

Notice again that in each case the formula requires any two sides and the included angle.

*Exercise 15J

Find the areas of the triangles in Exercise 15I, Questions 1 to 6.

15.11 Miscellaneous Exercises

1. Simplify the following expressions :

   (a) $\cos 37° \cos 23° - \sin 37° \sin 23°$

   (b) $\sin 28° \cos 42° + \cos 28° \cos 48°$

   (c) $\sin\left(\frac{\pi}{3} + x\right) - \sin\left(\frac{\pi}{3} - x\right)$

   (d) $\cos\left(\frac{\pi}{6} + x\right) + \cos\left(\frac{\pi}{6} - x\right)$

   (e) $\sin\left(\frac{2\pi}{3} - x\right) + \sin\left(x - \frac{\pi}{3}\right)$

2. Prove the following identities :

   (a) $\dfrac{\sin\theta + \sin 3\theta + \sin 5\theta}{\cos\theta + \cos 3\theta + \cos 5\theta} = \tan 3\theta$

   (b) $\dfrac{\sin(x-y) + \sin x + \sin(x+y)}{\cos(x-y) + \cos x + \cos(x+y)} = \tan x$

   (c) $\cos(A+B+C) + \cos(A+B-C) + \cos(A-B+C)$

   $+\cos(-A+B+C) = 4\cos A \cos B \cos C$

3. Solve the equation $4\tan^2 x + 12\sec x + 1 = 0$ giving all solutions in degrees, to the nearest degree, in the interval $-180° < x < 180°$. (AEB)

4. Solve the equation $\sqrt{3}\tan\theta - \sec\theta = 1$ giving all solutions in the interval $0° < \theta < 360°$. (AEB)

5. Prove the identity $\sin 3A = 3\sin A - 4\sin^3 A$. Hence show that $\sin 10°$ is a root of the equation $8x^3 - 6x + 1 = 0$. (AEB)

6. Prove the identity $\tan\theta + \cot\theta = 2\operatorname{cosec} 2\theta$. Find, in radians, all the solutions of the equation $\tan x + \cot x = 8\cos 2x$ in the interval $0 < x < \pi$. (AEB)

*7. Find the area of triangle ABC given

   (a) $a = 42$ cm, $b = 31$ cm, $C = 58.1°$

   (b) $A = 17.6°$, $b = 127$ m, $c = 98$ m

*8. A triangle has sides of length 2 cm, 3 cm and 4 cm. Find the area of the triangle.

*9. In triangle PQR, $R = 42.5°$, $p = 9$ m and $q = 12.2$ m. Find the area of the triangle and the length of the third side, r.
   Deduce the distance of R from the line PQ.

*10. In triangle XYZ, $x = 17$, $y = 28$ and angle $X = 34°$. Find the length of the remaining side and the size of angles Y and Z.

*11. Solve triangle PQR given

(a) $P = 14.8°, R = 59.1°, r = 87$ m.

(b) $P = 67°$, $p = 73$ m, $q = 42$ m.

(c) $p = 22$ cm, $q = 89$ cm, $r = 100$ cm.

*12. $a = 27$ m, $b = 32$ m and $c = 30.6$ m in triangle ABC. Find the smallest angle of the triangle, and its area.

16 DATA ANALYSIS

Objectives

After studying this chapter you should

- understand various techniques for presentation of data;
- be able to find mean, mode, median, quartiles and standard deviation.

16.0 Introduction

"Statistics is like garbage - you have to know what to do with it before you collect it"

The following page shows the amount spent per pupil in all of the Education Authorities in 1986. The information was presented in this way to enable readers to see how their local Authority fared compared with others. From the point of view of showing changing patterns in spending and regional differences the data is unintelligible and boring.

In this chapter you will see how masses of data such as this can be reduced to a form from which you can gain useful information and present it in a manner which easily and interestingly conveys these ideas to other readers. You may have met some of the basic techniques before, or possibly more advanced techniques, and it is not the purpose of this unit to give a detailed explanation of all the techniques.

What can be done to make this data more understandable and interesting?

Most of your ideas will come under three main headings:

(a) **Sorting** - putting into order and/or grouping.

(b) **Summary measures** - finding single values which give important facts about the various parts of the data.

(c) **Illustration** - using various forms of diagrams to bring out patterns more clearly and present data in a more immediate manner.

PUPIL TEACHER RATIOS — SECONDARY | Costs 1983-4 to 1986-7 — UNIT COSTS — SECONDARY

	PUPIL TEACHER RATIOS SECONDARY					UNIT COSTS SECONDARY				
	1983/4	1984/5	1985/6	1986/7	change 1985/6 1986/7	1983/4	1984/5	1985/6	1986/7	change 1985/6 1986/7
LONDON										
ILEA	13.0	12.8	12.4	12.1	-1.47%	£1,588	£1,754	£1,904	£2,011	5.64%
Barking and Dagenham	16.1	16.1	16.1	15.8	-2.17%	£1,027	£1,108	£1,200	£1,266	5.47%
Barnet	14.2	13.9	14.6	14.5	-0.07%	£1,036	£1,134	£1,110	£1,162	4.75%
Bexley	17.0	16.9	16.4	16.1	-1.38%	£987	£1,044	£1,099	£1,147	4.40%
Brent	13.6	12.7	11.4	11.2	-1.25%	£1,465	£1,630	£1,887	£2,063	9.35%
Bromley	15.9	15.7	15.9	15.7	-0.98%	£1,058	£1,126	£1,193	£1,299	8.87%
Croydon	16.7	15.6	15.5	14.7	-5.12%	£1,058	£1,126	£1,324	£1,428	7.82%
Ealing	14.8	14.2	14.3	13.6	-4.86%	£1,310	£1,455	£1,513	£1,673	10.55%
Enfield	15.4	14.8	15.0	14.9	-0.84%	£1.024	£1,070	£1,127	£1,208	7.14%
Haringey	13.0	12.5	12.4	11.9	-4.26%	£1.527	£1,765	£2,010	£2,039	1.46%
Harrow	14.3	13.9	14.4	14.5	0.94%	£1,247	£1,324	£1,392	£1,419	1.93%
Havering	16.1	15.8	15.5	14.6	-5.51%	£1,081	£1,142	£1,235	£1,271	2.89%
Hillingdon	15.8	15.8		16.2		£1,095	£1,176		£1,313	
Hounslow	14.9	15.3	15.7	15.4	-2.20%	£1,014	£1,059	£1,111	£1,175	5.78%
Kingston-upon-Thames	16.4	15.8	14.7	14.3	-2.30%	£946	£1,037	£1,187	£1,296	9.21%
Merton	18.0	18.1	16.6	16.8	1.24%	£876	£911	£1,007		
Newham	13.4	12.7	11.3	12.8	13.00%	£1,303	£1,408	£1,609	£1,628	1.15%
Redbridge	15.9	15.7	15.7	15.3	-2.88%	£1,129	£1,194	£1,267	£1,317	3.96%
Richmond-upon-Thames	16.2	16.7	16.3	16.4	0.60%	£1,116	£1,131	£1,217	£1,175	-3.42%
Sutton	17.1	17.1	16.9	16.7	-1.28%	£963	£1,010	£1,038	£1,127	8.63%
Waltham Forest	13.5	13.4	12.8	12.5	-2.20%	£1,290	£1,429	£1,525	£1,662	8.98%
METROPOLITAN DISTRICTS										
Bolton	16.3	15.9	15.5	15.6	0.43%	£889	£962	£1,052	£1,110	5.56%
Bury	16.0	15.7	15.6	15.4	-1.22%	£1,026	£1,128	£1,191	£1,229	3.12%
Manchester	15.8	14.4	13.8	13.6	-1.44%	£1,114	£1,212	£1,348	£1,443	7.04%
Oldham	16.5	16.0	15.5	15.1	-2.88%	£913	£972	£1,062	£1,131	6.51%
Rochdale	14.7	14.9	14.8	14.4	-2.69%	£1,052	£1,113	£1,191	£1,212	1.75%
Salford	15.8	15.4	15.2	15.3	0.49%	£970	£1,057	£1,158	£1,206	4.14%
Stockport	16.6	16.5	16.1	15.8	-1.90%	£901	£971	£1,070	£1,133	5.93%
Tameside	15.8	15.8	15.4	15.9	3.47%	£966	£1,036	£1,154	£1,159	0.40%
Trafford	16.2	16.1	15.7	16.4	4.16%	£1,110	£1,173	£1,317	£1,346	2.23%
Wigan	15.5	15.5	15.1	15.5	2.47%	£928	£998	£1,111	£1,156	4.11%
Knowsley	15.1	14.1	14.8	14.2	-4.20%	£1,107	£1,227	£1,315	£1,490	13.29%
Liverpool	16.9					£1,081				
St. Helens	15.9	15.6	15.2	14.8	-3.13%	£971	£1,050	£1,112	£1,214	9.22%
Sefton	16.7	16.7	16.8	16.6	-1.54%	£911	£964	£1,019	£1,081	6.06%
Wirral	17.5	16.2	15.8	15.9	0.77%	£931	£1,000	£1,130	£1,179	4.36%
Barnsley	16.7	16.6	16.2	15.3	-5.74%	£935	£1,021	£1,136	£1,190	4.71%
Doncaster	15.8	16.6	16.5	16.9	2.31%	£959	£1,002	£1,125	£1,144	1.64%
Rotherham	16.8	16.5	15.9	16.0	0.61%	£874	£940	£1,029	£1,125	9.30%
Sheffield	15.8	15.4		14.8		£1,044	£1,135		£1,333	
Gateshead	16.4	15.8	15.7	15.3	-2.52%	£989	£1,097	£1,143	£1,202	5.18%
Newcastle upon Tyne	15.1	15.1	15.4	17.2	11.55%	£1,109	£1,201	£1,278	£1,317	3.05%
North Tyneside	15.0	15.9	14.0	13.7	-2.17%	£1,025	£1,036	£1,232	£1,297	5.28%
South Tyneside	15.1	14.8	15.3	15.2	-067%	£1,1012	£1,082	£1,149	£1,226	6.70%
Sunderland	16.0	15.6	15.4	15.2	-1.01%	£926	£1,009	£1,103	£1,153	4.56%
Birmingham	15.9	15.9	15.4	15.3	-0.50%	£911	£990	£1,083	£1,167	7.79%
Coventry	16.2	15.3	14.8	14.0	-5.35%	£986	£1,069	£1,179	£1,261	6.97%
Dudley	17.1	16.4	15.6	15.4	-1.44%	£867	£937	£1,055	£1,143	8.37%
Sandwell	15.4	15.4	14.4	14.5	0.98%	£1,000	£1,079	£1,207	£1,315	8.93%
Solihull	16.9	16.9	16.3	16.2	-0.76%	£856	£898	£1,008	£1,046	3.82%
Walsall	14.0	14.4	14.0	13.4	-4.30%	£1,029	£1,066	£1,154	£1,265	9.54%
Wolverhampton	15.0	14.8	14.5	15.0	3.53%	£1,027	£1,105	£1,184	£1,260	6.41%
Bradford	17.9	16.8	16.5	16.6	0.24%	£890	£965	£1,055	£1,156	9.59%
Calderdale	17.5	16.8	16.5	16.6	0.24%	£890	£965	£1,055	£1,156	9.59%
Kirklees	17.3	17.1	16.6	16.3	-2.15%	£851	£910	£983	£1,041	5.85%
Leeds	18.7	16.0	16.0	14.2	-11.12%	£887	£976	£1,043	£1,253	20.11%
COUNTIES										
Avon CC	16.3	16.4	16.3	16.2	-1.02%	£987	£1,062	£1,114	£1,174	5.35%
Bedfordshire CC	17.5	16.9	16.9	16.8	-0.37%	£972	£1,035	£1,109	£1,143	3.06%
Berkshire CC	16.0	15.7	15.6	15.6	-0.16%	£982	£1,045	£1,129	£1,149	1.77%
Buckinghamshire CC	16.1	15.9	15.8	15.9	0.94%	£1,076	£1,136	£1,200	£1,286	7.13%
Cambridgeshire CC	16.8	16.9	16.5	16.2	-1.92%	£954	£996	£1,071	£1,129	5.35%
Cheshire CC	16.9	16.9	16.6	16.5	-0.48%	£1,004	£1,045	£1,118	£1,195	6.90%
Cleveland CC	16.2	16.1	15.4	15.8	2.84%	£970	£1,030	£1,131	£1,203	6.34%
Cornwall CC	16.8	16.8	16.5	16.4	-0.85%	£911	£975	£1,051	£1,088	3.52%
Cumbria CC	16.1	16.0	15.7	15.4	-1.75%	£968	£1,014	£1,131	£1,225	8.37%
Derbyshire CC	17.5	17.3	16.6	16.0	-3.68%	£932	£995	£1,099	£1,173	6.78%
Devon CC	17.0	16.8	16.7	16.7	-0.29%	£919	£976	£1,048	£1,102	5.11%
Dorset CC	17.1	17.0	16.3	16.4	0.51%	£872	£919	£995	£1,066	7.11%
Durham CC	16.7	16.8	17.3	16.5	-4.61%	£899	£964	£1,032	£1,133	9.73%
East Sussex CC	17.0	17.1	17.1	16.7	-2.13%	£939	£994	£1,031	£1,098	6.49%
Essex CC	17.2	17.0	16.8	16.6	-1.49%	£945	£1,013	£1,105	£1,169	5.73%
Gloucestershire CC	17.3	17.2	17.0	16.0	-6.00%	£929	£985	£1,055	£1,126	6.74%
Hampshire CC	16.8	17.1	17.0	16.7	-1.52%	£951	£1,001	£1,053	£1,132	7.57%
Heref'd & Worcester CC	18.0	17.2	16.8	16.7	-0.18%	£887	£964	£1,020	£1,065	4.46%
Hertfordshire CC	15.9	15.8	15.6	15.0	-4.03%	£961	£1,016	£1,093	£1,176	7.55%
Humberside CC	16.8	16.2	16.6	16.6	0.08%	£920	£968	£1,023	£1,081	5.58%
Isle of Wight CC	18.3	18.1	18.1	17.1	-5.88%	£911	£960	£1,050	£1,114	6.06%
Kent CC	17.1	16.8	16.7			£904	£996	£1,038	£1,093	5.32%
Lancashire CC	16.9	16.7	16.5	16.0	-3.45%	£951	£1,019	£1,093	£1,174	7.49%
Leicestershire CC	16.2	16.0	15.4	15.2	-1.22%	£968	£1,063	£1,157	£1,242	7.35%
Lincolnshire CC	17.5	17.1	16.8	16.3	-2.66%	£977	£1,058	£1,103	£1,194	8.21%
Norfolk CC	16.8	16.6	16.3	16.1	1.69%	£958	£1,008	£1,102	£1,162	5.43%
Northamptonshire CC	16.7	16.3	16.0	16.4	-2.48%	£923	£980	£1,069	£1,112	4.00%
Northumberland CC	17.5	17.2	16.8	16.4	-2.61%	£888	£943	£1,036	£1,092	5.47%
North Yorkshire CC	16.6	16.4	16.6	16.4	-1.32%	£967	£1,046	£1,100	£1,110	0.87%
Nottinghamshire CC	15.6	15.3	15.0	14.9	-0.51%	£1,007	£1,077	£1,180	£1,258	6.56%
Oxfordshire CC	17.2	17.3	16.8	16.5	-2.14%	£921	£972	£1,037	£1,098	5.88%
Shropshire CC	16.2	16.0	15.9	15.8	-0.94%	£949	£1,013	£1,109	£1,174	5.85%
Somerset CC	17.5	17.7	17.7	16.9	-4.42%	£913	£967	£1,025	£1,102	7.59%
Staffordshire CC	16.4	16.4	16.6	16.5	-0.54%	£956	£1,037	£1,102	£1,155	4.76%
Suffolk CC	17.3	16.8	17.0	16.8	-1.50%	£873	£941	£1,004	£1,063	5.88%
Surrey CC	16.3	16.5	16.0	15.7	-1.97%	£1,029	£1,085	£1,183	£1,258	6.31%
Warwickshire CC	17.2	17.1	16.8	16.6	-1.09%	£930	£981	£1,069	£1,113	4.08%
West Sussex CC	17.2	16.9	16.7	16.6	-0.84%	£879	£936	£989	£1,020	3.08%
Wiltshire CC	17.0	17.3	17.1	16.9	-1.17%	£926	£994	£1,056	£1,126	6.58%

In recent years new techniques have been developed under the umbrella of 'Exploratory Data Analysis' (EDA). These are attempts to simplify some of the more traditional sorting procedures and diagrams to improve on the information they portray. The name 'exploratory' is used as such methods are particularly useful when dealing with data that you are looking at for the first time. They will be used in this chapter alongside the more traditional methods.

Few people nowadays undertake statistical research of any length with pencil and paper. Many computer packages have been produced to carry out analysis, you may have already met these in other subject areas. Many packages are limited to particular techniques and can be restrictive in some kinds of research. The most useful are the spreadsheet style packages. These not only allow all the normal spreadsheet functions of manipulating rows and columns but allow a wide range of analysis to be performed.

Find out from your computer department what they have available and try to follow through this work with a computer. Most of the diagrams and tables in this chapter could be produced using such packages.

16.1 Stem and leaf diagrams

When you are faced with a large amount of data such as the figures on school spending it is difficult to answer questions like 'What are the highest and lowest spending authorities?' 'Do they all spend pretty much the same or are there some particularly high or low spenders?'

Pupil Teacher Ratios	Frequency
11.0 - 11.9	2
12.0 - 12.9	3
13.0 - 13.9	1
14.0 - 14.9	6
15.0 - 15.9	4
16.0 - 16.9	5
17.0 - 17.9	0

With small amounts of data it is usually sufficient to simply write the values in order, but with more than just a handful of data items some kind of grouping is required. The **frequency table** simply shows the number of items in each category or group. For example the pupil teacher ratios for London Authorities in 1986/7 would be listed as shown opposite. Note that the class limits are given to the same degree of accuracy as the original data, this avoids any overlap or confusion. Open ended groups e.g.'22.0 and over' are sometimes used where there are a lot of scattered items at one end. Open ended groups can cause inaccuracies and difficulties in later work, as do tables where groups are of uneven size, and these are best avoided. Tables are the backbone of official statistics publications where a number of variations can be shown at one time.

Stem	leaf
11	29
12	158
13	6
14	355679
15	3478
16	12478
17	

A modern alternative to the frequency table is the **stem and leaf diagram**. The stem is chosen in the same manner as the groups in a frequency table, so for the above data these would be the whole numbers. The stem and leaf of the above data would then take the form opposite.

The advantages of these over conventional tables are:

(i) the actual values are recorded in the table and can be used in later work;

(ii) the length of row gives a good visual indication of the spread of results.

With figures where the data range covers more than one significant figure some rounding needs to be used. The 'Unit Costs' for London in 1986/7 would be as shown opposite.

11	35677
12	177
13	0012
14	23
15	
16	367
17	
18	
19	
20	146

When you wish to compare two sets of data, e.g. London and Counties, you can draw a 'back-to-back' stem and leaf as shown opposite.

Pupil Teacher Ratio 1986/7

London		Counties
92	11	
158	12	
6	13	
976553	14	9
8743	15	02467889
87421	16	0001223444445555666677778899
	17	1

Another useful EDA technique is the **dotplot** where each item is stored as a dot on a continuous scale. The data for London Unit Costs would be shown as below.

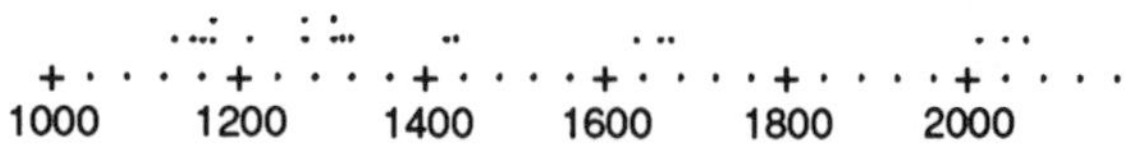

Whilst they usefully show the spread of data it is difficult to read off exact values.

Exercise 16A

In Questions 1 and 2 use a computer if possible.

1. Draw frequency tables for the Pupil Teacher Ratios in the Metropolitan Districts and Counties in 1986/7. Comment on any differences in the pattern of pupil/teacher ratios in the three types of area.

2. Draw stem and leaf diagrams for the Unit Costs in 1986/7 for the Metropolitan Districts and Counties. Use these along with the one in the text for London to comment on the pattern of spending in the three types of area.

3. Use the data from the table below 'Notifiable offences...' to answer the following.

   (a) Add together the figures for the three areas in each of the three years. Express these as a percentage of the total crimes in that year and put the results in a table.

   (b) What does your table tell you about the pattern of crime over that period?

   (c) Calculate the % of "violence against the person" crimes for Northern Ireland only in 1985. Does this support the view that Northern Ireland is a more violent place to live?

Notifiable offences recorded by the police: by type of offence

England & Wales, Scotland, and Northern Ireland *Thousands*

	England & Wales			Scotland			Northern Ireland		
	1971	1984	1985	1971	1984	1985	1971	1984	1985
Notifiable offences recorded									
Violence against the person	47.0	114.2	121.7	5.0	9.2	10.7	1.4	3.4	3.5
Sexual offences	23.6	20.2	21.5	2.6	2.4	2.6	0.2	0.5	0.7
Burglary	451.5	897.5	871.3	59.2	112.1	100.7	10.6	22.4	20.2
Robbery	7.5	24.9	27.5	2.3	4.5	4.4	0.6	2.0	1.8
Theft and handling stolen goods	1003.7	1808.0	1884.1	104.6	215.8	208.9	8.6	28.7	29.5
Fraud and forgery	99.8	126.1	134.8	9.4	29.1	30.6	1.5	3.1	3.7
Criminal damage	27.0	497.8	539.0	22.0	79.0	79.5	7.4	4.4	3.2
Other notifiable offences	5.6	10.4	12.2	5.9	22.7	24.6	0.5	2.2	2.0
Total notifiable offences	1665.7	3449.1	3612.1	211.0	474.8	462.0	30.8	66.7	64.6

Activity 1

The worksheet on 'World Data' shown here gives various facts about countries from four key world regions. Use this as a piece of ongoing research through this chapter. If you have computer facilities you will be able to work individually otherwise split into groups to do different regions. By drawing frequency charts/stem and leaf diagrams compare life expectancy, GNP, literacy, etc. within the regions. How do the underdeveloped regions compare with Western Europe?

World Data

Populn. - Population in 1984 in millions
Area - in thousands of km²
GNP - Gross National Product, roughly speaking the annual wealth (US$) produced by a country divided by the number of inhabitants.
* Denotes data not available.

Life - average lifespan (life expectancy)
Doct - the ratio of patients to doctor
Read - adult literacy, i.e, the % of adults able to read.

African States

Row	State	Populn.	Area	GNP	Life	Doct	Read
1	Egypt	45.9	1001	720	60	800	44
2	Nigeria	96.5	924	730	50	10540	34
3	Zimbabwe	8.1	391	760	57	6650	69
4	Camaroon	9.9	475	800	54	*	*
5	Botswana	1.0	600	960	58	9250	*
6	Tunisia	7.0	164	1270	62	3620	62
7	Libya	3.5	1760	8520	59	660	*
8	Ethiopia	42.2	1222	110	44	88120	15
9	Mali	7.3	1240	140	46	25380	10
10	Zaire	29.7	2345	140	51	*	55
11	Malawi	6.8	118	180	45	52960	25
12	Niger	6.2	1267	190	43	*	10
13	Tanzania	21.5	945	210	52	*	79
14	Uganda	15.0	236	230	51	22180	52
15	C.A.R.	2.5	623	260	49	23090	33
16	Somalia	5.2	638	260	46	15630	60
17	Benin	3.9	113	270	49	16980	28
18	Rwanda	5.8	26	280	47	10260	50
19	Kenya	19.6	583	310	54	7540	47
20	Sierra L.	3.7	72	310	38	17670	15
21	Guinea	5.9	246	330	38	*	20
22	Ghana	12.3	239	350	53	6760	*
23	Sudan	21.3	2506	360	48	9070	32
24	Senegal	6.4	196	380	46	13060	10
25	Chad	4.9	1284	*	44	*	15
26	Mozambique	13.4	802	*	46	33340	33
27	Liberia	2.1	111	470	50	8550	25
28	Zambia	6.4	753	470	52	7110	44
29	Lesotho	1.5	30	530	54	*	52
30	Ivory Co.	9.9	322	610	52	*	35

South & Central American States

Row	State	Populn.	Area	GNP	Life	Doct	Read
1	Nicaragua	3.2	130	860	60	2290	90
2	Dominican	6.1	49	970	64	1390	67
3	Peru	18.2	1285	1000	59	*	80
4	Ecuador	9.1	284	1150	65	*	81
5	Guatamala	7.7	109	1160	60	*	*
6	Costa Rica	2.5	51	1190	73	*	90
7	Jamaica	2.2	11	1150	73	*	90
8	Paraguay	3.3	407	1240	66	1310	84
9	Colombia	28.4	1139	1390	65	*	81
10	Cuba	9.9	115	*	75	600	95

South & Central American States (cont'd)

Row	State	Populn.	Area	GNP	Life	Doct	Read
11	Chile	11.8	757	1700	70	950	*
12	Brazil	132.6	8512	1720	64	1200	76
13	Panama	2.1	77	1980	71	1010	85
14	Uruguay	3.0	176	1980	73	510	94
15	Mexico	76.8	1973	2040	66	1140	83
16	Argentina	30.1	2767	2230	70	*	93
17	Venezuela	16.8	912	3410	69	930	82
18	Trinidad	1.2	5	7150	69	1390	95
19	Haiti	5.4	28	320	55	*	23
20	Bolivia	6.2	1099	540	53	1950	63
21	Honduras	4.2	112	700	61	*	60
22	El Salvador	5.4	21	710	65	3220	62

West European States

Row	State	Populn.	Area	GNP	Life	Doct	Read
1	Greece	9.9	132	3770	75	390	*
2	Portugal	10.2	92	1970	74	450	78
3	Spain	38.7	505	4440	77	360	*
4	Ireland	3.5	70	4970	73	780	98
5	Italy	57.0	301	6420	77	750	98
6	UK	56.4	245	8570	74	680	99
7	Belgium	9.9	31	8610	75	380	99
8	Austria	7.6	84	9140	73	580	99
9	Holland	14.4	41	9520	77	480	99
10	France	54.9	547	9760	77	460	99
11	Finland	4.9	337	10770	75	460	100
12	Germany	61.2	249	11130	75	420	99
13	Denmark	5.1	43	11170	75	420	99
14	Sweden	8.3	450	11860	77	410	99
15	Norway	4.1	324	13940	77	460	99
16	Switzerland	6.4	41	16330	77	390	99

East European States

Row	State	Populn.	Area	GNP	Life	Doct	Read
1	Yugoslavia	23.0	256	2120	69	670	85
2	Hungary	10.7	93	2100	70	320	99
3	Poland	36.9	313	2100	71	550	98
4	Albania	2.9	29	*	70	*	*
5	Bulgaria	9.0	111	*	71	400	*
6	Czechos.	15.5	128	*	70	350	*
7	Romania	22.7	238	*	71	650	98

16.2 Typical data

There are two basic questions that you need to ask about data:

(a) What is a typical value for a particular group of data?

(b) How closely does all the data conform to this typical value?

There are many different values that can be taken as typical, usually referred to as **measures of central tendency**. Each of these has an associated **measure of spread** which indicates how widespread the data is. The most useful are:

(a) mode and range;

(b) median and percentiles;

(c) mean and standard deviation.

Mode and range

These are the simplest and subsequently crudest measures available. The **mode** is defined as the most frequently occurring item or group of items.

The data opposite is part of an analysis of accidents on which insurance claims were submitted. The three sets of data illustrate the different types of data that occur.

(a) **Qualitative** - involves no meaningful numbers, e.g. 'Use of Vehicle'.

(b) **Discrete** - numerical data with only a fixed number of options e.g. 'Casualties'.

(c) **Continuous** - numerical data with infinite options, the only restriction being accuracy of measurement, e.g. 'Cubic Capacity'.

What is the modal value in each case?

With cubic capacity the modal group is '1501 -2000'. One problem with this is that the value could depend on the particular groupings. Because of this, attempts to find a precise mode are pointless.

With 'Use of Vehicle' you can say that the most common form of use was 'Pleasure'. The mode is in fact the only value you can use with qualitative data.

With 'Casualties' the mode is clearly 0. This measure however ignores the rest of the data.

Another problem with the mode occurs when two or more categories have equal highest frequencies. (See London Pupil/ Teacher Ratios in last unit.)

Use of a Vehicle

Pleasure	4550
Journey to/from work	1217
Business	1244
Motor Trade	40
Hire or reward	92
Total	7143
(Unknown	825)

Casualties

0	7383
1	448
2	103
3	23
4	10
5	0
6	1
Total	7968

Cubic Capacity

Up to 1000	706
1001-1500	2558
1501-2000	3011
2001-2500	269
2501-3000	162
Over 3001	97
Total	6803
(Unknown	1165)

The **range**, which is the **difference** between the highest and lowest value, is difficult to calculate from the data as presented (it has no meaning in the qualitative case) but could simply be found from the raw data. In neither of the two quantitative cases is it particularly informative. If you look at the 'Life Expectancy' in the data met earlier however, the highest and lowest values are of great interest. Find out what these values are.

The main difficulty with the range however is that it only needs one extreme value at each end to totally distort the data.

Median and percentiles

The title 'measures of central tendency' suggests that you are looking for a value in the middle. This is exactly what the median does. If 5 people are put in order of height, then the median height would be that of the middle person.

Note that the middle item of five is the third. In general if there are n items of data then the median is found at the $(n + 1)/2$th value. Clearly with an even number of items this will fall exactly half way between two values.

Medians can easily be found from stem and leaf diagrams. For example using the Life Expectancy figures for African States, you obtain the plot opposite, from which, since n=30, you can readily read off the median value.

3	88	
4		
4	3	
4	445	
4	66667	
4	899	
5	0011	Median = 50
5	2223	
5	444	
5	7	
5	89	
6	0	
6	2	

With data in groups you can only obtain an estimate (see why stem and leaf are better!).

Using the Literacy figures for Africa you get a frequency table which is shown opposite.

Literacy (%)	Freq.
10 - 19	6
20 - 29	4
30 - 39	5
40 - 49	3
50 - 59	4
60 - 70	3
70+	1
Total	26

The median is the (26+1)/2 = 13.5th item of data.

This must be 3.5/5 = 0.7 of the way up the 30-39 group.

The median therefore is 29.5 + (0.7 x 10) = 36.5

Note that 29.5 is the lowest rounded value which could be in the 30-39 group and is called the **lower class boundary**.

This method is called **linear interpolation**, which you may have met elsewhere, and assumes that the frequency goes up in a straight line. The result is therefore only an estimate.

Activity 2

(a) Work out the median life expectancies for Central & South America, Western Europe and Eastern Europe using stem and leaf diagrams. Comment on your results.

(b) The information opposite gives details of property deals carried out in a particular year. Use the number of deals (No. 000s) column to estimate the median price of property deals that year.

Residential Property Deals England and Wales 1989

Price	No. 000s	%	Value (£m)	%
Under £10,000	124	8.4	472	0.6
10-20,000	175	11.9	2,622	3.2
20-30,000	226	15.4	5,706	6.9
30-50,000	310	21.2	12,361	15.0
50-100,000	470	32.0	32,628	39.6
100-250,000	142	9.7	19,860	24.1
over £250,000	21	1.4	8,718	10.6
Total	1, 468	100	82,367	100

The median divides the data into two halves, i.e. it has 50% of the data above it and 50% below. Using the same idea you could in fact divide the data into any fraction you like. One of the most useful is to divide the data into quarters. The data for Life Expectancy in Africa is shown opposite.

Frequency	Stem	leaf
2	3	88
2	4	
3	4	3
6	4	445
11	4	66667
14	4	899
(4)	5	0011
12	5	2223
8	5	444
5	5	7
4	5	89
2	6	0
1	6	2

The first quarter is given by the $(30+1)/4 = 7.75$th item. Since the seventh and eighth item are both 46 this is 46. This is called the **lower quartile**.

The third quarter or **upper quartile** is given by $3 \times 7.75 = 23.25$th item, again with repeated values is 54.

In the table opposite, the running total or cumulative frequencies from each end have been shown to help you find these values.

A commonly used measure is the **interquartile range**, the difference between the two quartiles i.e. $54 - 46 = 8$. The **semi-interquartile range** is half this value.

The interquartile range gives the range within which the middle half of the data lie. In conjunction with the median you can see that the data is fairly evenly spread out about the middle.

To find these values from a frequency table you could use a linear interpolation method, but this can be difficult and the assumption of linearity between values is not always a good one. A commonly used alternative is to plot a **cumulative frequency curve**. You first need to find the cumulative frequency or running total. Look at the Literacy data for Africa shown opposite.

Literacy (%)	Freq.	Cumulative Freq.
10 - 19	6	6
20 - 29	4	10
30 - 39	5	15
40 - 49	3	18
50 - 59	4	22
60 - 70	3	25
70+	1	26

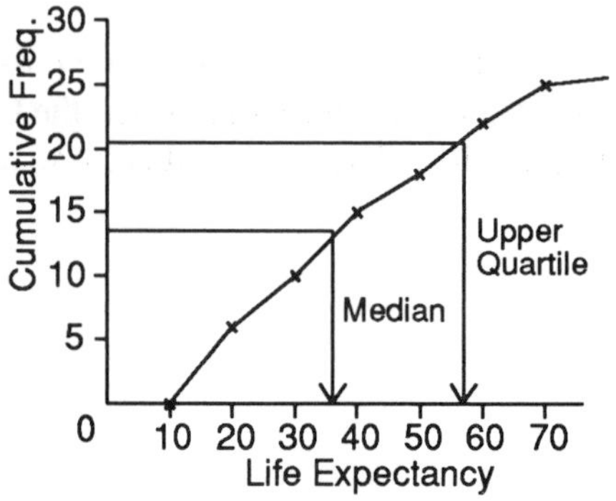

Note that the cumulative frequency values are related to the **upper class boundaries**, e.g. 10 in the second row tells you that 10 states had a literacy rate of 29.5% or less. You therefore plot a graph of cumulative frequencies against upper class boundaries.

The median and quartiles can be read off at the 13.5th, 6.75th and 20.25th values respectively. Although the results depend on graphical accuracy the fact that a curve is used rather than a straight line gives a more realistic result.

This same idea can be used for any other percentiles but the only other ones in use are the 5% and 95% values.

The median and quartiles are commonly used measures. The one criticism made of them is that they do not consider all the data and ignore the tail ends. This can however be an advantage in that they are not prone to distortion by extremes.

Activity 3

In this activity use a method appropriate to the data.

(a) Using the World Data worksheet find the median and inter-quartile range of the patient/doctor ratios in each of the four areas. Comment on your results.

(b) Find the median and quartiles for
  (i) Cubic Capacity
  (ii) Casualties
  from the 'Analysis of Insurance Claims' data earlier in this unit.

(c) The data below shows the population of the UK in millions over this century and predicted values for the future. Find the median and interquartile range for:
  (i) 1901 (ii)1941 (iii)1991 (iv)2015.

Comment on your results in particular with reference to what the possible implications on future Government planning might be.

Age and sex of the population

United Kingdom — Millions

	0-4	5-14	15-29	30-44	45-59	60-64	65-74	75-84	85+	All ages
Census enumerated										
1901	4.4	8.0	10.8	7.5	4.6	1.1	1.3	0.5		38.2
1911	4.5	8.4	11.2	8.9	5.6	1.2	1.6	0.6		42.1
1921	3.9	8.4	11.2	9.3	7.0	1.5	1.9	0.7		44.0
1931	3.5	7.6	11.8	9.7	8.0	1.9	2.5	1.0		46.1
Mid-year estimates										
1941	3.4	6.8	9.2	10.3	8.5	2.3	3.2	1.3		44.9
1951	4.3	7.0	10.2	11.2	9.6	2.4	3.7	1.8		50.3
1961	4.3	8.1	10.3	10.5	10.6	2.8	4.0	1.9	0.3	52.8
1971	4.5	8.9	11.8	9.8	10.2	3.2	4.8	2.2	0.5	55.9
1976	3.7	9.2	12.4	10.0	9.8	3.1	5.1	2.3	0.5	56.2
1981	3.5	8.1	12.8	11.0	9.5	2.9	5.2	2.7	0.6	56.4
1983	3.6	7.6	13.1	11.1	9.4	3.2	5.0	2.8	0.6	56.3
1984	3.6	7.4	13.3	11.2	9.3	3.3	4.8	2.9	0.7	56.5
1985										
Males	1.9	3.7	6.8	5.7	4.6	1.5	2.2	1.0	0.2	27.6
Females	1.8	3.5	6.6	5.6	4.7	1.7	2.8	1.9	0.5	29.0
Total	3.6	7.3	13.4	11.3	9.3	3.1	4.9	2.9	0.7	56.6
Projections										
1987	10.7		13.5	11.6	9.2	8.0		3.8		56.9
1991	11.0		12.9	12.1	9.5	7.9		4.0		57.5
1996	11.7		11.6	12.6	10.5	7.7		4.2		58.3
2001	12.0		10.8	13.2	11.0	7.6		4.4		59.0
2006	11.7		11.0	12.6	11.6	7.9		4.5		59.3
2011	11.1		11.7	11.3	12.1	8.8		4.5		59.4
2015	10.8		12.0	10.6	12.6	9.1		4.5		59.6

Mean and standard deviation

So far in this text the word 'average' has been avoided. In fact all measures of central tendency are averages, though if asked to find the average most people would calculate the mean. The mean is found by adding together all the values in the data and dividing by the number of items. In notation form you write this:

$$\bar{x} = \frac{\Sigma x}{n}$$

So the mean of 5, 5, 6, 8 and 15 is $\frac{(5+5+6+8+15)}{5} = 7.8$

But what does the mean mean?

If you imagine the numbers above being balanced on a 20 cm strip, to balance the strip you would need to put the pivot at a point 7.8 cm from the end.

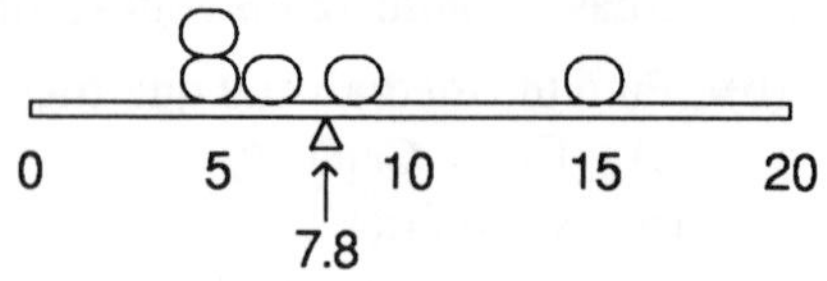

The mean is mathematically equivalent to the centre of gravity. The mean then 'balances' all of the data available. Although it does use all the data it is prone, as in this case, to distortion by odd extreme values.

Data presented in the form of a stem and leaf diagram can easily be used to calculate the mean as the original values are still recorded. When data is stored in a frequency table a quicker method can be used. The Insurance data for the number of casualties is shown in the table opposite.

Casualties	Freq.
0	7383
1	448
2	103
3	23
4	10
5	0
6	1
Total	7968

This table tells us that there were 7383 accidents with no casualties, 448 with one, etc. Therefore the total of all casualties can be found by:

$$\begin{aligned}\Sigma x = &\ (0\times7383)+(1\times448)+(2\times103)+(3\times23)\\ &+(4\times10)+(5\times0)+(6\times1)\\ &=769\end{aligned}$$

So $\quad \bar{x} = \frac{769}{7968} = 0.097$

As with the median when data is given in a grouped table you can only estimate the mean. Here you must repeat the above procedure but use the group mid-mark as the x value. Using 'Cubic Capacity' data from the Insurance data shown opposite:

Cubic Capacity	Mid value	Freq.
Up to 1000	750.5	706
1001 - 1500	1250.5	2558
1501 - 2000	1750.5	3011
2001 - 2500	2250.5	269
2501 - 3000	2750.5	162
Over 3000	3250.5	97
Total		6803

$$\begin{aligned}\Sigma x &= (750.5\times706)+(1250.5\times2558)+\ldots\ldots\\ &=10\,365\,651.5\end{aligned}$$

So $\quad \bar{x} = \frac{10\,365\,651.5}{6803} = 1524$

Note that the final answer has been rounded to a whole number in recognition of accuracy.

What are the assumptions that have been made and how true are they likely to be?

What other possible sources of error are there? (Hint: How were the mid-marks of the open ended groups chosen? Did it matter?)

Activity 4

(a) Find the mean life expectancy in the four areas in the World Data information, using the stem and leaf diagrams drawn earlier.

(b) From the 'Age and Sex of the Population' table in the last activity find the mean age of the population in the years

(i) 1901 (ii) 1941 (iii) 1991 (iv) 2015

Compare these values with the medians calculated in the last activity. Under what circumstances would you expect these two values to be approximately the same?

To accompany the mean it seems appropriate to have a measure of spread which incorporates all of the data. These are the life expectancies of the Middle Eastern states:

Yemen Arab Rep.	45	Yemen PDR	47
Jordan	64	Syria	63
Israel	75	Iran	61
Iraq	60	Oman	53
Libya	59	Saudi Arabia	62
Kuwait	72	U.A.E.	72

The mean is 61.1. To look at the way these differ from the mean you need to look at the differences between each value and the mean, i.e.

−16.1	−14.1
+2.9	+1.9
+13.9	−0.1
−1.1	−8.1
−2.1	+0.9
+10.9	+10.9

Add these differences up and you should not be too surprised to find this gives zero. In order to avoid this the differences are squared and to give an overall measure you sum these,

$$\Sigma(x-\bar{x})^2 = 16.1^2 + 14.1^2 + ... + 10.9^2 = 972.92$$

As it stands the figure will increase with more data so it needs to be averaged out. You also need to compensate for the squaring so you square root the final answer. This measure is the **standard deviation**. In this case

$$s = \sqrt{\left(\frac{972.92}{12}\right)} = 9.00$$

In general, the standard deviation is given by:

$$s = \sqrt{\frac{\Sigma(x-\bar{x})^2}{n}}$$

But what does the standard deviation stand for?

One of the difficulties with the standard deviation is that it is difficult to explain to a layperson what it represents. It is at its most useful in comparing different sets of figures, i.e. is one set of data more spread out than another? A rule of thumb often used is that when the data follows a bell shaped pattern (i.e. most data is close to the mean) 95% of data lies within **two** standard deviations from the mean.

The formula above is a rather clumsy method for actually calculating the standard deviation. Another formula more commonly used is:

$$s = \sqrt{\frac{\Sigma x^2}{n} - \bar{x}^2}$$

Also note that the **variance** is defined as the square of the standard deviation, s^2.

This has the advantage that Σx^2 and Σx can be found cumulatively, i.e.

Value	Σx	Σx^2
45	45	2025
47	92	4234
64	156	8330
63	219	1229
75	294	17924
.		
.		
.		
72	733	45747

$$\bar{x} = \frac{733}{12} = 61.1$$

$$s = \sqrt{\frac{45747}{12} - (61.1)^2} = 9.00$$

Activity 5

Noting that $\bar{x} = \dfrac{\Sigma x}{n}$, prove that $s^2 = \dfrac{\Sigma x^2}{n} - \bar{x}^2$.

If it was not for this alternative formula calculators would find this very difficult to calculate. As it is most modern calculators have the function to calculate this. Find out how to calculate the mean and standard deviation on your calculator.

Activity 6 Do personal stereos help you concentrate?

A simple mathematical puzzle is shown on the worksheet on the next page. The purpose of this experiment is to see whether people can complete the puzzle more quickly if they are using a personal stereo at the time. As a group design an experiment to test this hypothesis. Calculate the mean and standard deviation of the times subjects took to complete the test with and without headphones and use these to report your findings.

Exercise 16B

1. Find the standard deviation of the Life Expectancies for the four regions in the World Data. What does this tell you about regional differences in these main areas?

2. The Unemployment Rates in three regions in the UK in 1989 were listed as shown in the table opposite.

   Find the mean and standard deviation for each region and comment on the regional differences in unemployment.

3. Calculating the standard deviation from data in a frequency table works in the same way as the mean. Σx and Σx^2 are found by multipling the value (or mid mark in the case of grouped tables) by the frequencies. Some calculators do this automatically. Find the standard deviations of

   (i) Casualties;

   (ii) Cubic Capacity

   as given in Insurance data earlier.

4. The OPCS monitors the ages of mothers giving birth to children. The data for 1941, 1951, 1971 and 1989 are shown opposite.

   Find the mean and standard deviation for each year and comment on the changes in pattern of the age at which women give birth.

East Anglia	**%**	**North-West**	**%**
Cambridge	5.8	Accrington	13.4
Gt. Yarmouth	9.7	Ashton U. Lyme	14.0
Ipswich	8.1	Birkenhead	18.6
Lowestoft	11.7	Blackburn	13.9
Norwich	9.1	Blackpool	11.2
Peterborough	11.8	Bolton	15.4
		Burnley	11.8
East Midlands		Bury	13.2
Chesterfield	12.4	Chester	12.2
Coalville	8.7	Crewe	10.0
Corby	22.3	Lancaster	11.8
Derby	8.4	Leigh	15.3
Kettering	13.2	Liverpool	18.1
Leicester	11.0	Manchester	12.3
Lincoln	13.7	Nelson	14.2
Loughborough	7.5	Northwich	15.7
Mansfield	13.2	Oldham	14.1
Northants	9.3	Preston	11.9
Nottingham	11.2	Rochdale	16.9
Sutton in Ashfield	9.1	Southport	15.7

	Thousands of Births			
Age of Mother	**1941**	**1951**	**1971**	**1989**
15 - 19	28.8	33.0	92.2	61.6
20 - 24	169.9	212.0	317.6	202.0
25 - 29	208.1	247.3	273.2	265.9
30 - 34	147.8	159.0	122.7	158.5
35 - 39	85.0	88.3	50.5	53.3
40 - 44	28.1	26.1	13.1	9.8
45 - 49	2.0	1.5	0.9	0.8

PUZZLE

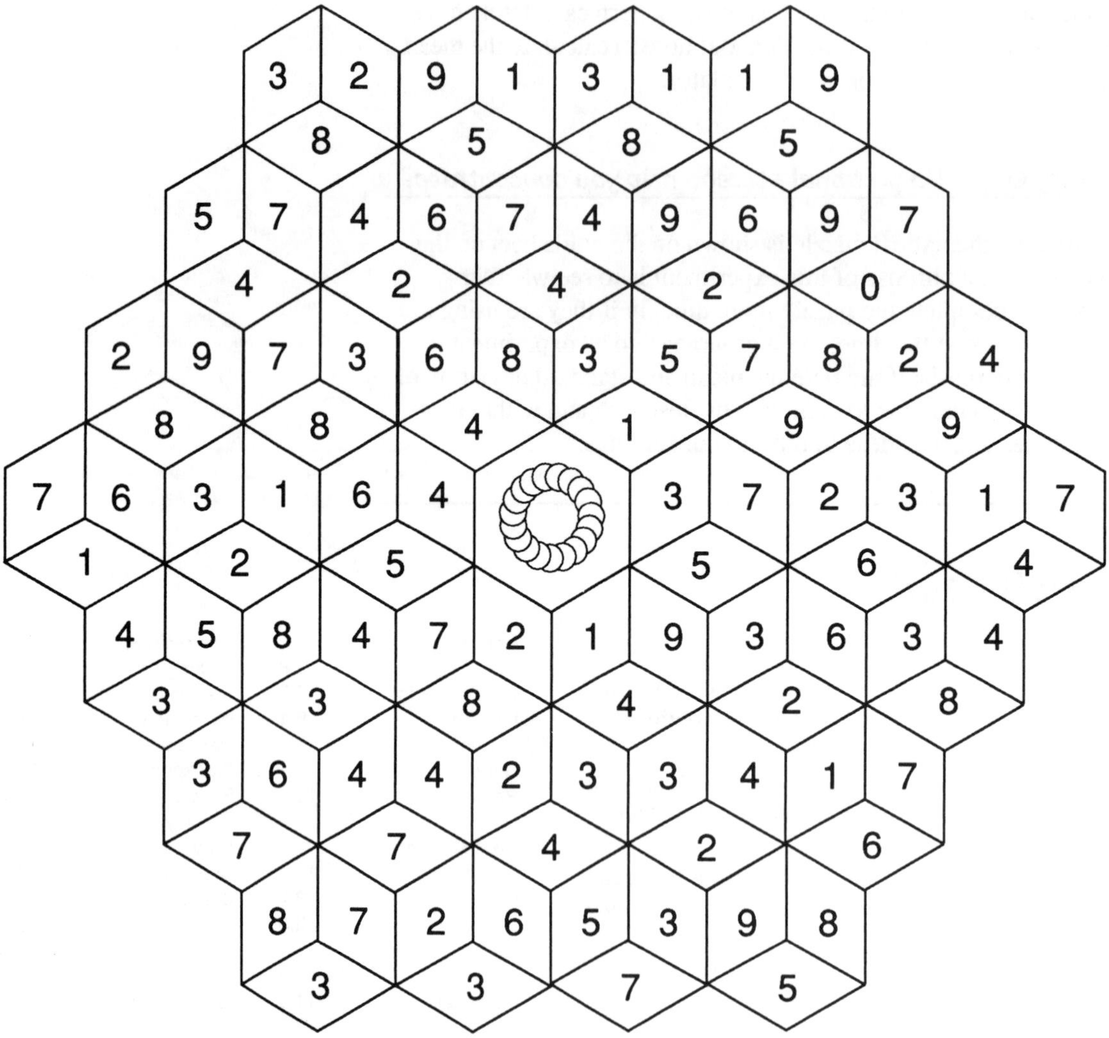

There are 14 hexagons on this grid where the three numbers add up to 15. Shade them in – they may overlap.

16.3 Illustrating results

So far all the techniques have been about simplifying the data with the main intention being your own understanding. When presenting your findings to others you will need to make them easy to understand and attractively presented. In this section look at various forms of diagrams which can help in this task.

Bar charts

These are the most commonly used form of diagram. Strictly speaking there are 3 types of bar chart, one for each type of data. The illustration below show these using the Insurance data.

In practice frequency diagrams are not often used as they are not particularly eyecatching and it is more common to see a bar chart used where the numbers are treated as qualitative.

Histogram

Used only for quantitative continuous data.

A proper continuous mathematical scale must be used along the bottom. There are no gaps between bars as they are drawn up to class boundaries.

Problems arise when groups have uneven sizes so open-ended groups are treated as the same size.

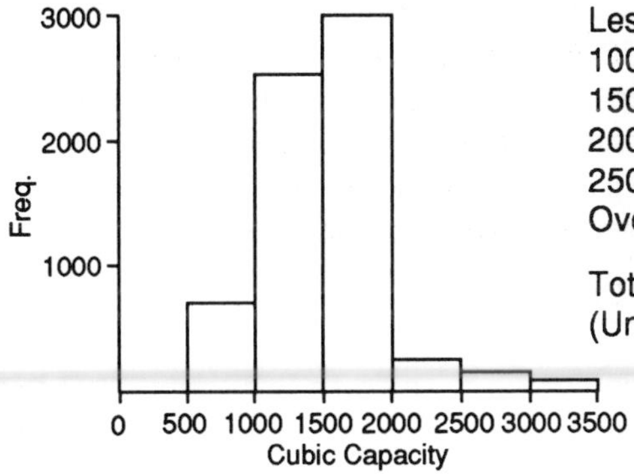

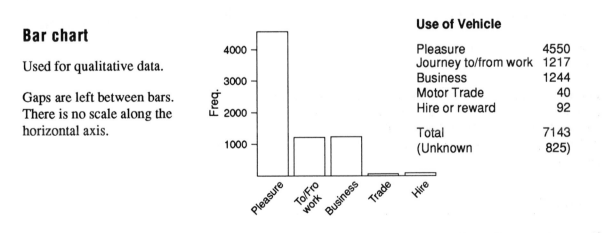

Cubic Capacity

Less than 1000	706
1000 - 1500	2558
1501 - 2000	3011
2001 - 2500	269
2501 - 3000	162
Over 3001	97
Total	6803
(Unknown	1165)

Bar chart

Used for qualitative data.

Gaps are left between bars. There is no scale along the horizontal axis.

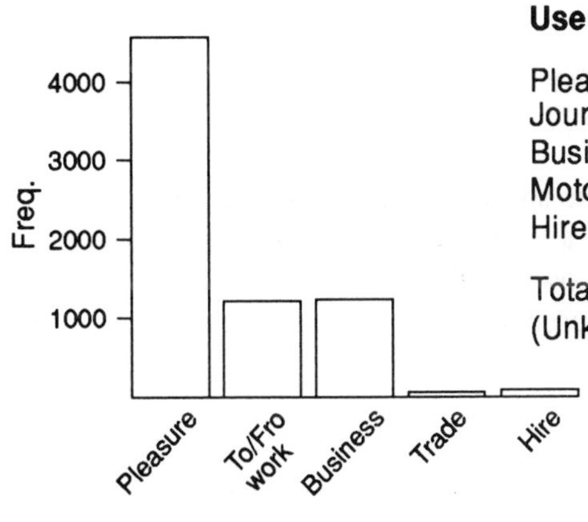

Use of Vehicle

Pleasure	4550
Journey to/from work	1217
Business	1244
Motor Trade	40
Hire or reward	92
Total	7143
(Unknown	825)

Frequency diagram

Used for quantitative discrete data.

A proper scale is used along the horizontal axis. Lines are used instead of bars to emphasize the discreteness.

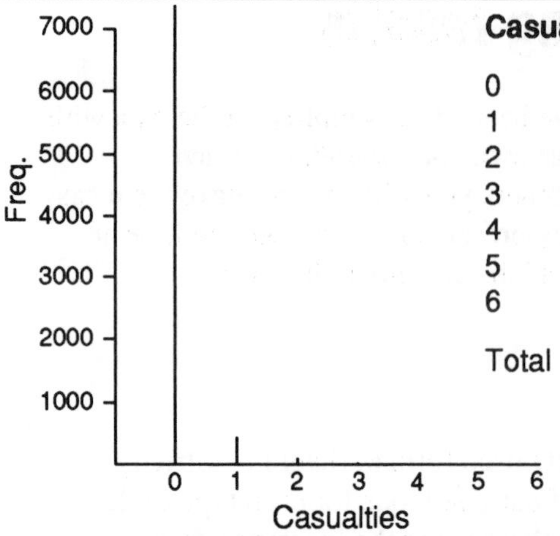

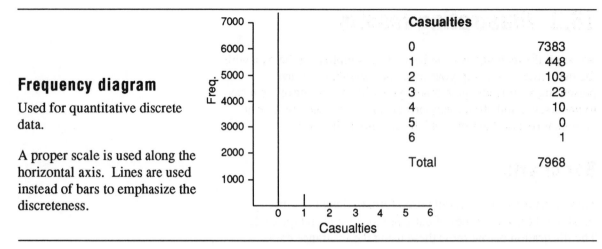

Casualties	
0	7383
1	448
2	103
3	23
4	10
5	0
6	1
Total	7968

Care needs to be taken where groups are of uneven size. Consider the data on 'Residential Property Deals' used in Activity 2. The histogram is shown opposite.

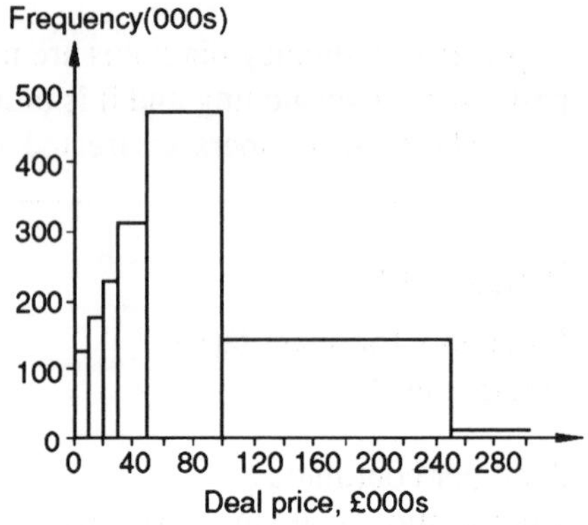

Although there were only 1.5 times as many deals in the 50-100 category compared to the 30-50 category, because your eye looks at areas, it appears that there are more than three times as many on the histogram. To compensate for this the frequencies can be adjusted to a standard group size so that the area represents the frequency. These are known as **relative frequencies**. i.e.

Price	Freq. per £10 000
Under 10 000	124
10 - 20 000	175
20 - 30 000	226
30 - 50 000	155
50 - 100 000	94
100 - 250 000	9.5
Over 250 000	1.4

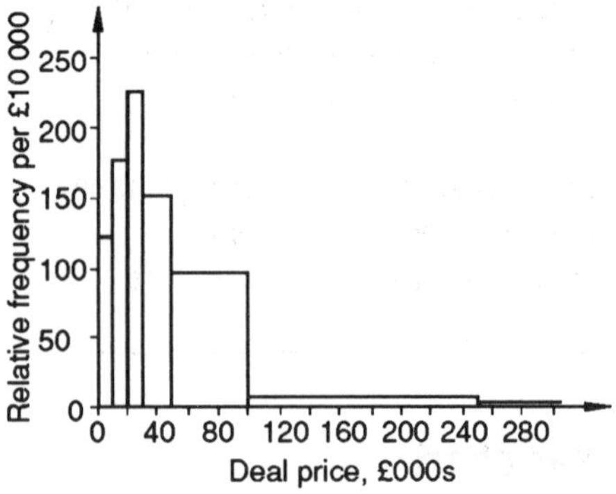

The resulting relative frequency histogram gives a much fairer view of the distribution of deals.

In some cases you may wish to show two sets of comparable data on one bar chart, this is called a **composite bar chart**. In the age distribution figures shown on the next page, three different methods have been used to show the male and female age group distributions.

Activity 7

Draw histograms for 1941 and 1989 using the 'Ages at which mothers give birth' data in Question 4, Exercise 16B.

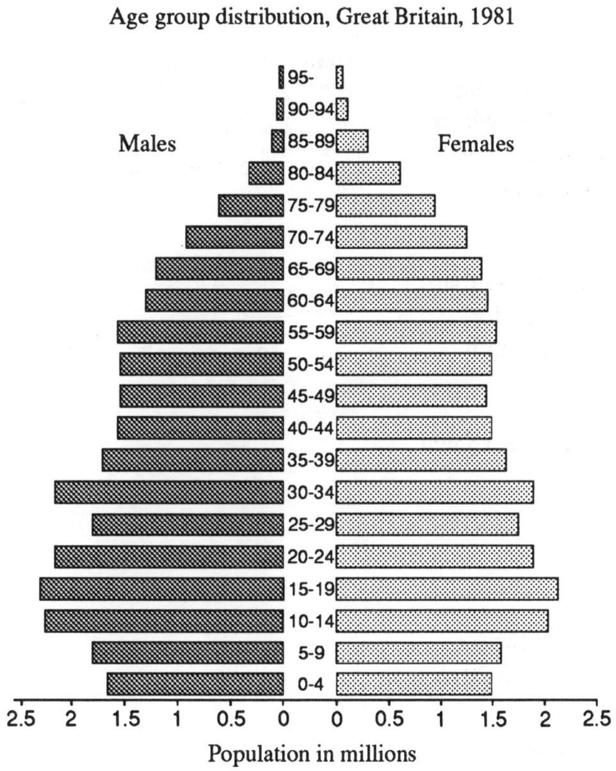

Bar charts are often used to show sets of comparable information side by side, as shown opposite. This is called a **composite bar chart**.

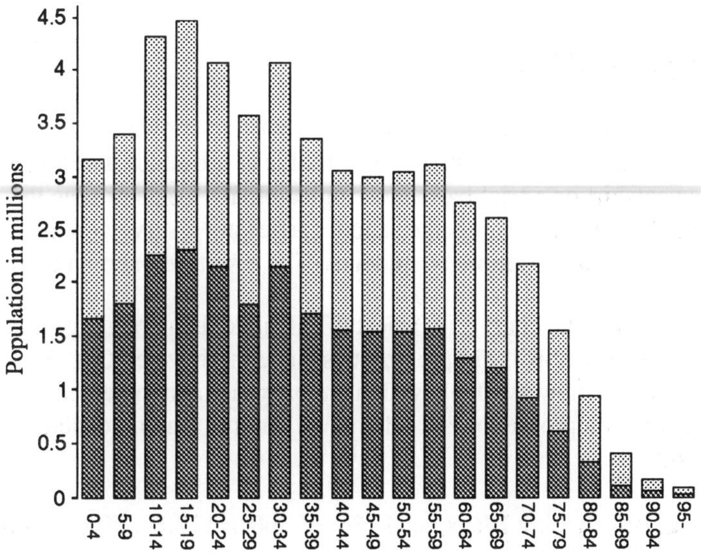

There are alternative ways this could have been shown, as is illustrated opposite and below.

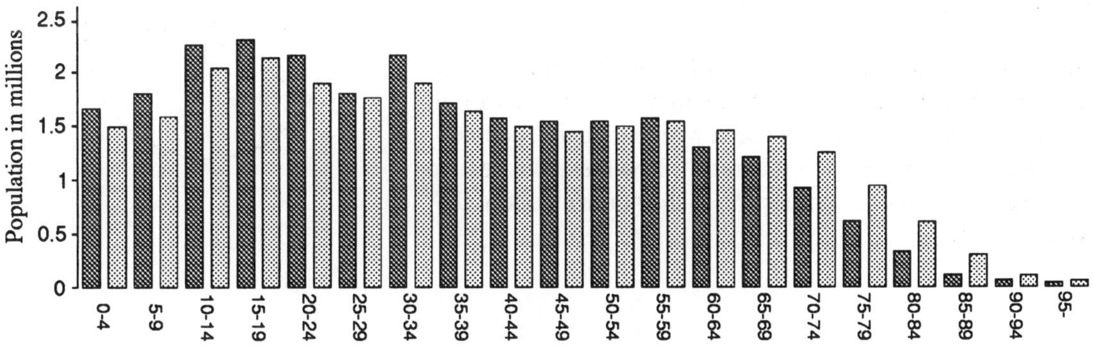

Box and whisker plot

This is an EDA technique that has become increasingly popular in recent years. It is drawn using the quartiles to make a box, with a line indicating the median. Lines or whiskers are then drawn to the extremities. The data for London Unit Costs used earlier would be as shown opposite.

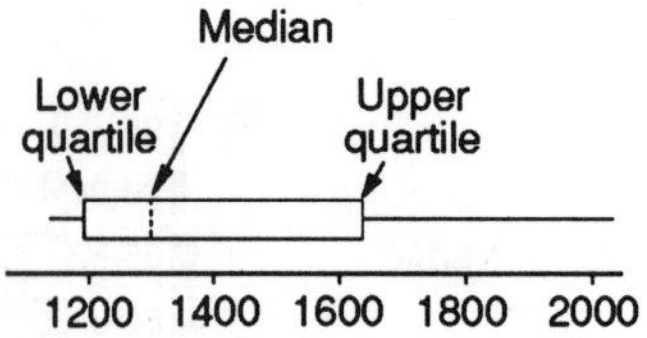

They are particularly useful when you wish to compare more than one set of data on the same scale. For example you can easily compare the Life Expectancies of Africa with Central & South America as shown opposite.

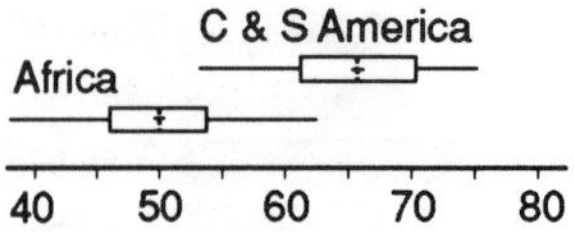

Where there are odd extreme items or 'outliers' these can be shown as crosses outside the normal whisker.

Activity 7

(a) Draw box and whisker plots for the 'Age and sex of the population' data given earlier for 1901, 1941, 1991 and 2015 using the same scale.

(b) Draw box and whisker plots for the patient/doctor ratios for Africa and Central & South America on the same axis.

Pie charts

Pie charts are commonly used if you wish to show how a total is split into component parts. A school is to introduce a new school sweatshirt on a trial basis in a single colour. To determine the likely range of colours the school carries out a survey on a representative sample of students. The results are shown opposite.

Prefered colour	Boys	Girls
Black	48	35
Grey	19	4
Blue	21	8
Green	4	1
Red	8	16
Total	100	64

To form a pie chart it is easiest to calculate the percentage in each group first (this is simple for boys since there were 100). Pie chart scales are now available which are broken down in percentages. If however a protractor is used you will simply find percentages of 360°.

e.g. Boys voting Black need 48% of 360° = 172.8°. The resulting pie chart is shown opposite.

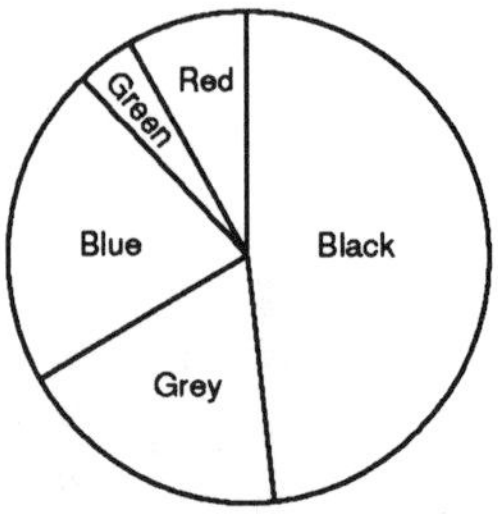

You might want to show the girls on a different pie chart, but since there are less of them a smaller chart should be drawn. Be careful however since, as you have already seen with bar charts, people perceive areas when they look at diagrams. You therefore need to draw the smaller pie chart in proportion to the **square root** of the radius of the larger.

For example if the boys' pie chart radius was 5 cm, area of girls' needs to be 64/100 = 0.64 times smaller, so the radius needs to be $\sqrt{0.64} = 0.8$ times smaller. Hence

$$\text{radius for girls} = 0.8 \times 5 = 4 \text{ cm}.$$

The two pie charts together are shown opposite.

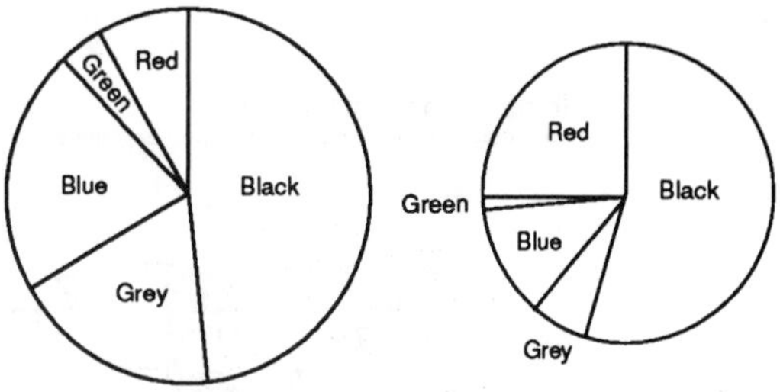

The following page shows some interesting ways that conventional diagrams have been made more eyecatching.

Other forms of diagram

Two forms of diagram are particularly useful when you have two sets of linked data. Where data is measured on a continuous scale, e.g. measurements taken over a period of time, a line graph is used as shown in the first diagram opposite.

Average half-hour audience: All adults Monday to Friday averaged

Capital Radio Rating (on 9.7m adult pop)

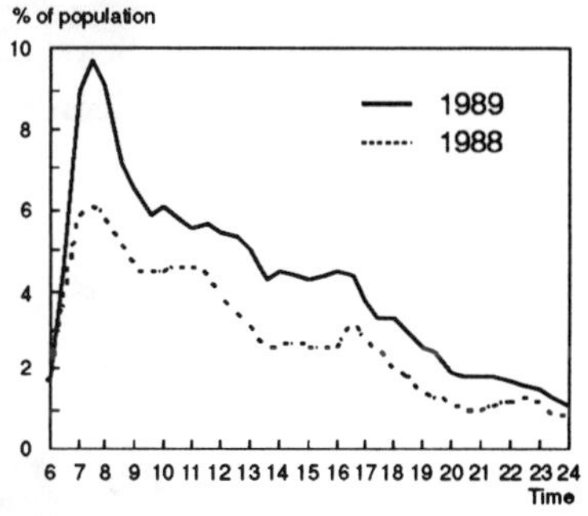

Capital Radio has gained significantly in audience across most of the day

Where the two values are measurements taken from individuals a scattergram can be used. For example suppose a scientist wishes to investigate whether reaction times are linked to pulse rates. The reaction time and pulse of some subjects are measured. Plotting these on a scattergram gives the diagram below.

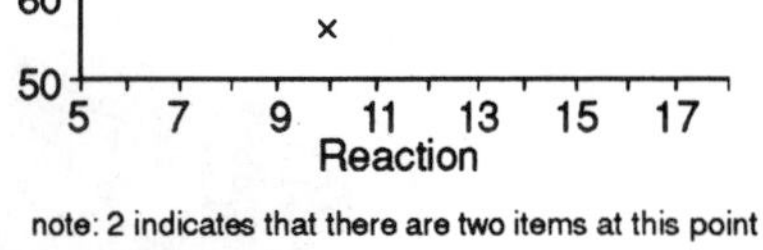

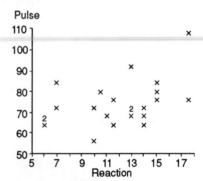

note: 2 indicates that there are two items at this point

In order to examine the link between two such variables you can mark the medians of the two variables on the graph. By examining the number of points in each quadrant an idea of the link or **correlation** between the two variables can be found.

In this case the points are evenly distributed so there appears to be little correlation between pulse and reaction time.

Deceptive diagrams

The page after next shows various diagrams from the media.

Discuss as a group why these perhaps might be misleading.

What could be done to make these more reasonable?

Interesting Illustrations

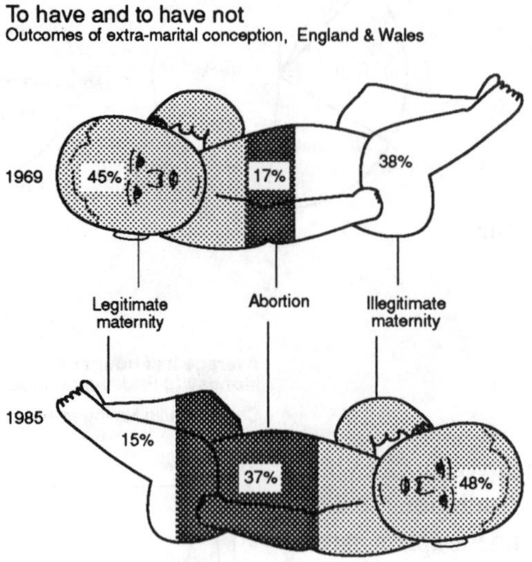
To have and to have not
Outcomes of extra-marital conception, England & Wales
1969
45%
17%
38%
Legitimate maternity
Abortion
Illegitimate maternity
1985
15%
37%
48%

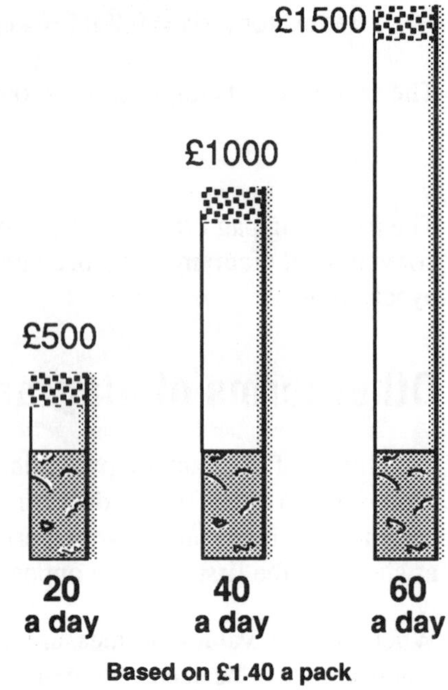
£500
£1000
£1500
20 a day
40 a day
60 a day
Based on £1.40 a pack

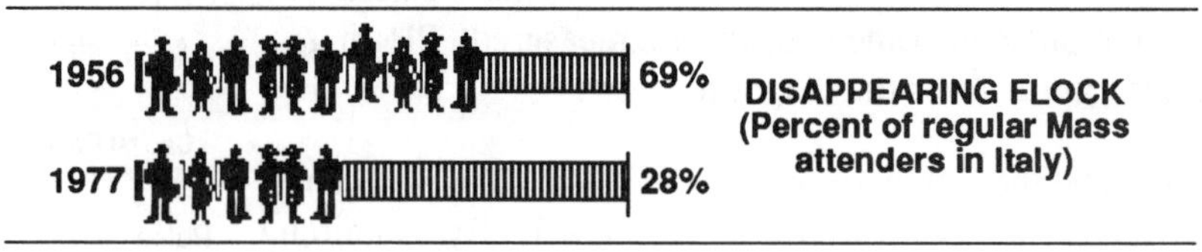
1956
69%
1977
28%
DISAPPEARING FLOCK
(Percent of regular Mass attenders in Italy)

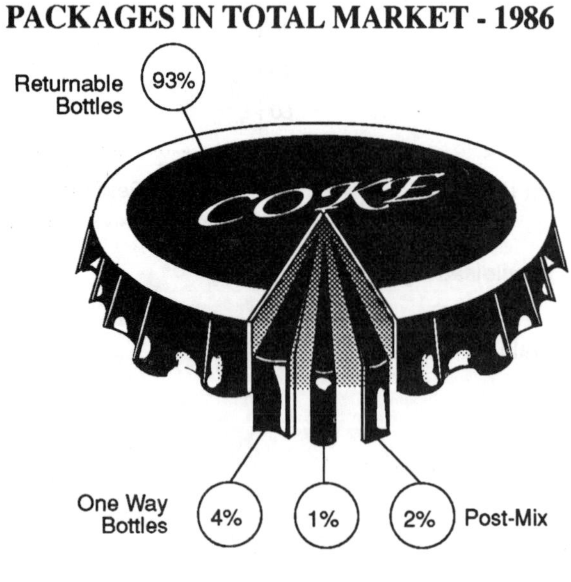
PACKAGES IN TOTAL MARKET - 1986
Returnable Bottles
93%
COKE
One Way Bottles
4%
1%
2%
Post-Mix

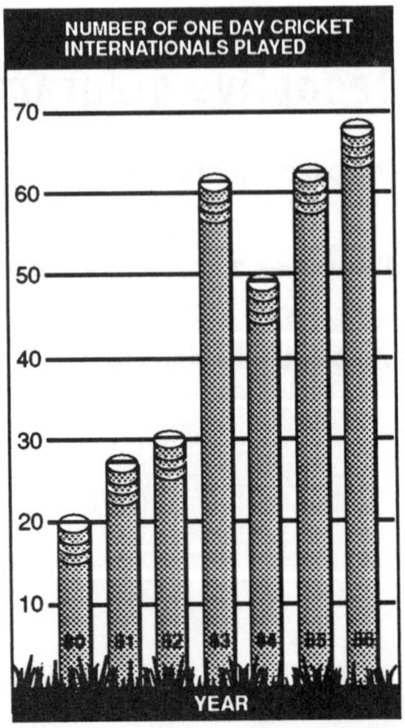
NUMBER OF ONE DAY CRICKET INTERNATIONALS PLAYED
70
60
50
40
30
20
10
YEAR

Deceptive diagrams

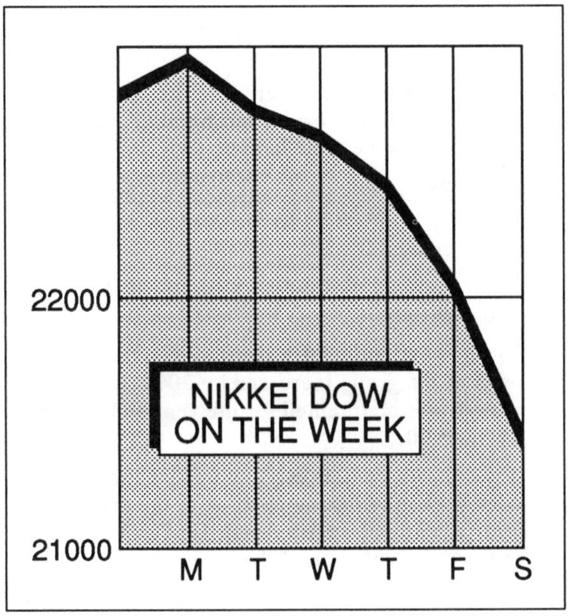
22000
21000
NIKKEI DOW
ON THE WEEK
M
T
W
T
F
S

Unions generally
All
Too little power 9%
Too much power 57%
About right 28%
Don't know 6%
Union members
17%
46%
34%
3%

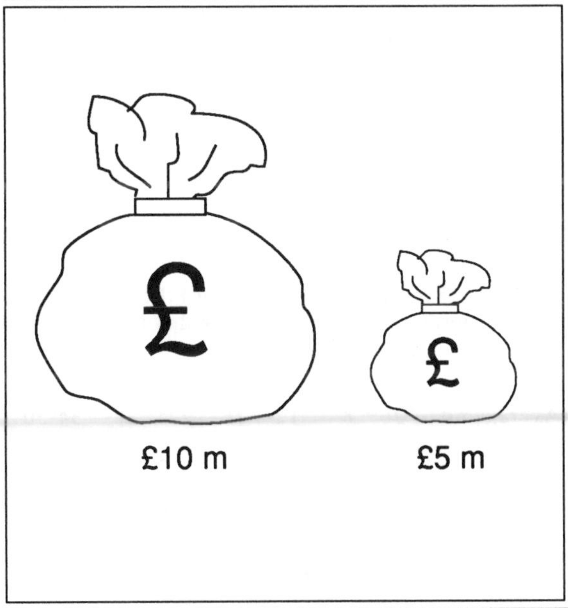
£
£
£10 m
£5 m

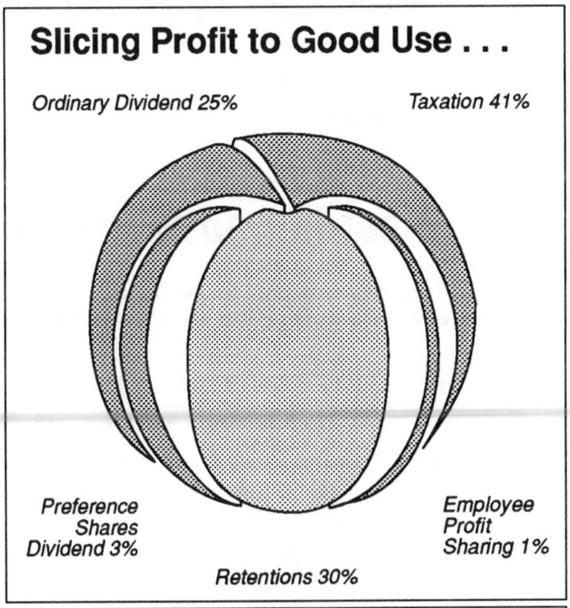
Slicing Profit to Good Use . . .
Ordinary Dividend 25%
Taxation 41%
Preference Shares Dividend 3%
Employee Profit Sharing 1%
Retentions 30%

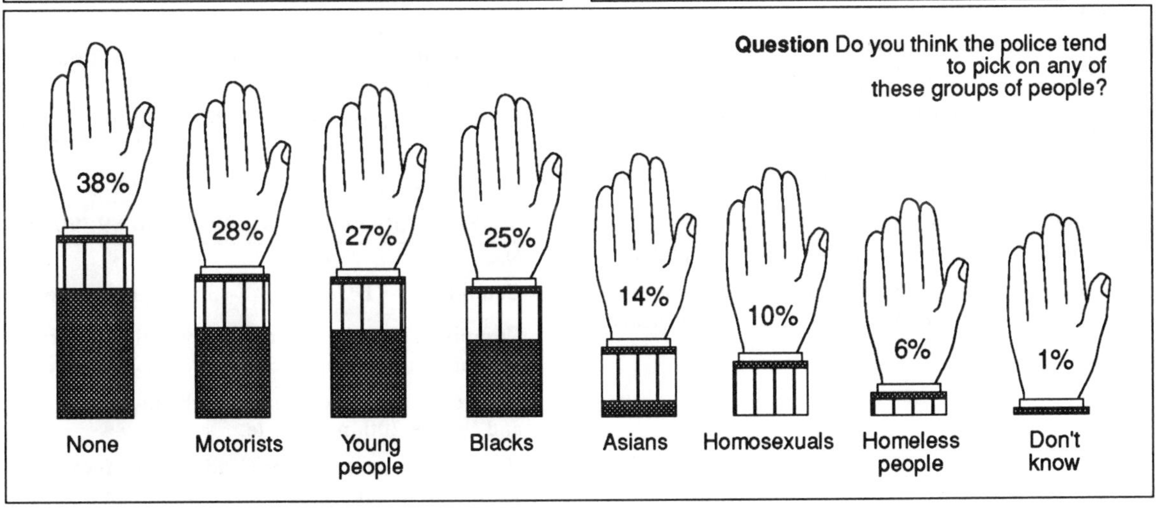
Question Do you think the police tend to pick on any of these groups of people?
38%
28%
27%
25%
14%
10%
6%
1%
None
Motorists
Young people
Blacks
Asians
Homosexuals
Homeless people
Don't know

Exercise 16C

1. The masses (measured to the nearest g) of washers are recorded in the table. Draw a histogram to illustrate the data.

Mass (g)	0-2	3-5	6-11	12-14	15-17
Frequency	5	6	14	4	3

2. 100 people were asked to record how many televsion programmes they watched in a week. The results were as follows:

Number of programmes	0-	10-	18-	30-	35-	45-	50-	60-
Number of viewers	3	16	36	12	12	9	3	0

Draw a bar chart to illustrate the data.

3. The table shows the sales, in millions of dollars, of a company in two successive years.

Year	Africa	America	Asia	Europe
1972	8.4	12.2	15.6	23.8
1973	5.5	6.7	13.2	19.6

Draw two pie charts which allow the total annual sales to be compared.

4. Five companies form a group. The sales of each company during the year ending 5th April, 1988, are shown in the table below.

Company	A	B	C	D	E
Sales (in £1000's)	55	130	20	35	60

Draw a pie chart of radius 5 cm to illustrate this information.

For the year ending 5th April, 1989, the total sales of the group increased by 20%, and this growth was maintained for the year ending 5th April, 1990.

If pie charts were drawn to compare the total sales for each of these years with the total sales for the year ending 5th April, 1988, what would be the radius of each of these pie charts?

If the sales of company E for the year ending 5th April, 1990, were again £60000, what would be the angle of the sector representing them?

16.4 Miscellaneous Exercises

1. The table shows the trunk diameters, in centimetres, of a random sample of 200 larch trees.

Diameter (cm)	15-	20-	25-	30-	35-	40-50
Frequency	22	42	70	38	16	12

Plot a cumulative frequency curve of these data.

By use of this curve, or otherwise, estimate the median and the interquartile range of the trunk diameters of larch trees.

A random sample of 200 spruce trees yields the following information concerning their trunk diameters, in centimetres.

Minimum	Lower quartile	Median	Upper quartile	Maximuum
13	27	32	35	42

Use this data summary to draw a second cumulative frequency curve on your graph.

Comment on any similarities or differences between the trunk diameters of larch and spruce trees.

2. 68 smokers were asked to record their consumption of cigarettes each day for several weeks. The table shown is based on the information obtained.

Average no. of cigs. smoked per day	0-	8-	12-	16-	24-	28-	34-50
No. of smokers	4	6	12	28	8	6	4

Illustrate these data by means of a bar chart.

3. The table below shows the marks, collected into groups, of 400 candidates in an examination. The maximum mark was 99.

Marks	0-9	10-19	20-29	30-39	40-49
No. of candidates	10	26	42	66	83

Marks	50-59	60-69	70-79	80-89	90-99
No. of Candidates	71	52	30	14	6

Compile a cumulative frequency table and draw the cumulative frequency curve.

Use your curve to estimate (a) the median, and (b) the 20th percentile.

If the minimum mark for Grade A was fixed at 74, estimate from your curve the percentage of candidates obtaining Grade A.

4. The frequency distribution given in the table refers to the heights, in cm, of 50 men corrected to the nearest 10 cm.

Height (cm)	140	150	160	170	180	190
Frequency	1	6	8	21	10	4

(a) State the least possible height of the one man whose height is recorded in the table as 140 cm.

(b) Draw on graph paper a histogram to illustrate the data from the table, drawing five columns, with the first column representing the seven shortest men. Label the axes carefully and explain clearly how frequency has been represented on your histogram.

(c) Draw a cumulative frequency diagram on graph paper for the data given in the table. From your diagram, estimate the upper and lower quartiles, the median height and the interquartile range.

5. In an agricultural experiment the gains in mass, in kilograms, of 100 pigs during a certain period were recorded as follows:

Gains in mass (kilos)	5-9	10-14	15-19	20-24	25-29	30-34
Frequency	2	29	37	16	14	2

Construct a histogram and a cumulative frequency polygon of these data. Obtain (a) the median and the semi-interquartile range, (b) the mean and the standard deviation.

Which of these pairs of statistics do you consider more appropriate in this case, and why?

(AEB)

6. In a certain industry, the numbers of thousands of employees in 1970 were as shown in the tables below, by age groups.

Age last birthday	15-19	20-24	25-29	30-34	35-39
No. of thousands	66	65	56	50	42

Age last birthday	40-44	45-49	50-54	55-59	60-64
No. of thousands	37	35	30	24	22

Calculate the arithmetic mean, median, variance and standard deviation of the ages of employees in the industry.
Estimate the percentage of the employees whose ages lie within one standard deviation of the arithmetic mean. (AEB)

7. Two hundred and fifty Army recruits have the following heights.

Height (cm)	165-	170-	175-	180-	185-	190-195
No.of recruits	18	37	60	65	48	22

Plot the data in the form of a cumulative frequency curve. Use the curve to estimate (a) the median height, (b) the lower quartile height.

The tallest 40% of the recruits are to be formed into a special squad. Estimate (c) the median (d) the upper quartile of the heights of the members of this squad.

17 CARTESIAN GEOMETRY

Objectives

After studying this chapter you should

- be familiar with cartesian and parametric equations of a curve;
- be able to sketch simple curves;
- be able to recognise the rectangular hyperbola;
- be able to use the general equation of a circle;
- be able to differentiate simple functions when expressed parametrically.

17.0 Introduction

You have already met the equation of a straight line in its cartesian form - that is, y expressed as a linear function of x.

Here you will extend the analysis to other curves, including circles and hyperbolas. You will also see how to differentiate to find the gradient of a curve when it is expressed in a parametric form.

17.1 Cartesian and parametric equations of a curve

You have already met the equation of a straight line in the form

$$y = mx + c$$

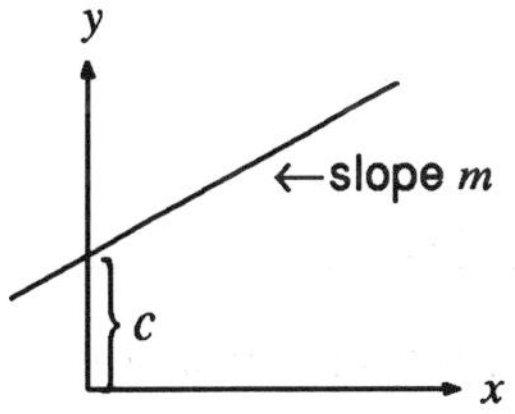

Here m is the slope of the line, and c the intercept on the y-axis (see diagram opposite)

This is an example of a **cartesian equation** since it gives a relationship between the two values x and y.

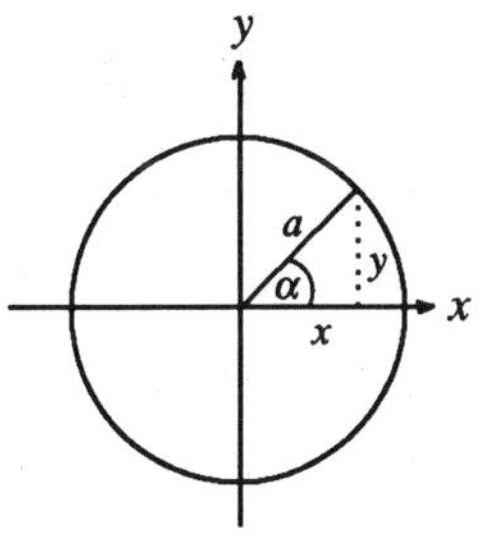

Similarly, the equation of a circle, centre origin, radius a, is given by

$$x^2 + y^2 = a^2 \qquad \text{(using Pythagoras)}$$

This is again a cartesian equation, but it can also be expressed as

$$\left.\begin{array}{l} x = a\cos\theta \\ y = a\sin\theta \end{array}\right\} \qquad 0 \le \theta \le 2\pi$$

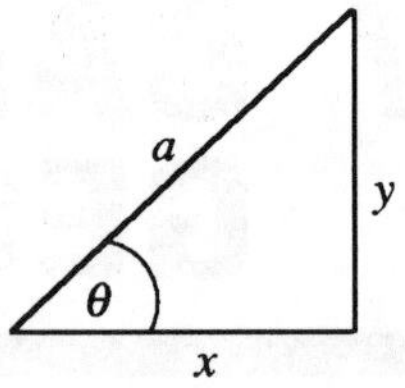

This is an example of a **parametric equation** of the circle and the angle θ is the parameter.

Example

A curve is given by the parametric equation

$$\left.\begin{array}{l} x = a\cos\theta \\ y = b\sin\theta \end{array}\right\} \qquad 0 \le \theta \le 2\pi$$

Find its cartesian equation.

Solution

To find the cartesian equation, you need to eliminate the parameter θ; now

$$\frac{x}{a} = \cos\theta \qquad \Rightarrow \qquad \cos^2\theta = \frac{x^2}{a^2}$$

$$\frac{y}{b} = \sin\theta \qquad \Rightarrow \qquad \sin^2\theta = \frac{y^2}{b^2}$$

But $\cos^2\theta + \sin^2\theta = 1$ giving

$$\frac{x^2}{a^2} + \frac{y^2}{b^2} = 1$$

This is in fact the equation of an ellipse as illustrated opposite when $a > b$.

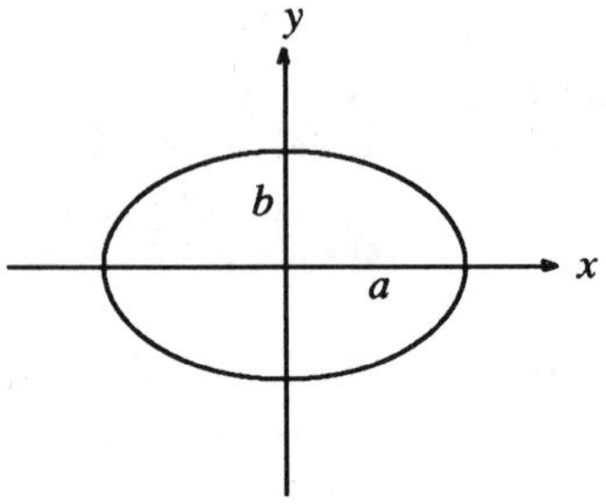

*Activity 1

Use a graphic calculator or computer program to find the shape of the curve

$$\frac{x^2}{a^2} + \frac{y^2}{b^2} = 1$$

when (a) $a = 1, \quad b = 1$

(b) $a = 1, \quad b = 2$

(c) $a = 1, \quad b = 3$

(d) $a = 2, \quad b = 1$

Example

A curve is given parametrically by

$$x = t^2 \quad y = t^3$$

Find its cartesian equation and sketch its shape in the xy plane.

Solution

Eliminating the parametric t,

$$y = t^3 = \left(x^{\frac{1}{2}}\right)^3 = x^{\frac{3}{2}}$$

Its sketch is shown opposite; for $t > 0$ and $t < 0$. There is a cusp at the origin.

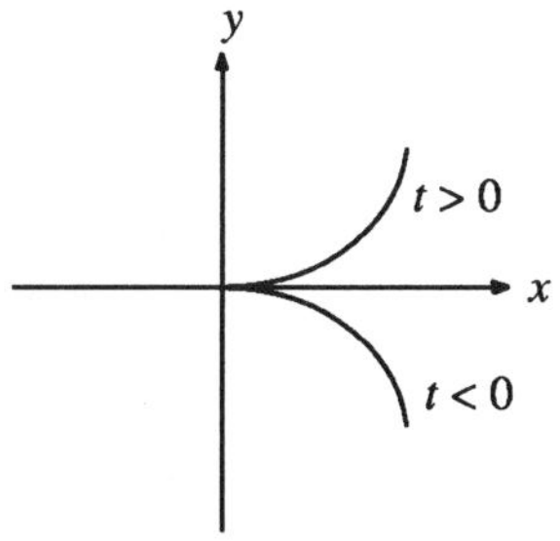

Exercise 17A

1. Find the cartesian equation of the curve when parametric equations are

   (a) $x = t^2, \quad y = 2t$

   (b) $x = 2\cos\theta, \quad y = 3\sin\theta$

   (c) $x = 2t, \quad y = \dfrac{1}{t}$

2. Find the stationary points of the curve when parametric equation are

   $$x = t, \qquad y = t^3 - t$$

   Distinguish between them.

3. Sketch the curve given parametrically by

   $$x = t^2, \quad y = t^3$$

   Show that the equation of the normal to the curve at the point A (4, 8) is given by

   $$x + 3y - 28 = 0$$

4. A curve is given by the parametric equations; for $\theta \geq 0$

   $$x = e^{\theta} + e^{-\theta}$$
   $$y = e^{\theta} - e^{-\theta}$$

   Find its cartesian equation.

17.2 Curve sketching

You have already met many examples of curve sketching. One way is to use your graphic calculator, or a graph plotting program on a computer, but you can often determine the slope of the curve analytically. This is illustrated for the function

$$y = \frac{3(x-2)}{x(x+6)}$$

First note **special** points of the curve

(a) $\quad y = 0 \quad \Rightarrow \quad x = 2$

(b) $\quad y \to \pm\infty$ as $x \to 0$ and as $x \to -6$
(since $x = 0$ and -6 give zeros for the denominator)

(c) Stationary points given by $\frac{dy}{dx}=0$ when

$$\frac{dy}{dx}=3\left\{\frac{1.x(x+6)-(x-2)(2x+6)}{x^2(x+6)^2}\right\}$$

$$=3\frac{\left(x^2+6x-2x^2-2x+12\right)}{x^2(x+6)^2}$$

$$=3\frac{\left(-x^2+4x+12\right)}{x^2(x+6)^2}$$

$$=-3\frac{(x+2)(x-6)}{x^2(x+6)^2}$$

This gives $x=-2$ and $x=6$ for the stationary points.

As you pass through $x=-2$, $\frac{dy}{dx}$ goes from negative to positive - hence **minimum** at $x=-2$ of value $\frac{3}{2}$.

Similarly there is a **maximum** at $x=6$ of value $\frac{1}{6}$.

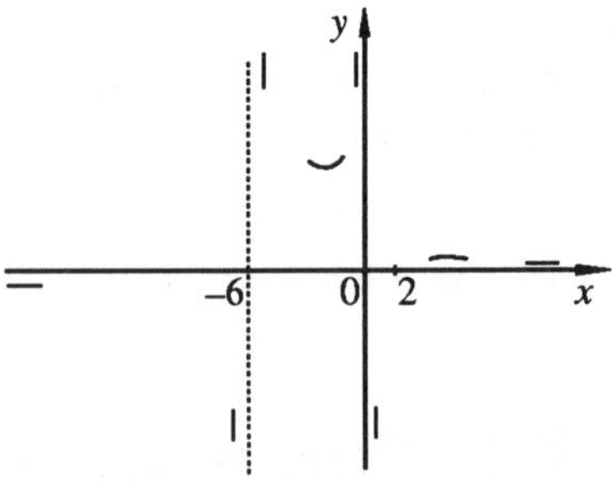

(d) As $x\to\infty$, $y\to 0$ and as $x\to-\infty$, $y\to 0$

These facts can now be plotted on a graph as shown opposite.

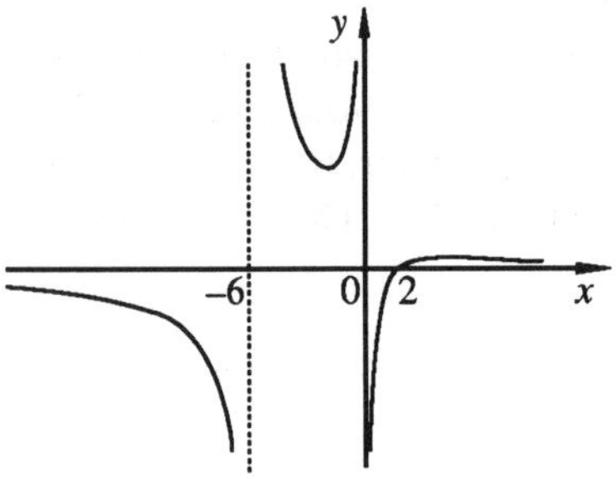

There is only one way that the curve can be completed. This is shown opposite.

Activity 2

Check this sketch by using a graphic calculator or graph plotting program.

Exercise 17B

In each case, without using a calculator or graph plotting program, sketch curves for the following functions. Then check your answers using a graphic calculator or graph plotting program.

1. $y = \dfrac{2x-1}{(x-2)^2}$

2. $y = \dfrac{2}{(x+1)}$

3. $y = \dfrac{x^2+1}{(x^2+x+1)}$

4. $y = \dfrac{4x+5}{(x^2-1)}$

17.3 The circle

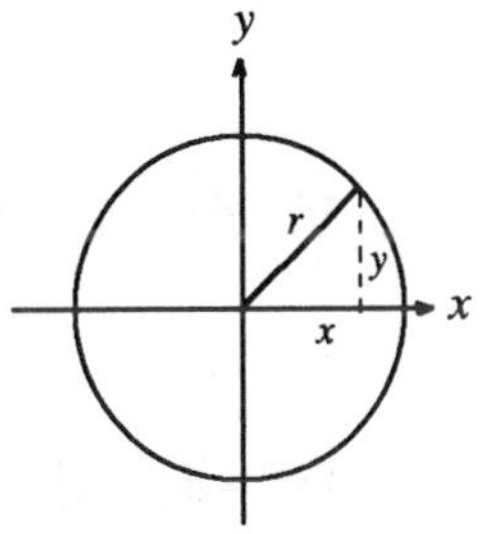

The equation of the circle, radius r, centre the origin, is clearly given by

$$x^2 + y^2 = r^2$$

How can you find the equation of a circle whose centre is not at the origin?

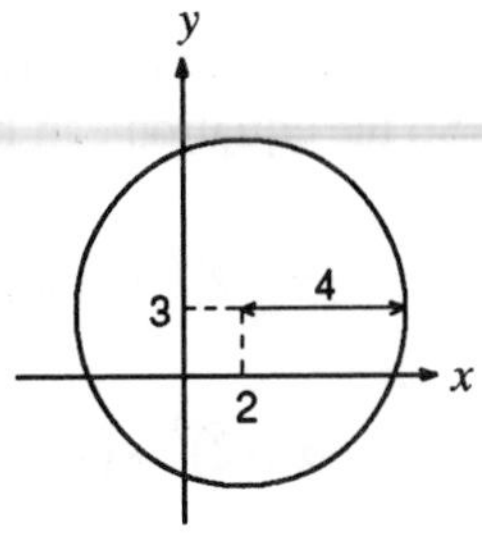

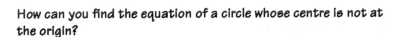

Suppose, you wish to find the equation of a circle, centre $x = 2$, $y = 3$ and radius 4, as illustrated opposite.

If (x, y) is any point on the circle, then the distance between (2, 3) and (x, y) is 4 units. Hence

$$(x-2)^2 + (y-3)^2 = 4^2 = 16$$

$$\Rightarrow \quad x^2 - 4x + 4 + y^2 - 6y + 9 = 16$$

$$\Rightarrow \quad x^2 - y^2 - 4x - 6y = 3$$

Activity 3

Find the equation of a circle, centre $x = a$, $y = b$, and radius r.

The equation in Activity 3 can be written as

$$\boxed{x^2+y^2-2ax-2by=r^2-a^2-b^2}$$

but, given such an equation, it is not so straightforward to find the centre (a, b) and radius r. This is shown in the next example.

Example

Find the centre and radius of the circle which has the equation

$$x^2+y^2-4x+2y=20$$

Solution

To find the centre, the L.H.S. must be written in the form

$$(x-a)^2+(y-b)^2$$

In this case,

$$(x-2)^2+(y+1)^2$$

since this gives

$$\left(x^2-4x+4\right)+\left(y^2+2y+1\right)$$

in which all the terms are correct except for the '+4' and '+1' terms. So the equation can be rewritten as

$$(x-2)^2+(y+1)^2-5=20$$

$$\Rightarrow \quad (x-2)^2+(y+1)^2=25=5^2$$

So it is the equation of a circle centre (2, –1), and radius 5.

One other special curve that is of great practical importance is the **rectangular hyperbola**, which has equation

$$\boxed{y=\frac{c}{x}} \quad (c \text{ constant})$$

For example if $c=1$,

$$y=\frac{1}{x},$$

you can see that $y \to 0$ as $x \to +\infty$.

What happens to y as $x \to -\infty$?

Similarly, as $y \to \pm\infty$, $x \to 0$, and the graph is shown opposite.

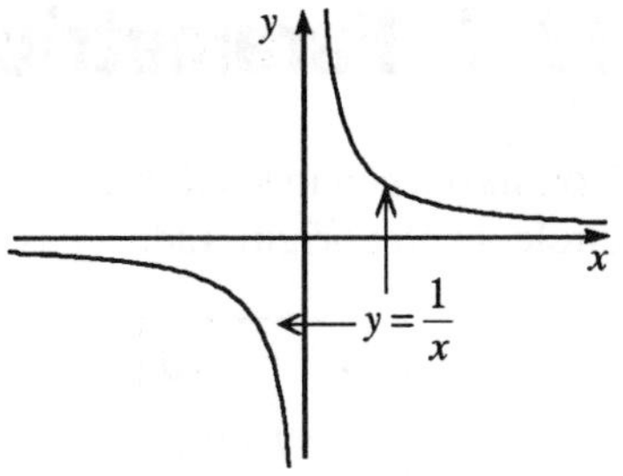

Activity 4

Sketch the curve $y = f(x)$ when

(a) $f(x) = \dfrac{2}{x}$

(b) $f(x) = -\dfrac{1}{x}$

(c) $f(x) = \dfrac{1}{x+1}$

Exercise 17C

1. Find the equation of the circle with

   (a) centre (1, 2), radius 3

   (b) centre (0, 2), radius 2

   (c) centre (–1, –2), radius 4.

2. Find the centre and radius of the circle whose equation is

   (a) $x^2 + y^2 + 8x - 2y - 8 = 0$

   (b) $x^2 + y^2 = 16$

   (c) $x^2 + y^2 + x + 3y - 2 = 0$

   (d) $2x^2 + 2y^2 - 3x + 2y + 1 = 0$

3. Find the equation of the tangent at the point (3, 1) on the circle

$$x^2 + y^2 - 4x + 10y = 8$$

*4. Find the equation of the circle which passes through the points (1, 4), (7, 5) and (1, 8).

17.4 Parametric differentiation

You have seen in section 17.1 that a parametric equation of the circle, centre origin, radius r is given by

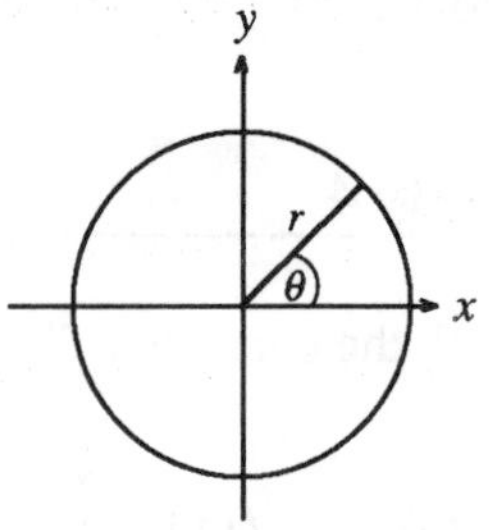

$$x = r\cos\theta$$
$$y = r\sin\theta$$

If you wanted to find the equation of the tangent at any point $P(r\cos\theta, r\sin\theta)$, then the gradient of the tangent is given by

$$\frac{dy}{dx} = \frac{dy}{d\theta} \bigg/ \frac{dx}{d\theta} \qquad \text{(function of function rule)}$$

$$= \frac{r\cos\theta}{-r\sin\theta}$$

$$= -\tan\theta$$

So the equation of the tangent is given by

$$(y - r\sin\theta) = -\tan\theta(x - r\cos\theta)$$

$$y\cos\theta - r\sin\theta\cos\theta = -\sin\theta x + r\sin\theta\cos\theta$$

$$y\cos\theta + x\sin\theta = 2r\sin\theta\cos\theta$$

Activity 5

Write the equation of the circle in the form

$$y = \sqrt{r^2 - x^2}$$

in order to find $\dfrac{dy}{dx}$ at the point P given by $x = x_0, \quad y = y_0$.

Hence find the equation of the tangent at P and show it is equivalent to the equation above, with $x_0 = r\cos\theta, \quad y_0 = r\sin\theta$.

Example

A curve is defined parametrically by

$$x = t^3 - 6t + 4$$

$$y = t - 3 + \frac{2}{t} \qquad (t \neq 0)$$

Find (a) the equation of the normal to the curve at the points when the curve meets the x-axis;

(b) the coordinates of their point of intersection.

Solution

Since $$\frac{dy}{dx}=\frac{dy}{dt}\bigg/\frac{dx}{dt}$$

$$=\left(1-\frac{2}{t^2}\right)\bigg/\left(3t^2-6\right)$$

$$=\frac{\left(t^2-2\right)}{3t^2\left(t^2-2\right)}$$

$$=\frac{1}{3t^2},$$

the gradient of the normal is

$$\left(y-\left(t-3+\frac{2}{t}\right)\right)=-3t^2\left(x-\left(t^3-6t+4\right)\right)$$

$$\frac{yt-t^2+3t-2}{t}=-3t^2\left(x-t^3+6t-4\right)$$

$$yt+3t^3x=3t^6-18t^4+12t^3+t^2-3t+2$$

The curve crosses the x-axis when $y=0$; i.e.

$$t-3+\frac{2}{t}=0$$

$$\Rightarrow\quad t^2-3t+2=0$$

$$\Rightarrow\quad (t-2)(t-1)=0$$

$$\Rightarrow\quad t=1,2$$

Equation of normal at $t=1$ is given by

$$y+3x=3-18+12+1-3+2$$

$$\Rightarrow\quad y+3x=-3,$$

and at $t = 2$,

$$2y + 24x = 192 - 288 + 96 + 4 - 6 + 2$$

$$\Rightarrow \quad y + 12x = 0.$$

These two lines intersect when

$$21x = 3 \quad \Rightarrow x = \frac{1}{3} \quad y = -4.$$

Exercise 17D

1. Show that the tangent at the point P, with parameter t, on the curve $x = 3t^2, \quad y = 2t^3$ has equation

$$y = tx - t^3$$

2. The parametric equation of a curve is given by $x = \cos 2t$, $y = 4\sin t$. Sketch the curve for $0 \le t \le \frac{\pi}{2}$, and show that

$$\frac{dy}{dx} = -\operatorname{cosec} t$$

3. A curve is given by

$$x = a\cos^2 t, \ y = a\sin^3 t, \ 0 < \frac{\pi}{2}$$

when a is a positive constant. Find and simplify an expression for $\frac{dy}{dx}$ in terms of t. (AEB)

4. A curve is described parametrically by the equation

$$x = \frac{1+t}{t}, \ y = \frac{1+t^3}{t^2}$$

Find the equation of the normal to the curve at the point where $t = 2$. (AEB)

17.5 Miscellaneous Exercises

1. Sketch the curve defined parametrically by

$$x = 2 + t^2, \quad y = 4t.$$

Write down the equation of the straight line with gradient m passing through the point $(1, 0)$. Show that this line meets the curve when

$$mt^2 - 4t + m = 0.$$

Find the values of m for which this quadratic equation has equal roots. Hence determine the equations of the tangents to the curve which pass through the point $(1, 0)$. (AEB)

2. Determine the coordinates of the centre C and the radius of the circle with equation

$$x^2 + y^2 + 4x - 6y = 12$$

The circle cuts the x-axis at the points A and B. Calculate the area of the triangle ABC.

Calculate the area of the minor segment of the circle cut off by the chord AB, giving your answer to three significant figures.

3. Sketch the curve C defined parametrically by

$$x = t^2 - 2; \quad y = t$$

Write down the cartesian equation of the circle with centre the origin and radius r. Show that this circle meets the curve C at points whose parameter t satisfies the equation

$$t^4 - 3t^2 + 4 - r^2 = 0$$

(a) In the case $r = 2\sqrt{2}$, find the coordinates of the two points of intersection of the curve and the circle.

(b) Find the range of values of r for which the curve and the circle have exactly two points in common. (AEB)

4. A curve is defined parametrically by

$$x=\frac{2t}{1+t},\quad y=\frac{t^2}{1+t}$$

Prove that the normal to the curve at the point $(1, \frac{1}{2})$ has equation $6y+4x=7$.

Determine the coordinates of the other point of intersection of this normal with the curve.

(AEB)

5. The parametric equations of a curve are

$$x=3(2\theta-\sin 2\theta)$$

$$y=3(1-\cos 2\theta)$$

The tangent and normal to the curve at point P

when $\theta=\frac{\pi}{4}$

meet the y-axis at L and M respectively.

Show that the area of the triangle PLM is

$$\frac{9}{4}(\pi-2)^2.$$

(AEB)

18 EVEN MORE CALCULUS

Objectives

After studying this chapter you should

- be able to differentiate and integrate basic trigonometric functions;
- understand how to calculate rates of change;
- be able to integrate using substitutions;
- be able to integrate by parts;
- be able to formulate and solve simple first order differential equations.

18.0 Introduction

In the earlier chapters 8, 11, 12 and 14 you met the concept of differentiation and integration. You should be familiar with the differentiation and integration of functions such as x^n, e^x and $\ln x$. In this chapter the range of functions is expanded to include the differentiation and integration of trigonometric functions and two important methods of integration, namely substitution and by parts, are dealt with. Finally, there is an introduction to the important topic of differential equations.

18.1 Derivatives of trig functions

Intuitive ideas

The derivative of a general function f(x) is given by

$$f'(x) = \lim_{h \to 0} \left\{ \frac{f(x+h) - f(x)}{h} \right\}$$

You are going to obtain the derivatives of $\sin x$, $\cos x$, and $\tan x$.

Remember that the derivative of a function at a given point is given by the **gradient** of that function at the given point.

Suppose you look at a sketch of the graph sin x and sketch in the tangents for values of x of:

$$-\frac{3\pi}{2}, -\pi, -\frac{\pi}{2}, 0, \frac{\pi}{2}, \pi, \frac{3\pi}{2}$$

This is shown opposite.

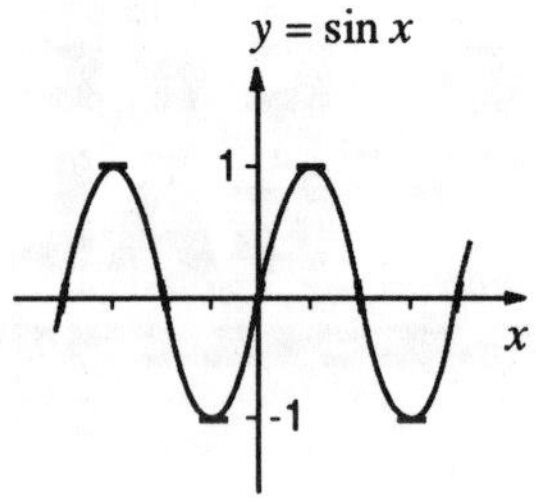

These tangent values when plotted against x will look like the sketch opposite.

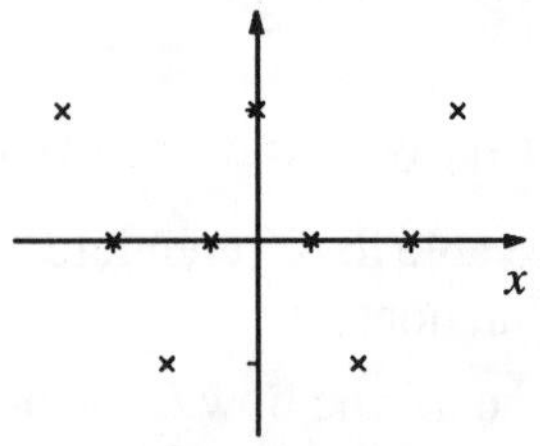

This suggests that the graph of the function for the tangent may be something like the sketch opposite.

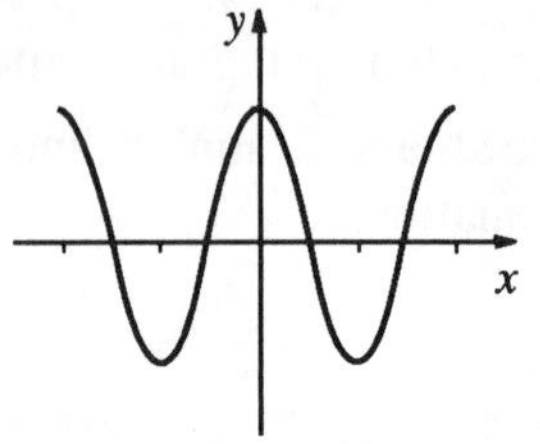

This sketch suggests that the derivative of sin x might be cos x, but this illustration is certainly not a proof.

Activity 1

By considering the graph of cos x, with tangents drawn at key points, show that the derivative of cos x might be – sin x.

Using a calculator or computer

The derivative of sin x is given by

$$\frac{d}{dx}(\sin x) = \lim_{h \to 0}\left\{\frac{\sin(x+h) - \sin x}{h}\right\}$$

Using a calculator or computer you can try some specific examples - using a set value for x and making h small.

Why is it not possible to take the actual value when $h = 0$?

For instance, setting $x = 0.2$ and $h = 0.00004$,

$$\begin{aligned}\frac{\sin(0.20004) - \sin(0.2)}{0.00004} &= \frac{0.198708533 - 0.198669331}{0.00004} \\ &= \frac{0.000039202}{0.00004} \\ &= 0.98005 \\ &= \cos(0.200083427)\end{aligned}$$

So, approximately

$$\frac{\sin(0.20004) - \sin(0.2)}{0.00004} \approx \cos(0.2)$$

Activity 2

Either calculate

$$\frac{\sin(x+h) - \sin x}{h}$$

for other values of x and very small values of h;

or write a computer programme to evaluate

$$\frac{\sin(x+h) - \sin x}{h}$$

for various values of x and very small values of h.

In each case show that

$$\frac{\sin(x+h) - \sin x}{h} \approx \cos x$$

Geometric proof

It is also possible to use the unit circle to demonstrate that, for example,

$$\frac{d}{dx}(\sin x) = \cos x$$

In the diagram, shown opposite, h is small, and

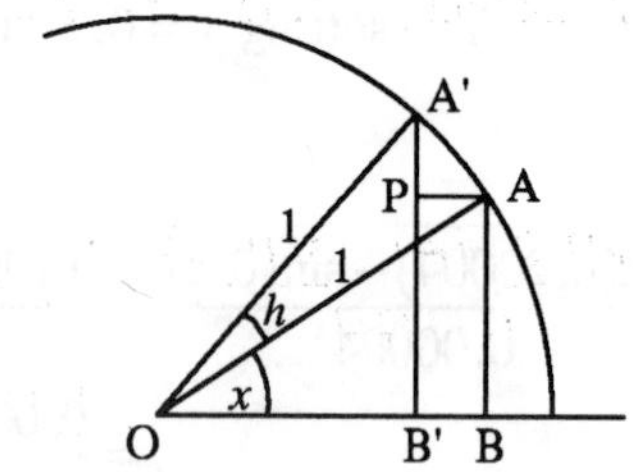

$$A'B' = \sin(x+h)$$

$$AB = \sin x$$

$$A'A = h \quad (\text{radius} \times \text{angle})$$

So $\quad \sin(x+h) - \sin x = A'P$

Now assume that when h is very small the arc $A'A$ is approximately straight.

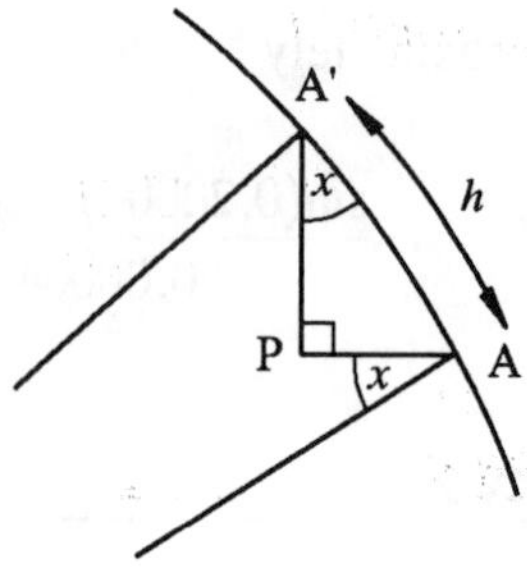

So for the 'triangle' $AA'P$,

$$\frac{\sin(x+h)-\sin x}{h} \approx \frac{A'P}{A'A} = \cos x$$

So, approximately, if h is very small

$$\frac{\sin(x+h)-\sin x}{h} \approx \cos x$$

Now, taking the limit as $h \to 0$, gives

$$\boxed{\frac{d}{dx}(\sin x) = \cos x}$$

Activity 3

By considering the same unit circle diagram, show that

$$\frac{\cos(x+h)-\cos x}{h} \approx -\sin x$$

and, taking the limit as $h \to 0$,

$$\boxed{\frac{d}{dx}(\cos x) = -\sin x}$$

To find the derivative of $\tan x$, formally you can use the quotient rule,

$$\frac{d}{dx}\left(\frac{u}{v}\right) = \frac{u'v - v'u}{v^2} \quad \left(u' = \frac{du}{dx},\ v' = \frac{dv}{dx}\right),$$

giving

$$\frac{d}{dx}(\tan x) = \frac{d}{dx}\left(\frac{\sin x}{\cos x}\right)$$

$$= \frac{\frac{d}{dx}(\sin x)\times\cos x - \sin x\times\frac{d}{dx}(\cos x)}{(\cos x)^2}$$

$$= \frac{\cos x\times\cos x - \sin x\times(-\sin x)}{(\cos x)^2}$$

$$= \frac{(\cos x)^2+(\sin x)^2}{(\cos x)^2}$$

$$= \frac{1}{(\cos x)^2}$$

This gives

$$\boxed{\frac{d}{dx}(\tan x) = (\sec x)^2}$$

Activity 4

Show that

$$\frac{d}{dx}(\cot x) = -\text{cosec}^2 x$$

So the three crucial results are

$$\frac{d}{dx}(\sin x) = \cos x \quad \text{or} \quad y=\sin x \Rightarrow \frac{dy}{dx} = \cos x$$

$$\frac{d}{dx}(\cos x) = -\sin x \quad \text{or} \quad y=\cos x \Rightarrow \frac{dy}{dx} = -\sin x$$

$$\frac{d}{dx}(\tan x) = \sec^2 x \quad \text{or} \quad y=\tan x \Rightarrow \frac{dy}{dx} = \sec^2 x$$

and, inverting these results

$$\int \cos x\, dx = \sin x + c$$

$$\int \sin x\, dx = -\cos x + c$$

$$\int \sec^2 x\, dx = \tan x + c$$

Why is it that we cannot find $\frac{d}{dx}(\tan x)$ when $x = \pm\frac{1}{2}\pi, \pm\frac{3}{2}\pi, \pm\frac{5}{2}\pi, \ldots$?

To differentiate $y = \sin kx$, where k is a constant, you can define a new variable z by $z = kx$, so that

$$y = \sin kx = \sin z,$$

giving $$\frac{dy}{dz} = \cos z.$$

But $$\frac{dy}{dx} = \frac{dy}{dz} \times \frac{dz}{dx} \qquad \text{(function of a function)}$$

and since $$z = kx$$

then $$\frac{dz}{dx} = k$$

So $$\frac{dy}{dx} = (\cos z) \times k$$

giving $$\frac{dy}{dx} = k \cos kx.$$

Exercise 18A

1. Find the derivative of

   (a) $\sin 2x$ (b) $\sin\frac{1}{2}x$

   (c) $\sin 100x$ (d) $\cos 3x$

2. Find $\frac{d}{dx}(\cos kx)$ and $\frac{d}{dx}(\tan kx)$

3. Differentiate

   (a) $\sin^2(2x)$ (b) $\sin 2x \cos 2x$

   (c) $\cos^3(\frac{1}{2}x)$ (d) $\tan^2(2x)$

4. Find $\frac{d}{dx}(\cos x)$ and $\frac{d}{dx}(\sec x)$.

   Hence determine

   $$\int \sec x \tan x \, dx.$$

18.2 Rates of change

From your earlier work on differentiation, you will recognise that the rate of change of a variable, say f, is given by $\frac{df}{dt}$, where t denotes time. Often though, f is a function of another variable, say x, so that you need to use the 'function of a function' rule,

$$\boxed{\frac{df}{dt} = \frac{df}{dx}\frac{dx}{dt}}$$

We will see in the next two examples, how this result is used.

Example

The radius of a circular oil slick is increasing at the rate of 2 m/s. Find the rate at which the area of the slick is increasing when its radius is (a) 10 m, (b) 50 m.

Solution

Now $\quad A = \pi r^2$

giving

$$\begin{aligned}\frac{dA}{dt} &= \frac{d}{dt}\left(\pi r^2\right)\\ &= \frac{d}{dr}\left(\pi r^2\right)\frac{dr}{dt} \quad \text{(using 'function of a function')}\\ &= 2\pi r\frac{dr}{dt}\\ &= 4\pi r, \quad \text{since } \frac{dr}{dt} = 2\,\text{m/s}.\end{aligned}$$

(a) When $r = 10\,\text{m}$, $\frac{dA}{dt} = 40\pi \approx 125.7\,\text{m}^2/\text{s}$.

(b) When $r = 50\,\text{m}$, $\frac{dA}{dt} = 200\pi \approx 628.3\,\text{m}^2/\text{s}$.

Example

A spherical balloon is blown up so that its volume increases at a constant rate of 10 cm^3/s. Find the rate of increase of the radius when the volume of the balloon is 1000 cm^3.

Solution

Now $$v = \frac{4}{3}\pi r^3$$

giving $$\frac{dv}{dt} = \frac{d}{dr}\left(\frac{4}{3}\pi r^3\right)\frac{dr}{dt}$$

$$= 4\pi r^2 \frac{dr}{dt}.$$

But $$\frac{dv}{dt} = 10$$

giving $$10 = 4\pi r^2 \frac{dr}{dt}.$$

Thus $$\frac{dr}{dt} = \frac{5}{2\pi r^2}.$$

When the volume is 1000 cm the radius can be calculated from

$$1000 = \frac{4}{3}\pi r^3$$

$$\Rightarrow \quad r = \left(\frac{750}{\pi}\right)^{\frac{1}{3}}$$

$$\Rightarrow \quad \frac{dr}{dt} = \frac{5}{2\pi}\left(\frac{750}{\pi}\right)^{-\frac{2}{3}} \approx 0.021$$

Exercise 18B

1. The radius of a circular disc is increasing at a constant rate of 0.003 cm/s. Find the rate at which the area is increasing when the radius is 20 cm.

2. A spherical balloon is inflated by gas being pumped at a constant rate of 200 cm^3/s. What is the rate of increase of the surface area of the balloon when its radius is 100 cm?

3. The volume of water in a container is given by xe^{-2x} cm^3 where x is the depth of the water in the container. Find the rate of increase of volume when the depth is 0.2 cm and increasing at a rate of 0.1 cm s^{-1}. Also determine when the rate of increase of volume is stationary.

(AEB)

4. The area of the region between two concentric circles of radii x and y $(x > y)$ is denoted by A. Given that x is increasing at the rate of 3 ms^{-1}, y is increasing at the rate of 4 ms^{-1}, and when $t = 0, x = 5$ m and $y = 2$ m, find

   (a) the rate of increase of A when $t = 0$;

   (b) the ratio of x to y when A begins to decrease;

   (c) the time at which A is zero.

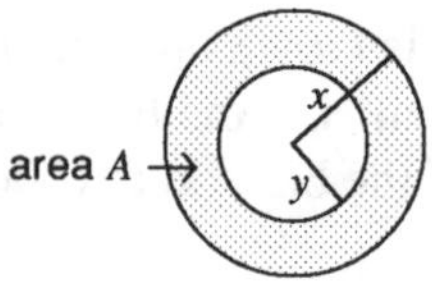

18.3 Integration by substitution

This method is the equivalent to using a change of variable when differentiating composite functions.

Activity 5

Differentiate

(a) $\left(2x^2-2\right)$ (b) $\left(3x^2+2\right)^5$

(c) $\left(4x^2-7\right)^6$ (d) $\left(4x^2-7\right)^n$

and use the above results to find

(a) $\int x\left(x^2-3\right)^5 dx$ (b) $\int x\left(x^2+2\right)^2 dx$

(c) $\int (3x-1)^5 dx$ (d) $\int x^2\left(x^3-1\right)dx$

(Check your results by differentiation.)

In general, if

$$y=\int f(x)dx$$

then $$\frac{dy}{dx}=f(x).$$

If we let $x=g(u)$ for some function g of a new variable u, then y becomes a function of u and

$$\frac{dy}{du}=\frac{dy}{dx}\times\frac{dx}{du}$$

$$\Rightarrow \quad \frac{dy}{du}=f(x)\frac{dx}{du}=f(g(u))\frac{dx}{du}$$

$$\Rightarrow \quad y=\int f(g(u))\frac{dx}{du}du$$

Example

Find $\int x(3x-1)^{\frac{1}{2}}dx$ using a suitable substitution.

Solution

If $u = 3x-1$ then $\frac{du}{dx} = 3$ and $x = \frac{u+1}{3}$. Hence the integral becomes

$$\begin{aligned}
\int x(3x-1)^{\frac{1}{2}}\frac{dx}{du}du &= \int\left(\frac{u+1}{3}\right)u^{\frac{1}{2}}\frac{du}{3} \\
&= \frac{1}{9}\int\left(u^{\frac{3}{2}}+u^{\frac{1}{2}}\right)du \\
&= \frac{1}{9}\left(\frac{2}{5}u^{\frac{5}{2}}+\frac{2}{3}u^{\frac{3}{2}}\right)+c \\
&= \frac{1}{9}\left(\frac{2}{5}(3x-1)^{\frac{5}{2}}+\frac{2}{3}(3x-1)^{\frac{3}{2}}\right)+c \\
&= \frac{2}{45}(3x-1)^{\frac{5}{2}}+\frac{2}{27}(3x-1)^{\frac{3}{2}}+c
\end{aligned}$$

Example

Find $\int_0^1 x\left(3x^2+2\right)^3 dx$

Solution

You can rewrite this integral using the substitution

$$u = \left(3x^2+2\right) \Rightarrow \frac{du}{dx} = 6x$$

The limits on u for the integration are determined from

$$x = 0 \Rightarrow u = 2$$

$$x = 1 \Rightarrow u = 5$$

Hence
$$\int_0^1 x(3x^2+2)^3\,dx = \int_2^5 x(3x^2+2)^3 \frac{dx}{du}\,du$$
$$= \int_2^5 x(3x^2+2)^3 \frac{1}{6x}\,du$$
$$= \int_2^5 \frac{1}{6}u^3\,du$$
$$= \left[\frac{1}{24}u^4\right]_2^5$$
$$= \frac{1}{24}\left[5^4 - 2^4\right]$$
$$= \frac{1}{24}(625-16)$$
$$= \frac{609}{24}$$

Exercise 18C

1. Find the following integrals, using the suggested substitution.

   (a) $\int x(x^2-3)^4\,dx$ $\quad (u = x^3 - 3)$

   (b) $\int x\sqrt{1-x^2}\,dx$ $\quad (u = 1 - x^2)$

   (c) $\int \cos x \sin^4 x\,dx$ $\quad (u = \sin x)$

   (d) $\int e^x\sqrt{1+e^x}\,dx$ $\quad (u = 1 + e^x)$

2. Using the substitution $x = 4\sin^2\theta$ or otherwise, show that
$$\int_0^2 \sqrt{x(4-x)}\,dx = \pi$$

3. Using the substitution $x = 3\tan\theta$, evaluate
$$\int_0^3 \frac{1}{(9+x^2)^2}\,dx$$

(AEB)

18.4 Integration by parts

Our second method of integration is a very important one which is particularly useful for a number of different integrals. You can see how it works by first differentiating with respect to x,

$$x \sin x + \cos x$$

Now use your answer to find the integral of $x \cos x$.

What form will the integral of $x \sin x$ take?

Check your answers by differentiating.

Activity 6

By assuming

$$\int x\, e^x dx = (ax + b)e^x + c$$

find the values of the constants a and b so that the result is valid.

(Hint: differentiate the R.H.S.)

By now you should be wondering if there is a more precise method of evaluating integrals of the type above, where the method requires inspired guesswork to start with. In fact, there is a more formal method.

If u and v are two functions of x then from your work on differentiation you know that

$$\frac{d}{dx}(uv) = v\frac{du}{dx} + u\frac{dv}{dx}$$

and integrating each side with respect to x gives

$$uv = \int v\frac{du}{dx}dx + \int u\frac{dv}{dx}dx$$

$$\Rightarrow \quad \boxed{\int u\frac{dv}{dx}dx = uv - \int v\frac{du}{dx}dx}$$

Example

Find $\int x \cos x \, dx$

Solution

Here $u = x$ and $\frac{dv}{dx} = \cos x$, so $v = \sin x$. This gives

$$\int x \cos x \, dx = x \sin x - \int \sin x . 1 \, dx$$

$$= x \sin x + \cos x + c$$

We can use the same method to find the integral in Activity 6.

Example

Find $\int x \, e^x dx$

Solution

Here $u = x$, $\frac{dv}{dx} = e^x$, giving $v = e^x$ and

$$\int x \, e^x dx = x \, e^x - \int e^x . 1 \, dx$$

$$= x \, e^x - e^x + c$$

$$= e^x (x - 1) + c$$

Activity 7

(a) Given that $\int x \cos x \, dx = x \sin x + \cos x + c$ show that

$$\int x^2 \sin x \, dx = x^2 \cos x + 2x \sin x + 2 \cos x + k$$

(b) Given that $\int x \, e^x dx = x \, e^x - e^x + c$ find

(i) $\int x^2 e^x dx$ (ii) $\int x^2 e^{-x} dx$

One of the difficulties with integration by parts is that of identifying u and $\frac{dv}{dx}$. For example, if

$$I = \int x \ln x \, dx$$

then taking $u = x$, $\frac{dv}{dx} = \ln x$ will not really work as you might not be able to solve for v. But taking

$$u = \ln x, \frac{dv}{dx} = x$$

gives $v = \frac{1}{2}x^2$, and

$$I = \tfrac{1}{2}x^2 \ln x - \int \left(\tfrac{1}{2}x^2\right)\frac{1}{x}\,dx$$

$$= \tfrac{1}{2}x^2 \ln x - \int \tfrac{1}{2}x \, dx$$

$$= \tfrac{1}{2}x^2 \ln x - \tfrac{1}{4}x^2 + c$$

It is also important to note that some functions which cannot be immediately integrated can be dealt with by writing the integrand as $1 \times$(function) since 1 can be integrated. This is illustrated below.

Example

Find $\int \ln x \, dx$

Solution

$$I = \int \ln x \, dx = \int 1 \times \ln x \, dx$$

So take $u = \ln x$, $\frac{dv}{dx} = 1$ to give $v = x$ and

$$I = x \ln x - \int x.\frac{1}{x}\,dx$$

$$= x \ln x - \int 1 dx$$

$$= x \ln x - x + c$$

Finally in this section it should be noted that we can have limits on integration in the usual way, for example

$$\int_0^{\frac{\pi}{2}} x\sin x\,dx = [-x\cos x]_0^{\frac{\pi}{2}} - \int_0^{\frac{\pi}{2}} 1(-\cos x)\,dx$$

$$= (0-0) + \int_0^{\frac{\pi}{2}} \cos x\,dx$$

$$= [\sin x]_0^{\frac{\pi}{2}}$$

$$= 1$$

Exercise 18D

1. Find $\int x^2 \ln x\,dx$.

2. By writing $\cos^3\theta$ as $\cos^2\theta\cos\theta$ find

   $$\int \cos^3\theta\,d\theta$$

   and hence show that

   $$\int_0^{\pi} \cos^3\theta\,d\theta = 0.$$

3. Evaluate $\int_0^{\frac{\pi}{2}} \sin^3 x\,dx$.

4. Find $\int x^3 \ln(4x)\,dx$ (AEB)

5. Use integration by parts twice to find

   $$\int x^2 \cos 2x\,dx$$

18.5 First order differential equations

You might well wonder why you have studied integration in such depth. The main reason is the crucial role it plays in solving what are known as **differential equations**. Here you will only be dealing with first order differential equations, which can be expressed, in general, in the form

$$\frac{dy}{dx} = f(x, y)$$

when $y = y(x)$ is an unknown function of x, and f is a given function of x and y.

Examples of such equations include

$$\frac{dy}{dx} = xy$$

$$\frac{dy}{dx} = x + y$$

$$\frac{dy}{dx} = \frac{x}{y} \qquad (y \neq 0)$$

but first you will see how they are formed.

As an example of the process, consider the problem of modelling the way in which human populations change.

An English economist, *Thomas Malthus*, in his 1802 article "An Essay on the Principle of Population" formulated the first model which attempted to describe and predict the way in which the magnitude of the human population was changing. In mathematical terms you can summarise his assumptions by introducing the variable $N = N(t)$ to represent the total population, where t is time. In a small time interval, say δt, Malthus argued that both births and deaths are proportional to the population size and the time interval. Hence in time δt, there will be $(\alpha N \delta t)$ births and $(\beta N \delta t)$ deaths where α, β are positive constants, and so the increase in the population size is given by

$$\delta N = \alpha N \delta t - \beta N \delta t = (\alpha - \beta) N \delta t$$

Writing $\alpha - \beta = \gamma$,and dividing by δt gives

$$\frac{\delta N}{\delta t} = \gamma N$$

Taking the limit as $\delta t \to 0$ results in the differential equation

$$\boxed{\frac{dN}{dt} = \gamma N}$$

Added to this is an initial condition; for example, $N = N_0$ at $t = 0$.

This is an example of a 'variable separable' differential equation, since it can be written in the form

$$\frac{1}{N}\frac{dN}{dt} = \gamma$$

and integration with respect to t,

$$\int \frac{1}{N}\frac{dN}{dt}dt = \int \gamma dt$$

$$\int \frac{1}{N}dN = \int \gamma dt$$

$$\Rightarrow \quad \ln N = \gamma t + c \quad (c \text{ constant})$$

$$\Rightarrow \quad N = e^{\gamma t + c}$$

$$= e^{\gamma t}e^{c}$$

$$\Rightarrow \quad N = Ke^{\gamma t} \quad \left(K = e^{c}\right)$$

But $\quad N = N_0$ at $t = 0$,

giving $\quad N_0 = Ke^0 = K$.

Hence the complete solution is

$$\boxed{N = N_0 e^{\gamma t}}$$

This solution is illustrated opposite for positive γ.

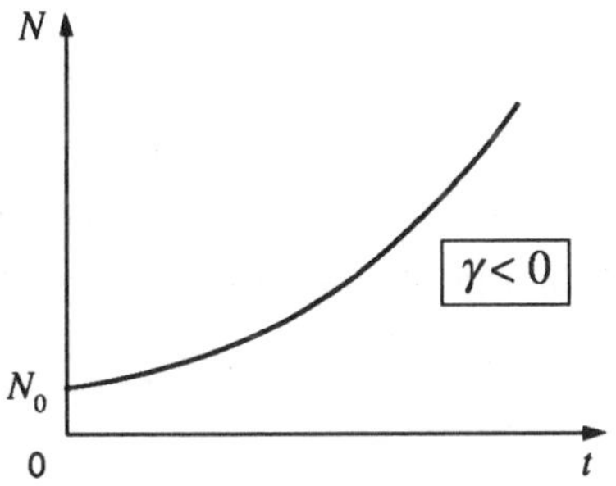

What does the solution look like when
(a) $\gamma = 0$ (b) γ is negative?

Activity 8

By differentiation check that $N = N_0 e^{\gamma t}$ satisfies the differential equation

$$\frac{dN}{dt} = \gamma N$$

You can see how to use this population model by applying it to the 1790 and 1800 USA population figures shown opposite.

Year	USA Population (in millions)
1790	3.9
1800	5.3

The time $t = 0$ corresponds to 1790, and $t = 1$ to 1800 etc; so

$$N_0 = 3.9$$

The model solution is

$$N(t) = 3.9e^{\gamma t}$$

and γ is determined by the population value at $t = 1$ (1800). This gives

$$5.3 = 3.9e^{\gamma}$$

$$\Rightarrow \quad e^{\gamma} = \frac{5.3}{3.9}$$

$$\Rightarrow \quad \gamma = \ln\left(\frac{5.3}{3.9}\right) \approx 0.03067$$

and

$$\boxed{N(t) = 3.9e^{(0.03067)t}}$$

What does this model predict for the population if t becomes large? Is this realistic?

Activity 9

Use the model above to predict the USA population for 1810 $(t = 2)$ to 1930 $(t = 14)$. Compare your prediction with the real values given opposite.

Can you explain any discrepancies in the prediction and real values?

Year	USA Population (in millions)
1810	7.2
1820	9.6
1830	12.9
1840	17.1
1850	23.2
1860	31.4
1870	38.6
1880	50.2
1890	62.9
1900	76.0
1910	92.0
1920	106.5
1930	123.2

The model gives a reasonably good fit for quite some time, but eventually predicts a population growing far too quickly.

Why does the model eventually go wrong?

Let us go back to the original assumption and consider what factors have been neglected. The model as it stands predicts the growth of a population in an ideal situation where there are no limits (e.g. food, land, energy) to continued growth. In 1837, Verhulst proposed an extension to the Malthusian model which took into account the 'crowding' factor. In his model, he assumed that the population change was proportional to

(i) the current population level N

(ii) the ratio of unused population resources to total population resources when it is assumed that a maximum population size of N_∞ can be sustained,

i.e. $$\frac{(N_\infty - N)}{N_\infty}$$

Thus

$$\frac{dN}{dt} = \gamma N \frac{(N_\infty - N)}{N_\infty}$$

i.e. $$\boxed{\frac{dN}{dt} = \gamma N - \frac{\gamma N^2}{N_\infty}}$$

When N is small, γN will be the dominant term on the right hand side, and so we are back with the Malthusian model; but as N becomes large, the $\dfrac{-\gamma N^2}{N_\infty}$ term becomes important.

This is again a first order differential equation, but much more difficult to solve.

*Activity 10

Show, by differentiating the expression below, that the Verhulst model has a solution given by

$$N(t) = \frac{N_\infty}{\left\{1 + \left[\dfrac{N_\infty}{N_0} - 1\right] e^{-\gamma t}\right\}}$$

where $N = N_0$ at $t = 0$.

Use your graphic calculator, or computer program to illustrate the shape of this function. For example, take $\gamma = 0.03$ and

(a) $N_0 = \frac{1}{2} N_\infty$

(b) $N_0 = \frac{1}{4} N_\infty$

(c) $N_0 = 2N_\infty$

What happens as $t \to \infty$?

Returning to simple first order differential equations, you will see how to solve them in the following two examples.

Example

For $x \geq 0$, solve $\dfrac{dy}{dx} = \dfrac{x}{y}$ given that $y = 1$ when $x = 0$.

Solution

You can write this as

$$y\frac{dy}{dx} = x$$

and integrating both sides with respect to x.

$$\int y\frac{dy}{dx}dx = \int x\,dx$$

$$\Rightarrow \quad \int y\,dy = \int x\,dx$$

$$\Rightarrow \quad \tfrac{1}{2}y^2 = \tfrac{1}{2}x^2 + K \quad (K \text{ constant})$$

Since $y = 1$ when $x = 0$,

$$\tfrac{1}{2} = 0 + K$$

$$\Rightarrow \quad K = \tfrac{1}{2}$$

and $\quad y^2 = x^2 + 1$

$$\Rightarrow \quad y = \sqrt{1 + x^2}$$

Example

Solve $\dfrac{dy}{dx} = \dfrac{y}{x}$ given that $y = 1$ when $x = 1$.

Solution

As before

$$\frac{1}{y}\frac{dy}{dx} = \frac{1}{x}$$

$$\Rightarrow \quad \int \frac{1}{y}\frac{dy}{dx}dx = \int \frac{1}{x}dx$$

$$\Rightarrow \quad \int \frac{1}{y}dy = \int \frac{1}{x}dx$$

$$\Rightarrow \quad \ln y = \ln x + C \qquad (C \text{ constant})$$

Writing $C = \ln K$,

$$\ln y = \ln x + \ln K$$

$$\Rightarrow \quad \ln y = \ln(Kx)$$

$$\Rightarrow \quad y = Kx$$

Since $y = 1$ when $x = 1$,

$$1 = K.1$$

giving $\quad K = 1$

and the solution

$$y = x.$$

Exercise 18E

Solve the following first order differential equations.

1. $3y\dfrac{dy}{dx} = 5x^2$ given that $y = 1$ when $x = 0$

2. $x\dfrac{dy}{dx} = 3y$ given that $y = 2$ when $x = 1$

3. $\dfrac{dy}{dx} = y^2$ given that $y = 1$ when $x = 1$

4. $\dfrac{1}{x}\dfrac{dy}{dx} = \dfrac{1}{(x^2+1)}$ given that $y = 0$ when $x = 0$

5. $e^x\dfrac{dy}{dx} = \dfrac{x}{y}$

6. $\dfrac{dy}{dx} = \dfrac{y+1}{x+2}$

7. $x\dfrac{dy}{dx} = \dfrac{1}{y} + y$

8. During the initial stages of the growth of yeast cells in a culture, the rate of increase in the number of cells is proportional to the number of cells present.

   If $n = n(t)$ represents the number of cells at time t, show that

   $$\frac{dn}{dt} = kn$$

   for some constant k. If the cells double in unit time, determine k, and solve for n in terms of t and the initial number of cells, n_0.

18.6 Miscellaneous Exercises

1. Differentiate (a) $\sin 3x$ (b) $\sec x \tan x$ (c) $\tan^2 x$.

2. Find

   (a) $\int \cos^4 x \sin x \, dx$

   (b) $\int \sin^3 x \, dx$

   (c) $\int \tan^2 x \sec^2 x \, dx$

3. The radius r of a circular ink spot, t seconds after it first appears, is given by

   $$r = \frac{1+4t}{2+t}$$

   Calculate

   (a) the time taken for the radius to double its initial value;

   (b) the rate of increase of the radius in cm s^{-1} when $t = 3$;

   (c) the value to which r tends as t tends to infinity. (AEB)

4. The volume of liquid V cm^3 in a container when the depth is x cm is given by

$$V = \frac{x^{\frac{1}{4}}}{(x+2)^{\frac{1}{2}}}, \qquad x > 0$$

(a) Find $\frac{dV}{dx}$ and determine the value of x for which $\frac{dV}{dx} = 0$.

(b) Calculate the rate of change of volume when the depth is 1 cm and increasing at a rate of 0.01 cm s^{-1}, giving your answer in $cm^3\ s^{-1}$ to three significant figures. (AEB)

5. (a) Differentiate $(1+x^3)^{\frac{1}{2}}$ with respect to x.

(b) Use the result from (a), or an appropriate substitution, to find the value of

$$\int_0^2 \frac{x}{\sqrt{(1+x^3)}}\,dx$$

6. Find the following integrals using the suggested substitution

(a) $\int \cos^5 x \sin x\,dx \qquad (u = \cos x)$

(b) $\int \frac{x}{\sqrt{1-x^2}}\,dx \qquad (u = 1-x^2)$

(c) $\int \frac{e^x}{(1+e^x)^2}\,dx \qquad (u = 1+e^x)$

7. (a) Use integration by parts to find

$$\int x^{\frac{1}{2}} \ln x\,dx$$

(b) Find the solution of the differential equation

$$\frac{dy}{dx} = (xy)^{\frac{1}{2}} \ln x$$

for which $y = 1$ when $x = 1$. (AEB)

8. Find the general solution of the following first order differential equations

(a) $(x-3)\frac{dy}{dx} = y$

(b) $xy\frac{dy}{dx} = \ln x$

(c) $\frac{dx}{dy} = \frac{yx}{x-1}$

19 ITERATION

Objectives

After studying this chapter you should

- understand the importance of graphical and numerical methods for the solution of equations;
- understand the principle of iteration;
- appreciate the need for convergence;
- be able to use several iterative methods including Newton's method.

19.0 Introduction

Before you begin studying this chapter you should be familiar with the basic algebraic and graph-plotting techniques covered in higher-level GCSE courses. You should also be able to differentiate at least simple algebraic functions: differentiation is covered in the Foundation Core. A number of examples and exercises involve trigonometry, but these are not essential and can be missed out if you have not covered that topic.

The solution of algebraic equations has always been a significant mathematical problem, and early Egyptian and Babylonian sources show how people of those civilizations were solving **linear**, **quadratic** and **cubic equations** more than three thousand years ago. The Egyptians often solved linear equations using an *aha* method (named after the Egyptian word for a heap, not because the answer came as a surprise!) in which they guessed an answer, tried it out, and then adjusted it; the Babylonians solved quadratic and cubic equations by using well-known algorithms together with written-out tables of values.

The spread of Greek mathematics, with its emphasis on elegance and precision, led to the disappearance of those early techniques among academic mathematicians, even if some of them survived among merchants, builders and other practical people. Instead, Mathematicians were more concerned to find general 'analytic' methods based on formulae for the exact solution of any equation of a particular type. Methods of solving quadratic equations were already known, but the first general method for solving a cubic equation was discovered by the Italian mathematician *Scipione del Ferro* in about 1500, and that for **quartics** by his compatriot *Ludovico Ferrari* some fifty years later.

At that point the process of discovery came to a stop, because no one was able to find a method for solving a general equation in x^5 or any higher power. For these equations, as they arose, people had to go back to the earlier trial-and-improvement methods, but the general slowness of those meant that the 'modern' analytic methods were much better. The development of electronic calculators and computers changed all this, however, so that nowadays it is often quicker to use a numerical method such as the Egyptians or Babylonians might have done than to spend time in developing a formula.

You will need a pocket calculator throughout the chapter; a graphic calculator will be particularly useful. Access to a computer with graph-plotting and/or programming facilities may be a further advantage.

19.1 Crossing ladders

In a narrow passage between two walls there are two wooden ladders, a green one 3 m long and a red one 2 m long; the ground is horizontal and the walls are vertical. Each ladder has its foot at the bottom of one wall and its top resting against the other wall. The green ladder slopes up from left to right and the red ladder slopes up from right to left. The ladders cross 1 m above the ground. How wide is the passage?

The first step in solving most problems of this kind is the creation of a mathematical model - not a model made of cardboard and glue, but a set of equations and other relations describing the mathematically important features of the situation.

Stop and think what these important factors are.

The essential facts are summarised in the diagram opposite, which shows the approximate positions and lengths of the ladders and the position of their crossing point. It denotes by x metres the distance to be found, and by u m, v m and w m respectively three other lengths that may be important. The diagram says nothing about the fact that the ladders are made of wood or that they are differently coloured, since these facts are irrelevant to the particular problem to be solved.

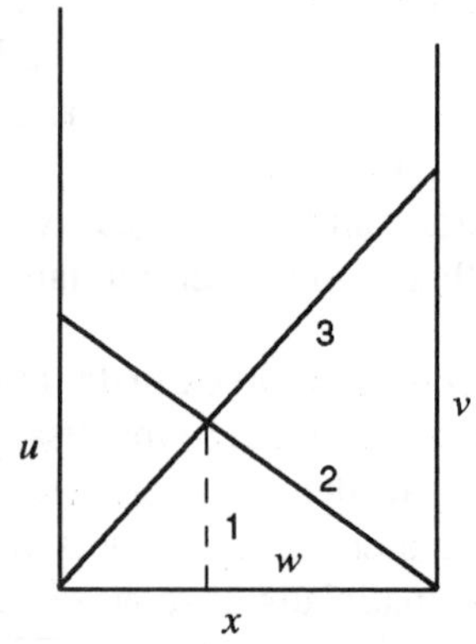

The ladder problem - find the length x

From the diagram, various relationships can be deduced.

Using similar triangles, $$\frac{w}{1} = \frac{x}{u}$$

Again using similar triangles, $$\frac{x-w}{1} = \frac{x}{v}$$

Adding these equations, $$\frac{x}{1}=\frac{x}{u}+\frac{x}{v}$$

$$\Rightarrow \quad \frac{1}{u}+\frac{1}{v}=1$$

Now by Pythagoras' theorem, $$u^2+x^2=4$$

$$\Rightarrow \quad u=\sqrt{4-x^2}$$

and similarly, $$v^2+x^2=9$$

$$\Rightarrow \quad v=\sqrt{9-x^2}$$

giving $$\frac{1}{\sqrt{4-x^2}}+\frac{1}{\sqrt{9-x^2}}=1.$$

All that remains is to solve this equation, and the value obtained for x is the width of the passage in metres.

Consider how you might obtain a solution.

Several methods of solution are possible, but you should have realised almost at once that this is not the sort of equation that can be solved by a simple algorithm (such as, "Take all the x terms to one side and all the numbers to the other"), nor is there a formula such as the one commonly used for quadratic equations. This equation cannot in fact be solved by any such 'analytic' method. Instead we are going to resort to methods which will lead us to very accurate approximations to solutions.

There are two approaches which may work, one involving numerical substitution and the other based on graphs. If you can find a positive numerical value for x which satisfies the equation, then clearly this is a solution. Random guessing is likely to take a long time, however, so any approach must be based on some kind of systematic trial and improvement. Later in this chapter several numerical methods are examined in detail. The alternative graphical approach is the subject of the next section.

19.2 Graphical methods

You should already be familiar with the idea of solving an equation by means of a graph: an example will remind you of the method.

Example

Solve $x^2 + 3x - 5 = 0.$

Solution

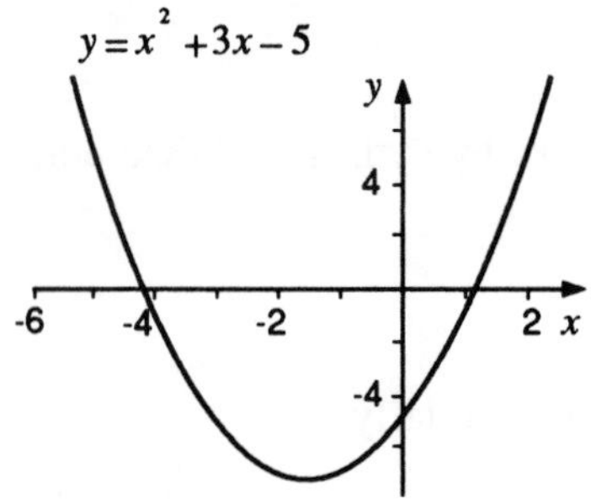

The diagram shows the graph of $y = x^2 + 3x - 5$, plotted from a table of values in the usual way. It crosses the x-axis at the points $(-4.2, 0)$ and $(1.2, 0)$ approximately - the graph certainly cannot be read to an accuracy greater than one decimal place - so the solutions of the equation are $x \approx -4.2$ and $x \approx 1.2$.

If you have the use of a graphic calculator or a computer with graph-drawing facilities, you can get the same result with much less effort. Draw the graph on the screen, and then use the computer mouse (or the <Trace> function on the calculator) to move the cursor to each of the crossing points in turn.

The same method can be used more generally to solve equations in higher powers of x. There are formulae (like the quadratic formula but much more complicated) for solving cubic and quartic equations, but the French mathematician *Evariste Galois* proved just under 200 years ago that no such formula can ever be found for general equations in powers of x higher than the fourth. As a bonus, the graphical method works for equations including sines, cosines, exponential and logarithmic functions, and so on. Look at some more examples.

Example

Solve the equation $2^x - 3 = 0$.

Solution

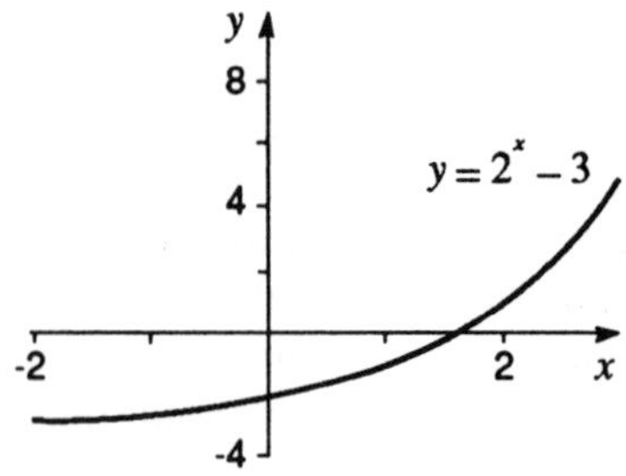

The diagram shows the graph of $y = 2^x - 3$, plotted from a table of values or drawn on a calculator or computer screen. The graph crosses the x-axis at (1.6, 0) approximately, and nowhere else, so $x \approx 1.6$ is the only solution of the equation.

Example

Find correct to one decimal place all the solutions of the equation $5\cos x - x = 0$, where x is expressed in radians.

Solution

The diagram shows the graph of $y = 5\cos x - x$. It crosses the x-axis three times, at (–3.8, 0), (–2.0, 0) and (1.3, 0), and so the equation has the three solutions, $x \approx -3.8$, $x \approx -2.0$, and $x \approx 1.3$.

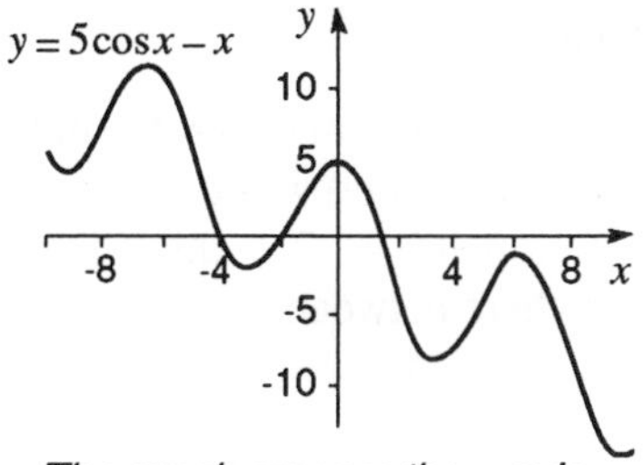

The graph crosses the x-axis three times

Plotting two graphs

The equation in the last example could have been rewritten in the form $5\cos x = x$, so an alternative approach would have been to plot two graphs, the graph of $y = 5\cos x$ and the graph of $y = x$, and to find their points of intersection. The advantage of this method is that both these are well-known functions whose graphs should be familiar, making it quick and easy to draw them. The diagram shows these two graphs, and it is evident that the values of x at the points of intersection correspond to those already found.

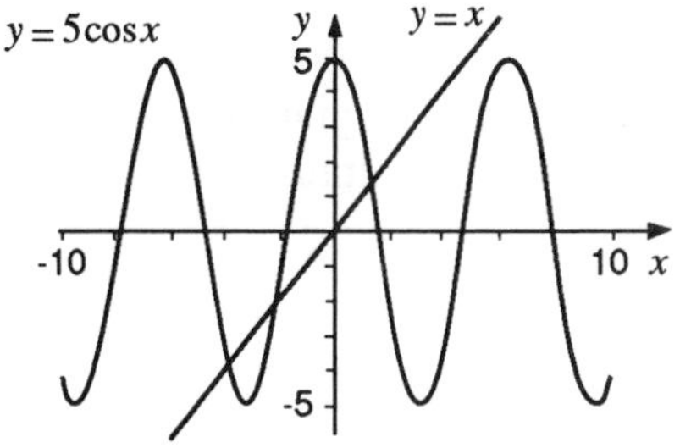

The two graphs intersect at three points

Example

By drawing two graphs, solve $x^3 + 2x - 4 = 0$.

Solution

The equation can be written as $x^3 = 4 - 2x$, and the diagram shows the graphs of $y = x^3$ and $y = 4 - 2x$. They intersect only once, at (1.2, 1.6), so the only solution of this cubic equation is $x \approx 1.2$.

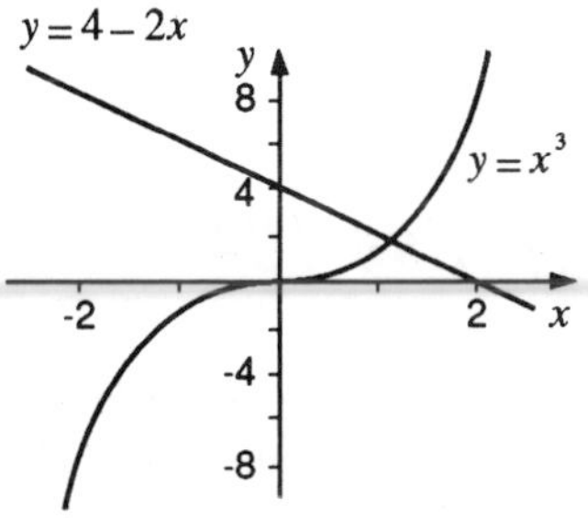

The equation could have been solved in other ways. It could have been rearranged in the form $2x = 4 - x^3$, or even as $x^2 = \frac{4}{x} - 2$, and either of these would have given the same result. Often there is no one right way to solve an equation graphically, but a whole collection of ways, some of which may be easier than others.

A possible difficulty

A particular difficulty arises when the graph is nearly flat at the point where it crosses the x-axis, or where two graphs are nearly parallel at their point of intersection. The next example provides an illustration.

Example

Solve the equation $3^x = x^2 + 2x$.

Solution

The first diagram opposite shows the graphs of $y = 3^x$ and $y = x^2 + 2x$, and while it is clear that there is one root of the equation at $x \approx -2.1$, the other (or others?) could be almost anywhere between 1.0 and 2.0.

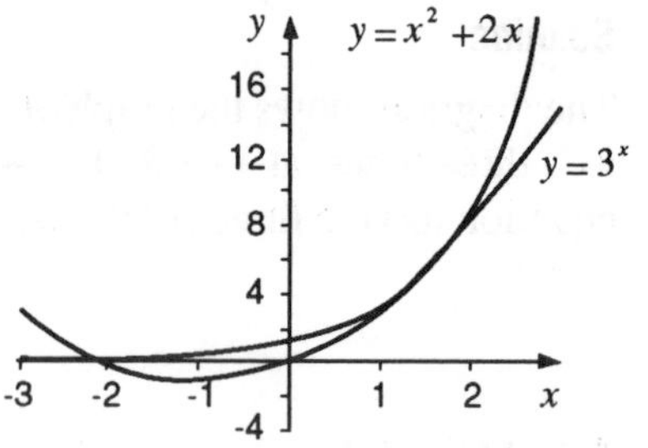

The second diagram showing the graph of $y = 3^x - x^2 - 2x$ is not much more helpful.

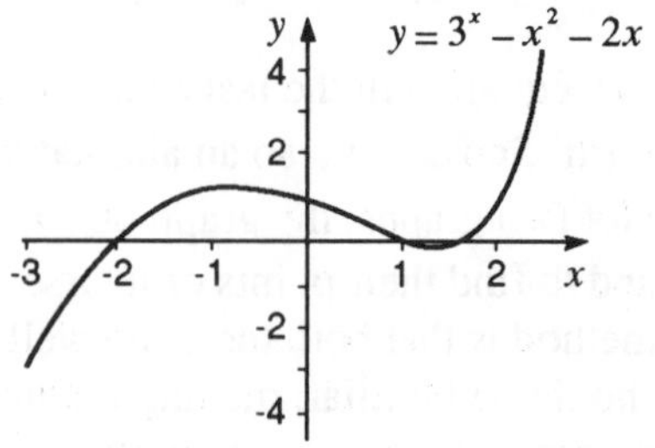

It is only in the third diagram with its exaggerated vertical scale that the other two solutions can be identified as $x \approx 1.0$ ($x = 1$ is actually an exact solution) and $x \approx 1.6$.

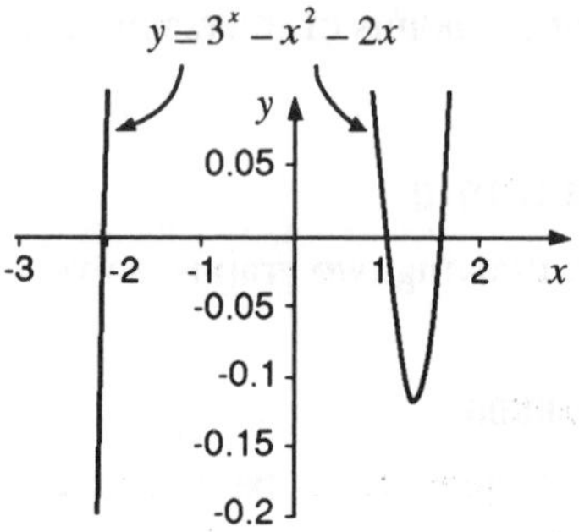

Function on a larger scale

Exercise 19A

Use graphical methods to find approximate solutions of the following equations, giving answers correct to one decimal place.

1. $x^2 - 1 = \dfrac{1}{x}$
2. $x^3 - 6x^2 + 11x - 5 = 0$
3. $x^4 = 2x + 1$
4. $2^x - 5x = 0$

*5. $\sin x = \cos 2x$ (answers between 0 and 2π only)

19.3 Improving accuracy

In the previous section all the solutions were given correct to one decimal place, but this is not always good enough. How might you get a more accurate answer - to two or three decimal places, say?

Stop and think about how you could obtain a more accurate answer.

You may have got a hint from the last example of Section 19.2 – with graphical methods, it is usually possible to get a more accurate answer by redrawing the graph on a larger scale. The next example illustrates this.

Example

Solve $x^3+2x^2-5=0$, giving your answer correct to three decimal places.

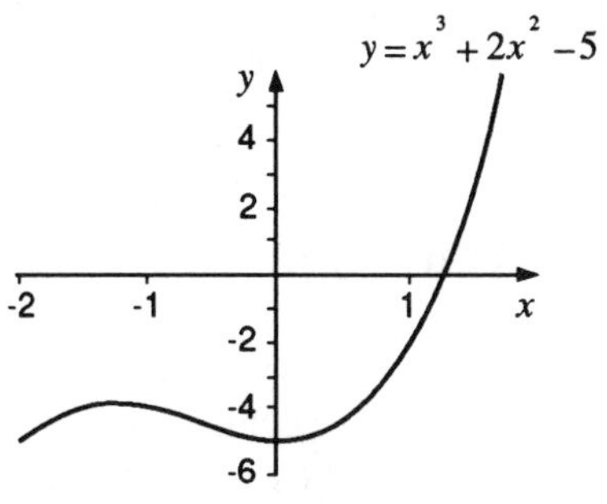

Graph of function for $-2 \le x \le 2$

Solution

The first diagram shows the graph of $y=x^3+2x^2-5$, plotted for values of x between -2 and 2. The equation clearly has only one root, which lies between 1 and 2, and a graphical estimate might suggest $x \approx 1.2$ to one decimal place.

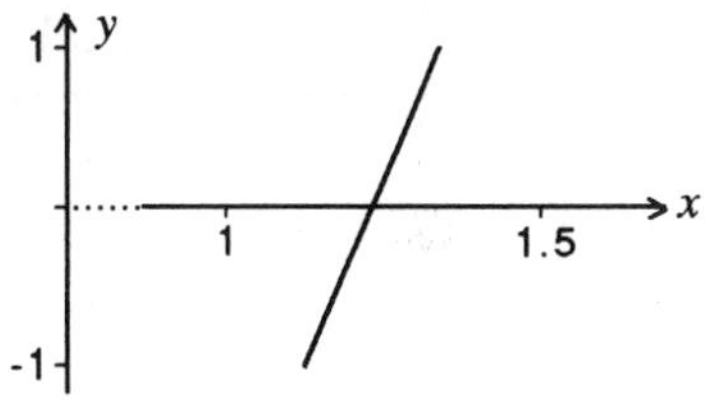

The same graph for $1 \le x \le 1.5$

The second diagram shows the same graph, but this time plotted only between $x=1$ and $x=1.5$ - notice that over this limited domain the graph is almost a straight line. On this larger scale it is possible to estimate the root more accurately, and to say that $x \approx 1.24$ to two decimal places.

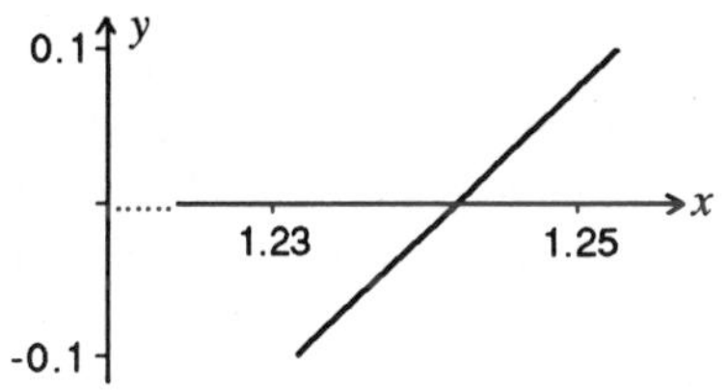

The same again for $1.23 \le x \le 1.25$

The third diagram increases the scale yet again, and shows the graph plotted over the domain $1.23 \le x \le 1.25$. Now the solution can be estimated even more accurately as $x \approx 1.242$ to three decimal places. Clearly there is no limit in theory to the accuracy that can be obtained by this method, but it is time-consuming.

Computers and calculators

The process can be carried out much more quickly with a computer graph package or a graphic calculator. Most graph-drawing software packages allow the user to change the scales without redrawing the whole graph, and by using this facility to 'zoom in' on the root the solution can be read quite easily to whatever level of accuracy is required.

Activity 1 *Graphic calculators*

The <Factor> command on the Casio *fx*-7000G is not widely used, but was designed for just this purpose. If you have such a calculator, try the following:

- <Range> $-10,\ 10,\ 5,\ -10,\ 10,\ 5$
- <Factor> 5 : <Graph> $Y = Xx^y3+2X^2-5$ <EXE>
- <Trace> and use the $\Rightarrow$ and $\Leftarrow$ keys to move the flashing dot close to the point where the graph crosses the x-axis, then <EXE> again.
- Repeat the last instruction as often as necessary - probably

three or four times - until you are satisfied with the accuracy of the x-value given on the screen.

---

*Accuracy

Although in theory there is no limit to the accuracy that can be obtained by a graphical method of this kind, it is difficult in practice to get solutions correct to more than five or six decimal places. Unless you are fond of very cumbersome pencil-and-paper arithmetic you will almost certainly use a calculator to work out the values to plot, and most calculators operate to no more than eight or ten significant figures at best. General-purpose computer packages have a similar limitation - six significant figures is not uncommon - making it impossible to obtain any more accurate result unless you are prepared to adjust the equation as well as the scales.

You should bear in mind too that many equations have **irrational** solutions - that is, the 'true' solutions are numbers that cannot be expressed exactly as fractions or decimals. Thus although it may be possible (in theory) to get as close to the true solution as you might wish, you may never be able to find its exact value. In real life this hardly matters - five or six decimal places is more than enough for any practical purpose - but a mathematician would be careful to distinguish a good decimal approximation from the 'exact' irrational solution.

Exercise 19B

Use a graphical method to solve each of the following equations correct to the stated level of accuracy:

1. $x^3 - 4x + 5 = 0$, to two decimal places
2. $x^5 - x^3 = 1$, to two decimal places
3. $2^x = x + 3$, to two decimal places (both solutions)
4. $2x^2 + 1 = \frac{1}{x}$, to three decimal places

*5. $x + \ln x = 0$, to three decimal places

19.4 Interval bisection

The graphical method of solving equations, as you will have realised, has two disadvantages. For one thing it tends to be quite time-consuming, though using a suitable calculator or computer can speed things up considerably. Secondly, however, it needs someone to read the graph, to estimate the position of the crossing point or move the cursor, and (if greater accuracy is required) to decide on the new range of values to be plotted.

These disadvantages are overcome, at least in part, by some of the algebraic methods discussed in the rest of the chapter. The chief benefit of such methods is that they can be expressed algorithmically in terms of yes/no decisions and routine operations, so eliminating the need for human intervention and making them suitable for programming into a computer or calculator.

Activity 2 *Guess a number*

Take a few minutes to play this game with another student. One of you thinks of a whole number between 1 and 100, and the other has to guess this number by asking no more than ten questions of a yes/no type. Play several rounds, taking it in turns to be the guesser, and try to find the most efficient strategy. How many questions do you really need?

In fact seven questions and a final 'guess' will do, as long as the questions are properly chosen. A skilful guesser might well have asked questions like the following:

Is your number more than 50?	Yes
Is it more than 75?	No
Is it more than 62?	Yes
Is it more than 69?	Yes
Is it more than 72?	No
Is it more than 70?	Yes
Is it more than 71?	Yes
The number is 72.	

At each stage, the guesser is roughly halving the number of possibilities. Initially the number could be anywhere between 1 and 100, but the first answer shows that it is actually between 51 and 100. Then it is between 51 and 75, then between 63 and 75, then between 70 and 75, then between 70 and 72, then between 71 and 72, and the final answer shows that it is 72.

If you played the game enough times you probably discovered this strategy (or something very similar) for yourself. If not, play two or three more rounds using this strategy, to be sure you understand how it works.

Locating a root

The same principle, known as **interval bisection** because at each stage the possible range of values is halved, can be applied to the solution of equations. If you know that a particular equation has a root between 2 and 3 (say), then you can ask whether the root is greater than 2.5, and so halve the interval in which it is to be found. By doing this repeatedly, you can eventually say that the root lies in an interval so small that you can give its value to whatever accuracy you want.

How do you find the first interval (i.e. between 2 and 3) ?

There are at least two practical methods of locating the root, either of which can be used alone but which are much better in combination. The first is to draw a quick rough graph; this does take a little time, but it shows how many roots there are altogether and helps you to avoid any of several possible traps.

The second method, which can be used on its own but which is much more reliable after you have sketched a graph, involves looking for a change of sign. If you find, for example, that $f(2)$ is negative and $f(3)$ positive, or vice versa, it follows that provided f is a continuous function then $f(x)$ is zero somewhere between $x = 2$ and $x = 3$.

The **change-of-sign method** is certainly more precise than the sketch graph in locating a root, but it does contain at least three possible traps. Firstly, it may well locate one root but miss another: unless you are very persevering (or know where to look) you are unlikely to find a root between (say) -11 and -10.

Secondly, the change-of-sign method will not work unless the graph of $y = f(x)$ is continuous over the interval in question. The diagram shows part of the graph of $y = \tan x$ for values of x (in radians) between 0 and 3. It is clear that $f(1) > 0$ and $f(2) < 0$, but equally clear that there is no root of the equation $f(x) = 0$ between 1 and 2.

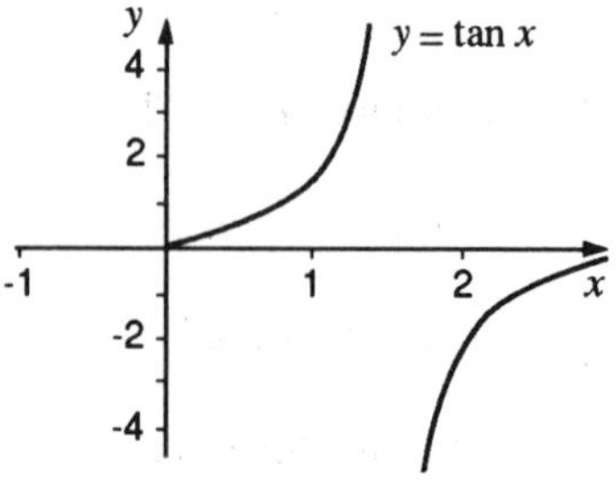

$f(1) < 0$ and $f(2) < 2$ but there is no root between 1 and 2

Thirdly, the change-of-sign method will not show up repeated roots (where the graph just touches the x-axis without crossing it), nor two roots close together. For example, the equation $6x^2 - 29x + 35 = 0$ has solutions $x = 2\frac{1}{3}$ and $x = 2\frac{1}{2}$, as you can check by factorising, but $f(2)$ and $f(3)$ are both positive and so give no indication that these roots exist.

In spite of these three problems, the change-of-sign method of locating roots is very important, and useful too when properly applied in conjunction with a sketch. It forms the basis of the interval bisection and linear interpolation methods discussed in this section and the next, and is commonly used at least at the start of the more sophisticated methods of solution considered later in the chapter.

The method in practice

Example

Solve $x^4 - 2x^3 - 1 = 0$, correct to two decimal places.

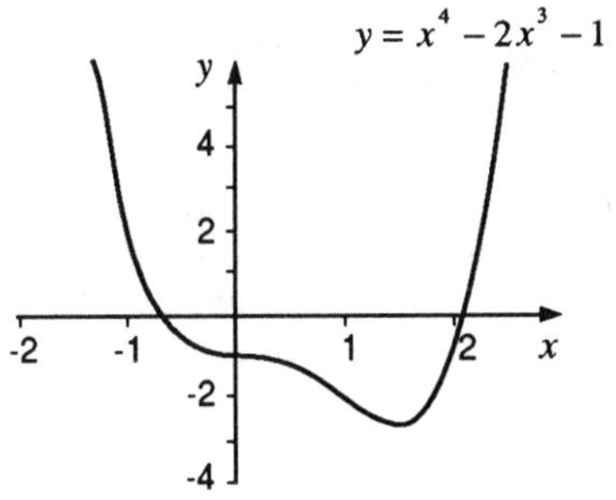

Solution

The diagram shows the graph of $y = x^4 - 2x^3 - 1$, and there are evidently two roots, one negative and close to -1, and the other positive and close to 2.

$f(-1) = 2$, $f(0) = -1$ and the change of sign shows that there is a root between -1 and 0.

$f(2) = -1$, $f(3) = 26$ and the change of sign shows that the second root lies between 2 and 3.

Consider the positive root first.

$f(2.5) \approx 6.8$ so the change of sign is between 2 and 2.5.

$f(2.2) \approx 1.1$ so the change is between 2 and 2.2.

(This is not exactly the midpoint of the interval, but is near enough and keeps the calculation fairly simple.)

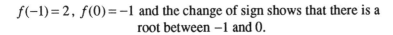

$f(2.1) \approx -0.1$ so the change is between 2.1 and 2.2.

$f(2.15) \approx 0.5$ so the change is between 2.1 and 2.15.

$f(2.12) \approx 0.1$ so the change is between 2.1 and 2.12.

$f(2.11) \approx 0.03$ so the change is between 2.1 and 2.11.

$f(2.105) \approx -0.02$ so the change is between 2.105 and 2.11.

This root is therefore 2.11 to two decimal places.

Similarly with the negative root,

$f(-0.5) \approx -0.7$ so the change is between -1 and -0.5.

$f(-0.7) \approx -0.1$ so the change is between -1 and -0.7.

$f(-0.85) \approx 0.8$ so the change is between -0.85 and -0.7.

$f(-0.78) \approx 0.3$ so the change is between -0.78 and -0.7.

$f(-0.74) \approx 0.1$ so the change is between -0.74 and -0.7.

$f(-0.72) \approx 0.02$ so the change is between -0.72 and -0.7.

$f(-0.71) \approx -0.03$ so the change is between -0.72 and -0.71.

$f(-0.715) \approx -0.01$ so the change is between -0.72 and -0.715.

So this root is -0.72 to two decimal places.

Exercise 19C

Use a sketch graph followed by a change-of-sign search to locate the roots of the equation $2^x - 2x - 3 = 0$. Then use an interval bisection method to find these solutions correct to two decimal places.

19.5 Linear interpolation

You may feel that the interval bisection method is unnecessarily slow. If $f(2) = -1$ and $f(3) = 26$, as in the last example with $f(x) = x^4 - 2x^3 - 1$, it is surely obvious that the root is likely to be closer to 2 than to 3. It is as a response to this very reasonable argument that the **linear interpolation** method has been developed.

You saw earlier how any graph drawn on a sufficiently large scale often looks very similar to a straight line, and the linear interpolation method makes use of this fact. The diagram shows a straight line drawn between the points (2, –1) and (3, 26). Since the line cuts the x-axis between 2 and 3 in the ratio 1 : 26, it must therefore cross the x -axis when $x = 2\frac{1}{27}$, which is approximately the point (2.04, 0). The second approximation produced by linear interpolation is therefore $x \approx 2.04$.

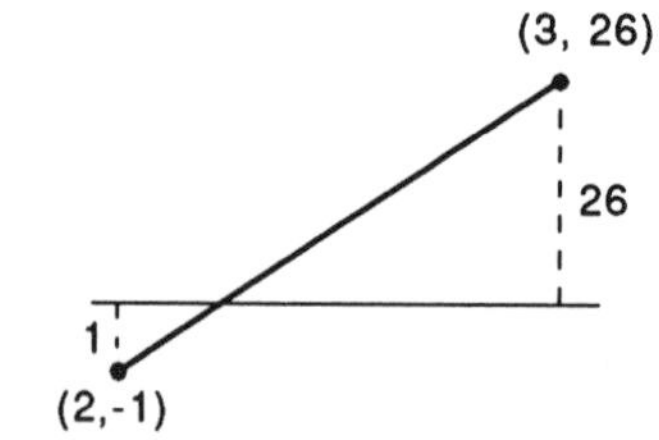

The principle of linear interpolation (not to scale)

Now $f(2.04) \approx -0.66$, and a new straight line can be drawn between (2.04, -0.66) and (3, 26). This divides the x-axis between 2.04 and 3 in the ratio 0.66 : 26, and therefore cuts it at

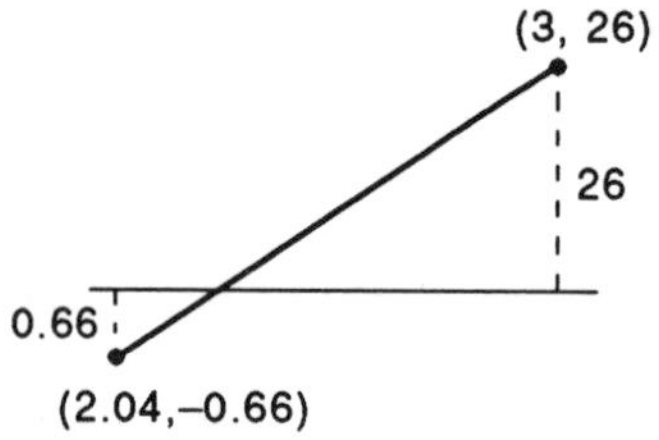

$$x = 2.04 + \left(\frac{0.66}{26.66}\right)(3 - 2.04) \approx 2.06.$$

$f(2.06) \approx -0.48$, and the line between (2.06, -0.48) and (3, 26) cuts the x-axis at (2.08, 0).

$f(2.08) \approx -0.28$, and the line between (2.08, -0.28) and (3, 26) cuts the x-axis at (2.09, 0).

$f(2.09) \approx -0.18$, and the line between (2.09, −0.18) and (3, 26) cuts the x-axis at (2.10, 0).

$f(2.10) \approx -0.07$, and the line between (2.10, −0.07) and (3, 26) cuts the x-axis at (2.102, 0).

After six interpolations, it seems fairly clear that the value is approaching a limit close to 2.10 or 2.11, and it is easy enough to check that $f(2.105) < 0$ and $f(2.115) > 0$, confirming the solution $x \approx 2.11$ to two decimal places. The negative root could be found in a similar way.

Consider a second example.

Example

Find the positive root of $10^x = x + 5$.

Solution

Rearrange the equation in the form $10^x - x - 5 = 0$, and write $f(x) = 10^x - x - 5$. The graph suggests a root between 0 and 1, and this is confirmed by $f(0) = -4$, $f(1) = 4$.

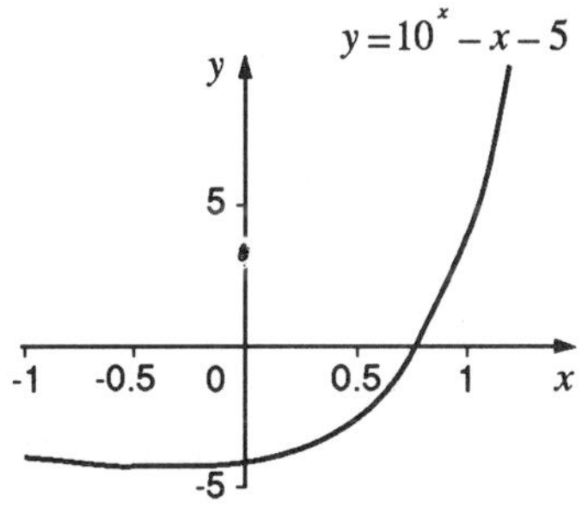

The line between (0, −4) and (1, 4) cuts the x-axis at (0.5, 0).

$f(0.5) \approx -2.34$, and the line between (0.5, −2.34) and (1, 4) cuts the x-axis at (0.68, 0).

$f(0.68) \approx -0.89$, and the line between (0.68, −0.89)and (1, 4) cuts the x-axis at (0.738, 0).

$f(0.738) \approx -0.27$, and the line between (0.738, −0.27) and (1, 4) cuts the x-axis at (0.755, 0).

$f(0.755) \approx -0.07$, and the line between (0.755, −0.07) and (1, 4) cuts the x-axis at (0.759, 0).

At this point you may guess that $x \approx 0.76$ is the solution correct to two decimal places, and since you know already that $f(0.755) < 0$, it remains only to check that $f(0.765) > 0$. This is indeed the case, so $x \approx 0.76$ to this level of accuracy.

Activity 3

Use a sketch graph followed by a change-of-sign search to locate the roots of the equation $x^3 - 4x^2 + 7 = 0$. Use linear interpolation to find each of these roots correct to two decimal places.

19.6 Rearrangement methods

Interval bisection and linear interpolation are fairly straightforward iterative methods for the solution of equations, but neither of them is particularly efficient. You have seen in the examples and exercises that it may easily take six or eight iterations to get a solution accurate to even two decimal places, and in a world where time is at a premium this is not good enough. Other quicker methods must therefore be considered.

Example

Solve the equation $x^5 + 3x^2 - 8 = 0$.

Solution

Let $f(x) = x^5 + 3x^2 - 8$; the graph of $y = f(x)$ shows clearly that there is only one root. Since $f(1) = -4$ and $f(2) = 36$, and since f is a continuous function, the solution lies between 1 and 2, probably close to 1.

Now the equation can be rearranged as $x^5 = 8 - 3x^2$, and this in turn can be written in the form $x = \sqrt[5]{8 - 3x^2}$. This equation can then be used as the basis of an **iteration** formula; i.e. one where, given an approximation x_0, a new approximation x_1 can be calculated, and then a new approximation x_2 can be calculated, etc. In this case the formula is

$$x_{n+1} = \sqrt[5]{8 - 3x_n^2}.$$

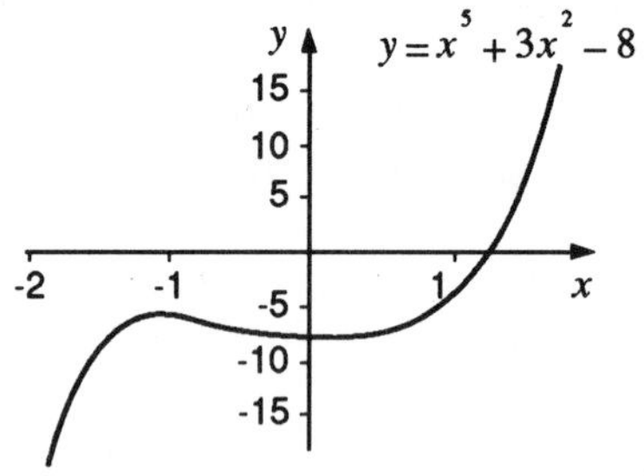

Substituting the first approximation $x_0 = 1$ gives $x_1 \approx 1.4$; substituting this result and then each of the others in turn gives $x_2 \approx 1.2$, $x_3 \approx 1.3$, $x_4 \approx 1.24$, $x_5 \approx 1.28$, $x_6 \approx 1.25$, $x_7 \approx 1.27$, $x_8 \approx 1.26$ and $x_9 \approx 1.26$ again. A quick check confirms that $f(1.255) < 0$ and $f(1.265) > 0$, so that the solution is $x \approx 1.26$ correct to two decimal places.

Although this has involved nine calculations (or iterations) and so is apparently no quicker than the previous methods, each iteration involves no more than the substitution of the previous result into a fairly simple formula. It is usually possible, in fact, to make the substitution using the value in the calculator directly, without the trouble of writing down each result and re-entering it: certainly a very simple program can be written for a programmable calculator or computer.

Example

Solve $x^2 + \sin x = 1$, with x in radians.

Solution

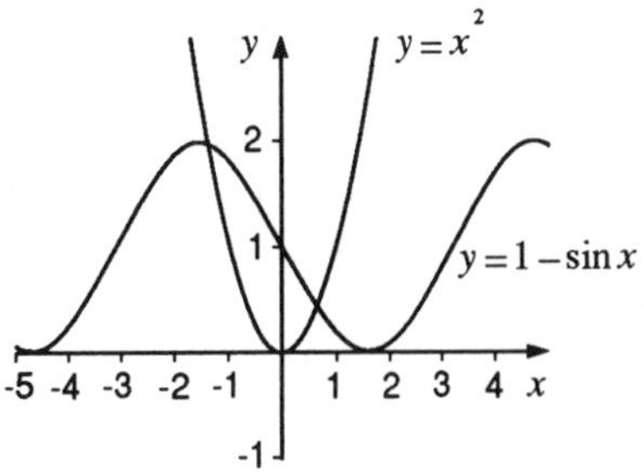

The equation can be rearranged as $x^2 = 1 - \sin x$, and from a sketch graph this has solutions at $x \approx 0.6$ and at $x \approx -1.4$. The rearrangement leads to an iteration formula

$$x_{n+1} = \sqrt{1 - \sin x_n}$$

and substituting $x_0 = 0.6$ gives in turn $x_1 \approx 0.66$, $x_2 \approx 0.622$, $x_3 \approx 0.646$, $x_4 \approx 0.631$, $x_5 \approx 0.640$, and $x_6 \approx 0.635$. Once again it is now easy to check that 0.635 and 0.645 give $x^2 + \sin x$ values respectively less than and greater than 1, so that the positive solution is $x \approx 0.64$ to two decimal places.

Substituting $x_0 = -1.4$, on the other hand, gives $x_1 \approx 1.41$ and $x_2 \approx 0.11$ and gradually moves in to the same solution as before. This is because the iteration formula has taken the positive square root, and so naturally gives only positive results. An alternative iteration formula with a negative square root would be equally valid:

$$x_{n+1} = -\sqrt{1 - \sin x_n}$$

and with $x_0 = -1.4$ this gives $x_1 \approx x_2 \approx -1.41$, which can be checked as correct in the usual way.

Exercise 19D

1. Show that the equation $x^3 + 2x - 6 = 0$ has just one solution, and locate it. Show that the equation can lead to the iteration formula

   $$x_{n+1} = \sqrt[3]{6 - 2x_n},$$

   and use this formula to find the solution correct to two decimal places.

2. Write down the equation whose solution can be found by using the iteration formula

   $$x_{n+1} = 1 + \frac{1}{x_n^2},$$

   and use the formula to find this solution correct to two decimal places.

3. Show that the equation $x^4 - 3x + 1 = 0$ has two solutions, and locate them approximately. Show that the equation can lead to two iteration formulae

   $$x_{n+1} = \sqrt[4]{3x_n - 1} \quad \text{and} \quad x_{n+1} = \frac{x_n^4 + 1}{3}$$

   and show that each of these formulae leads to just one solution. Find each solution correct to two decimal places.

4. Find a suitable iteration formula for the equation $x^3 - x^2 - 5 = 0$, and solve the equation correct to two decimal places.

5. Use an iterative method to solve the equation $x^x = 2$ correct to three decimal places.

19.7 Convergence

Exercise 19D should have started you thinking. Why is it, for example, that in Question 3 one iteration formula would work only for the smaller root and the other only for the greater? Why do some formulae seem to work faster than others? Why do some formulae not lead to a root at all, but give results that swing wildly from side to side?

These are all questions concerned with the **convergence** of the iterative process, and while it is useful for you to have a general understanding of the idea, you do not need to go deeply into the theory. If you want to study convergence more deeply than this section allows, look at an undergraduate textbook on numerical analysis.

Consider the equation $x^2 - 5x + 2 = 0$, to be solved using the formula $x_{n+1} = \sqrt{5x_n - 2}$. The diagram shows two graphs, those of $y = x$ and $y = \sqrt{5x-2}$ respectively; their points of intersection correspond to the solutions of the equation. The first approximation x_0 is substituted into the formula and gives a value - call it y_0 - which then becomes x_1 : this process is illustrated by the arrows.

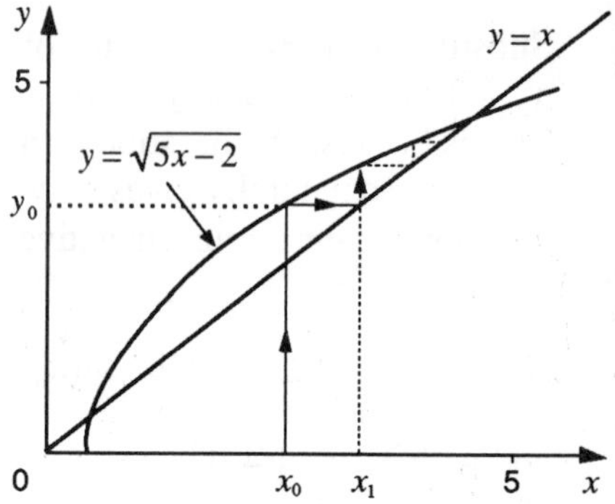

The principle of iteration

As the iteration is repeated, the arrows build into some sort of pattern. In this particular case, they are moving (slowly) closer to the right-hand point of intersection, and so will eventually lead to that solution.

If you try to apply the same method to find the left-hand point of intersection, you will fail no matter how hard you try - the arrows will either converge onto the right-hand point or diverge altogether. On the other hand, the iteration formula

$$x_{n+1} = \frac{x_n^2 + 2}{5}$$

(illustrated in a similar way in the second diagram) converges quite neatly onto the left-hand point of intersection and cannot be persuaded to lead to the upper solution.

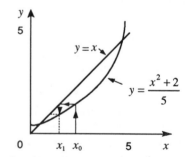

An alternative iteration formula for the lower root

Test for convergence

If you want to know whether or not a particular iteration formula will converge, it is often easiest in practice to apply the formula three or four times and look at the pattern of results. If the results are getting gradually closer together they are probably converging on a solution; if not, you are unlikely to find the solution using this formula. There is a more formal test, however, that you might want to use in a particular case.

Suppose that the iteration formula is $x_{n+1} = g(x_n)$, and that the derivative of $g(x)$ is $g'(x)$. Then it can be shown - the proof is not attempted here - that a **necessary** and **sufficient** condition for the formula to **converge** on the true solution λ is that

$$-1 < g'(\lambda) < 1.$$

This condition is all very well, except that the value of λ is what you are trying to find! In practice, therefore, it is usual to look for an x-interval containing both the unknown λ and the first approximation x_0 such that $|g'(x)| < 1$ throughout the interval. In the example above, if $g(x) = \sqrt{5x-2}$ then $g'(x) = \dfrac{5}{2\sqrt{5x-2}}$.

This has absolute value less than 1 if $x > 1.65$, and so can converge on the upper solution (given a suitable first approximation) but not the lower. On the other hand, if $g(x) = \dfrac{x^2+2}{5}$ then $g'(x) = \dfrac{2x}{5}$,

which lies between −1 and 1 only when $-2.5 < x < 2.5$; it thus converges only to the lower solution.

Exercise 19E

Use a graph to locate approximately the root or roots of each of the equations opposite. Rearrange each equation to give an iteration formula, and test each formula to determine whether it will lead to any or all of the roots. Repeat with another rearrangement if necessary, until all the roots are obtainable. Find each root correct to one decimal place.

1. $x^3 - 3x - 4 = 0$
2. $x^4 + 2x^3 = 5$.
3. $3^x = 3x + 2$.

19.8 Newton's method

The diagram shows part of the curve $y = f(x)$, where the equation to be solved is $f(x) = 0$. It also shows an approximate solution x_n and the tangent to the curve at the point (x_n, y_n). If this tangent cuts the x-axis at the point $(x_{n+1}, 0)$, then it is clear in this case that x_{n+1} is a better approximation than x_n to the true root λ.

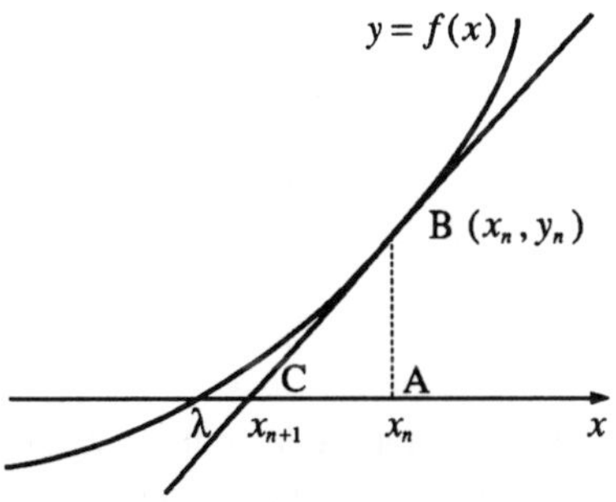

Newton's method for solving $f(x) = 0$

Now the gradient of BC is $\dfrac{\text{BA}}{\text{AC}}$, which is $\dfrac{y_n}{(x_n - x_{n+1})}$.

But $y_n = f(x_n)$, and the gradient of the tangent is $f'(x_n)$,

so $$f'(x_n) = \frac{f(x_n)}{(x_n - x_{n+1})}.$$

Rearranging this gives **Newton's iteration** formula (sometimes known as the Newton-Raphson formula):

$$x_{n+1} = x_n - \frac{f(x_n)}{f'(x_n)}$$

This can be used to obtain a sequence of results leading to a root in the same way as the iteration formulae discussed in Section 19.6; its main advantage over those formulae is that it tends to converge much more quickly.

Example

Solve the equation $x^3 + 3x^2 - 12 = 0$, correct to two decimal places.

Solution

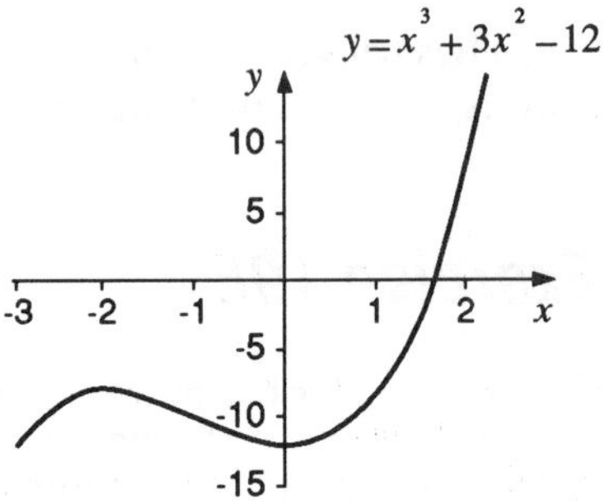

From a graph, there is just one solution, which lies between 1 and 2. Take $x_0 = 1.5$ as a first approximation.

$f(x) = x^3 + 3x^2 - 12$, so $f'(x) = 3x^2 + 6x$.

Applying Newton's formula,

$$\begin{aligned} x_1 &= 1.5 - \frac{f(1.5)}{f'(1.5)} \\ &= 1.5 - \frac{-1.875}{15.75} \\ &= 1.62. \end{aligned}$$

Applying the formula again,

$$\begin{aligned} x_2 &= 1.62 - \frac{f(1.62)}{f'(1.62)} \\ &= 1.62 - \frac{0.125}{17.59} \\ &= 1.613. \end{aligned}$$

And it is not difficult now, after just two iterations, to check that $f(1.605) < 0$ and that $f(1.615) > 0$, so giving $x \approx 1.61$ correct to two decimal places.

Example

Solve the equation $x^5 = 5x^2 - 2$, giving your answers correct to three decimal places.

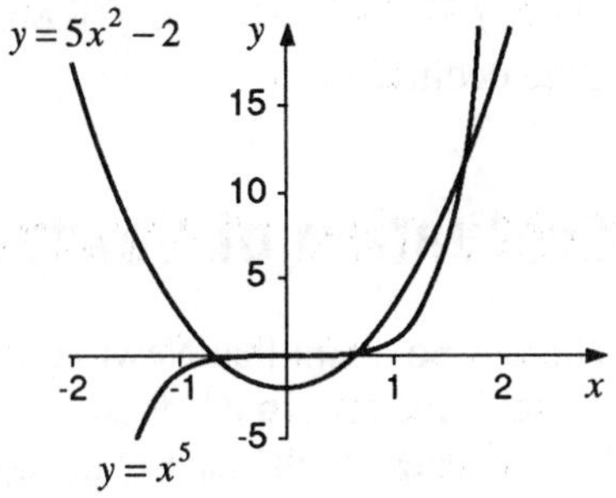

Solution

From a graph, there are solutions at $x \approx -0.6$, $x \approx 0.6$ and $x \approx 1.6$ respectively. Newton's method works only for equations in the form $f(x) = 0$, so a rearrangement gives $f(x) = x^5 - 5x^2 + 2$ and $f'(x) = 5x^4 - 10x$.

If $x_0 = -0.6$, then

$$\begin{aligned} x_1 &= -0.6 - \frac{f(-0.6)}{f'(-0.6)} \\ &= -0.6 - \frac{0.122}{6.648} \\ &= -0.618. \end{aligned}$$

If $x_1 = -0.618$, then

$$\begin{aligned} x_2 &= -0.618 - \frac{f(-0.618)}{f'(-0.186)} \\ &= -0.618 - \frac{0.00023}{6.909} \\ &= -0.618. \end{aligned}$$

$f'(-0.6185) < 0$ and $f'(-06175) > 0$, so $x \approx -0.618$ to three decimal places.

If $x_0 = 0.6$ then $x_1 = x_2 = 0.651$; and if $x_0 = 1.6$ then $x_1 = 1.619$ and $x_2 = 1.618$, which can similarly be confirmed as sufficiently accurate. Thus $x \approx -0.618, 0.651$ or 1.618 to three decimal places.

Example

Solve $\cos x = x^3$, where x is in radians, correct to three decimal places.

Solution

A sketch graph shows just one root, close to 0.9. Rearranging the equation gives $f(x) = \cos x - x^3$ and $f'(x) = -\sin x - 3x^2$.

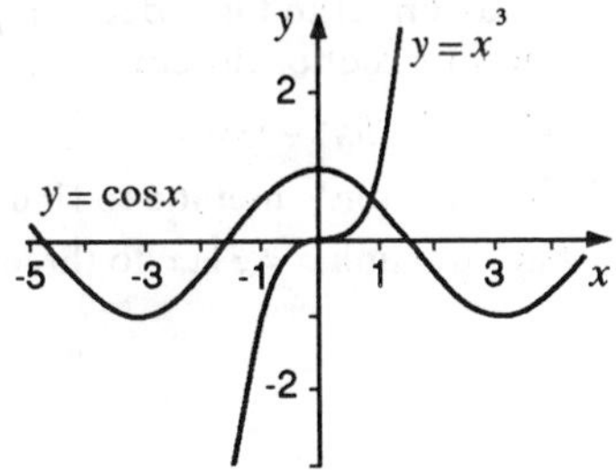

If $x_0 = 0.9$, $x_1 = 0.9 - \dfrac{-0.107}{-3.213} = 0.867$

$$x_2 = 0.867 - \frac{-0.0046}{-3.017} = 0.866$$

$$x_3 = 0.866 - \frac{-0.0016}{-3.0116} = 0.865.$$

Since $f(0.8645) > 0$ and $f(0.8655) < 0$, $x \approx 0.865$ correct to three decimal places.

Evaluation of Newton's method

There is no doubt that Newton's method is a very useful one, and it does have certain advantages over the methods discussed earlier. It converges much faster than any of the previous methods and also the same formula can be used for each of the roots.

The method is not perfect, however, and it does have a number of disadvantages. The first of these is that $f(x)$ has to be differentiated, and your ability to do this will depend on your knowledge of calculus techniques. Then, the first approximation must normally be fairly close to the root you are trying to find, making a reasonable graph almost essential. Finally, the method can become unreliable if the graph of $y = f(x)$ has a turning point or inflexion close to the root - in such a case a different iterative method may prove more effective.

In general, however, you will find the most effective strategy for the solution of difficult equations to be the following:

1. Draw a graph or graphs to locate the root(s) approximately.
2. Use a change of sign and a single linear interpolation to get a good first approximation.
3. Apply Newton's method once or twice (or more).
4. Verify that your answer has the accuracy you require.

Exercise 19F

1. Show that the equation $x^3 - 2x^2 + 4 = 0$ has a root close to $x = -1$. Use Newton's method to find this root correct to two decimal places.
2. Find correct to three decimal places the smallest positive root of the equation $x^4 - 3x^3 + 5x^2 - 1 = 0$.
3. Use Newton's method to find both solutions of the equation $x = 3\ln x$ to three decimal places.
4. Find $\sqrt[3]{10}$ using $x_0 = 2$ and two applications of Newton's method, and calculate the percentage error from the 'true' value obtained from a calculator.

*5. Solve $x^x = 5$ correct to four decimal places.

19.9 The ladders again

With the techniques covered in this chapter it is possible to complete the solution of the ladder problem introduced in Section 19.1. The problem, you will recall, was as follows:

In a narrow passage between two walls there are two wooden ladders, a green one 3 m long and a red one 2 m long. Each ladder has its foot at the bottom of one wall and its top resting against the other wall. The green ladder slopes up from left to right and the red ladder slopes up from right to left. The ladders cross 1 m above the ground. How wide is the passage?

This problem led to the equation

$$\frac{1}{\sqrt{4-x^2}}+\frac{1}{\sqrt{9-x^2}}=1$$

which was left unsolved at that time.

Although it is possible to attempt a graphical or numerical solution of the equation as it stands, it is probably better to simplify it by getting rid of the fractions and the roots. Multiplying the whole equation by both square roots,

$$\sqrt{9-x^2}+\sqrt{4-x^2}=\sqrt{4-x^2}\sqrt{9-x^2}.$$

Squaring,

$$\left(9-x^2\right)+2\sqrt{9-x^2}\sqrt{4-x^2}+\left(4-x^2\right)=\left(4-x^2\right)\left(9-x^2\right).$$

Collecting terms,

$$\begin{aligned}2\sqrt{9-x^2}\sqrt{4-x^2} &= \left(4-x^2\right)\left(9-x^2\right)-\left(9-x^2\right)-\left(4-x^2\right)\\ &= 23-11x^2+x^4.\end{aligned}$$

Squaring again,

$$4\left(9-x^2\right)\left(4-x^2\right) = \left(23-11x^2+x^4\right)^2$$

$$144-52x^2+4x^4 = 529-506x^2+167x^4-22x^6+x^8$$

$$\therefore \quad x^8-22x^6+163x^4-454x^2+385=0.$$

Now let $f(x)=x^8-22x^6+163x^4-454x^2+385$ and draw the graph of $y=f(x)$ for $0\le x\le 2$, since any valid solution must certainly lie within these bounds.

The diagram shows the result, and it is clear that there are two solutions, close to $x = 1.2$ and $x = 1.9$ respectively.

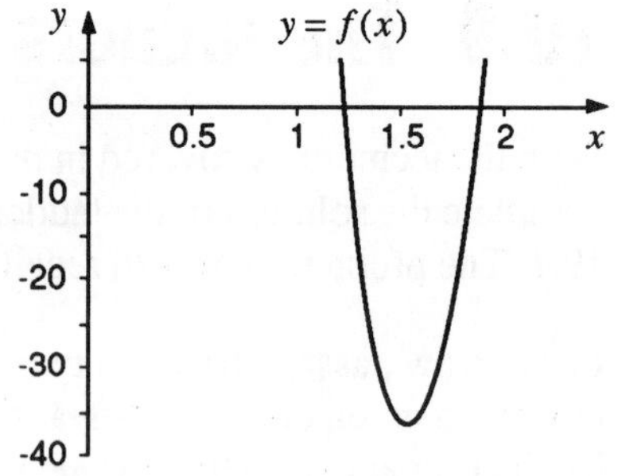

Graph of function for $0 \le x \le 2$

Now $f'(x) = 8x^7 - 132x^5 + 652x^3 - 908x$: this is the step which perhaps justifies the algebra, because differentiating the original equation would have been very messy.

Applying the Newton-Raphson formula with $x_0 = 1.2$,

$$\begin{aligned} x &= 1.2 - \frac{f(1.2)}{f'(1.2)} \\ &= 1.2 - \frac{7.84}{-263} \\ &= 1.23 \text{ to two decimal places.} \end{aligned}$$

Similarly,

$$\begin{aligned} x_2 &= 1.23 - \frac{f(1.23)}{f'(1.23)} \\ &= 1.23 - \frac{0.285}{-241} \\ &= 1.23 \text{ again.} \end{aligned}$$

It is easy to check that $f(1.225) > 0$ and $f(1.235) < 0$, confirming that this solution is accurate to the nearest centimetre.

Similarly, taking $x_0 = 1.9$,

$$\begin{aligned} x_1 &= 1.9 - \frac{f(1.9)}{f'(1.9)} \\ &= 1.9 - \frac{5.12}{194} \\ &= 1.87 \text{ to two decimal places.} \end{aligned}$$

A second iteration gives 1.87 again and this solution of $f(x) = 0$ can similarly be shown to have the necessary accuracy. However, a few moments of thought, possibly by sketching the positions of the ladders, will show you that the passage certainly cannot be 1.87 m wide. Sometimes squaring the original equation (as we have done in this case) leads to some phantom roots being introduced and so one ought to spend a little time checking that the answer obtained does solve the original problems.

The other root of $x \approx 1.23$ does work and so the passageway must be approximately 123 cm wide.

*Activity 4 Iterative chaos

Use a computer or a programmable calculator to investigate sequences given by the iteration formula $x_{n+1} = kx_n(1 - x_n)$, with $x_0 = 0.7$, for different values of k between 1 and 4. The results could be quite chaotic!

19.10 Miscellaneous Exercises

1. Show that the equation $x^3 - x - 2 = 0$ has only one real root, and that this root lies between 1 and 2. Use an iterative method to determine its value accurate to three decimal places.

2. Determine graphically the number of solutions of the equation
$$x^2 - 4 = \frac{1}{x},$$
and estimate their values.

3. Show that the equation $2^x = 3x + 2$ has two solutions, and find each of them correct to two decimal places.

4. Find correct to two decimal places all the solutions of the equation
$$x^4 + 2x^3 - 11x^2 - 12x + 21 = 0.$$

5. Find correct to four decimal places the smallest positive root of the equation
$$7x^3 - 19x^2 + 14x - 3 = 0.$$

6. Solve the equation $xe^x = 1$, correct to two decimal places.

7. Without using any calculator functions other than +, −, × and ÷, find $\sqrt{3}$ correct to six decimal places.

8. Find correct to two decimal places the coordinates of the points at which the circle $x^2 + y^2 = 16$ meets the rectangular hyperbola $x(y+1) = 9$.

9. Show that
$$x_{n+1} = (9x_n - 5)^{\frac{1}{3}}$$
is an iteration formula for the solution of the equation
$$x(x^2 - 9) + 5 = 0$$
Show that this equation has a root between −4 and −3, and use the given iteration formula with $x_0 = -3$ to find this root correct to 2 decimal places, showing that your answer has this accuracy. (AEB)

*10. In a circle whose radius is 10 cm, a segment of area 50 cm² is cut off by a chord AB. Show that AB subtends an angle θ radians at the centre of the circle, where $\theta - \sin\theta = 1$. Solve this equation and hence find the perimeter of the segment in cm correct to two decimal places.

11. Show that the equation $x^3 - x^2 - 2 = 0$ has a root α which lies between 1 and 2.

(a) Using 1.5 as a first approximation for α, use the Newton-Raphson method once to obtain a second approximation for α, giving your answer to 3 decimal places.

(b) Show that the equation $x^3 - x^2 - 2 = 0$ can be arranged in the form $x = \sqrt[3]{(f(x))}$ where $f(x)$ is a quadratic function.

Use an iteration of the form $x_{n+1} = g(x_n)$ based on this rearrangement and with $x_1 = 1.5$ to find x_2 and x_3, giving your answers to 3 decimal places. (AEB)

20 PROBABILITY

Objectives

After studying this chapter you should

- understand how the probability of an event happening is measured;
- recognise whether or not events are related in any way;
- be able to assess the likelihood of events occurring;
- understand and be able to determine conditional probabilities.

20.0 Introduction

'Sue is more likely than Jane to be head girl next year.'

'It will probably rain for the fête tomorrow.'

'A European football team has a better chance of winning the next world cup than a South American one.'

'Reza is 'odds on' to beat Leif in the chess final.'

All these sentences express an opinion that one outcome is more likely than another but in none of them is there any attempt to say by how much. Yet if you want to take out insurance against bad weather for the fête the insurance company you approach must have a way of calculating the probability or likelihood of rain to know how much to charge.

So how can you assess the chance that some event will actually happen?

20.1 Theoretical probability: symmetry

Many intuitive ideas of chance and probability are based on the idea of **symmetry**. Consider the following questions:

If you toss a coin repeatedly, how many times will it come down heads?

If you roll a die how often will you get a four?

If you roll two dice several times, how often will you get two sixes?

For the second question, your answer should be about one in six times provided the die is a fair one. Another way of expressing this is to say that the probability of obtaining 4 is

$$\frac{1}{6} \quad \Rightarrow \quad p(4) = \frac{1}{6}.$$

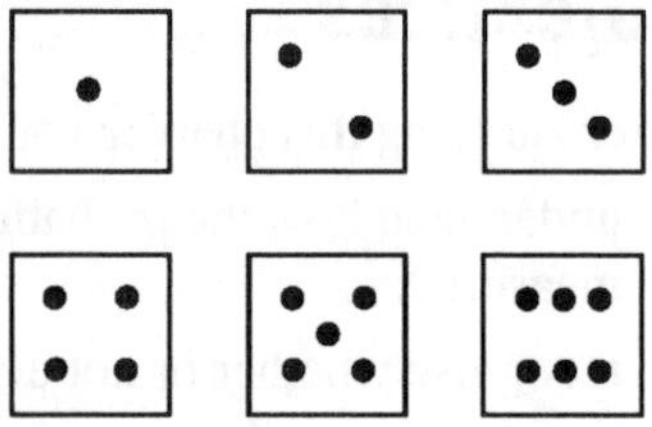

The answer is dependent on the idea of symmetry. That is, every possible outcome (namely 1, 2, 3, 4, 5 and 6) is equally likely to occur. So the probability of any one score must be $\frac{1}{6}$.

Sometimes, though, you must be very careful to make sure that you have a complete list of **all** the possible outcomes of the event under consideration.

Listing all the equally likely outcomes can be very tedious so you may find it simpler and clearer to show them in a diagram.

For example, when two dice are rolled there are thirty six possible outcomes which can be shown very neatly in a diagram (see opposite).

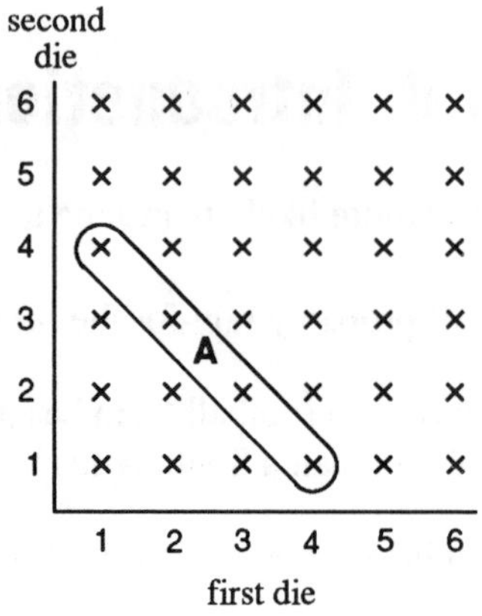

This is called the **sample space**. You can see by looking at the crosses in the area labelled **A** that, for example,

$$P(\text{total} = 5) = \frac{4}{36} = \frac{1}{9}.$$

This sort of diagram can be adapted to other problems so it is very useful.

What is $P(\text{total} = 7)$**?**

Example

Two of the five reserves for the school ski trip, Tamsin, John, Atanu, Robin and David can have places now that a couple of people have had to drop out. How likely is it that John and Tamsin will be chosen to go?

Solution

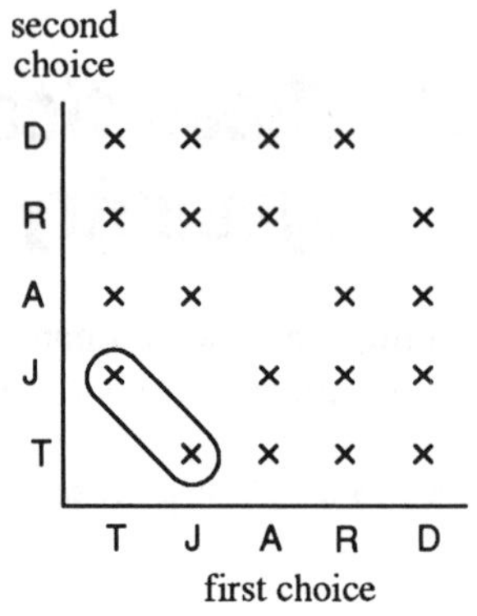

Only the two cases indicated out of the twenty in the diagram opposite are situations when John and Tamsin are chosen, so

$$P(\text{T and J}) = \frac{2}{20} = \frac{1}{10}.$$

You know that with **one** die there are six different possible outcomes and the diagram for **two** dice showed that there are thirty six possible outcomes in this case.

How many will there be if three dice are used?

What sort of diagram could be drawn to show the different results?

As one die needs a one-dimensional diagram which gives six possibilities and two dice need a two-dimensional diagram to show thirty six outcomes, a sensible idea to try for three dice would be a three-dimensional picture.

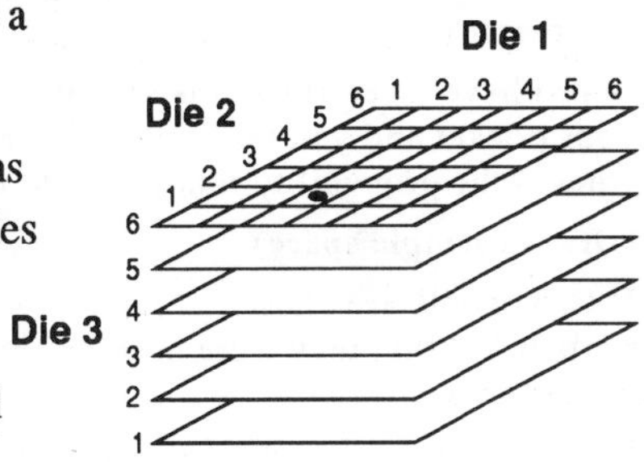

The diagram opposite shows six of the two-dimensional diagrams in layers on top of each other so there are $6 \times 36 = 216$ possibilities in this case or 6^3.

The • in the diagram represents 3 on the first die, 2 on the second and 6 on the third.

The number of dice used appears as a power in these examples so it should be possible to work out the total number of outcomes when more than three dice are used.

Example

What is the probability of getting five sixes when five dice are rolled?

Solution

Five dice produce $6^5 = 7776$ outcomes.

Only one outcome is all sixes, so

$$P(\text{five sixes}) = \frac{1}{7776}.$$

Example

What is the probability that there will be at least one head in five tosses of a fair coin?

Solution

Five coins produce $2^5 = 32$ outcomes.

Only T T T T T does not contain at least one head, so

$$P(\text{at least one H}) = \frac{31}{32}.$$

Exercise 20A

1. What is the probability of choosing an even number from the set of numbers {1, 2, 3, 5, 6, 7, 8, 10}?
2. When two six-sided dice are rolled what is the probability that the product of their scores will be greater than six?
3. If you have three 10p coins and two 50p coins in your pocket and you take out two at random, what is the probability that they add up to 60p? (Draw a sample space)
4. If two people are chosen at random what is the probability that they were born on the same day of the week.
5. List the ways in which one head and five tails may be obtained from six tosses of a coin.
6. Two dice are rolled and the 'score' is the product of the two numbers showing uppermost. If the probability is $\frac{11}{36}$ that the score is at least N, what is the value of N?
7. Pierre and Julian each roll one die. If Pierre's shows the higher number then he wins 7p, otherwise he loses 5p. Explain why this is fair. If Pierre were to add three dots to convert his two to a five how will it affect his winning?
8. A card is chosen at random from a pack of fifty-two. It is replaced and a second card is selected. What is the probability that at least one is a picture card (Jack, Queen, King)? (Sketch a sample space but don't bother with all the crosses.)
9. Eight people are seated at random round a table. What is the probability that Sharif and Raijit will be next to each other?

20.2 Empirical probability: experiment

Mathematicians' early interest in the subject of probability in the seventeenth century came largely as a result of questions from gamblers in France. Since dice, cards, etc. were used, the situations involved had outcomes which were equally likely. All the arguments then could be based on symmetry. You must also be prepared, however, for other situations which do not have properties of symmetry.

It was possible to answer the question about the die as there were six possible outcomes which were equally likely to occur as the cube is a simple regular solid. However, you might find questions about a **cuboctahedron** not as simple to answer.

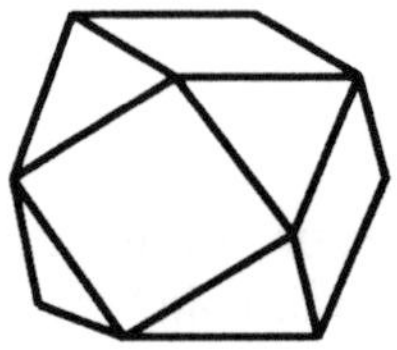

Cuboctahedron

This solid is formed by cutting equilateral triangles from the corners of a cube to produce six square and eight triangular faces.

What is the probability of the solid ending with a square facing upwards when it is rolled?

Perhaps it depends on how many of the faces are squares. Or does considering the areas of the squares as a fraction of the total surface area seem more likely?

Without testing and evidence nobody will believe any answer you give to the question so you will need to experiment to find the probability of a square facing upwards.

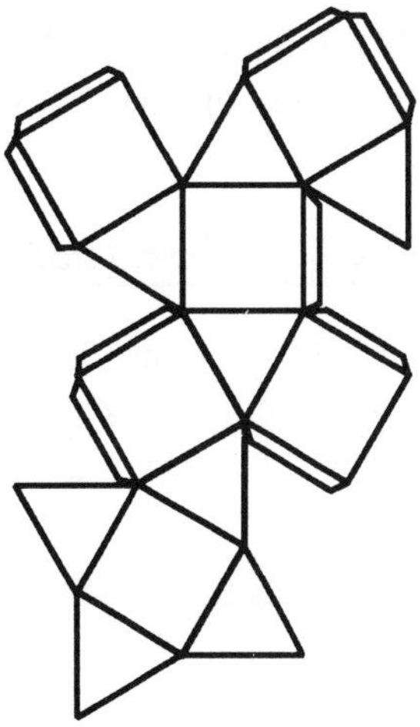

Net of a cuboctahedron

Activity 1

Find the answer for yourself by making the solid from a copy of the net. Be prepared to roll it a lot of times.

You can see the probability graphically by plotting the number of rolls on the x-axis and the fraction of the times a square is facing upwards on the y-axis.

You could, for example, see a square seven times in the first ten goes and nine times in the next ten goes, so a table could start:

No. of squares in 10 goes	7	9	
Total no. of squares	7	16	
Total no. of rolls	10	20	30
Fraction (probability)	$\frac{7}{10} = 0.7$	$\frac{16}{20} = 0.8$	

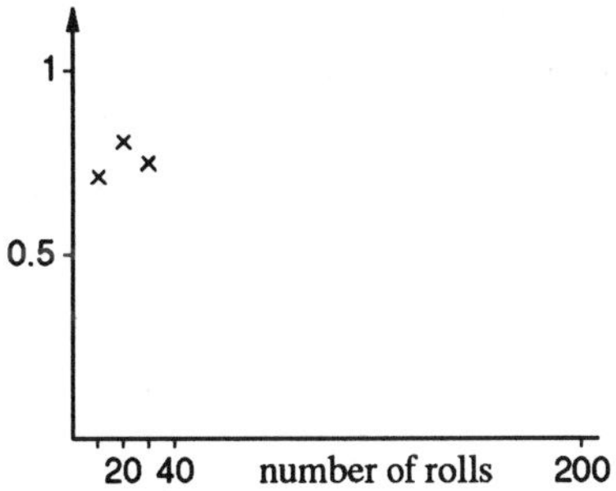

Of course, if several people are doing this experiment you could put your results together to achieve a more reliable answer.

What you will often find from experiment is that the fraction calculated will gradually cease to vary much and will become closer to the value called the **probability.**

What is the probability of a square not appearing uppermost?

From this experiment you will have produced an **empirical probability**; i.e. one based on experience rather than on a logical argument.

The idea of experiment and observation then gives a probability equal to

$$\frac{\text{the number of times a square was upwards}}{\text{the number of attempts}}$$

So if you saw it happen on 150 out of 200 times you will have come to the conclusion that

$$P(\text{square}) = \frac{150}{200} = \frac{3}{4}.$$

In reality, if the true probability was $\frac{3}{4}$, you will be unlikely to get exactly 150 out of 200 - but you should be somewhere near it.

Activity 2 Coin tossing

Toss an unbiased coin 100 times, and record the total fraction of heads after every 10 goes. Plot these on a graph of fraction of heads against number of goes. Does this indicate that the coin is a fair one?

20.3 Empirical probability: observation

How likely is it that the writer of this text is alive now? It is hard to conduct an experiment on this but if I am forty now and writing this in 1991 then you can make use of observations on the life expectancies of forty year old males.

Male age	Average life expectancy beyond present age	Probabilityof surviving at least 5 years
35	38.1	0.993
36	37.1	
37	36.2	
38	35.2	
39	34.3	
40	33.3	0.988
41	32.4	
42	31.5	
43	30.5	
44	29.6	
45	28.7	0.979

Data like this is needed by insurance companies for their life policies and some people will look at figures for sunshine hours and rainfall when planning holidays.

Probability is of interest to people working in economics, genetics, astronomy and many other fields where it may be difficult to experiment but data can be gathered by observation over a long period.

Example

Jane travels to school on the train every weekday and often sees rabbits in a field by the track. In four weeks her observations were

Number of rabbits seen	0	1	2	3	4	5	6	7	8
Number of occasions	0	3	5	7	2	1	0	1	1

What is the probability that on her next journey she will see at least two rabbits?

Solution

$$P(\text{at least two rabbits}) = \frac{17}{20} = 0.85,$$

as on $5+7+2+1+0+1+1 = 17$ days out of the 20 she saw two or more rabbits.

Exercise 20B

1. Using the information from the example above, what is the probability that Jane sees:

   (a) 3 or 4 rabbits; (b) 6 rabbits;
   (c) at least one rabbit?

2. The number of visitors to the UK from North America in 1988 is given below in categories to show mode of travel and purpose of visit.

	Air	Sea	
Holiday	1269	336	
Business	605	17	(in
Friends and relatives	627	55	1000s)
Miscellaneous	324	39	

If you were to have met a visitor from North American in 1988 what would have been the probability that the visitor

(a) was here on business;

(b) came by sea;

(c) came by air to visit friends or relatives;

(d) was here on business if you know the visitor came by sea?

20.4 Combined events

Complement

In the empirical case you will have obtained a value for probability by considering, for example, the number of times a square face finished uppermost as a fraction of the total number of rolls as

$$P(\text{square}) = \frac{\text{no. of times square finished upwards}}{\text{no. of trials}}$$

and this is also called **relative frequency**.

The largest value this fraction can take is one, when a square face appears every trial, and the smallest it can be is zero, when a triangle is uppermost on each go, so

$$0 \le \text{probability} \le 1.$$

Another result that may be obvious is that the number of times with a square facing up plus the number of times with a triangle facing up equals the number of trials.

Hence

$$\frac{\text{no. of times with square up}}{\text{no. of trials}} + \frac{\text{no. of times triangle up}}{\text{no. of trials}} = 1$$

$$\Rightarrow \quad P(\text{square}) + P(\text{not square}) = 1$$

which is written in general as

$$\boxed{P(A) + P(A') = 1}$$

where A' means 'not A' or the '**complement** of A'.

You may well have used this idea earlier when you answered the question in Section 20.2 about how likely it is for a square not to appear on the top face when a cuboctahedron is rolled.

Intersection

Take a cube and mark on its different faces three black circles, one black cross and two red crosses

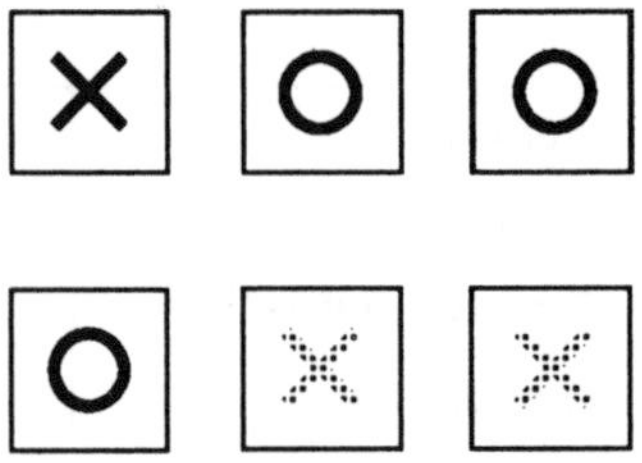

When it is rolled, what are the probabilities of getting

$P(\text{red})$, $P(\text{black})$, $P(\text{circle})$ **and** $P(\text{cross})$ **?**

What is the likelihood of getting a black symbol and a cross?

You can see that just one of the cube's six faces is covered by this description, so

$$P(\text{black and cross}) = \frac{1}{6}.$$

This is often written as

$$P(\text{black} \cap \text{cross}) = \frac{1}{6}$$

and is called the **intersection** of the two events, 'black' and 'cross'.

Another way of showing all the possibilities is illustrated opposite.

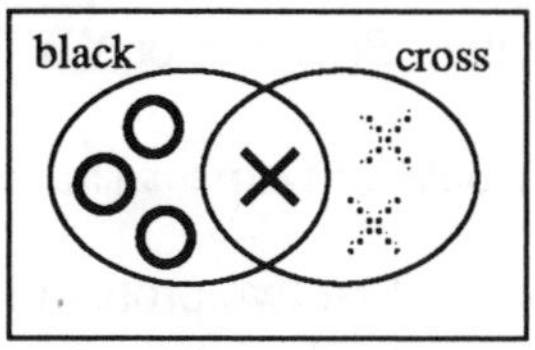

or

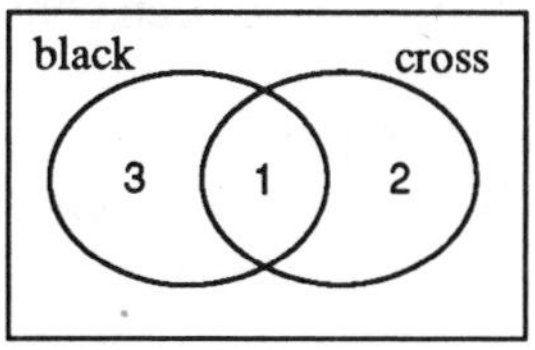

These are called **Venn diagrams** after *John Venn*, an English mathematician and churchman, who studied logic and taught at Cambridge.

What is the value of P(red and cross)?

You may have noticed that

$$P(\text{red and cross}) + P(\text{black and cross}) = P(\text{cross}).$$

If you were asked for the probability of a circle **and** a red symbol finishing uppermost from a single roll you should realise that

$$P(\text{red and cross}) = 0$$

as the two cannot happen at the same time. These are called **mutually exclusive** events as the occurrence of either excludes the possibility of the other one happening too.

Union

Eight teams are entered for a knock-out netball tournament and two of these are the YWCA and the Zodiac youth club.

What is the probability that the YWCA or Zodiac will reach the final?

('or' here means one or the other or both, more technically called the 'inclusive disjunction'.)

How the competition will run is shown opposite but until the draw is made no names can be entered.

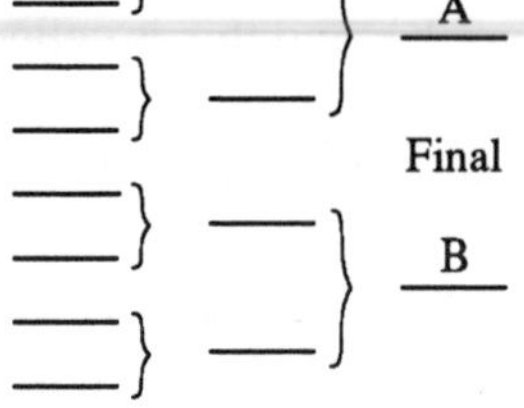

A diagram like the one you used earlier shows all the different possible ways in which the two final places A and B may be filled by the competing teams.

From the figure opposite you can see that

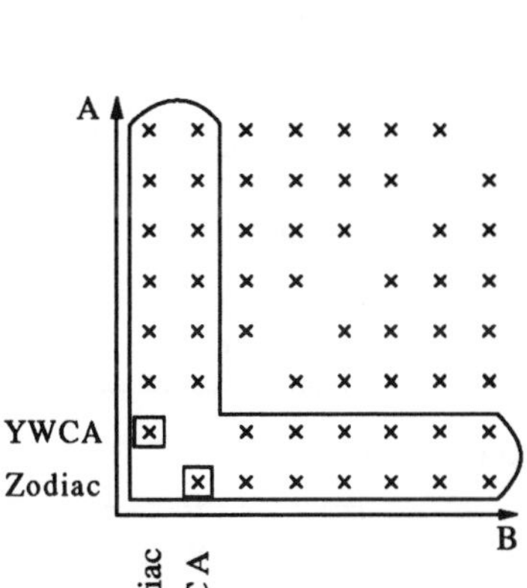

(a) $P(\text{Zodiac in final}) = \dfrac{14}{56}$

(b) $P(\text{YWCA in final}) = \dfrac{14}{56}$

(c) $P(\text{Zodiac or YWCA}) = \dfrac{26}{56}.$

Note that $P(\text{Zodiac or YWCA}) \neq P(\text{Zodiac}) + P(YWCA)$.

Why would you expect these not to be equal?

When the first two probabilities (a) and (b) were worked out, the two cases marked with squares in the diagram were included in each answer. When the probabilities are added together, these probabilities have been counted twice.

These correspond to the two ways of having both Zodiac and YWCA in the final. Their probability is given by

$$P(Z \text{ and } Y) = \frac{2}{56}$$

and you can see that

$$P(Z \text{ or } Y) = P(Z) + P(Y) - P(Z \text{ and } Y).$$

Taking off the $P(Z \text{ and } Y)$ ensures that these two events are not counted twice.

Checking with the figures you get

$$\frac{14}{56} + \frac{14}{56} - \frac{2}{56} = \frac{26}{56}$$

which is true.

Note that it is common to use the notation $P(Z \cup Y)$ for $P(Z \text{ or } Y)$, and this is called the **union** of events Z and Y.

Is it ever true that $P(A \text{ or } B) = P(A) + P(B)$?

If it is, then $P(A \text{ and } B)$ must be zero and this means that the events are what is called **mutually exclusive**. A Venn diagram could be drawn and would look like the one here with no overlap. So if

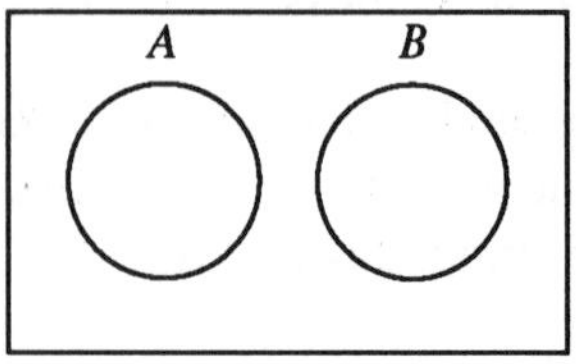

$$P(A \text{ and } B) = 0$$

then $$P(A \text{ or } B) = P(A) + P(B).$$

In general though,

$$\boxed{P(A \text{ or } B) = P(A) + P(B) - P(A \text{ and } B)}$$

and in set notation

$$\boxed{P(A \cup B) = P(A) + P(B) - P(A \cap B)}$$

and this can be illustrated by the Venn diagram opposite. The intersection of the two sets, $A \cap B$, is shown whilst the union, $A \cup B$, is given by everything inside A and B.

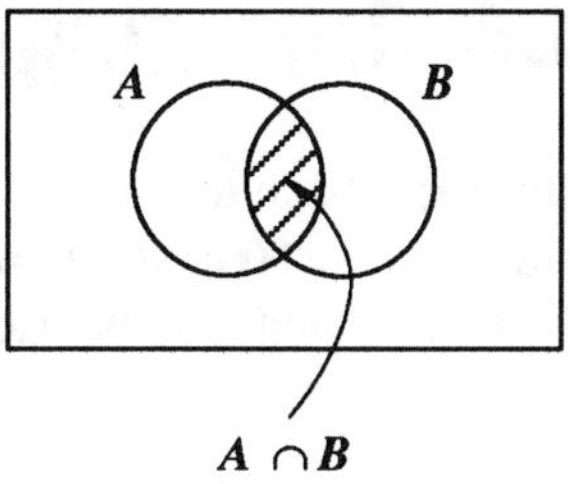

Exhaustive probabilities

The cube you looked at marked with crosses and circles had faces as shown opposite

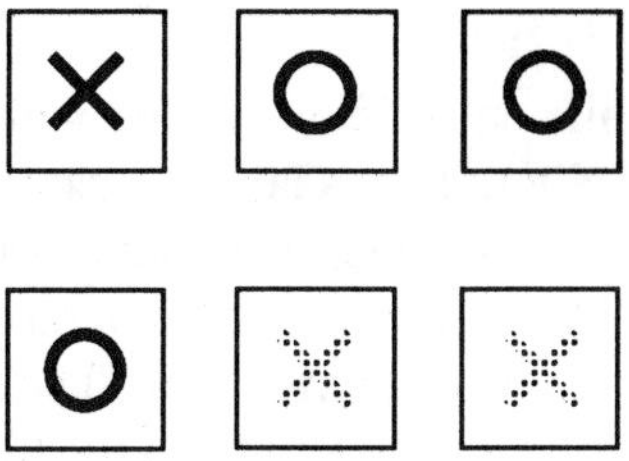

What is the value of $P(\text{black} \cup \text{cross})$?

Since each of six symbols was black or a cross then

$$P(\text{black} \cup \text{cross}) = 1$$

and the events 'getting a black symbol 'and 'getting a cross' are said to form a pair of **exhaustive events.** Between them they exhaust all the possible outcomes and therefore all the probability, i.e. one.

So, if A and B are exhaustive events, $P(A \text{ or } B) = 1$, or

$$\boxed{P(A \cup B) = 1}$$

Exercise 20C

1. In a class at school $\frac{1}{2}$ of the pupils represent the school at a winter sport, $\frac{1}{3}$ represent the school at a summer sport and $\frac{1}{10}$ do both. If a pupil is chosen at random from this group what is the probability that someone who represents the school at sport will be selected?
2. If the probability that Andrea will receive the maths prize this year is $\frac{1}{3}$ and the probability that Philson will win it is $\frac{1}{4}$, what is the chance that one of them will get it?
3. In a certain road $\frac{1}{5}$ of the houses have no newspapers delivered. If $\frac{1}{2}$ have a national paper and $\frac{2}{3}$ have a local paper, what is the probability that a house chosen at random has both?
4. Consider the following possible events when two dice, one red and one green, are rolled:

   A : the total is 3

   B : the red is a multiple of 2

   C : the total is ≤ 9

   D : the red is a multiple of 3

   E : the total is ≥ 11

   F : the total is ≥ 10.

   Which of the following pairs are exhaustive or mutually exclusive?

   (a) A, B (b) A, D (c) C, E

   (d) C, F (e) B, D (f) A, E

20.5 Tree diagrams

Another approach to some of the problems examined earlier would be to use **'tree diagrams'**. These are sometimes called decision trees and may be used in other subjects such as business studies.

Example

While on holiday, staying with Rachel in Kent in the South East, Gabrielle saw a very large black bird. Rachel noticed that it was, in fact, not all black and they looked in a bird book to find what it might have been. The facts they discovered are shown in the tree diagram opposite.

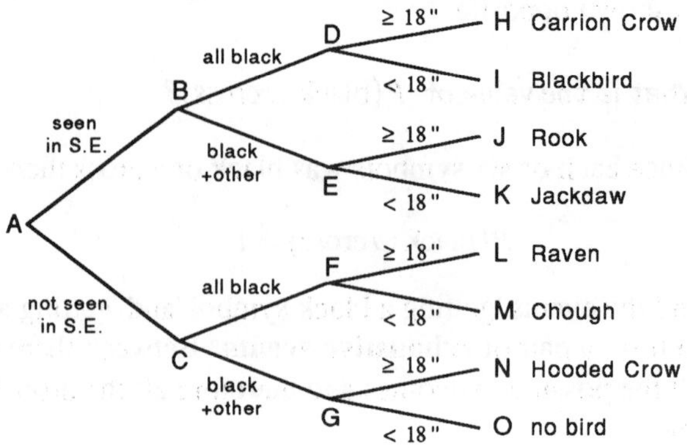

By following along the branches from the left to the right can you decide what they actually saw?

Solution

As they were in Kent you should have moved from A to B. Since the bird was not all black, B to E is the correct choice next, and if the bird was very large then E to J tells you it was a rook.

You can also use the tree diagram to find proportions and probabilities.

Example

If there are equal numbers of boys and girls in your school and you know that

$\frac{1}{4}$ of the boys and $\frac{1}{10}$ of the girls walk in every day,

$\frac{1}{3}$ of the boys and $\frac{1}{2}$ of the girls get a lift

and the rest come by coach, determine

(a) the proportion of the school population that are girls who come by coach;

(b) the proportion of the school population that come by coach.

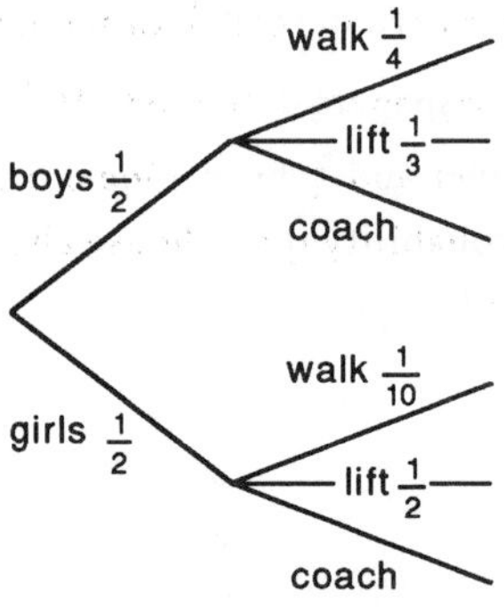

Solution

The branches have missing entries but these can be calculated from the facts already known. Since

$$\frac{1}{4} + \frac{1}{3} = \frac{7}{12}$$

of the boys have been accounted for, there remains $\frac{5}{12}$ who must use the coach.

Similarly, the proportion of girls going by coach is given by

$$1 - \left(\frac{1}{10} + \frac{1}{2}\right) = \frac{4}{10} = \frac{2}{5}.$$

All the values are entered on the diagram opposite, so that the answers to (a) and (b) are now easy to see.

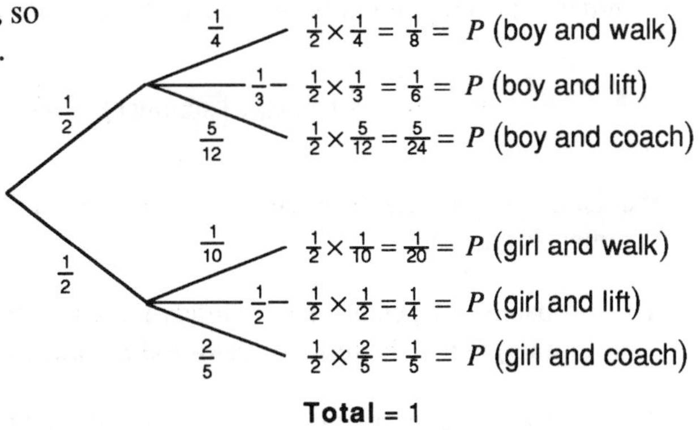

(a) $\frac{1}{2} \times \frac{2}{5} = \frac{1}{5}$

(b) $\frac{1}{5} + \frac{1}{2} \times \frac{5}{12} = \frac{49}{120}.$

Example

When Sam and Jo play in the hockey team the probability that Sam scores is $\frac{1}{3}$ and that Jo scores is $\frac{1}{2}$, regardless of whether or not Sam does.

What is the probability that neither will score in the next game?

Solution

The tree diagram opposite shows that the answer is $\frac{2}{3} \times \frac{1}{2} = \frac{1}{3}$.

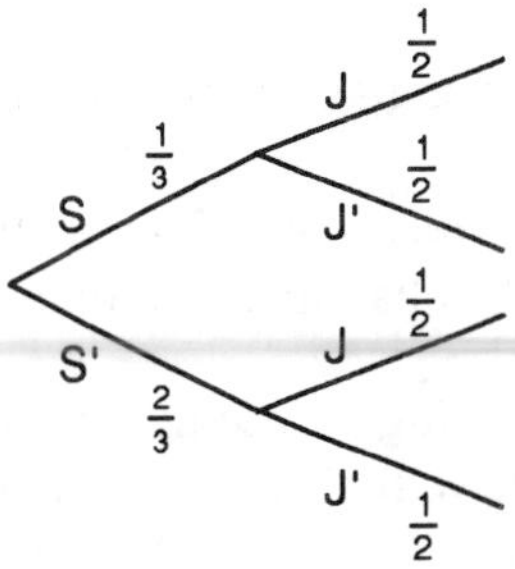

Exercise 20D

1. The probability that a biased die falls showing a six is $\frac{1}{4}$. The biased die is thrown twice.

   (a) Draw a tree diagram to illustrate the probabilities of 'throwing a six' or 'not throwing a six'.

   (b) Find the probability that exactly one six is obtained.

2. In each round of a certain game a player can score 1, 2, 3 only. Copy and complete the table which shows the scores and two of the respective probabilities of these being scored in a single round.

Score	1	2	3
Probability	$\frac{4}{7}$		$\frac{1}{7}$

3. A bag contains 7 black and 3 white marbles. Three marbles are chosen at random and in succession, each marble being replaced after it has been taken out of the bag.

   Draw a tree diagram to show all possible selections.

   From your diagram, or otherwise, calculate, to 2 significant figures, the probability of choosing:

   (a) three black marbles;

   (b) a white marble, a black marble and a white marble in that order;

   (c) two white marbles and a black marble in any order;

   (d) at least one black marble.

   State an event from this experiment which, together with the event described in (d), would be both exhaustive and mutually exclusive.

20.6 Conditional probability

Your assessment of how likely an event is to occur may well depend on some other event or variable. If you were asked, "What is the probability that it will rain next Monday?" your answer would depend on the time of year you were asked. If the question were in winter then $\frac{1}{2}$ might be a realistic assessment but in summer your reply might be $\frac{1}{10}$. This can be written

$$P(\text{rain next Monday} \mid \text{summer}) = \frac{1}{10},$$

that is, the probability of rain next Monday, given that it is summer, is one tenth.

This probability depends on a definitely known condition, (that is, it is summer) hence the term '**conditional probability**'.

As another example, consider the following problem:

If the probability of a school pupil wearing glasses is $\frac{1}{9}$, does it make any difference to how likely you think it is that the next one you see will wear glasses if you know that the pupil is female?

Is P (wearing glasses) **the same as** $P(\text{wearing glasses} \mid \text{female})$**?**

It should be possible to find out by considering a large sample, perhaps when having lunch or at a main entrance.

There is nothing new in the idea of conditional probability and you may well have realised that you have used it already. Conditional probabilities appeared on branches of the tree diagram to do with pupils' transport in the last section. The fractions on the branches after the initial ones were conditional probabilities as they definitely depended on the previous ones. The transport tree could have been labelled

$$B = \text{boy},\ G = \text{girl},\ W = \text{walk},\ L = \text{lift},\ C = \text{coach}.$$

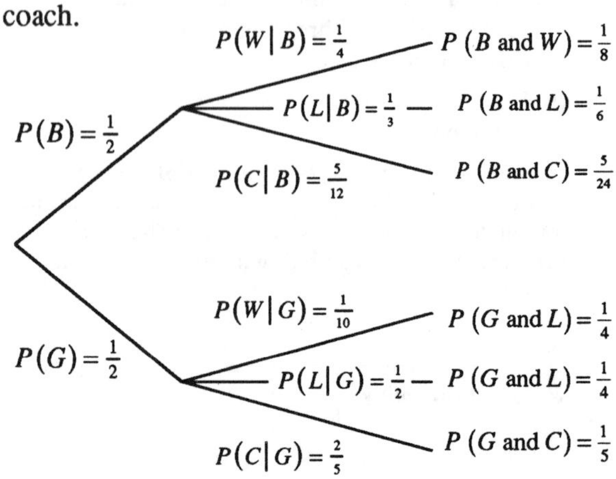

You can readily see that $P(B \text{ and } W) = \frac{1}{8}$

since $\quad P(B \text{ and } W) = \frac{1}{2} \times \frac{1}{4} = \frac{1}{8}.$

Now $\quad P(B) = \frac{1}{2}$, and $P(W \mid B) = \frac{1}{4}$,

leading to $\quad P(B \text{ and } W) = P(B) \times P(W \mid B)$

or $$P(W \mid B) = \frac{P(W \text{ and } B)}{P(B)}$$

This is a very useful equation when working with conditional probability and holds in general. That is, if A and B are two events,

then $$P(A \mid B) = \frac{P(A \text{ and } B)}{P(B)}$$

Example

If you roll two dice, one red and one green, what is the probability that the red one shows a six if the total on the two is 9?

Solution

Since you know that the total is 9 you need only look at the four crosses enclosed by the curve in the diagram opposite as they indicate all the possible ways of getting the 9 required. Now just considering these four, what is the chance that the red one shows 6?

$$P(r=6 \mid r+g=9) = \frac{1}{4}$$

as only one of the four crosses has a six on the red.

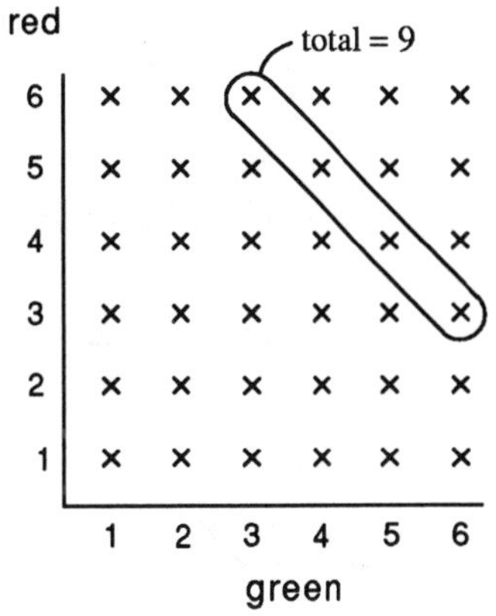

Example

Class 7C has 18 boys and 12 girls in it and 7K is made up of 12 boys and 16 girls. If you pick one of their registers and a pupil from it at random, what is the probability that you select

(a) a girl (b) from 7C if the choice is a girl?

Solution

(a) $$P(\text{girl}) = \frac{1}{2}\times\frac{2}{5}+\frac{1}{2}\times\frac{4}{7}$$

$$= \frac{1}{5}+\frac{2}{7} = \frac{17}{35}.$$

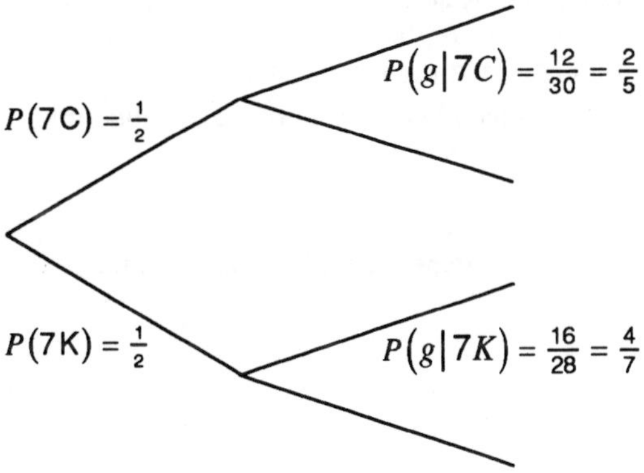

(b) $$P(7C \mid \text{girl}) = \frac{P(7C \text{ and girl})}{P(\text{girl})}$$

$$= \frac{\frac{1}{2}\times\frac{2}{5}}{\frac{17}{35}}$$

$$= \frac{1}{5} \div \frac{17}{35} = \frac{7}{17}.$$

You might wonder why the answer to (a) was not

$$\frac{\text{no. of girls}}{\text{no. of pupils}} = \frac{12+16}{30+28} = \frac{28}{58} = \frac{14}{29}.$$

Why does this argument give the wrong answer?

The reason this method does not produce the correct answer here is that the pupils are not all equally likely to be chosen. Each pupil in 7C has a probability of

$$\frac{1}{2} \times \frac{1}{30} = \frac{1}{60}$$

of being selected, but for those in 7K it is

$$\frac{1}{2} \times \frac{1}{28} = \frac{1}{56}.$$

Exercise 20E

1. Two cards are drawn successively from an ordinary pack of 52 playing cards and kept out of the pack. Find the probability that:
   (a) both cards are hearts;
   (b) the first card is a heart and the second card is a spade;
   (c) the second card is a diamond, given that the first card is a club.
2. A bag contains four red counters and six black counters. A counter is picked at random from the bag and not replaced. A second counter is then picked. Find the probability that:
   (a) the second counter is red, given that the first counter is red;
   (b) both counters are red;
   (c) the counters are of different colours.
3. The two events A and B are such that
   $$P(A) = 0.6,\ P(B) = 0.2,\ P(A|B) = 0.1.$$
   Calculate the probabilities that:
   (a) both of the events occur;
   (b) at least one of the events occur;
   (c) exactly one of the events occur;
   (d) B occurs, given that A has occurred.
4. In a group of 100 people, 40 own a cat, 25 own a dog and 15 own a cat and a dog. Find the probability that a person chosen at random:
   (a) owns a dog or a cat;
   (b) owns a dog or a cat, but not both;
   (c) owns a dog, given that he owns a cat;
   (d) does not own a cat, given that he owns a dog.

20.7 Independence

In the previous section the answer to, "What is the probability that it will rain next Monday?" depended on the fact that you were told or knew about the season.

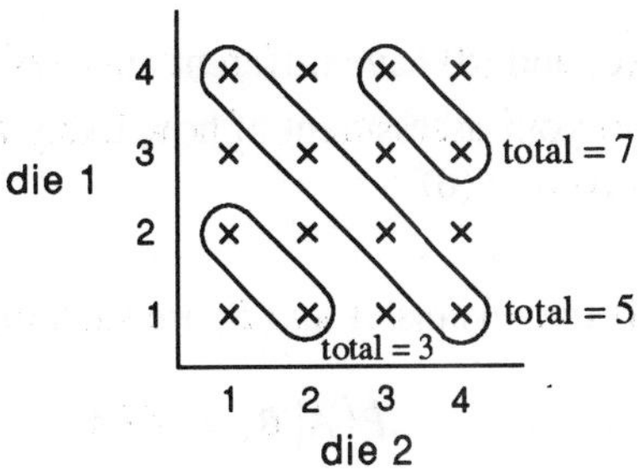

When two tetrahedral dice are rolled there are sixteen possible outcomes, as shown in the diagram opposite.

What is $P(\text{total}) = 7$?

Now if I tell you that my cat has a broken leg, what is

$$P\,(\text{total} = 7 \mid \text{my cat has a broken leg})?$$

The answer is $\frac{2}{16}$ to both of these questions.

The replies are the same because the two things discussed, the chance of a total of 7 and my cat having a broken leg, are independent. Other examples may not be as immediately obvious.

Example

What is the value of

(a) $P(\text{total} = 5)$ (b) $P(\text{total} = 5 \mid \text{red} = 2)$

(c) $P(\text{total} = 3)$ (d) $P(\text{total} = 3 \mid \text{red} = 2)$?

Solution

(a) From the sample space diagram above

$$P(\text{total} = 5) = \frac{4}{16} = \frac{1}{4}.$$

(b) Again $P(\text{total} = 5 \mid \text{red} = 2) = \dfrac{1}{4}$

since there is only one event (red = 2, green = 3) out of four possible events for red = 2.

(c) $P(\text{total} = 3) = \dfrac{2}{16} = \dfrac{1}{8}.$

(d) $P(\text{total} = 3 \mid \text{red} = 2) = \dfrac{1}{4}.$

The answers to (a) and (b) are both $\frac{1}{4}$, so the answer to ,"How likely is a total of 5?", is independent of (not affected by) the fact that you were told in (b) that the red score was 2.

(c) and (d) have different answers, however, $\frac{1}{8}$ and $\frac{1}{4}$ respectively, so your assessment of how likely a total of 3 is depends on the fact given in (d).

If two events, A and B, are such that

$$P(A|B) = P(A)$$

then they are said to be **independent**. Otherwise they are **dependent.**

In Section 20.5 there were examples of both cases. The tree diagram showing how pupils travelled to school included

$$P(\text{walk} \mid \text{boy}) = \frac{1}{4}$$

and $$P(\text{walk} \mid \text{girl}) = \frac{1}{10},$$

so how likely you think a pupil is to walk would depend on their sex.

On the other hand, in another example in Section 20.5, the chance of Jo scoring was not related to how likely Sam was to score so these events were independent. (In a tree diagram to show two events the branches are duplicated after each initial one if the second event is independent of the first.)

Example

In one year at school, 25 out of 154 failed the end of term maths exam. One class was particularly badly behaved and 7 out of 31 of them failed. Does bad behaviour in class affect how likely a pupil is to fail the test?

Solution

$$P(\text{fail}) = \frac{25}{154} = 0.162 \text{ (to 3 d.p.)}$$

$$P(\text{fail} \mid \text{badly behaved class}) = \frac{7}{31} = 0.226 \text{ (to 3 d.p.).}$$

Since these are certainly different the events are dependent, so the answer is 'Yes'.

Example

A family has three children. What is the probability that all three are the same sex? If you know at least two of them are girls what is the probability that they are all the same sex? Has this piece of information been of any help?

Solution

The possible combinations are shown below.

At least two girls	G	G	G	all same sex
At least two girls	G	G	B	
At least two girls	G	B	G	
	G	B	B	
At least two girls	B	G	G	
	B	G	B	
	B	B	G	
	B	B	B	all same sex

$$P(\text{all same sex}) = \frac{2}{8} = \frac{1}{4}$$

$$P(\text{all same sex} \mid \text{at least 2 girls}) = \frac{1}{4}.$$

So the events are independent, and the answer is 'No'.

Starting from the definition of independence,

$$P(A) = P(A \mid B)$$

$$= \frac{P(A \text{ and } B)}{P(B)}$$

$$\Rightarrow \quad P(A)\, P(B) = P(A \text{ and } B).$$

Testing to see whether or not $P(A) \times P(B)$ is, in fact, equal to $P(A \text{ and } B)$ can also be used as a test for independence. So in our last example,

$$P(\text{at least two girls}) = \frac{4}{8} = \frac{1}{2}$$

$$P(\text{all three the same sex}) = \frac{2}{8} = \frac{1}{4}$$

$$P(\text{at least two girls and all three the same sex}) = \tfrac{1}{8}.$$

Since $\frac{1}{2} \times \frac{1}{4} = \frac{1}{8}$ you can see that these events are independent.

If A and B are independent then the occurrence of B does not affect the likelihood of A happening and similarly it seems very likely that the non-occurrence of B should have no effect.

If A and B are independent, then

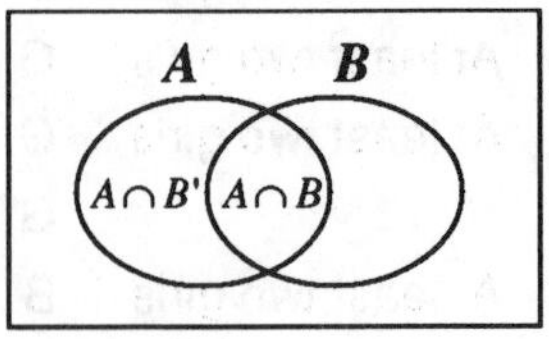

$$P(A \text{ and } B) = P(A)\,P(B)$$

$$P(A) - P(A \text{ and } B) = P(A) - P(A)\,P(B)$$

$$\Rightarrow \quad P(A \text{ and } B') = P(A) - P(A)\,P(B)$$

$$= P(A)\left(1 - P(B)\right)$$

$$\Rightarrow \quad P(A \text{ and } B') = P(A)\,P(B').$$

So A and B' are also independent.

Exercise 20F

1. A card is selected at random from an ordinary pack of 52. If

   A = the card is an ace

   D = the card is a diamond

   P = the card is a picture (Jack, Queen or King)

   R = the card is from a red suit

   X = the card is not the three of diamonds or the two of clubs,

   find the values of the following:

   (a) $P(A)$ (b) $P(A|D)$ (c) $P(D)$

   (d) $P(D|P)$ (e) $P(D|R)$ (f) $P(P)$

   (g) $P(P|A)$ (h) $P(P|A')$ (i) $P(A|X)$

   (j) $P(D|X')$ (k) $P(X|D)$ (l) $P(R|X)$

2. Decide which of the following pairs of events from Question 1 are independent:

   (a) A, D (b) D, P (c) P, A

   (d) R, X (e) D, R (f) D, R'

3. Work out the six probabilities on the branches labelled a to f and also the value of g.

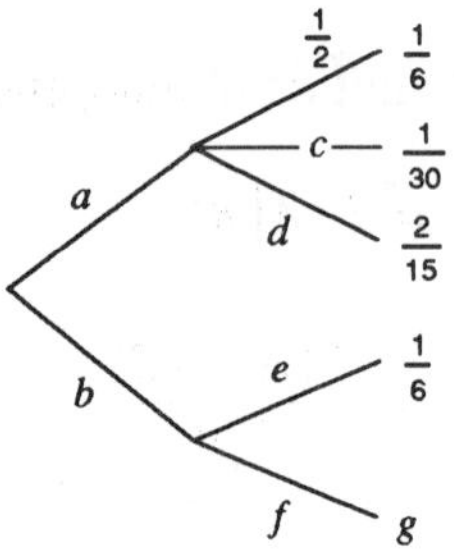

4. Two boxes, A and B, each contain a mixture of black discs and white discs. A contains 8 black and 7 white while B has 5 black and 7 white. A box is selected at random and a disc taken from it.

   Draw a tree diagram and calculate the probability that:

   (a) the disc is white;

   (b) the disc came from B if it is white.

5. A box contains 60 balls each of which is either red, blue or white. If the numbers of these are in the ratio 6:3:1 how many are there of each?

   By drawing a tree diagram, find the probability that when two balls are drawn at random together:

   (a) they are the same colour;

   (b) no red ball is drawn;

   (c) they are both white if you are told they are the same colour.

6. In a quiz competition the first question is worth one point and answered correctly with probability $\frac{5}{6}$. After any question is answered correctly the contestant receives one worth a point more than the previous one. After a wrong answer the contestant receives a one point question and two consecutive wrong answers eliminates the competitor.

   If the probabilities of correctly answering 2, 3 and 4 point questions are $\frac{4}{5}$, $\frac{3}{4}$ and $\frac{2}{3}$ respectively, calculate the probability that after four rounds the contestant has:

   (a) been eliminated;

   (b) scored at least six points.

7. In May, three mornings out of every five on average are fine.

   When the weather is fine Sarita walks to work with probability $\frac{1}{2}$, goes on the bus with probability $\frac{1}{3}$ and drives when she does not walk or use the bus. She never walks when the weather is wet and drives four times as often as she uses the bus. The probability of her arriving late when she walks in is $\frac{1}{2}$ and when she uses the bus it is $\frac{1}{4}$. She is always on time when she drives.

   On a particular May morning what is the probability that Sorita:

   (a) arrives on time;

   (b) travels by bus and is late?

   If she arrives late what is the probability that it is a fine morning?

20.8 Miscellaneous Exercises

1. One die has the numbers 1, 2, 3, 4, 5, 6 on its faces and another has 1, 1, 2, 2, 3, 3 on its faces. When the two are rolled together what is the probability that one of the scores will divide exactly into the other?

2. There are prizes for the first two runners home in a race with six competitors. What is the probability that:

   (a) both Dave and Raj will win prizes;

   (b) neither Dave nor Raj will win a prize?

3. A two digit number is written down at random. What is the probability that it:

   (a) is divisible by 5; (b) is divisible by 3;

   (c) is greater than 50; (d) is a square number?

4. When four coins are tossed together, what is the probability of at least three heads?

5. A counter starts at the point (0, 0). A coin is tossed and when a tail results it moves one unit to the right. When a head is seen it moves one unit upwards.

   What is the probability that after three goes it is still on the x-axis?

6. **Buffon's Needle** Take some ordinary pins and draw a set of straight parallel lines across a sheet of paper so that they are the same distance apart as the length of a pin. Drop ten pins onto the lined paper several times and record your results in the same way as in Section 20.2, noting how many lie across a line. Draw a graph and estimate the probability of a pin crossing a line when dropped.

7. **Off-centre spinner** Make a hexagonal spinner and put a cocktail stick or something similar through a point to divide AB in the ratio 2 : 3.

   What are the probabilities of the various scores?

8. Four unbiased coins are tossed together. For the events A to D below, say whether statements (a) to (e) are true or false and give a reason for each answer.

   A = no heads $\quad$ B = at least one head

   C = no tails $\quad$ D = at least two tails

(a) A and B are mutually exclusive;

(b) A and B are exhaustive;

(c) B and D are exhaustive;

(d) A' and C' are mutually exclusive.

9. In a class of 30 pupils, 17 have a dog, 19 have a cat and 5 have neither. If a member of the form is selected at random what is the probability that this pupil has both a cat and a dog?

10. The probability that Suleiman will be chosen to play in goal for the next match is $\frac{1}{4}$ and the probability that Paul will be selected for that position is $\frac{2}{5}$. Find the probability that:

(a) Suleiman or Paul will be selected to play in goal;

(b) neither of them will be asked to play in goal.

11. A number is to be formed by arranging the digits 1, 4, 7, and 8 in some order.

If A = the number is odd

and B = the number is greater than 4000,

find the value of:

(a) $P(A)$ (b) $P(B)$ (c) $P(B|A)$

(d) $P(A \cap B)$ (e) $P(A'|B)$.

12. John does $\frac{3}{5}$ of the jobs that come into the workshop and Dave does the rest. If 35% of John's work and 55% of Dave's work is perfect, find the probability that a job done in the workshop will be done:

(a) perfectly;

(b) by Dave if it was not done perfectly.

13. A warehouse receives 60% of its supplies from factory A, 30% from B and the rest from C.

A sends large, medium and small items in the ratio 1 : 3 : 2.

B's supplies are $\frac{1}{3}$ large size and no small size.

C provides three times as many medium as small items and no large ones.

If an item is selected at random from the warehouse, what is the probability that it is:

(a) medium;

(b) from B and large;

(c) from C if it is found to be medium?

14. A box contains 8 discs of which 5 are red and 3 are blue. One is selected at random and its colour noted. It is returned to the box together with an extra one of the other colour. This process is repeated twice more.

What is the probability that:

(a) the third disc selected is red;

(b) more reds are selected than blues;

(c) the third disc is red if there are more blues shown than reds?

15. At a fete, one of the games consists of throwing a 2p coin onto a large board of coloured squares, each 2 inches by 2 inches. If a coin lies completely within a single square it is returned to a player with another 2p, otherwise it goes to the organiser. A 2p coin has a diameter of 1 inch. By considering where the centre of the coin must land for a win, work out the player's probability of success.

How much money should the organiser expect to take in one hundred goes?

To make more profit, you could draw up a board to use with 10p coins. What size should the square be if the player is to have a probability of $\frac{1}{3}$ of winning? (Answer to the nearest mm.)

16. A circular spinner has three sections numbered 1, 2 and 3. If these numbers came up twenty-five, thirty and forty-five times in an experiment, what do you consider the likely values for the angles of the sectors?

17. Twenty discs numbered 1 to 20 are put at random into four boxes with five in each.

What is the probability that numbers 15 and 19 will be in the same box?

Would the answer be different if the discs had been split into five groups of four?

18. A forgetful teacher leaves his mark book in a room where he has had a lesson once in every three occasions on average. If he teaches three lessons in different rooms in the morning, what is the probability that:

(a) he will arrive at the lunch break having lost his mark book;

(b) he left it in the second room if he finished the morning without it?

19. Three bags, A, B and C, each contain three 5p coins and two 2p coins. A coin is selected at random from A and placed in B. A coin is drawn from B and put in C. Finally, a coin is drawn from bag C. Find the probability that:

(a) the coin selected from C is a 2p;

(b) the coin selected from A was a 5p if the one from C was a 2p.

Explain why the answer to (a) might have been expected. Repeat (a) for x 2p coins and y 5p coins, showing all your working.

20. Four girls each try to catch a ball and the probability that each will succeed is independently $\frac{2}{3}$.

    What is the probability that it will:

    (a) not be caught;

    (b) be caught?

21. Three students, Dave, Jane and Mary, share a house. Each of the girls is twice as likely as Dave to receive a telephone call in the evening. The probabilities that each will be out on any evening are independently $\frac{1}{2}$, $\frac{2}{5}$ and $\frac{3}{5}$ respectively. If the telephone rings one evening find the probability that the call is:

    (a) for Jane who is in;

    (b) for someone who is out;

    (c) for Dave given that it is for someone that is out.

22. Two gamblers play a game with two coins. The first tosses them and pays the second £1 for each head showing. Then the second has a turn and pays £1 for each tail showing. After each has had one go what is the probability that the first player has made a profit?

23. A school has three minibuses and the probability that each is free after school is independently $\frac{2}{5}$.

    Find the probability that after school on a particular day:

    (a) at least one minibus is free;

    (b) all the minibuses are free if at least one is free.

24. A set of dominoes consists of twenty eight pieces, each of which shows two sets of spots from zero to six, and no two dominoes are the same. A single domino is selected at random. Show the 28 possibilities on a diagram.

    What is the probability that:

    (a) the smaller number is 2;

    (b) it is a double;

    (c) it contains neither a 4 nor a 5?

25. Three coins are tossed. Event X is that at least one head and at least one tail result. Event Y is that at most one head shows. Are events X and Y independent?

21 MATHEMATICAL MODELLING

Objectives

After studying this chapter you should

- understand how mathematical models are formulated, solved and interpreted;
- appreciate the power and limitations of mathematics to solve practical problems.

21.0 Introduction

Throughout this text, you will have seen many techniques applied to a variety of problems. This has often involved setting up a mathematical model to describe the problem, and this concept was introduced in Section 1.2.

You now have many more mathematical techniques available to solve problems, and in this last chapter you will need to use many of them!

For each case study, the following procedure will be observed:

- specify the real problem
- set up a mathematical model
- determine the mathematical problem
- solve the mathematical problem
- interpret the solution
- use the solution or improve the model.

21.1 Stock control

Specify the real problem

In this case study you will consider a problem faced by management in industry. Every large organisation needs a policy for controlling its stock levels. The simple model for stock control considered here is fundamental to many large firms. Here is a particular example.

(i) Data on costs associated with stock handling are as follows. The **ordering cost** (cost of administrative processing) is estimated to be £25 per order. The annual **holding cost** of an item in store (mainly interest charges being paid on borrowed capital, or loss of interest which could be made on that capital if it were lent elsewhere) is assessed at 17% of the goods' price.

(ii) The ordering of stock is at the disposal of the person managing the stockholding, who must take two decisions:

- how much to order
- when to order.

(iii) The problem is to find the cheapest decisions.

Set up a model

If there were no systematic attempt to 'manage' the stock-keeping then ,for any particular item held in store, the graph of stock level against time would look like the graph opposite.

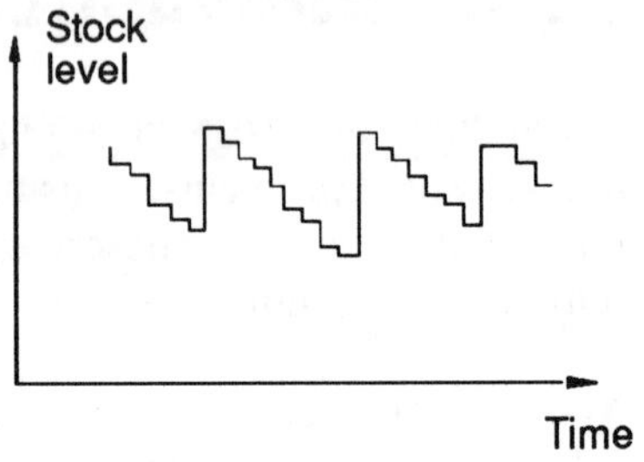

Each vertical jump upwards represents a re-stocking, and the downward 'staircases' represent usage of stock.

You can simplify and idealize the problem by making the following assumptions:

(a) that orders are placed at regular intervals, each order being for the same quantity;

(b) that the order is placed just as stocks run out (since holding cost increases with amount of stock held) and is filled instantaneously;

(c) that the rate of usage is constant and that the stock level can vary continuously.

These three assumptions may be summarized by their effect on the 'realistic' graph of stock level against time shown above. The 'idealized' graph is shown opposite. There is now a regular series of 'teeth' of height equal to the reorder quantity.

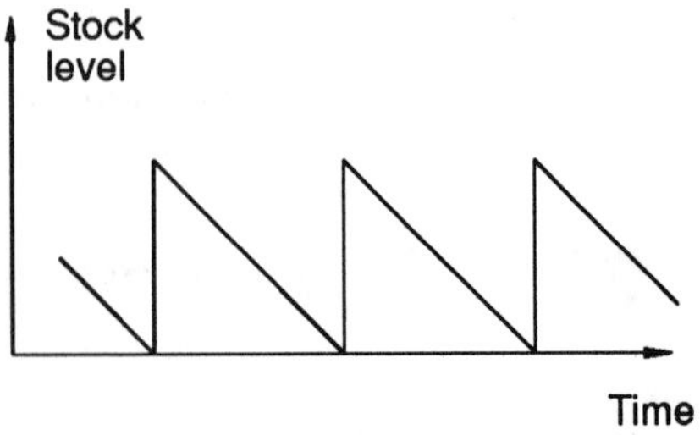

Formulate the mathematical problem

Introduce variables

Let the reorder quantity be q items and the rate of usage u items per year. The total annual cost (annual ordering cost plus annual holding cost) for the stock is denoted by £y, and the (constant) price of each individual item by £P.

Relate the variables

Total annual cost has been defined as annual ordering cost plus annual holding cost. From the data given above

ordering cost per order = £25, and

annual holding cost per item = 17% of its cost price

= £(0.17P).

Rate of usage is u items per year, and there are q items in each order. The annual number of orders placed is therefore u/q, so that

$$\text{annual ordering cost} = £\left\{25 \times \frac{u}{q}\right\}$$

The 'idealized' graph shows that stock level drops from q to 0 at a uniform rate between successive orders. It follows that the average stock level is $\frac{1}{2}q$ items. Each item held costs £(0.17P) per year. Hence

$$\text{annual holding cost for entire stock} = £\left(0.17P \times \frac{1}{2}q\right)$$

The total annual cost, £ y, can be expressed in terms of P, q and u:

$$\boxed{y = \frac{25u}{q} + \frac{0.17Pq}{2}}$$

Mathematical problem

In the boxed formula above, P and u are assumed constant. The mathematical problem is to find a positive value of q which minimises y if such exists.

Solve the mathematical problem

The graph of the function y has a minimum for a positive value of q, as illustrated opposite.

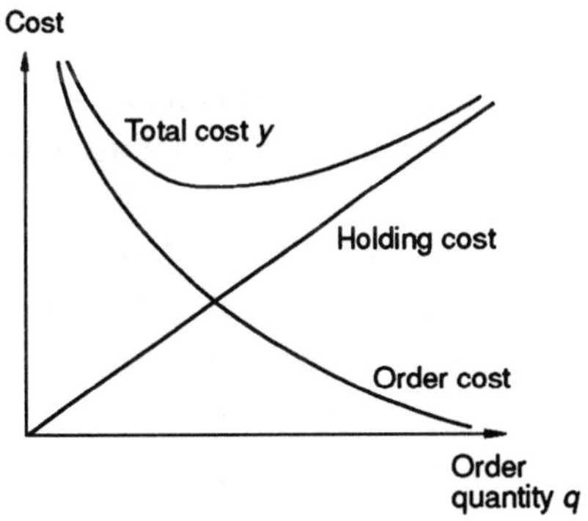

To find the stationary point, you differentiate y with respect to q, remembering that P and u are constants. This gives

$$\frac{dy}{dq} = -\frac{25u}{q^2} + \frac{0.17P}{2}$$

The value of q for which $\frac{dy}{dq}$ is zero is given by the equation

$$-\frac{25u}{q^2}+\frac{0.17P}{2}=0\ .$$

This gives the solution for q as

$$\boxed{q=\sqrt{\frac{2\times 25u}{0.17P}}}$$

Interpret the solution

The optimal order quantity is given as

$$\sqrt{\frac{2\times 25\times \text{annual usage}}{0.17\times\ \text{cost price per item}}}$$

More generally, the optimal order quantity is

$$\sqrt{\frac{2\times \text{ordering cost}\times \text{annual usage}}{\text{holding cost per item}}}$$

so that

(a) higher holding cost (higher price) means a smaller optimal order quantity;

(b) higher annual usage implies a larger optimal order quantity, but (for example) it takes a four-fold increase in usage to double the optimal order quantity.

The two qualitative predictions agree with what one would expect.

Improve the model

The model contains some unrealistic features for which allowance should be made.

(a) It assumes that orders are placed at the moment stock runs out, and that they are instantaneously satisfied. There is in fact a gap, called the lead time, between the placing of an order and goods' arrival.

(b) Stock may be allowed to run out before restocking (the associated run-out cost can be assessed and traded off against the reduced holding cost).

(c) Demand is not steady.

(d) Prices vary with time.

Incorporating these features would make the mathematics vastly more complicated, and it is often a balance between realism and complex mathematics that has to be sought.

Activity 1 Using the model

Find the optimal order quantity when $P = 2$ and

(a) $u = 50000$ (b) $u = 5000$ (c) $u = 500$.

In each case, also find the number of orders made per year.

21.2 Dipstick

Specify the real problem

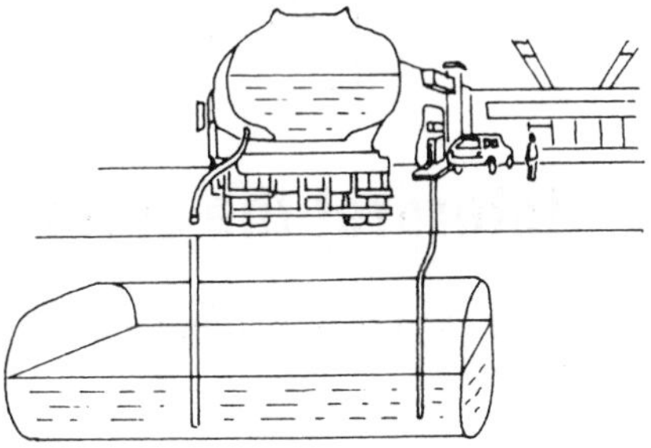

Petrol stations very rarely run out of petrol. This is due partly to efficient deliveries but also to precise stock control.

Each type of petrol (4 star, unleaded, diesel) is stored in an underground tank and the amount left in each tank is carefully monitored using some form of dipstick.

Our problem is to design the calibration on a dipstick.

Set up a model

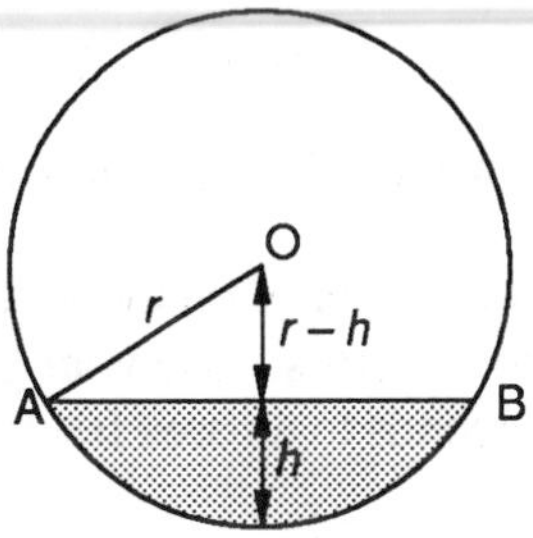

It is easy to measure the **height**, say *h*, left in the tank. However, the volume will be proportional to the **cross-sectional area** - not the height. Suppose the cross-section is a circle (it is in fact elliptical). You will need to find the relationship between the shaded area , *A*, and the height, *h*, and so provide a ready reckoner to convert height to area.

Formulate the mathematical problem

For simplicity, take $r = 1$ m. For values of *h* from 0 to 1.0, you need to find the angle, θ, and hence the cross-sectional area of oil.

Solve the mathematical problem

You can see that, with θ in degrees,

$$\cos\theta = \frac{r-h}{r} = 1 - h \quad (\text{since } r = 1)$$

The area of the sector OAB is given by

$$\left(\frac{2\theta}{360}\right)\times\pi\times1^2=\frac{\pi\theta}{180}$$

whereas the area of the triangle OAB is given by

$$2\times\left(\frac{1}{2}\times(1-h)\times1\sin\theta\right)=(1-h)\sin\theta .$$

Hence the cross-sectional area of oil is given by

$$\frac{\pi\theta}{180}-(1-h)\sin\theta$$

The whole cross-sectional area of the tank is π, so the fraction A' of the whole area which corresponds to the oil is given by

$$A'=\frac{\theta}{180}-\frac{(1-h)}{\pi}\sin\theta$$

Interpret the solution

You can use this formula to complete a ready reckoner.

Activity 2

Complete the task opposite by using the equation

$$\cos\theta=1-h$$

to determine θ for given h, and the formula above to find A'.

Plot a graph of A' on the vertical axis against height h on the horizontal cross. Use your graph to estimate the height that corresponds to an area fraction of

(a) 0.05 (b) 0.10.

h	$\theta°$	A'
0	0	0
0.1	25.84	0.019
0.2	36.87	0.052
...	...	...
...	...	...
1.0	90	0.500

You are now in a position to design the dipstick. Part of it is shown opposite. The height on the left hand side is linear, whereas the area fraction is not. Since $h=0.2$ corresponds to $A'=0.05$ approximately, you can see that $A'=0.05$ is indicated at the same level as $h=0.2$.

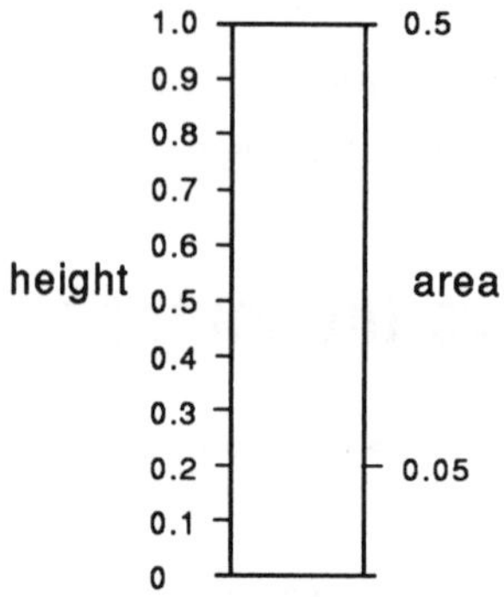

Activity 3

Use your graph to find the values of h which correspond to $A' = 0.1, 0.15, 0.2, \ldots, 0.45$, and use these values to complete the dipstick calibration.

21.3 Dicey games

Specify the real problem

Throw 3 dice
Entry Fee : 10p
Win
£1 for 18
50p for 17, 16, 15
20p for 14, 13, 12

You have to organise a game of chance at the school fete in which contestants pay a 10p entry fee to roll three dice. The total score is recorded and there are money prizes for high scores. The problem is to decide whether these prizes will give sufficient incentive for people to enter the game, and sufficiently low for you, the organiser to make a profit!

Set up a model

The model here is straightforward - you associate a probability of $\frac{1}{6}$ with obtaining any number 1, 2, ..., 6 with **one** roll of a dice.

Formulate the mathematical problem

The mathematical problem is to determine the expected winnings/ losses for a contestant.

Solve the mathematical problem

To find the expected winnings, you must find the probabilities of obtaining a total score of 18, 17, ..., 12 since these are the scores which attract a prize.

What is the probability of obtaining 18?

Activity 4

Complete the table below which gives the probabilities of a total sum of 3, 4, ... 18.

3	4	5	6	7	8	9	10	11	12	13	14	15	16	17	18
$\frac{1}{216}$													$\frac{6}{216}$	$\frac{3}{216}$	$\frac{1}{216}$

(Check that your sum of the probabilities is 1.)

With these values for the probabilities you can now determine the expected winnings/losses for a contestant. They will win

£1 with a probability of $\frac{1}{216}$

50p with a probability of $\frac{19}{216}$

20p with a probability of $\frac{61}{216}$

Check from your table in Activity 4 the values $\frac{19}{216}$, $\frac{61}{216}$ used above.

So the contestant has an expected profit/loss, in pence, of

$$100 \times \frac{1}{216} + 50 \times \frac{19}{216} + 20 \times \frac{61}{216} - 10$$

$$= \frac{2270}{216} - 10$$

$$= \frac{110}{216}$$

$$\approx \tfrac{1}{2}\text{p}.$$

Interpret the solution

Since, on average, a participant will win $\frac{1}{2}$p, if 100 people play the game during the fete, you will expect to lose about

$$100 \times \tfrac{1}{2}\text{p} = 50\text{p}$$

which will not be of much help to the school funds!

Improve the model

Its not really the model that needs improving, but the money prizes on offer.

Activity 5

Suggest new prizes so that on average a contestant will lose about 5p per game.

21.4 Postscript

The three case studies in this chapter should be sufficient to show you that applying maths can be very useful, but this is not the whole story. The real world is a very complex system and it is up to mathematicians to use their knowledge and skills to help the human race to find optimum solutions to problems.

The ability to perform and understand mathematical techniques and concepts is something to be proud of and to nurture throughout your life. It can at times be frustrating when, for example, integrals do not work out – but the delight and joy in completing a mathematical task correctly is an experience that no one can take away!

APPENDIX : PARTIAL FRACTIONS

Given the expression $\frac{1}{x-2}-\frac{1}{x+4}$ and asked to find its integral, you can use work from Section 14.4 to give

$$\int\left(\frac{1}{x-2}-\frac{1}{x+4}\right)dx=\ln(x-2)-\ln(x+4)+c$$

$$=\ln\left(k\frac{(x-2)}{x+4}\right) \quad (c=\ln k)$$

If the same problem had been presented as

$$\int\frac{6}{x^2+2x-8}dx$$

this may have caused some difficulty.

However, since $\frac{6}{x^2+2x-8}\equiv\frac{1}{x-2}-\frac{1}{x+4}$ you can 'solve' the problem. Writing

$$\frac{6}{x^2+2x-8}\equiv\frac{1}{x-2}-\frac{1}{x+4}$$

means that you have expressed $\frac{6}{x^2+2x-8}$ in **partial fractions.**

Expressing a function of the form $\frac{1}{g(x)}$ when $g(x)$ is a polynomial in x in terms of its partial fraction is a very useful method which enables you to evaluate $\int\frac{1}{g(x)}dx$. So firstly you need to find out how to find partial fractions. The approach is illustrated in the following example.

Example

Writing

$$\frac{x-1}{(3x-5)(x-3)}=\frac{A}{(3x-5)}+\frac{B}{(x-3)}$$

find the values of A and B.

Solution

If the previous equation is true, then multiplying both sides by the denominator gives

$$x-1=A(x-3)+B(3x-5)$$

This must hold for **any** value of x. So, for example, if $x=3$, then

$$(3-1)=A(3-3)+B(9-5)$$

$$\Rightarrow \quad 2=4B$$

$$\Rightarrow \quad B=\tfrac{1}{2}$$

Similarly, $x=\tfrac{5}{3}$ gives

$$\tfrac{5}{3}-1=A(\tfrac{5}{3}-3)+B(5-5)$$

$$\Rightarrow \quad \tfrac{2}{3}=-\tfrac{4}{3}A$$

$$\Rightarrow \quad A=-\tfrac{1}{2}$$

So $$\frac{x-1}{(3x-5)(x-3)}=\frac{-\frac{1}{2}}{(3x-5)}+\frac{\frac{1}{2}}{(x-3)}$$

You can check this by putting the R.H.S. over a common denominator:

$$\begin{aligned}\text{R.H.S.}&=\frac{-\frac{1}{2}(x-3)+\frac{1}{2}(3x-5)}{(3x-5)(x-3)}\\&=\frac{-\frac{1}{2}x+\frac{3}{2}+\frac{3}{2}x-\frac{5}{2}}{(3x-5)(x-3)}\\&=\frac{x-1}{(3x-5)(x-3)}\end{aligned}$$

Also note that an alternative to substituting values in the identity

$$x-1=A(x-3)+B(3x-5)$$

is to compare coefficients. So for 'x' terms,

$$[x] \quad 1=A+3B$$

and for the constant term

$$[\text{ct}] \quad -1=-3A-5B$$

These two equations can be solved for A and B.

Check that $a = -\frac{1}{2}$, $B = \frac{1}{2}$ satisfies both equations.

Activity 1

(a) By writing $\dfrac{1}{(x+4)(x-5)}$ as $\dfrac{A}{x+4} + \dfrac{B}{x-5}$ show that

$$1 = A(x-5) + B(x+4)$$

and hence find the values of A and B.

(b) By writing $\dfrac{2x+1}{(x-4)(x+1)}$ as $\dfrac{A}{x-4} + \dfrac{B}{x+1}$ find the values of A and B and hence express $\dfrac{2x+1}{(x-4)(x+1)}$ in partial fractions.

(c) Express $\dfrac{11x+12}{(2x+3)(x+2)(x-3)}$ in partial fractions of the form

$$\frac{A}{2x+3} + \frac{B}{x+2} + \frac{C}{x-3}.$$

A quadratic expression in the denominator cannot always be expressed in terms of linear factors, for example $\dfrac{1}{x^2+1}$ or $\dfrac{2x+1}{x^2+3}$.

Now $\dfrac{2x+1}{x^2+3}$ could be written as $\dfrac{2x}{x^2+3} + \dfrac{1}{x^2+3}$; this would suggest that when writing an expression where one of the factors is quadratic, there may be two unknowns to find.

For example, $\dfrac{2x+1}{(x-3)(x^2+3)}$ could be written as

$$\frac{A}{x-3} + \frac{Bx}{x^2+3} + \frac{C}{x^2+3} = \frac{A}{x-3} + \frac{Bx+C}{x^2+3}$$

and multiplying both sides by $(x-3)(x^2+3)$

gives $\quad 2x+1 = A(x^2+3) + (Bx+C)(x-3)$

or $\quad 2x+1 = x^2(A+B) + x(C-3B) + 3(A-C).$

Activity 2

Find the values of A, B and C for the expression above.

Activity 3

Express in terms of partial fractions

$$\frac{6x^2-13}{(x-1)(x-2)\left(x^2+x+5\right)}$$

You should note the result that

$$\int \frac{2x}{x^2+a^2}\,dx = \ln\left(x^2+a^2\right)+c$$

as this will be very useful in integrating partial fractions.

Activity 4

Verify the result above by differentiating the R.H.S. and showing that it is equal to the integral.

Example

Find $\displaystyle\int \frac{(3-x)}{(x+1)\left(x^2+3\right)}\,dx$

Solution

You must first find the partial fractions by writing

$$\frac{(3-x)}{(x+1)\left(x^2+3\right)} = \frac{A}{(x+1)} + \frac{Bx+C}{\left(x^2+3\right)}$$

This gives

$$3-x = A\left(x^2+3\right)+(Bx+C)(x+1)$$

Substituting

$$x=-1 \quad \Rightarrow \quad 4=4A \quad \Rightarrow \quad A=1$$

$$\left[x^2\right] \quad \Rightarrow \quad 0=A+B \quad \Rightarrow \quad B=-1$$

$$[\text{ct}] \quad \Rightarrow \quad 3=3A+C \quad \Rightarrow \quad C=0$$

Hence

$$\int \frac{(3-x)}{(x+1)(x^2+3)}dx = \int \frac{1}{(x+1)} - \frac{x}{(x^2+3)}dx$$

$$= \ln(x+1) - \tfrac{1}{2}\ln(x^2+3) + C$$

Activity 5

Find $\displaystyle\int \frac{(4+3x)}{(x-3)(x^2+4)}dx$

One further case arises when a quadratic expression in the denominator does **not** factorise. You can regard this case as optional.

A further complication arises when there is a repeated factor. For example,

$$\frac{1}{(x+2)(x-1)^2}$$

What form will the partial fraction take?

Here you can write

$$\frac{1}{(x+2)(x-1)^2} = \frac{A}{(x+2)} + \frac{B}{(x-1)} + \frac{C}{(x-1)^2}$$

For multiplying throughout by $(x+2)(x-1)^2$ gives

$$1 = A(x-1)^2 + B(x+2)(x-1) + C(x+2)$$

and, for

$$x=1 \quad \Rightarrow \quad 1 = C.3 \quad \Rightarrow \quad C = \tfrac{1}{3}$$

$$x=-2 \quad \Rightarrow \quad 1 = A(-3)^2 \quad \Rightarrow \quad A = \tfrac{1}{9}$$

$$[x^2] \quad\quad 0 = A + B \quad \Rightarrow \quad B = -\tfrac{1}{9}$$

So $\displaystyle\frac{1}{(x+2)(x-1)^2} = \frac{\tfrac{1}{9}}{(x+2)} - \frac{\tfrac{1}{9}}{(x-1)} + \frac{\tfrac{1}{3}}{(x-1)^2}$

Example

Integrate $\displaystyle\frac{1}{(x+2)(x-1)^2}$

Solution

You have already seen that

$$\frac{1}{(x+2)(x-1)^2} = \frac{\frac{1}{9}}{(x+2)} - \frac{\frac{1}{9}}{(x-1)} + \frac{\frac{1}{3}}{(x-1)^2}$$

So that

$$\int \frac{1}{(x+2)(x-1)^2}\,dx = \int \frac{\frac{1}{9}}{(x+2)}\,dx - \int \frac{\frac{1}{9}}{(x-1)}\,dx + \int \frac{\frac{1}{3}}{(x-1)^2}\,dx$$

$$= \frac{1}{9}\ln(x+2) - \frac{1}{9}\ln(x-1) - \frac{1}{3}.\frac{1}{x-1} + k$$

$$= \frac{1}{9}\ln\left(\frac{x+2}{x-1}\right) - \frac{1}{3(x-1)} + k$$

(since $\ln A - \ln B = \ln\left(\frac{A}{b}\right)$)

The method can be further extended to factors of higher degree than 2. So, for example, suppose

$$f(x) = \frac{1}{(x-1)^2(x+2)^2}$$

What form will the partial fraction take?

In all the examples so far considered of the form

$$\frac{f(x)}{g(x)}$$

when f and g are both polynomials in x, it has always been the case that the degree of f is less than the degree of g. So if g is a quadratic function, the methods so far can deal with the case where f is of the form

$$f(x) = a + bx \qquad (a, b \text{ constants})$$

But suppose f is also a quadratic function.

What happens when both f and g are quadratic expressions?

The method will be illustrated with an example.

Example

Express $\dfrac{x^2+5}{x^2-5x+6}$ in terms of its partial fraction.

Hence find the value of

$$\int_4^5 \frac{x^2+5}{x^2-5x+6}\,dx$$

Solution

You can write

$$\frac{x^2+5}{x^2-5x+6} = \frac{x^2+5}{(x-3)(x-2)}$$

$$= A + \frac{B}{(x-3)} + \frac{C}{(x-2)}$$

Multiplying throughout by $(x-3)(x-2)$ gives

$$x^2+5 = A(x-3)(x-2) + B(x-2) + C(x-3)$$

and

$$\begin{array}{llllll} x=2 & \Rightarrow & 9 = C(-1) & \Rightarrow & C=-9 \\ x=3 & \Rightarrow & 14 = B(1) & \Rightarrow & B=14 \\ [x^2] & & 1 = A & \Rightarrow & A=1 \end{array}$$

Hence

$$\frac{x^2+5}{x^2-5x+6} = 1 + \frac{14}{x-3} - \frac{9}{x-2}$$

and

$$\int_4^5 \frac{x^2+5}{x^2-5x+6}\,dx = \int_4^5 1\,dx + 14\int_4^5 \frac{1}{x-3}\,dx - 9\int_4^5 \frac{1}{x-2}\,dx$$

$$= [x]_4^5 + 14[\ln(x-3)]_4^5 - 9[\ln(x-2)]_4^5$$

$$= (5-4) + 14(\ln 2 - \ln 1) - 9(\ln 3 - \ln 2)$$

$$= 1 + 23\ln 2 - 9\ln 3$$

Activity 6

Express $\frac{x^2+x+1}{\left(x^2-1\right)}$ in partial fractions and hence find

$$\int \frac{x^2+x+1}{\left(x^2-1\right)}\,dx$$

Returning to the general case of $\frac{f(x)}{g(x)}$, consider now what happens if the degree of $f(x)$ is greater than that of $g(x)$. For example,

$$\frac{x^3+x^2-1}{\left(x^2-4\right)}$$

What form will the partial fractions take for the above function?

Activity 7

Find $\int \frac{x^3+x^2-1}{\left(x^2-4\right)}\,dx$

Finally in this section it should also be noted that expressing in terms of partial fractions can be helpful in differentiation as well as integration.

Activity 8

By putting $y=\frac{x+1}{(x-2)(x+5)}$ into partial fractions, obtain

(a) $\frac{dy}{dx}$ (b) $\frac{d^2y}{dx^2}$ (c) $\frac{d^ny}{dx^n}$

Exercise

1. Express in partial fractions

   (a) $\dfrac{x}{(2-x)(1+x)}$ (b) $\dfrac{3x-1}{(3x+1)(x-2)}$

   (c) $\dfrac{2x}{x^2+2x-3}$ (d) $\dfrac{3}{(x-2)^2(x+2)}$

   (e) $\dfrac{2x^2-3}{x\left(x^2+2\right)}$ (f) $\dfrac{x^2+2x}{x^2-9}$

   (g) $\dfrac{1}{(x-1)^2(x+1)}$ (h) $\dfrac{3x}{(x+3)\left(x^2+1\right)}$

2. Evaluate $\displaystyle\int_3^4 \frac{2x-1}{(x-2)(5-x)}\,dx$

3. Evaluate $\displaystyle\int_0^{\frac{3}{4}} \frac{1-x}{(x+1)\left(x^2+1\right)}\,dx$

4. Find $\displaystyle\int \frac{2x^2+2x+3}{(x+2)\left(x^2+3\right)}\,dx$

5. Find $\displaystyle\int \frac{x^3+2x^2-10x-9}{(x-3)(x+3)}\,dx$

ANSWERS

The answers to the questions set in the Exercises are given below. Answers to questions set in some of the Activities are also given where appropriate.

1 THE NATURE OF MATHEMATICS

Activity 3

28

Exercise 1A

1. (a) $-11^\circ C$ (b) $-5^\circ C$ (c) $-18^\circ C$
2. 1016; 181.7 cm
5. (a) 4 (b) 5
6. (a) No (b) Yes

Exercise 1B

1. $r \approx 5.42$ cm, $h \approx 10.84$ cm
3. Competitor number 6
4. $a=2$, $b=2$

Exercise 1C

1. (a) 4.2×10 (b) 4.2×10^{-1} (c) 1.57×10^{-2}
   (d) 1.952×10^{2} (e) 2.38796×10^{3} (f) 2.8×10^{-3}
2. (a) 2700 (b) 0.0352 (c) 0.701
   (d) 56.5
4. (a) 1.152×10^{-2} (b) 1.37548×10^{0}
   (c) 3.5853×10^{-2}
6. 6.696×10^{8} mph; 5.866×10^{12} miles/year
7. 3.9×10^{4} km

2 USING GRAPHS

Activity 1

(a) 262.5 Fr (b) £21.21 (c) 289.7 Fr
(a) 241.5 Fr (b) £19.21 (c) 268.7 Fr

Activity 2

(a) $86^\circ F$ (b) $50^\circ F$ (c) $38^\circ F$

Activity 4

(a) $x\neq5$ (b) $x\neq1$ (c) $x\geq2$
(d) all x (e) $x\neq0$ (f) $x\neq1$

Exercise 2A

1. (a) 6 (b) 3 (c) 2
   (d) a^2+2 (e) $(1-a)^2+2$
2. (a) 1 (b) -1 (c) does not exist
   (d) $\frac{1}{a^2}$ $(a\neq0)$ (e) $\frac{1}{(1-a)}$ $(a\neq1)$

Exercise 2B

1. (a) odd (b) odd (c) neither
   (d) even
3. (a) odd (b) neither (c) neither
   (d) even (e) even

Miscellaneous Exercises

1. 31.5
2. (a) $x\neq0$; $0<f(x)$
   (b) $x>3$; $0<f(x)$
   (c) $x\leq6$; $0\leq f(x)$
   (d) $x\neq2,-3$; $0<f(x)$ and $f(x)\leq-0.16$
3. (a) Yes (b) No (c) Yes
   (d) Yes (e) Yes
4. (a) $-\frac{1}{8}$ (b) $-\frac{1}{7}$ (c) $-\frac{1}{9}$ (d) $-\frac{1}{16}$
5. (a) neither (b) odd (c) even

3 FUNCTIONS

Activity 1

Only $x=1$

Exercise 3A

1. (a) $f_0 g = x^3 - 1$, $\quad g_0 f = (x-1)^3$

   (b) $f_0 g = \sqrt{x-2}$, $\quad g_0 f = \sqrt{x} - 2$

   (c) $f_0 g = \frac{1}{x+1}$, $\quad g_0 f = \frac{1}{x} + 1$

   (d) $f_0 g = \frac{1}{x^2} - 1$, $\quad g_0 f = \frac{1}{x^2 - 1}$

   (e) $f_0 g = x$, $g_0 f = x$

   (f) $f_0 g = x$, $g_0 f = x$

2. $f_0 g = 1 + \frac{1}{x^2}$, $g_0 f = \left(1 + \frac{1}{x}\right)^2$

3. $h_0 g_0 f = \frac{1}{x^2 - 3}$

Activity 2

$$R = \left(\frac{T}{k}\right)^{\frac{2}{3}}$$

Exercise 3B

1. $x-2$
2. $\frac{1}{4}(x+1)$
3. $\frac{1}{4}(x+2)$
4. x
5. $1-x$
6. $\frac{3}{x}$, $(x \neq 0)$
7. $\frac{1}{x} - 2$, $(x \neq 0)$
8. $5 - \frac{1}{(x-2)}$, $(x \neq 2)$

Activity 4

$f^{-1}(x) = \frac{1}{4}(x+3)$

Exercise 3D

1. many to one
2. one to one
3. many to one
4. many to one
5. many to one
6. one to one
7. one to one
8. many to one

Exercise 3E

2. 6000 tonnes; every 7 days; zero stock level reached

Miscellaneous Exercises

1. (a) $f^{-1}(x) = \frac{1}{3}(x+2)$

   (b) $f^{-1}(x) = \frac{1}{3}(4-x)$

   (d) $f^{-1}(x) = \sqrt{x+1}$, $(x \geq -1)$

   (f) $f^{-1}(x) = \frac{1}{(x+4)}$, $(x \neq -4)$

4 GRAPH TRANSFORMS

Exercise 4B

2. (a) unaltered

   (b), (c) and (d) altered

Exercise 4C

2. (a) $y = 2f(x)+1$

   (b) $y = 4 - f(x)$

   (c) $y = g(x+4)+2$

   (d) $y = -2g(x)+1$

   (e) $y = f(x+1)+41$

Miscellaneous Exercises

2. (a) $y = f(2x)+1$

   (b) $y = 1 - g(x+1)$

3. function odd

5 SOLVING PROBLEMS

Exercise 5A

1. (a) 254 (b) −15 (c) 101
   (d) 27.3 (e) 2.66 (f) 11.7

2. (a) $p=81$, $q=69$
   (b) $m=23$, $n=-27$
   (c) $k=32$, $\ell=3$
   (d) $x=-5$, $y=-14$
   (e) $p=-0.182$, $q=14.9$
   (f) $u=-1.55$, $v=-2.82$

3. (a) $a\leq 13$ (b) $b>16$ (c) $c\geq 8$, $c\in\mathbb{N}$
   (d) $d>-9.43$ (e) $e\geq 13$ (f) $f\geq 4$, $f\in\mathbb{N}$
4. 34 tables, 66 chairs
5. 12 hardbacks, 8 paperbacks
6. 6 minutes
7. 1516 units.

Exercise 5B

1. (a) $10x+14y$ (b) a^2-ab
   (c) $18\ell^2m-15\ell m^2$ (d) $2p^3-3p^2q^2+p^2$
   (e) $2h^4k^4+3h^4k^5$

2. (a) x^2+3x+2 (b) $x^2-2x-15$
   (c) $x^2-10x+16$ (d) x^2+x-30
   (e) $x^2-3x-70$

3. (a) $2x^2-13x+21$ (b) $2x^2+5x+3$
   (c) $3x^2-4x-160$ (d) $2a^2-3ab-2b^2$
   (e) $2m^3+10m^2n^2-nm-5n^3$

4. (a) x^2+2x+1 (b) p^2-6p+9
   (c) $x^2-20x+100$ (d) $x^2+2ax+a^2$
   (e) $4x^2-20x+25$

5. (a) $2a^2-b^2$ (b) $3y^2+8y-1$
   (c) $2n+23$ (d) $m^2+2m-18$
   (e) $v^2-10uv-3u^2$

6. (a) $3(2x+5)$ (b) $u(u-3)$
   (c) $3p(p+8)$ (c) $6ab^2(2ab-1)$
   (e) $5y(x^2+3)-35$

7. (a) $(x+4)(x+2)$ (b) $(x+6)(x-5)$
   (c) $(x-2)(x-5)$ (d) $(x+4)(x+1)$
   (e) $(x-10)(x+7)$ (f) $(x-9)(x-1)$
   (g) $(x+8)(x-2)$ (h) $(x-12)(x+7)$

8. (a) $(x-4)(x+4)$ (b) $x(x-25)$
   (c) $(2x+1)(x+3)$ (d) $(2x+1)(x-4)$
   (e) $(3x+4)(x-5)$ (f) $2(x+1)(x-3)$
   (g) $(3x-10)(x+2)$ (h) $(10x+8)(10x-8)$

9. (a) $(5x-2)(x+1)$ (b) $(4x-3)(x+2)$
   (c) $(2x+1)(2x-3)$ (d) $3(2x-3)(x+4)$
   (e) $(3x-5)(2x+5)$ (f) $(4x-5)(3x+2)$

Activity 3

(a) $x=-9,\ 3$ (b) $x=-m,\ -n$

(c) $x=\frac{1}{2},\ -2$

Exercise 5C

1. (a) 1, −4 (b) 5, −10 (c) 9, −8
   (d) 7, 11 (e) −2, −48 (f) 20, 30
   (g) $\frac{3}{2}$, 5 (h) $\frac{7}{2}$, −3 (i) 5, −3
   (j) $\frac{7}{3}$, −2
2. Length 13 m, width 10 m
3. Height $\frac{3}{2}$ m

Exercise 5D

1. (a) 3, $-\frac{3}{2}$ (b) 3.27, −4.28
   (c) 11.58, 8.42 (d) 14.58, −20.58
2. (a) 1.70, −4.70 (b) 6.19, 0.81
   (c) −1.76, −6.24 (d) 77.8, −102.8
3. 85 m
4. 52 cm

Activity 8

(a) $p=2$, $q=7$ (b) $x=2\pm\sqrt{7}$

(c) (i) $1\pm\sqrt{2}$ (ii) $\frac{3}{2}\pm\frac{\sqrt{29}}{2}$

Exercise 5E

1. (a) 5.32, −1.32 (b) 8.45, 3.55
   (c) 1.62, −0.62 (d) 13.23, −23.23
   (e) 3.87, 0.13 (f) 1.26, −2.06
   (g) 31.7, −1.67 (h) 38.8, −15.8
2. (a) $x \to \infty$ (b) $-\frac{25}{4}$ (c) 190
   (d) 475, $x = -15$
3. (a) 34.14 or 5.86 (b) 800 m²

Exercise 5F

1. (a) 1.22, −0.936 (b) 0.0753, −0.781
   (c) 3.90, −1.56 (d) 15.6, −4.27
   (e) 0.384, 0.116 (f) 20.8, 3.06
2. (a) none (b) two (c) two
   (d) one (e) two (f) one
3. (a) 4.25 (b) 24.05 m
4. 4.82 cm

Exercise 5G

1. (a) 21 (b) 36 (c) ±12
   (d) 5 (e) −22 (f) 9, $-\frac{15}{2}$
   (g) 8, −7 (h) 0, 10 (i) $\frac{3}{2}$, 5
   (j) 11.43, −7.43
2. 1.618
3. £1.45
4. 14p

Exercise 5H

1. (a) $x \le -6$, $x \ge 11$ (b) $x < \frac{1}{3}$, $x > 1$
   (c) $x \le -7$, $x \ge 9$ (d) $x < -60$, $x > -50$
2. (a) $x > 1.24$, $x < -3.24$ (b) $1.55 \le x \le 6.45$
   (c) $-18.6 < x < -5.37$ (d) $x < -9.16$, $x > 10.9$
3. (a) $-5 \le x \le 12$ (b) $-8.83 < x < -3.17$
   (c) $\frac{20}{3} < x < 10$ (d) $-8.61 < x < 6.78$
   (e) $0.770 \le x \le 3.90$ (f) $0.739 < x < 4.83$
4. $0 < a < 1 + \sqrt{3}$

Exercise 5I

1. (a) $-1 \le a \le -\frac{1}{5}$ (b) $4 < b < 16$
   (c) $c \le 3$, $c \ge 4\frac{1}{2}$ (d) $-27 \le d \le 6$
   (e) $-5.42 < e < 1.25$ (f) $-14 \le f \le \frac{134}{9}$
2. (a) $x = 1$
   (b) $x = -14, -13, -12, -11, 6, 7, 8, 9$
3. (a) $1 < x < 2.27$, $5.73 < x < 7$
   (b) $x > 2.61$, $-2 < x < 0$, $x < 4.61$
   (c) $-8.37 < x < -1.13$
4. (a) $-15 \le C^\circ \le 35$ (b) $0 \le C^\circ \le 20$
5. (a) 3.5 s (b) $15.625 \le d \le 28.125$

Miscellaneous Exercises

1. 12 short, 4 long
2. £13522.50 or £43382.82
3. 10 to 40 minutes
4. (a) 7.40 am (b) 4.47 pm
5. $0 \le Q \le 104$
6. 75 at £16 each
7. 257 mph
8. 73 mph
9. 21 km/hour
10. about 4.22
11. 1.1618
12. 81 cm
13. (a) $100 - 400t$, $60 - 300t$
    (b) about $11\frac{1}{2}$ minutes
14. 60 m × 20 m
15. (a) $x = -\frac{1}{2}$ (b) $x < -9$, $-1 < x < 8$
    (c) $x = \pm 2$, ± 3 (d) $x = 4$
    (e) $x = 0, 6, -8$ (f) $x = -2, 2$

6 EXTENDING ALGEBRA

Exercise 6A

1. (a) (i) $x^2 + x - 2$ (ii) $x^2 + 5x - 3$
   (iii) $x^2 - 5x - 36$
   (b) (i) $x = 4, 1, -2$ (ii) $x = -3, 0.54, -5.54$
   (iii) $x = -4\frac{1}{2}, -4, 9$

3. (a) 1, 0.59, 3.41 (b) −1, 6, −8

(c) $\frac{1}{2}$, −3, 3

4. 1 cm side

Exercise 6B

1. (b) $x = -2.34$
2. (a) −19.9, 28.4, 66.5 (b) −2.84, 5.39, −6.55

Activity 4

(b) $(x-2)(x+1)$ (c) $x^2 - x - 2$

(d) $(qx - p)$

Exercise 6C

2. A : 2; C : 1; D : 3
3. (a) $(x-1)$ (b) $(x-2)$ (c) $(x-1)$

(d) $(2x+1)$ (e) $(3x-2)$

Exercise 6D

1. (a) 307 (b) 321 (c) 341 (d) 523
2. (a) $x^3 + 5x^2 + 2x + 6$ (b) $x^3 - x - 5$

(c) $x^2 + 2x - 4$

3. (a) $x^3 + 5x^2 + 4x + 1$ (b) $x^3 + x^2 - 6x - 3$

(c) $2x^2 - 7$ (d) $3x^4 + x^3 - 6x^2 + 4x + 1$

4. (a) $x + 7$ (b) $2x^2 - x - 1$

(c) $x^2 - 6x + 3$ (d) $x + 2$

Exercise 6E

1. (a) −1, −3, −5, 1 (b) 1, 2, −2, −9
2. −3, −1, 1 (repeated), 2

Exercise 6F

1. (a) −40 (b) 40
2. (a) $x^2 + x - 10$, 40 (b) $x - 10$, −40

Exercise 6G

1. (a) 7 (b) 61 (c) −488
2. $p = 3$
3. $p = -3$, $q = -10$
4. $(x+2)$, $(x+8)$

Exercise 6H

1. (a) $\sqrt{12}$ (b) $\sqrt{700}$ (c) $-\sqrt{30}$
2. (a) $2\sqrt{13}$ (b) $5\sqrt{3}$ (c) $2\sqrt{30}$

(d) $7\sqrt{5}$

3. (a) $2\sqrt[3]{2}$ (b) $3\sqrt[3]{2}$ (c) $2\sqrt[4]{3}$
4. (a) $\sqrt{2} + 1$ (b) $\frac{\sqrt{21} + 3}{4}$ (c) $\frac{2}{3}\left(\sqrt{5} + \sqrt{2}\right)$

(d) $\frac{3\sqrt{2}}{2}$ (e) $\frac{\sqrt{14} + 2}{2}$

Miscellaneous Exercises

1. (a) $(x-5)$ (b) $(x+2)$
2. (a) −1, 5, 0.62, −1.62

(b) 3, 1, 8, −8

3. (a) $(x-7)\left(x^2 - 1\right) - 13$

(b) $x^4 + 3x^3 - 6x^2 + 9x - 16 + \frac{33}{(x+2)}$

4. (a) −15 (b) 297
5. $a = 8$
6. $(x-8)$, $(x+3)$
7. $3x^2 - 7x + 2$
8. $(x+1)$, $(x-10)$, $(x-3)$
9. (a) $\frac{(x-1)}{2}$ (b) $\frac{6a^2}{(2+a)}$

(c) $\frac{(m-2)(m+2)}{2m}$ (d) $\frac{1}{3}(3x-1)$

(e) $x^2 + x + 1$

10. (a) 9 (b) 0; $(x+1)(2x-1)(x-1)$
11. 30
13. (a) (i) $p - 2q$ (ii) $x^2 + 3xy - y^2$

(iii) $(a-b)(2a+3b)$

(b) (i) $(x-3a)(x+a)$ (ii) $(p+12q)(p-2q)$

(iii) $(a-b)(a-4b)(a+3b)$

14. $x(2x-3)(2x+3)\left(4x^2 + 9\right)$

7 STRAIGHT LINES

Activity 2

(a) 20 (b) 182

Exercise 7A

1. $\frac{20}{37}$, 0.541
2. 1.72 m s^{-2}
3. 0.7466 m s^{-2}
4. 1 minute 45 seconds
5. $y=3x+5$ (a) £9.5 (b) £14 (c) £41

Exercise 7B

1. (a) 3, −1 (b) −4, −3 (c) $\frac{1}{2}$, 5

   (d) $-\frac{6}{5}, -\frac{1}{2}$ (e) 4, 0 (f) 1, 0

   (g) −1, 0 (h) 0, 5
2. (a) −4, 9 (b) $-\frac{1}{2}$, 3 (c) $\frac{3}{2}$, −2

   (d) $\frac{1}{2}, -\frac{3}{2}$
3. $y = 3x-14$
4. $y = -\frac{1}{3}x + \frac{22}{3}$
5. $y = 2x-5$
6. $y = 2x-8$
7. $y = -\frac{4}{3}x$

Exercise 7C

1. $y=2x-1$
2. $y=-x$
3. (1, 1)
4. $2y=5-x$

Exercise 7E

1. (a) 5 (b) 12.0 (c) 8.49 (d) 14.3
2. $\left(\frac{3}{2}, 2\right)$, $\left(5, \frac{5}{2}\right)$, $(1, -2)$, $\left(\frac{3}{2}, -1\right)$
3. 5

Miscellaneous Exercises

1. 105 Fr/£
2. −1.675 m s^{-2}
3. (a) 1 (b) $\frac{3}{2}$ (c) $-\frac{3}{2}$ (d) $-\frac{14}{9}$
4. (a) 5, 3 (b) −1, 1 (c) $\frac{1}{2}$, 0

   (d) $\frac{1}{3}$, 2 (e) $\frac{5}{2}, -\frac{11}{2}$ (f) $-\frac{3}{4}, -\frac{1}{4}$
5. $y = 2x-11$
6. $y = 4x+21$
7. $3y+4x=15$
8. 52 cm
9. $4y+x=59$
10. $2y+3x-5=0$
11. $y = 5x-20$
12. $\left(\frac{3}{5}, \frac{3}{5}\right)$
13. $5y=3x+9$
14. $6y=5x-2$

8 RATES OF CHANGE

Exercise 8B

1. (a) $4x$ (b) $2x+1$ (c) $2t+4$ (d) $2x-1$

   (e) $12l$ (f) $10-\frac{2x}{5}$ (g) $\frac{2y}{9}+3$ (h) $\frac{2n-5}{2}$

   (i) $1-12v$ (j) $\frac{3}{2}x+\frac{1}{5}$
2. (a) −7 (b) 5 (c) $23\frac{5}{6}$ (d) $\frac{9}{4}$ (e) 71
3. (a) 16 m s^{-1} (b) −7 m s^{-1}

Exercise 8C

1. (a) $3x^2+10x+3$ (b) $18t^2-20t+2$

   (c) $10x-\frac{1}{x^2}$ (d) $3x^2-1$ (e) $\frac{3t^2+3}{5}$
2. (a) $2(x+2)$ (b) $3x^2-1$

   (c) $3s^2+\frac{4}{3}s+\frac{1}{9}$ (d) $\frac{8}{3}y^2+\frac{2}{3}y$

   (e) $3x^2-5+\frac{1}{x^2}$

3. (a) 9 (b) $\frac{13}{4}$ (c) (2, 19)
   (d) (−1, 18) (e) (2, 41), (1, 18)

4. (a) $\frac{1}{3}$ (b) $\frac{3}{16}$ (feet per year)

Exercise 8D

1. (−2, 55) max; (6, −201) min
2. (a) $\left(\frac{3}{2}, \frac{5}{2}\right)$ min
   (b) (3, 18) min, (−3, −18) max
   (c) (−7, −469) min, (5, 395) max
   (d) (2, 12) min
3. (b) 50, 680
4. 47.6 mph

Exercise 8E

1. 5 m^2
2. (a) 13.33 m^2 (b) 7.59 m^2
3. 20 m
4. 120 m
6. 120, 239, 159 mm

Exercise 8F

1. (a) $-\frac{6}{x^7}$ (b) $9x^2 - \frac{4}{x^3}$
   (c) $20q^3 + 12q^2 + \frac{9}{q^4}$ (d) $8t^7 + \frac{18}{t^7}$
   (e) $-\frac{2}{x^5}$ (f) $-\frac{6}{5x^3}$
   (g) $-\frac{2}{t^2} + \frac{14}{t^5}$ (h) $\frac{x}{2} + \frac{9}{4x^4}$
2. (a) 2.5 (b) 11 (c) 449.5
3. (a) 4 (b) 308 (c) −1

Exercise 8G

1. (a) $y = 10x - 12$ (b) $y = 2x - 3$
   (c) $y = -2x - 12$
2. (a) $y = 9 - x$ (b) $8y = 128x + 527$
   (c) $7y = 24 - x$

3 (a) 4 (c) 3

Miscellaneous Exercises

1. (a) $2x + 4$ (b) $3x^2 - 8x + 17$
   (c) $3x^2 + 4x + 1$ (d) $2x - \frac{2}{x^2}$
   (e) $3x^2 - 2 - \frac{1}{x^2}$
2. (a) $20x^3 - \frac{6}{x^3}$ (b) $-\frac{18}{t^5}$ (c) $6y^5 + \frac{10}{y^3}$
   (d) $-\frac{2}{p^2} - \frac{2}{p^3}$ (e) $-\frac{18}{25x^3} + \frac{8}{25}x$
3. (a) $y = 8x - 15$ (b) $3y + x = -4$
4. (b) $10x - 2$
5. 15625 cm^3
6. (a) $v = 3t^2 - 24t + 45$
   (b) $t = 3$ s or 5 s (c) $t = 4$ s
7. (a) 75
8. (b) 9, −4
9. $a = 100, b = 10000$
10. 3

9 POWERS

Exercise 9A

1. (a) 4 (b) 2 (c) 3
   (d) $\frac{1}{2}$ (e) $\frac{2}{5}$ (f) −1
2. (a) 2.45 (b) 2.15 (c) 2.24
   (d) 0.839 (e) 0.707
3. (a) $\frac{1}{2}$ (b) $\frac{1}{3}$ (c) $\frac{1}{4}$ (d) $-\frac{1}{4}$
4. (a) £409.84 (b) £222.25
5. 14.35%
6. (a) £1732 (b) £790 (c) £2990

Exercise 9B

1. (a) 8 (b) 9 (c) 100 000 (d) 10 000
   (e) 32 (f) 4
2. (a) 1310 (b) 0.552 (c) 187 (d) 4.64
   (e) 0.552 (f) 0.0421
3. (a) $\frac{1}{4}$ (b) $\frac{1}{8}$ (c) $\frac{1}{4}$ (d) $\frac{1}{625}$

4. (a) 0.316 (b) 0.405 (c) 55.9
   (d) 0.188

5. (a) 1 (b) 2.5 (c) $-\frac{1}{2}$
   (d) $-\frac{1}{3}$ (e) $\frac{2}{3}$ (f) $-\frac{3}{4}$

6. (a) $5\sqrt{p}$ (b) $\frac{6}{q}$ (c) $\frac{10}{\sqrt{x}}$
   (d) $\frac{3}{4\sqrt{y}}$ (e) $\frac{1}{2}m\sqrt{m}$ (f) $\frac{12}{t^2\sqrt{t}}$

7. (a) 20.3% (b) 58.7%

Exercise 9C

1. (a) $1+2x+x^2$ (b) $1+3x+3x^2+x^3$
   (c) $1+4x+6x^2+4x^3+x^4$
   (d) $1+5x+10x^2+10x^3+5x^4+x^5$

2. (a) $a^2+2ax+x^2$ (b) $a^3+3a^2x+3x^2a+x^3$
   (c) $a^4+4a^3x+6a^2x^2+4ax^3+x^4$
   (d) $a^5+5a^4x+10a^3x^2+10a^2x^3+5ax^4+x^5$

3. (a) $9-12x+4x^2$
   (b) $8+60p+150p^2+125p^3$
   (c) $625-250m+\frac{75}{2}m^2-\frac{5}{2}m^3+\frac{1}{16}m^4$

Exercise 9D

1. (a) 6 (b) 5 (c) 10 (d) 20 (e) 3

2. $\begin{pmatrix}3\\2\end{pmatrix}$; $\begin{pmatrix}4\\2\end{pmatrix}$

Exercise 9E

1. (a) 84 (b) 792 (c) 1 144 066
2. 60, 1260, 210, 9 979 200
3. 12 650
4. 210
5. 4368
6. 13 860

Exercise 9F

1. (a) $1+8x+24x^2+32x^3+16x^4$
   (b) $125-150p+60p^2-8p^3$
   (c) $46656-23328a+4860a^2-540a^3+\frac{135}{4}a^4-\frac{9}{8}a^5+\frac{1}{64}a^6$
   (d) $32m^5+240m^4n+720m^3n^2+1080m^2n^3+810mn^4+243n^5$
   (e) $16-16r+6r^2-r^3+\frac{1}{16}r^4$

2. (a) 15360 (b) −16 800
   (c) $10\,500\,000\,p^3$ (d) $495\times3^4\times2^8\times\ell^8$
   (e) $-120\times\frac{5^{10}}{6^7}$

3. (a) 1.05 (b) 1.22 (c) 0.932 (d) 8.12
   (e) 98 000 000 (f) 1 770 000

Miscellaneous Exercises

1. (a) $\frac{1}{3}$ (b) $\frac{3}{2}$ (c) $\frac{1}{2}$ (d) $\frac{1}{8}$

2. (a) $\frac{1}{4}$ (b) $-\frac{1}{2}$ (c) $-\frac{2}{3}$ (d) −1

3. (a) 1.262 (b) −0.631 (c) −5.048
   (d) 1.577

4. (a) 25 741 485 (b) 51 527 245

5. (a) $1+5x+10x^2+10x^3+5x^4+x^5$
   (b) $81+54x+\frac{27}{2}x^2+\frac{3}{2}x^3+\frac{1}{16}x^4$
   (c) $64-576p+2160p^2-4320p^3+4860p^4-2916p^5+729p^6$

6. (a) 6 (b) −540 (c) 664 (d) −5760
7. −280

10 TRIGONOMETRY

Activity 2

(a) $2\pi r$ (b) $\frac{\pi r\theta}{180}$ (c) $\theta=1$ radian

Exercise 10A

1. (a) 210° (b) 540° (c) 114.6° (d) 165°
2. (a) 0.218 radians (b) 1.265 radians
   (c) 3.665 radians (d) 0.349 radians

Activity 4

(a) πr^2 (b) $\dfrac{\theta}{2\pi}$ (c) $\frac{1}{2}r^2\theta$

Exercise 10B

1. (a) $\dfrac{5}{3}$ radians (b) 30207 cm^3
2. $r = 10$ cm, $\theta = 2$ radians
3. 0.4 ms^{-1}

Exercise 10C

1. (a) 2.61 (b) 3.22 (c) 1.88
2. (a) $\dfrac{1}{\sqrt{2}}$ (b) $-\dfrac{1}{\sqrt{2}}$ (c) $-\dfrac{1}{\sqrt{2}}$

   (d) $\dfrac{1}{\sqrt{2}}$ (e) $-\dfrac{1}{\sqrt{2}}$ (f) 1

   (g) −1 (h) −1

Exercise 10D

1. 60°, 300°
2. 45°, 225°
3. 14.5°, 165.5°
4. 210°, 330°
5. 14.0°, 194.0°, 374.0°, 554.0°
6. −0.340 radians, $-\pi + 0.340$ radians
7. ±1.23 radians
8. (b), (c) and (e)

Exercise 10E

1. 0°, 180°, 360°
2. 90°, 210°, 330°
3. 41.4°, 120°, 240°, 318.6°
4. $\dfrac{3\pi}{4}$, $\dfrac{7\pi}{4}$
5. 18.4°, 198.4°

Miscellaneous Exercises

1. $\dfrac{5\pi}{12}$
2. $\dfrac{\pi}{3}$
3. 7.4 cm
4. (a) $\dfrac{\pi}{4}$ (b) 1.288 radians (c) 3.121 radians
5. $\dfrac{\pi}{2}$
6. 0.8 radians
7. (a) 135°, 315° (b) $\dfrac{\pi}{6}$, $\dfrac{5\pi}{6}$, $\dfrac{7\pi}{6}$, $\dfrac{11\pi}{6}$

   (c) 129°

   (d) $\dfrac{7\pi}{18}$, $\dfrac{11\pi}{18}$, $\dfrac{19\pi}{18}$, $\dfrac{23\pi}{18}$, $\dfrac{31\pi}{18}$, $\dfrac{35\pi}{18}$
8. (a) 45°, 225° (b)1.89, 5.03 radians

   (c) 19.59°, 90°, 160.5°

   (d) 120°, 240°
9. (a) 9.2°, 99.2° (b) 0°, 180°, 360°

   (c) 0°, 60°, 120°, 180°, 240°, 300°, 360°

11 GROWTH AND DECAY

Exercise 11A

1. 1.61
2. −0.69
3. −0.288
4. 0
5. 0.575
6. 0.41
7. 1.1
8. 4.25
9. 0.55
10. 1.39

Exercise 11B

1. 2.32
2. 0
3. −0.415
4. 1.46
5. −2.58
6. 0.63
7. 1.68
8. 0.50
9. −4.1

10 −0.38

Exercise 11C

1. 2
2. 4
3. 3
4. -4
5. $-\frac{1}{2}$
6. $\frac{1}{2}$
7. 3
8. $\frac{1}{2}$

Miscellaneous Exercises

1. (a) 1.39 (b) -0.768 (c) 1.30 (d) 0
   (e) 0.699 (f) -0.878 (g) 0.577
   (h) 0.104 (i) 0.566 (j) 3 (k) 2
   (l) -3
2. $a = 30$, $k = 0.0995$, 10.05 hours

12 INTEGRATION

Exercise 12A

1. About 3

Exercise 12B

1. (a) 100 (b) 55 (c) 80
2. (a) $\int_0^{10}(x+5)\,dx$ (b) $\int_{20}^{30}(8-0.1t)\,dt$
   (c) $\int_{-2}^{3}(2x+15)\,dx$
3. (b) 99
4. (a) 120 (b) 50 (c) 2887.5
   (d) 126.16
5. (b) 62.5 m
6. (a) 3100 (b) 6150

Exercise 12C

1. (a) x^2+7x+c (b) $10t-\frac{1}{2}t^2+c$
   (c) $2.8w+5.7w^2+c$ (d) $-14x-\dfrac{11x^2}{2}+c$
2. (a) 30 (b) 46.5 (c) 54 (d) 115

Exercise 12D

1. $\dfrac{1}{10}x^{10}+c$
2. $-\dfrac{1}{7x^7}+c$
3. $-\dfrac{1}{4x^4}+c$
4. $\dfrac{x^5}{5}+\dfrac{x^8}{8}+c$
5. $\ln x-\dfrac{1}{x}+c$
6. $\dfrac{3}{4}x^8+c$
7. $-\dfrac{3}{2t^2}+c$
8. $\ln w^2+c$
9. $e^p-\dfrac{3p^2}{2}+c$
10. $2q+\dfrac{1}{2q^2}+c$
11. $\dfrac{x^4}{8}+c$
12. $\dfrac{x^8}{6}+c$
13. $-\dfrac{3}{4y^2}+c$
14. $x^2-\dfrac{2}{3}\ln x+c$
15. $\dfrac{1}{4}e^k-\dfrac{1}{2k^2}+c$
16. $\dfrac{3}{4}x-\dfrac{x^6}{12}+c$
17. $e^m+\dfrac{2}{15m^3}+c$
18. $\dfrac{5x^3}{6}-\dfrac{x^2}{4}+\dfrac{x}{2}+c$
19. $\dfrac{z^3}{15}-\dfrac{1}{5}\ln z+c$
20. $2x-\ln x+c$

Exercise 12E

1. (a) $\frac{250}{3}$ (b) 132.25 (c) $\frac{5}{6}$

(d) $2e^3 - \frac{2}{e^2} + \frac{35}{3}$ (e) $4 + \ln 3$

(f) 0.516 to 3 significant figures

2. (a) 40.5 (b) 13.0 (c) 0.375

(d) 2.12

3. $\frac{1}{6}$

4. $\frac{2}{11}, \frac{20}{11}$

Exercise 12F

1. (a) $h = 2t - 5t^2 + 1000$ (b) $t = 14.34$

2. (a) $x = 5t + \frac{1}{2}t^2 - \frac{1}{12}t^3 - 30$

(b) $x(7.7) > 0$, $x(7.8) < 0$

3. (a) $C = \frac{1}{3}Q^3 - \frac{3}{2}Q^2 + 5Q + 5$

(b) 114

Miscellaneous Exercises

1. (a) $\frac{5x^2}{2} + 2x + c$ (b) $\frac{t^4}{8} + \frac{2t^3}{9} + c$

(c) $7\ln p - \frac{1}{2}p^2 + c$ (d) $\frac{1}{4s^5} + c$

(e) $\frac{x^3}{3} - \frac{4}{x} - 4x + c$

2. (a) $e^{15} + 2249$ (b) $e^3 - e^{-3} + 36$

(c) $\frac{3}{10} + \ln 4$ (d) $3\frac{5}{6}$ (e) $-\frac{5}{12}$

3. $A = \frac{5}{12}$, $B = \frac{8}{3}$

4. 11

5. 3

6. (a) $\frac{8}{3}$ (b) $\frac{20}{3}$ (c) $e^2 - 5$

7. (a) $2 - \ln 3$ (b) $\frac{e^{-1}}{2} - \frac{e^{-4}}{2} + \frac{3}{2}\ln 4$

8. (a) (i) $0.003t^3 + 0.04t^2 + 0.01t$

(ii) $36 - 0.003t^3 - 0.04t^2 - 0.01t$

(b) (i) 0.053 litres (ii) 1.58 litres

(c) (i) 34.6 litres (ii) 16.7 litres

9. (b) (i) 1.129×10^5 (ii) 8.144×10^5

10. (a) 13 (d) −14

11. (b) (i) 66 (ii) 112

13 SEQUENCES AND SERIES

Exercise 13A

1. (a) $3 \times 2^{n-1}$ (b) $36 \times \left(\frac{1}{2}\right)^{n-1}$

(c) $2 \times (-3)^{n-1}$ (e) $90 \times \left(-\frac{1}{3}\right)^{n-1}$

(e) 10^n (f) $(-1)^{n-1}6$ (g) $\frac{1}{4} \times \left(\frac{1}{3}\right)^{n-1}$

2. (a) 315 (b) 118 096 (c) 0.6641

(d) 83.33 (e) 18 620 (f) 16.01

3. (a) 11th (b) 14th (c) 10th

4. (a) 9 (b) 1708

5. £9050

Exercise 13B

1. (a) $\frac{320}{3}$ (b) 135 (c) 200 (d) - (e) $\frac{1}{9}$

2. (a) 0.111111... (b) $\frac{37}{99}$

3. (a) $\frac{52}{99}$ (b) $\frac{358}{999}$ (c) $\frac{193}{990}$

4. (a) 42 (b) 0.125

5. 211.6 cm³

6. (a) 16.963 s (b) 49.4 m

Exercise 13C

1. (a) 105 (b) 252 (c) 78 (d) 2500

2. (a) $u_n = 3n - 2$, $S_n = \frac{n}{2}(3n - 1)$

(b) $u_n = 3 + 9n$, $S_n = \frac{n}{2}(9n + 15)$

(c) $u_n = 65-5n$, $S_n = \frac{n}{2}(125-5n)$

(d) $u_n = \frac{1}{2}(3n-1)$, $S_n = \frac{n}{4}(1+3n)$

3. 1840 cm

Exercise 13D

1. (a) 536 (b) 45 (c) 1162
   (d) 277.2 (e) 385 (f) 409.125
2. -8, 621
3. (a) 10 (b) 19
4. 5.5
5. £76 300

Exercise 13E

1. (a) $5^2+6^2+7^2+\ldots+15^2$
   (b) $1+3+5+\ldots+19$
   (c) $1+2+3+\ldots+n$
   (d) $\frac{1}{3}+\frac{2}{4}+\frac{3}{5}+\ldots+\frac{8}{10}$
   (e) $4^2+5^2+6^2+\ldots+98^2$
2. (a) $\sum_{r=1}^{25}\frac{1}{r}$ (b) $\sum_{r=0}^{40}(10+r)$ (c) $\sum_{r=1}^{n}r^3$
   (d) $\sum_{r=0}^{12}3^r$ (e) $\sum_{r=1}^{n}(5r+1)$ (f) $\sum_{r=0}^{16}14+3r$
   (g) $\sum_{r=0}^{n}5\times10^r$ (h) $\sum_{r=1}^{20}\frac{r}{(r+1)(r+2)}$
3. (a) $\sum_{r=10}^{99}r$ (b) $\sum_{r=1}^{60}(2r-1)$
   (c) $\sum_{r=10}^{20}r^2$ (d) $\sum_{r=0}^{14}(7r+1)$
4. (a) $\sum_{r=0}^{18}(19-r)$ (b) $\sum_{r=1}^{40}\frac{1}{r}$ (c) $\sum_{r=0}^{6}(r-3)^2$

Exercise 13F

1. (a) 10 (b) 100 (c) 731 (d) 8.8×10^{16}
   (e) $\frac{7}{3}$ (f) 3
2. (a) $\sum_{r=1}^{6}\frac{(-1)^{r+1}}{r}$ (b) $\sum_{r=1}^{12}(-1)^r r^2$
   (c) $\sum_{r=0}^{50}12(-0.2)^r$
3. (a) 84 (d) 32 (e) 44 (f) 36

Exercise 13G

1. (a) $\sum_{r=1}^{20}r=210$ (b) $\sum_{r=1}^{10}r^2=385$
   (c) $2\sum_{r=1}^{15}r^2=2480$ (d) $2\sum_{r=1}^{50}r=2550$
   (e) $\sum_{r=1}^{13}(2r-1)=169$ (f) $\sum_{r=1}^{10}r^3=3025$
2. 165
3. (a) 4515 (b) 13959 (c) 861
4. 6461

Miscellaneous Exercises

1. (a) 102.4 mm (b) 15 (c) 42
2. (a) $4\times(1.5)^{n-1}$ (b) $256-6n$
   (c) $10\times(0.2)^{n-1}$ (d) $0.32n-0.15$
3. (a) 810 (b) 1062 880 (c) -330
   (d) 960
4. 21
5. (a) 249 (b) 22
6. -4, 7
7. (a) 15 (b) 26250
8. (a) 0.98 (b) 297
9. $\pm\frac{1}{3}$, 81, 162

14 FURTHER CALCULUS

Exercise 14A

1. (a) $6x$ (b) $12x^2$ (c) 2 (d) 0 (e) $\frac{2}{x^3}$
   (f) $24x-24$ (g) 0 (h) e^x (i) $-\frac{1}{x^2}$

2. (a) $24x$ (b) $-\frac{72}{x^5}$ (c) e^x (d) $\frac{2}{x^3}$ (e) 0

Exercise 14B

1. (a) $x = -\frac{3}{4}$, minimum

 (b) $x = 2$, minimum; $x = -2$, maximum

 (c) $x = \frac{-2+\sqrt{19}}{3}$, minimum

 $x = \frac{-2-\sqrt{19}}{3}$, maximum

 (d) $x = 1$, point of inflection

 (e) $x = \ln 4$, minimum

 (f) none

2. (a) maximum at $x = \frac{2+a}{3}$

 minimum at $x = a$

 (b) minimum at $x = \frac{2+a}{3}$

 maximum at $x = a$

Exercise 14C

1. (a) $16(2x-5)^7$ (b) $10\left(x^2+x^3\right)^9\left(2x+3x^2\right)$

 (c) $-\frac{1}{(x-2)^2}$ (d) $-\frac{6}{(3x+1)^3}$

 (e) $\frac{1}{2}\frac{1}{\sqrt{x+1}}$ (f) $6\left(e^x-x\right)^5\left(e^x-1\right)$

 (g) $\frac{3}{(3x+4)}$ (h) $\frac{1}{2\sqrt{x}}e^{\sqrt{x}}$

2. (a) $x=0$ (b) $x=-4$ (c) $x=1$

 (d) $x=\pm 1$

3. -0.964° C / min; -0.290° C / min

4. 0.48 millions / year

5. (a) $2e^{2x}$; $\frac{e^{2x}}{2}+c$

 (b) $-e^{-x}$; $-e^{-x}+c$

6. $2xe^{x^2}$; $\frac{1}{2}e^{x^2}+c$

7. $\ln(x+2)+c$

Exercise 14D

1. (a) $\frac{(2x+1)^5}{10}+c$ (b) $-\frac{1}{(x-5)}+c$

 (c) $2\sqrt{x+1}+c$ (d) $\frac{1}{6}(4x-1)^{\frac{3}{2}}+c$

2. (a) $\ln 2$ (b) $\frac{1}{2}\ln 3$

3. (a) $\frac{1}{3}\ln(3x+2)+c$ (b) $\frac{1}{2}\ln\left(x^2+1\right)+c$

 (c) $\ln\left(1+e^x\right)+c$

4. $\frac{1}{2}\left(1-\frac{1}{e}\right)$

Exercise 14E

1. (a) $e^x(x+1)$ (b) $x+2x\ln x$

 (c) $\frac{-2\left(x^2+x+3\right)}{\left(x^2-3\right)^2}$ (d) $\frac{xe^x}{(1+x)^2}$

2. (a) $x=-1$ (b) $x=0$, $x=0.607$

 (d) $x=0$

3. Root of $(1+x)\ln(1+x)=1$

4. $\frac{-3}{2(2x-1)^2}\sqrt{\frac{2x-1}{x+1}}$

5. $\frac{e^x(2+x)}{2\sqrt{e^x(x+1)}}$

6. $\frac{1}{\sqrt{x}}\left(\frac{1}{(x-2)}-\frac{\ln(x-2)}{2x}\right)$

7. $x=1$, minimum

 $x=-2$, maximum

9. $x=0,\ 2$

Miscellaneous Exercises

1. (a) $x=\frac{5}{2}$, minimum

 (b) $x=\frac{3}{4}$, maximum

 (c) $x=-1$, maximum; $x=-\frac{1}{3}$, minimum

(d) $x=4$, maximum; $x=-2$, minimum
(e) $x=1$ minimum

2. (a) $-24(5-3x)^7$ (b) $\dfrac{-1}{2\sqrt{x}\left(\sqrt{x}+1\right)^2}$

(c) $(\ln 3)\,3^x$ (d) $\sqrt{\dfrac{1-x}{1+x}} \times \dfrac{1}{(1-x)^2}$

(e) $\ln 2$ (f) $\dfrac{2e^{-x^{-2}}}{x^3}$

3. $3e^{3x-1}$; $\dfrac{1}{3}e^{3x-1}+c$

4. $\dfrac{(2x-4)^6}{12}+c$

5. $\dfrac{1}{3}\ln\left(\dfrac{17}{8}\right)$

6. $\dfrac{2x}{x^2+1}$; $\dfrac{1}{2}\ln 2$

15 FURTHER TRIGONOMETRY

Exercise 15B

1. (a) $\dfrac{1}{2\sqrt{2}}\left(\sqrt{3}+1\right)$ (b) $\dfrac{1}{2\sqrt{2}}\left(\sqrt{3}+1\right)$

(c) $\dfrac{1}{2\sqrt{2}}\left(1-\sqrt{3}\right)$ (d) $\dfrac{1}{2\sqrt{2}}\left(\sqrt{3}-1\right)$

(e) $\left(2+\sqrt{3}\right)$ (f) $-\left(2+\sqrt{3}\right)$

(g) $-\dfrac{1}{\sqrt{2}}$ (h) $\dfrac{1}{2\sqrt{2}}\left(\sqrt{3}-1\right)$

(i) $2-\sqrt{3}$

Exercise 15D

1. (a) $-2\sin 4x\sin x$ (b) $2\cos 9x\sin 2x$

(c) $2\cos\dfrac{11}{2}x\cos\dfrac{7}{2}x$ (d) $2\sin 8x\cos 5x$

(e) $4\cos\dfrac{2\pi}{5}\cos\dfrac{\pi}{3}\cos\dfrac{\pi}{5}$ (f) $4\sin 50\cos 35\cos 25$

(g) $2\cos 90\cos 24$

2. $\dfrac{\sqrt{3}}{\sqrt{2}}$

3. (a) $\cos 12x+\cos 2x$ (b) $\cos 3x+\cos 2x$
(c) $\cos 2\theta-\sin 4\theta$
(d) $\sin 270^\circ+\cos 60^\circ=-0.5$

5. $4\cos 3x\cos 4x\cos 5x$

6. $\sin 4x\sin 8x$

Exercise 15E

1. $5\sin(x+0.927)$
2. $5\cos(x-0.644)$
3. $17\sin(x-0.490)$
4. $\sqrt{40}\cos(x+0.322)$
5. $29\sin(x-0.810)$
6. $\sqrt{197}\cos(x-0.071)$
7. $\sqrt{2}\cos(2x+0.464)$
8. $\sqrt{34}\sin\left(\frac{1}{2}x+0.540\right)$

Exercise 15F

1. $\dfrac{\pi}{2}$, 3.990 and 5.435 radians
2. $\pm 70.5^\circ$, $\pm 120^\circ$
3. 63.4°, 101.3°, 243.4°, 281.3°
4. 114.5°
5. $\dfrac{\pi}{4}$, 1.047, 2.094, $\dfrac{3\pi}{4}$
6. 1.257, 2.513 radians
7. 0.841, 2.094 radians

Exercise 15G

1. $\pm\dfrac{2\pi}{3}$
2. 0°, 60°, 120°, 180°
3. 66.4°
4. 115.2°, 244.8°
5. 0, π, 2π
6. 60°, 109.5°

7. 1.878, 4.405 radians
8. 30°, 150°, 210°, 330°
9. 210°, 330°
10. 0.474, 2.667 radians
11. 45°, 60°, 120°, 135°
12. ±30°, ±90°, ±150°

Exercise 15H

1. $n = 97.0$ m, $L = 107.3°$, $\ell = 111$ m
2. $y = 7.62$ cm, $Z = 23.2°$, $X = 36.8°$
3. $C = 36.5°$, $B = 94.5°$, $b = 168$ m
4. $P = 30.2°$, $Q = 122.8°$, $q = 15.4$ cm
5. $D = 37°$, $e = 6.56$ m, $f = 5.87$ m
6. $U = 46.4°$ $V = 90°$, $v = 5.8$ m

Exercise 15I

1. $A = 116°$, $B = 40.5°$, $C = 23.6°$
2. $d = 4.98$ m, $E = 26.2°$, $F = 140°$
3. $n = 32.5$ mm, $L = 73.5°$, $M = 35.5°$
4. $X = 22.1°$, $Y = 41.1°$, $Z = 116.8°$
5. $P = 12.7°$, $Q = 77.3°$, $R = 90°$
6. $v = 144$ m, $V = 102°$, $W = 41.4°$

Exercise 15J

1. 46.8 cm²
2. 14.7 m²
3. 312.0 mm²
4. 12.5 m²
5. 180 cm²
6. 4195 m²

Miscellaneous Exercises

1. (a) $\cos 60 = 0.5$ (b) $\sin 70$ (c) $\sin x$
   (d) $\sqrt{3}\cos x$ (e) $\sin x$
3. 108°, −108°
4. 60°, 180°
6. $\frac{\pi}{24}, \frac{5\pi}{24}, \frac{13\pi}{24}, \frac{17\pi}{24}$
7. (a) 553 cm² (b) 1882 m²

8. 2.905 cm²
9. 37.1 m², 8.24 m, 9.00 m
10. $z = 29.8$, $Y = 67.1°$, $Z = 78.9°$
11. (a) $Q = 106.1°$, $p = 25.9$ m, $q = 97.4$ m
    (b) $Q = 32.0°$, $R = 81.0°$, $r = 78.4$ m
    (c) $P = 11.6°$, $Q = 54.4°$, $R = 114°$
12. 51.0°, 381 m²

16 DATA ANALYSIS

Exercise 16A

3. (a)

	1971	1984	1985
Violemce against the person	2.3	3.2	3.3
Sexual Offences	1.4	0.6	0.6
Burglary	27.3	25.9	24.0
Robbery	0.5	0.8	0.8
Theft and handling stolen goods	58.5	51.4	51.3
Fraud and forgery	5.8	4.0	4.1
Criminal Damage	3.0	14.6	15.0
Other notifiable offences	0.6	0.9	0.9
Total (1000s)	1907.5	3990.7	4138.5

(b) Although the given table does not indicate this, the figures for 1984 and 1985 are not strictly comparable with those for 1971 because of changes made by new counting rules which were introduced at the beginning of 1980.

(c) 5.4%

Activity 3

(a)

	Median	IQ range
African States	10400	15385.5
South and Central American States	1255	730
West European States	455	160
East European States	475	312.5

(b)

	Median	Lower quartile	Upper quartile
Cubic capacity	1522	1193	1803
No. of casualties	0	0	0

(c)

	Median	IQ range
(i) 1901	24.5	26.5
(ii) 1941	19.7	32.0
(iii) 1991	21.1	38.2
(iv) 2015	25.1	38.9

Activity 4

(a)

	Mean Life expectancy
African States	49.9
South and Central American States	65.7
West European States	75.5
East European States	70.3

(b)

	Mean
1901	27.3
1941	36.5
1991	37.8
2015	39.9

Exercise 16B

1.

	Standard deviation
African States	5.84
South and Central American States	5.83
West European States	1.46
East European States	0.70

2.

	Mean	Standard deviation
East Anglia	9.37	2.08
East Midland	11.67	3.79
North West	14.33	2.26

3. Casualties: Mean $=0.0965$, S.D $=0.386$

   Cubic capacity: Mean $=1524$, S.D $=460$

4.

	Mean	S.D
1941	27.3	6.13
1951	27.9	5.96
1971	25.6	5.57
1989	26.8	5.53

Exercise 16C

4. 5.5 cm, 6 cm; 50°

Miscellaneous Exercises

1. 27 - 28 cm, 7 - 9 cm
3. (a) 46 (b) 29; 9%
4. (a) 135 cm (c) 176, 162, 170, 14
5. (a) 17, 4 (approx) (b) 17.85, 5.57
6. 34.9, 32.7, 186.5, 13.7, 61%
7. (a) 180.5 (b) 175.5 (c) 187 (d) 189.5

17 CARTESIAN GEOMETRY

Exercise 17A

1. (a) $y^2=4x$ (b) $\frac{x^2}{4}+\frac{y^2}{9}=1$ (c) $y=\frac{2}{x}$

2. Min $\left(\frac{\sqrt{3}}{3},-2\frac{\sqrt{3}}{9}\right)$ Max $\left(-\frac{\sqrt{3}}{3},2\frac{\sqrt{3}}{9}\right)$

4. $x^2-y^2=4$

Exercise 17C

1. (a) $x^2+y^2-2x-4y=4$

   (b) $x^2+y^2-2y=0$

   (c) $x^2+y^2+2x+4y=11$

2. (a) $(-4,1)$; 5 (b) $(0,0)$; 4 (c) $\left(-\frac{1}{2},-\frac{3}{2}\right)$; $\frac{3}{\sqrt{2}}$

   (d) $\left(\frac{3}{4},-\frac{1}{2}\right)$; $\frac{\sqrt{5}}{4}$

3. $6y+x=9$

4. $2x^2+2y^2-15x-24y+77=0$

Exercise 17D

3. $-\frac{3}{2}\sin t$

4. $3y-x=\frac{21}{4}$

Miscellaneous Exercise s

1. $y=m(x-1)$; $m=\pm 2$
2. (−2, 3), 5, 12, 11.2
3. (a) (2, 2) and (2, −2) (b) $r>2$
4. $\left(14,-\frac{49}{6}\right)$

18 EVEN MORE CALCULUS

Exercise 18A

1. (a) $2\cos 2x$ (b) $\frac{1}{2}\cos\frac{1}{2}x$

   (c) $100\cos 100x$ (d) $-3\sin 3x$

2. $-k\sin kx$; $k\sec^2 kx$

3. (a) $4\sin 2x\cos 2x$ (b) $2\left(\cos^2 2x-\sin^2 2x\right)$

   (c) $\frac{3}{2}\cos^2\left(\frac{1}{2}x\right)\sin\left(\frac{1}{2}x\right)$ (d) $4\tan 2x\sec^2 2x$

4. $-\cos x\ \mathrm{cosec}^2 x$; $\tan x\sec x$; $\sec x+c$

Exercise 18B

1. 0.377 cm²/s

2. $0.2\ \text{cm}^2/\text{s}$

3. $0.0402\ \text{cm}^3/\text{s},\ x=\frac{1}{2}$

4. (a) 14π (b) $\frac{4}{3}$ (c) 3

Exercise 18C

1. (a) $\frac{1}{10}\left(x^2-5\right)^5$ (b) $-\frac{1}{3}\left(1-x^2\right)^{\frac{3}{2}}$

(c) $\frac{1}{5}\sin^5 x$ (d) $\frac{2}{3}\left(1+e^x\right)^{\frac{3}{2}}$

3. $\frac{(\pi+2)}{216}$

Exercise 18D

1. $\frac{x^3}{3}\ln x-\frac{x^3}{9}+C$

3. $\frac{2}{3}$

4. $\frac{1}{4}x^4\ln(4x)-\frac{x^4}{16}+C$

5. $\frac{1}{4}\left(2x^2\sin 2x+2x\cos 2x-\sin 2x\right)+C$

Exercise 18E

1. $y^2=\frac{2}{3}\left(\frac{5x^3}{3}+\frac{3}{2}\right)$

2. $y=2x^3$

3. $y=\frac{1}{2-x}$

4. $y=\frac{1}{2}\ln\left(x^2+1\right)$

5. $y^2+2(x+1)e^{-x}=A$

6. $y=-1+A(x+2)$

7. $x^2=A\left(1+y^2\right)$

8. $k=\ln 2,\ n=n_0 2^t$

Miscellaneous Exercises

1. (a) $3\cos 3x$ (b) $\sec x\left(\tan^2 x+\sec^2 x\right)$

(c) $2\tan x\sec^2 x$

2. (a) $-\frac{1}{5}\cos^5 x+K$ (b) $-\cos x+\frac{1}{3}\cos^3 x+K$

(c) $\frac{1}{3}\tan^3 x+K$

3. (a) $\frac{1}{3}$ (b) 0.28 cm/s (c) 4

4. (a) 2 (b) $0.000481\ \text{cm}^3/\text{s}$

5. (a) $\frac{3x^2}{2}\left(1+x^3\right)^{-\frac{1}{2}}$ (b) $\frac{4}{3}$

6. (a) $-\frac{1}{6}\cos^6 x+C$

(b) $-\sqrt{1-x^2}+C$

(c) $-\frac{1}{\left(1+e^x\right)}+C$

7. $\frac{2}{3}x^{\frac{3}{2}}\ln x-\frac{4}{9}x^{\frac{3}{2}}+C;\quad y=\left(\frac{1}{3}x^{\frac{3}{2}}\ln x-\frac{2}{9}x^{\frac{3}{2}}+\frac{11}{9}\right)^2$

8. (a) $y=A(x-3)$ (b) $y^2=A+(\ln x)^2$

(c) $y^2+A=2x-2\ln x$

19 ITERATION

Exercise 19A

1. $x\approx 1.3$
2. $x\approx 0.7$
3. $x\approx -0.5,\ x\approx 1.4$
4. $x\approx 0.2,\ x\approx 4.5$
5. $x\approx 0.5,\ x\approx 2.6,\ x\approx 4.7$ (twice)

Exercise 19B

1. $x\approx -2.46$
2. $x\approx 1.24$
3. $x\approx -2.86,\ x\approx 2.44$
4. $x\approx 0.590$
5. $x\approx 0.567$

Exercise 19C

$x\approx -1.30,\ x\approx 3.25$

Activity 3

$x\approx -1.16,\ x\approx 1.77,\ x\approx 3.39$

Exercise 19D

1. $x \approx 1.46$
2. $x^3 - x^2 - 1 = 0$; $x \approx 1.47$
3. $x \approx 1.31$, $x \approx 0.34$
4. $x_{n+1} = \sqrt[3]{x_n^2 + 5}$; $x \approx 2.12$
5. $x_{n+1} = 2^{\left(\frac{1}{x_n}\right)}$; $x \approx 1.560$

Exercise 19E

1. $x_{n+1} = \sqrt[3]{3x_n + 4}$; $x \approx 2.2$
2. $x_{n+1} = \dfrac{5}{x_n^3} - 2$; $x \approx -2.4$; $x_{n+1} = \left(\dfrac{5 - x_n^4}{2}\right)^{\frac{1}{3}}$;

   $x \approx 1.2$
3. $x_{n+1} = \dfrac{3^{x_n} - 2}{3}$; $x \approx -0.5$; $x_{n+1} = \dfrac{\ln(3x_n + 2)}{\ln 3}$;

   $x \approx 1.8$

Exercise 19F

1. $x \approx -1.13$
2. $x \approx 0.519$
3. $x \approx 1.857$; $x \approx 4.536$
4. $f(x) = x^3 - 10$; $x_1 = 2.166\ldots$; $x_2 = 2.154\ldots$; 0.003%
5. $x \approx 2.1294$

Miscellaneous Exercises

1. $x \approx 1.521$
2. $x \approx -1.9$ or -1.8; $x \approx -0.3$ or -0.2; $x \approx 2.1$
3. $x \approx -0.42$; $x \approx 3.72$
4. $x \approx -3.68$; $x \approx -2.04$; $x \approx 1.04$; $x \approx 2.68$
5. $x \approx 0.3964$ (the other two are 0.6472 and 1.6708)
6. $x \approx 0.57$
7. $x_{n+1} = \frac{1}{2}\left(x_n + \dfrac{3}{x_n}\right)$; $x_0 = 1.5$, gives $x \approx 1.732051$ after just three iterations.
8. $x^4 - 15x^2 - 18x + 81 = 0$; (2.02, 3.45), (3.75, 1.40)
9. −3.25
10. $\theta \approx 1.9346$; perimeter ≈ 35.81 cm
11. (a) 1.733 (b) $f(x) = x^2 + 2$; 1.613, 1.663

20 PROBABILITY

Exercise 20A

1. $\dfrac{4}{8} = \dfrac{1}{2}$
2. $\dfrac{22}{36} = \dfrac{11}{18}$
3. $\dfrac{3}{5}$
4. $\dfrac{1}{7}$
5. Six ways
6. 16
7. $P(\text{Pierre wins}) = \dfrac{15}{36} = \dfrac{5}{12}$;

   $P(\text{Julian wins}) = \dfrac{7}{12}$;

   $P(\text{Julian wins}) = \dfrac{1}{2}$
8. $\dfrac{69}{169}$
9. $\dfrac{2}{7}$

Exercise 20B

1. (a) $\dfrac{9}{20}$ (b) 0 (c) 1
2. (a) $\dfrac{605 + 17}{\text{total}} = \dfrac{622}{3272} = 0.19$

   (b) 0.14 (c) 0.19 (d) $\dfrac{17}{447} = 0.04$

Exercise 20C

1. $\dfrac{1}{2} + \dfrac{1}{3} - \dfrac{1}{10} = \dfrac{11}{15}$
2. $\dfrac{1}{3} + \dfrac{1}{4} = \dfrac{7}{12}$ (mutually exclusive)
3. $\dfrac{11}{30}$
4. (a) neither (b) exclusive (c) exclusive
   (d) exhaustive (e) neither (f) exclusive

Exercise 20D

1. (b) $\frac{3}{8}$
2. $\frac{2}{7}$
3. (a) 0.34 (b) 0.063 (c) 0.19 (d) 0.97
   Choosing all 3 white marbles

Exercise 20E

1. (a) $\frac{1}{17}$ (b) $\frac{13}{204}$ (c) $\frac{13}{51}$
2. (a) $\frac{1}{3}$ (b) $\frac{2}{15}$ (c) $\frac{8}{15}$
3. (a) 0.02 (b) 0.78 (c) 0.76 (d) $\frac{1}{30}$
4. (a) 0.5 (b) 0.35 (c) 0.375 (d) 0.4

Exercise 20F

1. (a) $\frac{4}{52}=\frac{1}{13}$ (b) $\frac{1}{13}$ (c) $\frac{13}{52}=\frac{1}{4}$
   (d) $\frac{3}{12}=\frac{1}{4}$ (e) $\frac{13}{26}=\frac{1}{2}$ (f) $\frac{12}{52}=\frac{3}{13}$
   (g) 0 (h) $\frac{12}{48}=\frac{1}{4}$ (i) $\frac{4}{50}=\frac{2}{25}$
   (j) $\frac{1}{2}$ (k) $\frac{1}{13}$ (l) $\frac{25}{50}=\frac{1}{2}$
2. a, b, d
3. $a=\frac{1}{3}$ $b=\frac{2}{3}$ $c=\frac{1}{10}$ $d=\frac{2}{5}$ $e=\frac{1}{4}$ $f=\frac{3}{4}$
   $g=\frac{1}{2}$
4. (a) $\frac{1}{2}\times\frac{7}{15}+\frac{1}{2}\times\frac{7}{12}=\frac{21}{40}$ (b) $\frac{\frac{1}{2}\times\frac{7}{12}}{\frac{21}{40}}=\frac{5}{9}$
5. 36, 18, 6;
   (a) $\frac{133}{295}$ (b) $\frac{46}{295}$ (c) $\frac{\frac{1}{118}}{\frac{133}{295}}=\frac{5}{266}$
6. (a) $\frac{19}{216}$ (b) $\frac{7}{12}$
7. (a) $\frac{39}{50}$ (b) $\frac{7}{100}$, $\frac{10}{11}$

Miscellaneous Exercises

1. $\frac{13}{18}$
2. (a) $\frac{1}{15}$ (b) $\frac{2}{5}$
3. (a) $\frac{1}{5}$ (b) $\frac{1}{3}$ (c) $\frac{49}{90}$ (d) $\frac{1}{15}$
4. $\frac{5}{16}$
5. $\frac{1}{8}$

8. (a) true $P(A\cap B)=0$ or $P(A|B)=0$
   (b) true $P(A\cup B)=1$
   (c) true $P(B\cup D)=1$
   (d) false $P(A'\cap C')=\frac{14}{16}=\frac{7}{8}$
9. $\frac{11}{30}$
10. (a) $\frac{1}{4}+\frac{2}{5}=\frac{13}{20}$ (b) $1-\frac{13}{20}=\frac{7}{20}$
11. (a) $\frac{1}{2}$ (b) $\frac{3}{4}$ (c) $\frac{5}{6}$ (d) $\frac{5}{12}$ (e) $\frac{4}{9}$
12. (a) 0.43 (b) $\frac{6}{19}$
13. (a) 0.575 (b) 0.1 (c) $\frac{3}{23}$
14. (a) $\frac{416}{720}=\frac{26}{45}$ (b) $\frac{239}{360}$ (c) $\frac{63}{242}$
15. $\frac{1}{4}$, £1, 57 mm
16. 90°, 108°, 162°
17. $\frac{4}{19}$, yes $\frac{3}{19}$
18. (a) $\frac{19}{27}$ (b) $\frac{6}{19}$
19. (a) $\frac{2}{5}$ (b) $\frac{7}{12}$ $\frac{x}{x+y}$
20. (a) $\frac{1}{81}$ (b) $\frac{80}{81}$

21. (a) $\frac{6}{25}$ (b) $\frac{1}{2}$ (c) $\frac{1}{5}$

22. $\frac{5}{16}$

23. (a) $\frac{98}{125}$ (b) $\frac{4}{49}$

24. (a) $\frac{1}{7}$ (b) $\frac{1}{4}$ (c) $\frac{17}{28}$

25. Yes

APPENDIX: PARTIAL FRACTIONS

Exercise

1. (a) $\dfrac{2}{3(2-x)}-\dfrac{1}{3(1+x)}$

   (b) $\dfrac{6}{7(3x+1)}+\dfrac{5}{7(x-2)}$

   (c) $\dfrac{1}{2(x-1)}+\dfrac{3}{2(x+3)}$

   (d) $\dfrac{3}{16(x+2)}+\dfrac{3}{4(x-2)^2}-\dfrac{3}{16(x-2)}$

   (e) $\dfrac{7x}{2(x^2+2)}-\dfrac{3}{2x}$

   (f) $1+\dfrac{5}{2(x-3)}-\dfrac{1}{2(x+3)}$

   (g) $\dfrac{1}{2(x-1)^2}-\dfrac{1}{4(x-1)}+\dfrac{1}{4(x+1)}$

   (h) $\dfrac{-9}{10(x+3)}+\dfrac{9(1+3x)}{30(x^2+1)}$

2. $\ln 4$

3. $\ln\left(\dfrac{7}{5}\right)$

4. $\ln(x+2)+\frac{1}{2}\ln(x^2+3)+C$

5. $\dfrac{x^2}{2}+2x+\ln(x-3)-2\ln(x+3)+C$

INDEX